JOHN CATT'S

Which School?

2020

Published in 2019 by
John Catt Educational Ltd,
15 Riduna Park,
Melton, Suffolk IP12 1QT UK
Tel: 01394 389850
Fax: 01394 386893
Email: enquiries@johncatt.com
Website: www.johncatt.com

Opinions expressed in this publication are those of the contributors,
and are not necessarily those of the publishers or the sponsors. We
cannot accept responsibility for any errors or omissions.

A CIP catalogue record for this book is available from the British
Library.

ISBN: 978 1 912906 65 9

Contacts

Editor
Jonathan Barnes
Email: jonathanbarnes@johncatt.com

Advertising & School Profiles
Tel: +44 (0) 1394 389850
Email: sales@johncatt.com

Distribution/Book Sales
Tel: +44 (0) 1394 389863
Email: booksales@johncatt.com

Website: www.schoolsearch.co.uk

Contents

How to use this guide

Which School? has been specifically designed with the reader in mind. There are clearly defined sections providing information for anyone looking at independent education in the UK today.

Are you looking for help and advice? Take a look at our editorial section (pages 5-48). Here you will find articles written by experts in their field covering a wide variety of issues you are likely to come across when choosing a school for your child. Each year we try to find a differing range of topics to interest and inform you about the uniqueness of independent education.

Perhaps you are looking for a school or college in a certain geographical region? Then you need to look first in the directories, which begin on page D307. Here you will find basic information about all the schools in each region complete with contact details. From this section you will be directed to more detailed information in the guide where this is available. An example of a typical directory entry is given below.

Are you looking for a certain type of school or college in your local area? Then you will need to look in the directories for your local area (see contents page for a list of all regions). Underneath each school you will find icons that denote the different types of schools or the qualifications that they offer.

Some of you may already be looking for a specific school or college. In which case, if you know the name of the school or college but are unsure of its location, simply go to the index at the back of the guide where you will find all the schools listed alphabetically. Page numbers prefixed with the letter D denote the directory section; those without, a detailed profile.

If, however, you need to find out more information on relevant educational organisations and examinations, then you can look in the appendices where you will find up-to-date information about the examinations and qualifications available (page 417). There is also a section giving basic details about the many varied and useful organisations in the education field (page 437).

The profile and directory information in this guide is also featured on **www.schoolsearch.co.uk**, which also includes social media links, and latest school news.

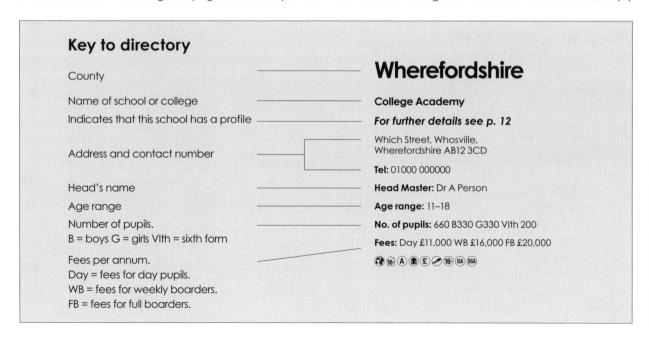

Key to directory

County

Name of school or college

Indicates that this school has a profile

Address and contact number

Head's name

Age range

Number of pupils.
B = boys G = girls VIth = sixth form

Fees per annum.
Day = fees for day pupils.
WB = fees for weekly boarders.
FB = fees for full boarders.

Wherefordshire

College Academy

For further details see p. 12

Which Street, Whosville,
Wherefordshire AB12 3CD

Tel: 01000 000000

Head Master: Dr A Person

Age range: 11–18

No. of pupils: 660 B330 G330 VIth 200

Fees: Day £11,000 WB £16,000 FB £20,000

Key to directory icons

Key to symbols:
- ⚲ Boys' school
- ⚲ Girls' school
- 🌐 International school
- 16⁺ Tutorial or sixth form college

Schools offering:
- Ⓐ A levels
- ⚐ Boarding accommodation
- £ Bursaries
- 16⁺ Entrance at 16+
- ⒾⒷ International Baccalaureate
- ✎ Learning support
- ✹ Vocational qualifications

The questions you should ask

However much a school may appeal on first sight, you still need sound information to form your judgement

Schools attract pupils by their reputations, so most go to considerable lengths to ensure that parents are presented with an attractive image.

Modern marketing techniques try to promote good points and play down (without totally obscuring) bad ones. But every Head knows that, however good the school prospectus is, it only serves to attract parents through the school gates. Thereafter the decision depends on what they see and hear.

When you choose a school for your son or daughter, the key factor is that it will suit them. Many children and their parents are instinctively attracted (or otherwise) to a school on first sight. But even if it passes this test, and 'conforms' to what you are looking for in terms of location and academic, pastoral and extracurricular aspects, you will need to satisfy yourself that the school does measure up to what your instincts tell you.

Research we have carried out over the years suggests that in many cases the most important factor in choosing a school is the impression given by the Head. As well as finding out what goes on in a school, parents need to be reassured by the aura of confidence which they expect from a Head. How they discover the former may help them form their opinion of the latter.

So how a Head answers your questions is important. Based on our research, we have drawn up a list of 24 points on which you may need to be satisfied. The order in which they appear below does not necessarily reflect their degree of importance to each parent, but how the Head answers them may help you draw your own conclusions:

- How accessible is the Head, whose personality is seen by most parents as setting the 'tone' of the school?

- Will your child fit in? What is the overall atmosphere?

- To which organisations does the school belong? How has it been accredited?

- What is the ratio of teachers to pupils?

- What are the qualifications of the teaching staff?

- How often does the school communicate with parents through reports, parent/teacher meetings or other visits?

- What is the school's retention rate? Do larger lower classes and smaller upper classes reflect a school's inability to hang on to pupils?

- What are the school's exam results? What are the criteria for presenting them? Are they consistent over the years?

- How does the school cope with pupils' problems?

- What sort of academic and pastoral advice is available?

- What is the school's attitude to discipline?

- Have there been problems with drugs or sex? How have they been dealt with?

- What positive steps are taken to encourage good manners, behaviour and sportsmanship?

- Is progress accelerated for the academically bright?

- How does the school cope with pupils who do not work?

- What is the attitude to religion?

- What is the attitude to physical fitness and games?

- What sports are offered and what are the facilities?

- What are the extracurricular activities? What cultural or other visits are arranged away from the school?

- What steps are taken to encourage specific talent in music, the arts or sport?

- Where do pupils go when they leave – are they channelled to a few selected destinations?

- What is the uniform? What steps are taken to ensure that pupils take pride in their personal appearance?

- What are the timetable and term dates?

- Is it possible to speak to parents with children at the school to ask them for an opinion?

What is a world class independent education?

Mike Buchanan, Executive Director of HMC, says great schools focus on the needs of the individual

"Whatever an education is, it should make you a unique individual, not a conformist; it should furnish you with the original spirit with which to tackle the big challenges. It should allow you to find values which will be your roadmap through life; it should make you spiritually rich, a person who loves whatever you are doing, wherever you are, whomever you are with; it should teach you what is important, how to live and how to die."

This quote from John Taylor Gatto, an American teacher of long standing, is not a bad definition for what most independent schools work towards alongside you and your children.

Well, there are plenty big challenges for young people and adults alike, not least navigating the childhood and teenage years in order to emerge as a well-rounded, physically and mentally healthy people with the resilience to cope with adult life and the vision to see joy in their life's purpose. Joy arises from the fulfilment of working closely with others for something meaningful; our families, our workmates, our teammates, our acquaintances are all sources of joy and fulfilment.

Learning to see joy in others is one of the big challenges of life. Too often we strive to place ourselves ahead of others in our desperate search for personal achievement, money, fame or position. In doing so, we often find fleeting pleasure but rarely long-lasting joy and fulfilment.

The best independent schools understand this, and they work towards two simple things. Firstly, maximising the achievements of the children and young people not merely their academic examination results and, secondly, developing them as people. They do this very simply. Firstly, they provide outstanding, expert teaching by experts in their fields which broadens and deepens each student's knowledge, understanding and skills. You can see this by observing how curious students are and whether they ask probing questions of their teachers. Secondly, the leadership of the school is entirely focused on teaching and learning, inside and outside the classroom by providing a myriad of opportunities that your child can and should take; look for the myriad. Thirdly and equally importantly, great schools focus on the needs, pastoral and academic, of the individual for whom they demonstrate great care and love; talk to those who experience this care and love about their experiences.

Those independent schools in the UK which follow these simple principles are leaders in the world which is why they are in such demand by the parents of the world.

Learning to see joy in others is one of the big challenges of life. Too often we strive to place ourselves ahead of others in our desperate search for personal achievement, money, fame or position. In doing so, we often find fleeting pleasure but rarely long-lasting joy and fulfilment.

The best independent schools understand this.

For more information about HMC, see page 45

Children and technology use

Dina Mallett, Headmistress of Cameron House School in London, advocates safe and effective screen time

There are many schools of thought about children and technology use but at the centre of the Venn diagram of all of the contradictory and controversial dos and don'ts is the fact that technology exists: it is present and it will play a huge part in our children's future.

We have been made very aware of the negative impact of screen time on children and of the correlation between social media and poor mental health. With this in mind, it would be very easy to keep children as far away from this danger but we cannot hide our children away from the online world, as advised by some, because it poses a threat. The thing is, so does climbing trees and crossing roads; and just as I would not leave a small child unattended with a pair of sharp scissors, neither would I leave them alone with unlimited access to the internet. What we must do is teach children to use technology safely to give them access to today's and tomorrow's world, and accept that technology is a wonderful tool for learning.

It is the responsibility of schools to ensure that this 'tool' is used safely. As a preparatory school, our modus operandi is to prepare our children for life beyond their primary phase of education; and this includes ensuring that they are up to date and ready for the technological world with the knowledge of how to navigate their way safely. It has been said again and again that the jobs that some of our children will have as adults do not even exist right now! The world moves at a rapid pace and our children must not be left behind. Sir Tim Berners-Lee, creator of the World Wide Web, stated, "The Web as I envisaged it, we have not seen it yet. The future is still so much bigger than the past."

At Cameron House School our children are well versed in both the skills of computing and online safety. The impressive projects and creations developed in our fantastic 'Robotics Club' are testament to the benefits of teaching and learning programming. Alongside reference books, our pupils from as young as Year 2 use the internet in school for independent research once they have been given the guidance of how to do so successfully. Our PSHE programme ensures that our children are taught how to use the internet safely and wisely, that they are aware of the existence of CEOP and, as they should with any worry, the importance of 'telling an adult' should they ever be faced with a technology issue.

It is important to consider how and why your children are using technology at home and for how long. Useful tips for parents include:

- Setting time limits for technology use.
- Having a family computer/tablet rather than children having their own – it is easier for a child to accept it being taken away if it is not their personal possession.
- Monitor and encourage usage in a communal space rather than bedrooms.
- Ask your child what they know about keeping safe online.

Further information about staying safe online can be found at:
Thinkyounow.co.uk
Internetmatters.org
Nspcc.org
Safetynetkids.org
Kidsmart.org

For more information about Cameron House School, see page 138

Introducing the EPQ

John Tyler, Deputy Head (Academic) at Dauntsey's, on a qualification that can be 'immensely rewarding'

The Extended Project Qualification (EPQ) was devised by Sir Mike Tomlinson in 2006, during his review of 16 to 19-year-olds' education and it became a compulsory part of the 14–19 Diploma taken by students in England and Wales between 2008 and 2013.

An EPQ consists of either a practical project, plus a 1,000-word report, or a 5,000-word dissertation. Everyone gives a ten-minute presentation on their work and answers questions from an audience. Each student has a supervisor and receives around 30 hours of teaching, as well as spending between 90 – 120 hours on the project itself.

The marking of an EPQ is designed to reflect the skills needed at university, with 20 per cent for planning and managing the workload, 20 per cent for use of resources, 40 per cent for developing and realising the project and 20 per cent for reviewing it. The result is worth more than an AS level in terms of university entrance points, with 28 points for the top grade of an A*, compared to just 20 points for the top grade of an A for an AS.

More and more universities and employers are recognising EPQs when they assess student applications. They like the EPQ as it helps develop skills such as critical thinking, problem-solving and creativity which are valuable not only for university study but also for the world of work. With a choice of just three or four A levels narrowing students' choice of subject, an EPQ can provide an opportunity to explore in depth another area of interest or something they have never had the chance to study. Completing an EPQ also provides content which a student can discuss in detail during interviews which can be a significant differentiator.

Doing an EPQ demands imagination, self-motivation, organisation and application. But a successfully executed EPQ can tip the balance in favour of one university applicant over another and some universities will even accept an excellent EPQ in lieu of a target grade in one A level subject. It is also great preparation for the shift in mental gear required at university, as it requires a high level of independent work and original thought.

The EPQ has been on offer at Dauntsey's since 2012, when it was completed in a pupil's own time. It has now been on the timetable since 2016. We view it as a bridge between school and university, a chance to explore an area that might be relevant to a future career and a taster of academic life after school. It is not only an intellectual and practical challenge but an intellectual task that can be immensely rewarding.

> 'The EPQ has been tremendous. It's a great chance to prove something to yourself and I really would recommend it to anyone.'

Thomas completed his EPQ on 'Altitude and Cognitive Function':

"I want to read medicine and thought that doing a related EPQ would help, as well as being an opportunity to look at a topic in depth. I'd already planned to climb Kilimanjaro, so that gave me the opportunity to do real-life experiments to test cognitive function as we were ascending. Before then, I'd been planning a 5,000-word essay but this way I was able to do far more.

I learned that I was surprisingly well-organised – I'm not in general life – particularly when it comes to getting up in the morning! But I needed to manage my time properly to get my research done while carrying on with my other studies.

The EPQ gives you targets and has shown me how to apply critical analysis to revision for my A levels in maths, physics, chemistry and biology, which has helped a lot. It's going to be invaluable at university."

Africa completed her EPQ by creating a solar-powered bike.

"The EPQ has been tremendous. It's a great chance to prove something to yourself and I really would recommend it to anyone. It's got me a lower offer to study at Nottingham – but I wanted to do the project anyway. It's great producing something yourself.

People didn't think my idea was going to work – but it does! Unlike most solar bikes, which have solar panels down the sides, it's got a solar canopy. It can also be powered by mains electricity and it does move on its own.

I live in Spain, so I had plenty of sun. I built it over the summer with a bit of supervision from my dad, but that was mainly to make sure I didn't burn the house down! My A levels helped. I'm taking maths, further maths, physics and chemistry and the physics was particularly useful. It helped me understand how solar panels work and how to set them up best.

It really helped that I wrote everything down, and it will definitely give me something to talk about at university!"

For more information about Dauntsey's see page 58

An orchestra of equals

Bryony Bell reports on how Chetham's is creating Olympians of the music world

In summer 2019 we watched the England women's football team reach the semi-finals of the FIFA World Cup for the second time in a row, after years on the sidelines. Increased investment in the women's game, and dramatic leaps in its media profile, saw the tournament thrill the nation as the Lionesses drew within reach of victory and players became household names.

The story isn't an isolated one. Increased investment after the 2012 Olympics still resonates in Team GB's sporting successes today, as children inspired by the London games train for their own medal attempts in 2020. Yet, for others inspired not by the sports themselves, but by the dance, music and creativity on show in the Olympics Opening and Closing ceremonies, the pathway has been less clear. Time and resources assigned to arts education have tumbled across the state education sector, and whilst there are numerous exceptional youth arts activities happening across the country, they're not always long term, connected, or accessible to children of all backgrounds. For those who discover a real talent, who are ready, at a young age, to commit the time and energy needed to join the elite, there are new hurdles to be faced. Cost, geography, the support of teachers, family and friends – all of these can be powerful barriers to success.

Wonderfully, many independent schools across the country offer bursaries for young musicians, dancers and performers, alongside athletes and academics. Yet how much more wonderful for these young people to join an elite training camp, an entire school community built around a shared talent and commitment. That's what's offered by the UK Government's Music and Dance schools – nine centres in England and Scotland where young artists join a programme in which talent is the only criterion for entry.

Boarding accommodation, funding up to full bursaries, and integrated arts and academic teaching create genuine meritocracies – elite institutions, but in no way elitist.

At Chetham's, the largest of the five Music schools within the scheme, 300+ young musicians live and learn in the heart of Manchester. Here they enjoy facilities to rival the country's leading conservatoires – purpose built rehearsal and practice rooms, two world class performance venues, and an unparalleled programme of individual tuition, music

> 'For Chethams ... it became a thrilling triumph.'

theory, chamber classes, improvisation and choral singing, all taught by leading professional musicians. In summer 2019 – two days before the women's world cup final – its flagship orchestra, Chetham's Symphony, became the first school ensemble to perform Mahler's colossal Symphony No. 8. "It's hard to imagine any place of secondary education where they would even contemplate it," said the ArtsDesk, "but for Chetham's…it became a thrilling triumph." Broadcast live on BBC Radio 3, with almost no performer above the age of 19, it brought together over two-thirds of the school's community, from the very youngest choristers, aged 8, to sixth formers just awaiting A-level results before joining top conservatoires and universities across the world.

These vast forces created a true orchestra of equals. Its leader, Molin, joined Chetham's from China, with generous bursaries recognising her precocious talent, and is now studying at the Royal College of Music. On The Bridgewater

Hall's mighty pipe organ was George, leaving Chetham's after ten years as a chorister, trumpeter, organist and singer to take up an organ scholarship at Cambridge. In the chorus was head girl Josephine, a hugely talented pianist and singer also predicted superb A-level results, and heading for a highly competitive academic programme at university. Principal bassoon was Jamie from Glasgow, aged just 16, fresh from his GCSEs and with a Wigmore Hall debut already under his belt. Younger still were the children's chorus members, mainly the choristers of Manchester Cathedral and Chetham's. Among them was Molly, aged 11 from Lancashire, inspired to sing after an outreach programme created by Chetham's and The Bridgewater Hall. 90% were in receipt of funding through the Department for Education's Music and Dance scheme; others from the Cathedral's choristership programme. With music at the very core of Chetham's being, those few who do pay full or partial fees can be confident that they include all music tuition, orchestral programmes, and over 300 performance opportunities each year. There's even a bespoke sports programme, Fit to Perform, designed around the special demands of music practice on students' growing bodies.

This elite training camp has already produced many of the Olympians of the music world. Its alumni fill concert halls across the world, as performers, conductors, composers and leaders of the music sector, as classical musicians, jazz artists, folk singers, electronic DJs and hip hop stars. It's a place where all remain welcome – as students, as audiences, as parents, alumni and friends – to play their part in an orchestra of equals.

For more information about Chetham's School of Music, see page 176

Top tips for dual working families

Rachel Gaynor, Deputy Head at Maltman's Green School, shares expert advice for parents choosing a school

Affordability is a big concern when it comes to education. Many parents choose the independent sector to give their children the best start in life, but may find that they need a dual income in order to do so. Having to factor in the costs of a childminder before and/or after school can suddenly make this dream unaffordable. If you fit into this category, how do you go about selecting a school that will meet both your educational and childcare needs? Here are some top tips as both a Deputy Head, and a parent, who has been there.

1. Decide on your ideal location

Consider whether you would rather your child went to a local independent school or if it would be easier to drop them off adjacent to where either of you work or commute from. Both have pros and cons so it is worth having this discussion. Locally will mean it is easier for your child to socialise, attend parties and weekend activities but will inevitably mean you need to pay for before and after school care. Nearer one of your places of work or the start of your commute may cut your fee bills, however, it will also mean you have to get your child up and ready earlier and you will spend more hours on the road, particularly at weekends.

2. Analyse your working hours

Is one of you able to work flexible hours or work from home? It might be worth talking to your employer about this, as dependent on your role, most are very understanding. Some parents manage to arrange things so one parent goes in to work later after the drop off but then works later into the evening, while the other goes into work early and is finished earlier in the day ready for pick up.

3. Do your research

Once you have narrowed down your search area if possible, arrange some childcare and head off to somewhere quiet such as a coffee shop, armed with an internet enabled device and a notepad. Away from the constant interruptions of family life you will have the time to go through each school's website to identify the type of education that the school offers, as well as the breakfast and after school care availability. If you need to use these services then the times that these are offered will be crucial when it comes to selecting a school. Do not forget to check if any holiday care is provided. Typically, because the school day is longer in the independent sector, the holidays tend to be longer and this needs to be factored into your research.

4. Make a shortlist

Based on your research, make a shortlist and be prepared to be brutal. It was at this point that I had to cross out some schools for my son that I really liked purely based on the availability of their breakfast and after school care. Some schools just didn't offer care until 8am, which was too late for me or didn't have a nursery provision to allow my son to stay in one school from nursery upwards, which I felt was important. Once you have your shortlist re-visit the websites and begin to form a list of any questions that you may have.

5. Phone the school to arrange a visit or attend an open day

For me, the phone calls were just as vital as visiting the school itself. I was looking to have interactions with polite, helpful and friendly members of the school community, and conversations which would hopefully mirror the ethos of the school that I had read about online. Of course, the conversation will need to open with an enquiry about the availability of spaces in the school. If a place is available then it is ideal if you a visit with your partner as you can both ask questions and get a real feel for the school. If you are unable to do this then it is worth visiting separately.

6. Look around and make a decision!

Once you have made your visits, it is time to make a decision. Enquire directly with the school about the next steps in terms of accepting a place. After having had this type of discussion with many parents over my career, I have noticed that often one school emerges as the clear favourite – it was certainly like this for me. Choosing a school is like buying a house – when you are in the right one you will know and you will be able to visualise your child there.

Armed with an understanding of the difficulties faced by dual working families, Maltman's Green launched a day-care facility for girls aged two and up in early 2017, providing year-round care from 7.30am to 6.30pm. This came as a welcome relief to our existing parents who had a little one that needed taking care of, as well as to new parents who wanted their daughter settled in a school that could see them right through to aged 11. Such was the demand for our Little Malties day care, that not long after opening, renovations were made to extend the space. Over the last few years we have gone one step further as we work to help meet the demands of working parents, and extended our out of hours provision right across the School. Girls in our Nursery are now offered the same year round care as those in our Little Malties setting, while girls in Reception to Year 6 can stay from 7.30am – 6.00pm, with holiday care provided onsite by an external provider.

As the saying goes, 'the proof is in the pudding', and the ever-increasing number of girls in our Breakfast and After School Clubs prove just how valuable a wrap-around-care provision is for busy parents.

Meet my bear!

My bears name is

Colour

Size (in cm)

My bear likes to

Owners name

For more information
about Maltman's Green,
see page 214

Embracing – and navigating – the digital age

Rachel Phelan, of Abbot's Hill School in Hertfordshire, explains how technology has impacted upon school life

Abbot's Hill School aims to prepare pupils for a lifetime of learning. Our historic campus offers modern facilities in a magnificent country setting, situated in over 70 acres of beautiful parkland on the outskirts of Hemel Hempstead, Hertfordshire. Our pupils are encouraged to aim high, enjoy learning and to grasp opportunities.

In a world where technology is constantly evolving and more accessible than ever before, we have chosen to embrace this at our school.

This includes inside the classroom, for teaching and learning, parent communications and pastoral care. Recognising that technology is increasingly part of our everyday lives, our goal is to create a modern learning environment in which pupils are taught to navigate the privileges and risks of the digital age.

At Abbot's Hill School, we recognise that technology can greatly enrich the curriculum and help to assist pupils' learning. We also realise that our pupils need to be aware of how to use technology safely.

Our Senior School pupils are each issued with a Chromebook device which is used to enhance their learning through the use of Google Classroom and associated apps. These pupils will all complete an Online Safety qualification to ensure that they are aware of the online dangers and the ways in which they can use the internet wisely.

The school has also run interactive sessions and talks for both pupils and parents on how to engage with technology in positive ways. The Director of Pastoral Care works closely with the school's ICT team and a board of parent volunteers who make up the dedicated Online Safety Community Group for the school. They work together to find practical ways to support families through the ever-changing developments in technology and any potential issues that they could cause.

We pride ourselves on our pastoral care and at Abbot's Hill; the individual pupil's well-being is at the heart of everything we do. This is reflected in all aspects of school life and starts from the moment a pupil enters the school.

Abbot's Hill was the first school in the country to begin using the AS Tracking tool for both Prep and Senior pupils. It is an online self-assessment which is completed by pupils up to three times in an academic year and monitor pupils' mental health in its results. This data is used by staff to inform proactive, targeted and evidence-based pastoral support for each individual child.

Parents also directly benefit from the use of technology at Abbot's Hill. All parents have access to a dedicated, secure Parent Portal which provides instant access to their children's timetables, reports, the school calendar and much more. Clubs and extra-curricular activities can be booked through this, as well as slots for parent consultation evenings. There is no need to rely on your daughter bringing home consent forms for an upcoming trip, you can complete these on the Parent Portal and the information will go straight back to the school. If you need to update your contact details, that is just the click of a button.

Over recent years, we have taken on feedback from our parent body about the most effective ways for the school to communicate with them. This greatly favoured digital communications, where parents can instantly access the information that they need. We have now developed a weekly e-mail bulletin for families which incorporates key school news items, reminders and letters for each year group across the school.

The Senior School Council voted unanimously to ensure that all Abbot's Hill pupils were issued with the same device to ensure there was no peer pressure to have the very best technology that they could afford. By equipping all pupils with the same Chromebook models, it allows the girls to have equal opportunity to learn in this way.

We take great pride in the quality of the teaching and learning at Abbot's Hill. Throughout the school, pupils are taught in small classes and receive personalised support, ensuring that they are stretched and supported at each stage of their education. Traditional methods of teaching and learning still have a key place in education and at our school, with technology acting as an additional educational tool to enhance and aid learning.

We have seen positive results in both pupils and teachers working together through dedicated Google Classrooms. Abbot's Hill School promotes learning in a supportive and nurturing environment in which children have the means and support to mature naturally. By using apps that enable teachers to assess learning, pre-teach material and completing assignments within guidelines that do not put pupils' at risk of online dangers, Abbot's Hill can ensure that technology enhances education where it is meaningful.

To experience Abbot's Hill School for yourself, come to our next Open Event. For further details, please visit www.abbotshill.herts.sch.uk or call us on 01442 240333. We look forward to welcoming you.

For more information about Abbot's Hill School, see page 84

Looking back to move forward as I cross the border

Dominic Findlay, the new Warden of Llandovery College in Wales, looks ahead to a fresh challenge

Many will consider that a third Headship should be easy and as I leave for the Brecon Beacons, I have been told: "it will be a walk in the park", "just repeat what you have always done and you will be fine."

Yet, on my appointment as Warden of Llandovery College from September 2019, the above comments simply do not apply. The need to understand the Welsh culture, the passion surrounding all aspects of the College community, the rich heritage of many incredible successes that have gone before and much more has made my move to Llandovery a really interesting career move.

Creating a culture full of opportunity for all of our pupils in the Independent Sector, one which sets us apart from our State School colleagues, is key to ensuring success. The pressures now being faced simply to survive in the current climate are many, yet all Heads must look forward to discovering ways of adding value both academically and pastorally to ensure parents believe that our product is worth investing in.

At Llandovery College, I have spent time speaking to many people in an attempt to discover exactly what it is that makes parents commit to sending their children to a small school on the edge of the Brecon Beacons. Looking back has been key to building a new and exciting development plan on which we will be able to move forward. Parents, pupils, staff, Old Boys and Girls, Governors, Trustees, local people and many others have given me their views on what makes Llandovery College so special as well as advice on how to develop it.

So what can be learnt from looking to the past? An understanding of how important the College is to many previous families is vitally important. I have met many former pupils who proudly claim: "I would be nowhere if it wasn't for my time at the College." Their stories are hugely powerful

to market to current and prospective pupils who themselves will be prospective parents and grandparents of the future.

Llandovery College has an incredible Old Llandoverian Society that helps raise funds, offers guidance to current pupils and demonstrates in real terms the end product of the education they received. Recently I was sent an article that showed that 550 full Welsh Rugby caps have been gained by former pupils, recent examples being George North and current Captains Alun Wyn Jones and, for the national women's rugby union team, Carys Phillips.

Taking this example and gaining a clear perspective of the sporting DNA and culture that is so important to so many at the College, I am now looking to develop this further in September. Such a rich sporting culture that has shaped so many former Llandoverians cannot be ignored and will help shape our current and future pupils over the coming years.

Recognising the valuable lessons of the past and how sport has helped shape pupils throughout and beyond their

school years has been incredibly powerful. Commitment, the importance of the concept 'team', the ability to demonstrate the School's values both in success and failure and much more are lessons that now sit with these young men and women as they build their careers in our ever changing world. Ours, like many other Independent Schools, will claim much in our marketing literature but ultimately it is these real life examples that help add reality to these claims.

In looking back we must also not forget the core purpose of any school and that is to educate as openly and as honestly as possible the youngsters in our care. Discovery, by turning our heads backwards to see what made the teacher 'a legend' or how they continually got outstanding results compared to others, is key. Alongside this, as educators, we need to challenge ourselves on a daily basis to ensure that we make a difference to the pupils in our care.

Looking back to help shape how we look forward is firmly engraved on my mind as I move to Llandovery College. Showing an understanding and respect to this, whilst striving to ensure that the educational experience we offer is forward looking, modern and fit for purpose in today's society is no mean task. It is a task that myself and my team at Llandovery College now face and we are ready for the challenge.

Do come and visit if you are ever stepping over the border and you will receive a passionate, Welsh welcome like no other!

"Edrych yn ol i symud ymlaen"

For more information about Llandovery College, see page 290

Curriculum 200 at Eagle House

Helen Brice, Deputy Academic, explains the reasoning behind the launch of a new approach to Years 5–8

It may sound rather obvious, but the magic of the independent education system is the ability and permission to be independent, unique and go above and beyond the 'typical'. There is no doubt that all schools strive to be 'outstanding' not only in the sense of being the best they can be, but to actually 'stand out'.

There are many aspects of school life that make Eagle House: drama productions for 150 children in a professional theatre, forward-thinking personal, social, citizenship and health education, a wide range of sporting opportunities for all and an extraordinary co-curricular activities programme.

On the academic side of school life, we were one of the first prep schools in the country to adopt the IPC (International Primary Curriculum) for Years 1–4. This enabled us to combine the teaching of the humanities, science and arts subjects into meaningful thematic units in which the children are encouraged to research, report and explore with a greater degree of freedom and independence, without losing the rigour of these distinct subjects. Pupils, staff and parents have offered nothing but praise for this new curriculum and every year we host staff from both state and independent schools who are keen to observe the curriculum in action in the hope of emulating what we offer.

By stark contrast, the curriculum beyond Year 4, examined through the Common Entrance examinations at 13+, has been around in the vast majority of prep schools up and down the country, since 1904! Whilst it has, of course, evolved over the past 115 years, it does continue to restrict a school's ability to be creative and devise a curriculum of their own for these senior years; a curriculum which builds on the foundations set in the early years and prepares the children for the world in which they will live. Certainly, producing a 'stand out' curriculum for these senior year groups has been a real challenge.

As senior schools have moved to Pre-Testing in Year 6 the concept of Common Entrance as an entrance exam to independent senior schools has become somewhat redundant. In addition, many top employers have criticised the current education system (both state and independent) for producing graduates that are not fit for the workplace. Top performances in school examinations do not necessarily correlate with success in the workplace and the skills valued, honed and practised in a typical school are not necessarily those that will be important to succeed in later life. Currently, a lot of curriculum time is lost, especially in the final two years to exam preparation. Exams are important and whilst they are still the method by which pupils are assessed and judged, they need to learn to do well in them. That said, we must not allow this to dominate to the detriment of the future success of these young people. We need to ensure they are 'Learning for Life'. We need to create and develop learners of the future. Learners who are engaged, reflective, communicative, motivated, resilient, organised, inquisitive.

As Eagle House celebrates its 200th Anniversary we need to ensure we are teaching a curriculum that will prepare children for the next 200 years. By one popular estimate, 65% of children entering primary school today will ultimately end up working in completely new job types that don't yet exist.

From September 2019 Eagle House will be launching our new Curriculum 200 for the pupils in Years 5–8. This rich, knowledge-based curriculum will continue where the IPC has finished. As pupils move into Year 5 and are taught by subject specialists, teachers have built the curriculum with topics that ignite passion and allow for relevant and meaningful cross-curricular links. Curriculum 200 will be a modular system with regular formal assessment to allow for the continual monitoring of progress every half term, rather than cramming for exams. Every lesson in every term will count. Exams will still take place in every year group from Years 5–8 but only in the summer term, providing up to 6 weeks additional teaching time over the course of the year.

Alongside new topics assessed through end of unit assessments, we will also be assessing pupils learning skills; their levels of engagement in class, whether they can be reflective, how communicative they are, their self-motivation, the resilience they show when faced with academic challenges and whether they are organised and inquisitive. Curriculum 200 includes a seven-point grading scale of all these key learning skills. Pupils will be graded each term and shown where, and more crucially, how they can develop in these vital areas.

In addition to the new, broader range of topics being taught, pupils in all year groups will complete a range of short independent learning projects throughout the year. These will take place in curriculum time due to the time gained from fewer sets of exams. These smaller but more frequent projects will enable pupils to have greater ownership of their learning and be able to develop the vital learning skills that employers value so highly.

For more information about Eagle House School, see page 198

A well-being led approach to examination success

Steve Winter, Deputy Head of Bethany School, outlines a 10-step plan for planning and preparation

Placing the well-being of pupils first ensures examination success. This has once again been evidenced at Bethany School by outstanding A level and GCSE results, including a record number of A level A*/A grades and GCSE grades 7-9. In March, it was announced that the School was in the top 2% of schools nationally for A level progress and Bethany School was one of the very few senior schools in the country to have been awarded the National Wellbeing award for Schools.

As we start a new academic year, the stress placed on pupils during assessments and examinations can be forgotten in the glow of successes from the A level and GCSE results days. At Bethany School, a great deal of thought goes into considering how pupil wellbeing can best be supported during the stressful exam period. We highlight the need to place the child at the centre of every decision and we believe that by doing so we will usually take the right approach. Key to our approach to pupil support during assessments and examinations is that strategies for promoting wellbeing are thought of and rehearsed at the start of the year so the routines and behaviours become normalised, offering maximum support to pupils when it comes to the examination period itself.

Bethany School's 10-step approach to promoting assessment and examination wellbeing starts with the adage 'planning and preparation prevents poor performance':

1. Begin preparation early: considering individual pupil needs at the start of the year means that all elements of examination preparation have been rehearsed.
2. Provide pupil and parent sessions on effective revision and mindful preparation for the examinations, support this with regular updates to pupils and parents on effective revision strategies.
3. Pupils with coursework 'pinch points' are supported through after-hours access to academic facilities.
4. Pupils with examination access arrangements are given the opportunity to practise in an examination environment (e.g. if taking examinations alone, they will have the opportunity to do this prior to the examination).
5. Staff work on individual strategies for pupils with anxieties around the examination room itself, so that they can rehearse beforehand how they will deal with that "over the threshold" moment.
6. With day pupils, parents are encouraged to practise the examination day routine at home so that pupils feel comfortable with the pre-exam routine and can identify any areas of difficulty or stress beforehand.
7. Run examination warm-ups for pupils to receive specific advice in the run up to the examination and can talk through any anxieties with their tutors. The shared experience of these can minimise individual anxieties.
8. Support pupils to keep up their energy levels and prevent fatigue during examinations by providing water and a cereal bar or fruit in the examination warm-ups.
9. Offer boarding pupils the opportunity to unwind by opening School sports facilities in the evenings and at weekends and make available early morning swimming which helps pupils work and exercise when they are most effective.
10. On results days, have Tutors, Housemasters/Mistresses and the Senior Staff (including Head of Sixth Form and UCAS Coordinator for A level results) available to share in pupils successes but also to provide appropriate counsel and support for those who have missed out on what they had hoped to achieve.

What we have found over the past three years of running this programme is, that for those pupils whose anxieties are well known, their performance loss in examinations is minimised by practising and rehearsing their strategies for assessments and examinations. Furthermore, our focus on the individual benefits all because we are mindful as a whole School community at all times of the need to be supportive during these stressful moments in young people's lives. However, it is not until after all issues arising from the Results Days have been resolved that we feel our job for the year is done. From very early on both Results Days we have Senior Staff and Tutors available to meet with pupils and families to provide valuable one to one counselling and support with next steps both for those who have exceeded their expectations but also for those who, for one reason or another, have not made the grade. Pupils and Parents are hugely grateful for the time that is spent with every individual who needs support on Results Days and, indeed, in the days afterwards.

Headmaster, Francie Healy, said "I am delighted for each and every Bethany School pupil who have received their results this month. Behind every headline are many individual success stories which sum up our ethos as a School: we know every pupil very well and put their wellbeing first. It is so rewarding when you see young people who we have come to know so well achieve their potential and, very often, beyond it. Thanks are due to the fantastic and supportive teachers and parents who have helped our pupils achieve these successes."

For more information about Bethany School, see page 188

The importance of creativity in extra-curricular opportunities

Mary Fowell, Director of Marketing and Admissions at Manor House School, on the growing demand for creative and expressive curricular enrichment opportunities

Founded in 1920, and soon to be celebrating its Centenary Year, Manor House School in Bookham is known for providing girls with a happy and nurturing smaller school environment, encouraging excellent academic results. One of the school's seven core values is 'Creative and Collaborative' and it is no surprise that Manor House was shortlisted for an Independent Schools Award in the Creative and Expressive Arts in 2018. As well as a wealth of sports clubs fostering high levels of participation and performance, music, singing and drama clubs are a popular choice with students and there is also increasing demand for creative and expressive curricular enrichment opportunities.

One such creative example that has seen significant growth in recent years is the provision of LAMDA (London Academy of Music and Dramatic Art) lessons which are taught as a co-curricular option and offered from Year 1 all the way up to Year 11. Over one third of pupils at Manor House now choose to take LAMDA. Examinations take place every year in the Spring term but LAMDA isn't just about results, it's about the girls gaining confidence in themselves to perform in front of others, working with their peers, improving their speaking and listening skills and learning about poetry and a variety of playwrights. The seven reasons for studying LAMDA include:

1. Reading fluently with understanding
2. Improving confidence in speaking and listening
3. Improving self-expression by expanding vocabulary
4. Memorising and recalling information
5. Delivering formal presentations
6. Working successfully alone and in a team
7. Creating and defending arguments

Sometimes the quietest and shyest of girls take LAMDA and really blossom over the year. For one pupil it can be finding the confidence to read aloud in class and be heard, and for another it can help to improve public speaking or interview skills.

Manor House runs an extensive extra-curricular clubs programme every term with up to 50 clubs and activities operating at any one time across all year groups before, during and after school. The ability to 'try something new' without pressure encourages girls to seek out new experiences, develop new interests and in turn build confidence, whilst making new friends. There is of course the added benefit of improving an existing skill or simply having sheer fun!

The 'creative clubs' on offer don't just stop at the subjects of Art, Music or Drama though. Opportunities are varied and include groups such as: Textiles Craft Club (learning new techniques in modern day textiles), a 'Gifted and Talented' Writing Club (a creative writing club which challenges girls to compose high quality writing on a competitive basis) and Bridge (teaching pupils social skills as well as offering a mental workout stimulating both halves of the brain in equal measure). Playing bridge uses and develops visualization, logical thinking, inferential analysis, problem solving skills, sequencing, lateral thinking, long and short-term memory and observation. Bridge is already on the national curriculum in some enlightened countries such as China and Poland. There is a photography club and even a Creative Media Club, where girls can learn how to make and change webpages, games and images.

There are, of course, the more traditional clubs on offer including Drama Clubs, Prep and Senior Bands, Music Theory Club and Junior and Senior Orchestral Clubs where the ability to perform and/or 'act out' in front of peers and audiences increase self-confidence, self-esteem and communication skills.

Additional music lessons are delivered throughout the school day in the facility of Meadow Cottage. We offer tuition in over 18 instruments encouraging participation in school productions and the annual 'Rock & Pop Concert'.

Art is taught across the School from Reception age to Year 11. Girls are encouraged to work in a variety of materials including paint, pencil, textiles, collage, clay, print-making, plaster and wire. Many of them choose to work big and the department prides itself on allowing the girls to pursue their own strengths and enthusiasms, resulting in stimulating and diverse work at GCSE level. There are four Art clubs – two for Preps, one for Seniors and one for GCSE students.

A popular senior scholarships programme awards scholarships in Art, Drama and Music (in addition to Sport) effective at Year 7 and most recently, new Year 3 scholarships, for Academic and Music, have been announced. These are effective from September 2020 (apply by mid-November 2019). To enquire, contact admissions@manorhouseschool.org or visit www.manorhouseschool.org. Following an open morning in October 2019, further open mornings will take place in February and May 2020.

For more information about Manor House School, see page 216

Why creativity and innovation are so important

Caroline Jordan, Headmistress at Headington School, considers what it takes to thrive in a technological age

What differentiates us from robots? This may sound like a stupid and, perhaps, irrelevant, question, but as the world of technology advances at a sometimes bewildering rate, it could in fact be the most important question of all.

The advance of robots, machine learning and artificial intelligence is already changing the job market beyond what we could have imagined a few short years ago. Increasingly, jobs which needed a skilled person in post can be automated. Soon, there may be very few things which machines cannot do at least as well, if not better – and more cheaply – than their human counterparts. The idea that a robot could put you out of a job would seem incredible were it not already happening all over the world.

In education, this is something that needs to be at the forefront of all our minds. If, as PwC predicts, as many as 30 per cent of UK jobs are at risk of being taken over by robots and AI by 2030, how do we prepare the children in our charge for this? How does this change what we need to teach and how our students need to learn?

There are some skills which are, however, uniquely human. Creativity and creative thinking appear to be beyond the capacity of artificial intelligence. These, then, are the skills we need to be focussing on developing. We already know how much employers value analytical thinking, innovation, creativity and originality. These are things which differentiate good candidates from excellent ones. In the future, this combination of skills may be what makes a human 'worth' employing over a robot.

When we think about the jobs of the future – and most of these do not yet exist, with an estimated 65 per cent of children entering primary school today destined to work in careers we can't envisage – it is clear that creativity has to be our defining skill. Creativity is no longer the remit of a small and specialist group of people, creatives, or artists, or thinkers, it is an essential skill which we will all need to succeed in our rapidly changing world.

How, then, do we develop these creative thinking skills? At Headington, this is something we have been thinking about for some time and we have this summer broken ground on a new Creativity & Innovation Centre. This will

> Creativity is no longer the remit of a small and specialist group of people, creatives, or artists, or thinkers, it is an essential skill which we will all need to succeed in our rapidly changing world.

become the new home for Fine Art, Sculpture, Photography, and Fashion Textiles at Headington, as well as a hub for cross-curricular learning with a focus on sustainability, enterprise and technology. We want to create the conditions that will foster creativity and ensure each girl lives up to their creative potential. Instead of defining themselves as 'arty' or 'creative' or 'good at Science' to the exclusion of other subjects, we want our girls to look at how skills and approaches from all subjects feed into each other to produce more interesting outcomes. How can we take what or how we learn in one subject and use it to make another area of learning more effective and successful? A fantastic new learning environment, exposing girls to new ideas and techniques and using purpose-built, state-of-the-art equipment and classrooms will help facilitate this but ultimately this approach needs to be part of everything we do, whether in our new centre or anywhere in the School.

Earlier this year, some of our younger girls combined Science, Art and Computing as they researched, designed and built model flying planes. While a computer might be able to follow instructions perfectly and execute a 'textbook' model plane, it takes a human touch to come up with something new, to take a wider view and to be truly creative. Young minds are uniquely placed to do this – they haven't yet accepted the orthodox approach and so are really very good at coming up with something original and fresh. This kind of cross-curricular creative learning is something we will be doing more of to help develop these skills further. It is our job to cultivate these skills, attitudes, behaviours and experiences in our learners. We will do this by encouraging girls to question, explore and investigate how things work and to ignite their creative spark. This means taking risks, getting things wrong, adapting and innovating, building resilience and growth mindset as we do so – more skills we know employers hugely value.

Education has moved some way beyond learning facts and processes by rote and, while there will always be a value to having a good knowledge base, the fact most of us have access to vast quantities of information at our fingertips means this is far less significant than it once was. All of us need to think creatively to prosper in a new digital world.

For more information about Headington School, see page 64

Confidence, courage and faith in your own ability

How Ellesmere College utilises the Combined Cadet Force (CCF) and the benefits for students

One of the key aspects to a full and enriched educational programme is the diversity of the co-curricular programme. Leading Independent schools, such as Ellesmere College have recognised for years that the breadth of opportunity to engage and build a platform for individual growth bears fruit both in and out of the classroom. One area where this is particularly relevant is that of the Combined Cadet Force (CCF).

There are CCF contingents in a large number of Independent schools across over the UK, and offer pupils a broad range of challenging, exciting, adventurous and educational activities.

"Our aim is to enable the development of personal responsibility, leadership and self-discipline. Each CCF is an educational partnership between the school and the Ministry of Defence, and a CCF may include Royal Navy, Royal Marines, Army or Royal Air Force sections." – Combined Cadet Force.

The importance and recognition of the programme and its merits to pupils is evident by the curriculum time devoted to this programme. Thursday afternoons are ring-fenced for this activity and all pupils from Year 9 to Year 13 have the opportunity to select an area (Army/Navy/RAF) and then follow the varied route each one has.

Camps and courses throughout the year enable cadets to build upon this weekly training, enabling the consolidation of the many skills learnt in different Ministry of Defence establishments and training facilities across the UK.

Cadets also have the opportunity to pursue the Duke of Edinburgh Award (DofE) schemes (Bronze, Silver and Gold), with a dedicated adventurous training camps at Easter and in the summer – offering incredible challenges and tasks that are both physically and mentally tough, but the rewards are incredible!

These activities enable them to acquire essential life skills, develop their leadership and management capabilities and use their initiative in unfamiliar and challenging environments. For many, the biggest barrier for educational achievement is often self-confidence and self-belief. Living in a world where league tables rule the educational fields and pupils are examined at most stages of their school life, the "real" skills of education are about building character, developing confidence and belief in their own abilities and the belief and trust in others; an area where the CCF comes into its own.

From day one, the programme structure gives the pupils the confidence in the journey they will follow. Many activities and training programmes are delivered by senior cadets and this peer to peer learning is an essential part of the respect and recognition which goes with the ranks. Pupils wear the uniform with pride and feel part of something "special" – a group that every member feels honoured to be part of.

The Year 9 programme is designed to allow all students the opportunity to engage in a wide variety of new skills and experiences as part of the wider CCF programme including climbing, kayaking, shooting, Theory of Flight and team building.

This approach allows the pupils to decide based on real experience and personal commitment the area they want to focus on post-Year 9. One of the many strong aspects of the course is its inclusiveness that welcomes everyone and values the contribution that each student can bring to the team.

Stephen Mullock, Deputy Head External Relations says of the CCF, "It is without doubt a most worthy activity that all pupils should have the chance to experience in their formative years. I have witnessed incredible changes in pupil's attention to detail, focus and time management but mainly of self-belief, the willingness to try something difficult and the perseverance to keep going. The results speak for themselves and the skills learnt in the CCF have certainly contributed to examination success and indeed University destinations".

The latter is also an important feature of the importance of choosing a school with a varied and detailed co-curricular programme. With Universities applications comes the opportunity to separate your own application from many other pupils applying for the same place. Those pupils who have led a varied and exciting extra-curricular experience are not only better suited for such courses but have the skills to cope with the process of studying away from home with a new group of people in unfamiliar surroundings; to the CCF cadets this is nothing they have not been through before!

As part of the broader picture, the co-curricular opportunities a school offers are just as important, if not more so, than the academic qualifications – the school has to value the individual, offer opportunity for all, meet success and failure head on, encourage pupils to learn, fail and to try again. This is the essential part of developing pupils and the building of skills which will not only help them be Life Ready, but will stay with them throughout their life; this is what a good education is about.

For more information about Ellesmere College see page 254

Educating the whole child

Headmaster Daniel Berry is delighted that Kirkham Grammar School continues to thrive and flourish in a very competitive market

At Kirkham Grammar School we are convinced that in an environment that currently has a high reputation, we must continue to strive to offer the very best to all of our pupils. When one stands still, one is in effect going backwards. Kirkham Grammar is a remarkable school within the North-West educational landscape. In nurturing well-qualified, compassionate, self-assured members of the community, our vision sets out the opportunity to look forward and plan without losing sight of what has come before. Every child travels through our school only once and deserves the very best. The family ethos of the school is fundamental and should be a key factor in driving our future plans for growth and expansion. Our seven-year vision views the Foundation from 3–18 years as the key to our current and future ongoing success. The school has a particular niche within the marketplace and we must be careful to consider this in our planning. The expectation for any potential family joining Kirkham Grammar School is to join us for the journey from Pre-School through to Sixth Form. Therefore, all the facilities we provide and develop are of equal importance.

So what is it that makes such a school so special and unique? The range of opportunities given to our pupils is the main reason for such an envious reputation.

I firmly believe from my years as a Headmaster that it is the breadth and balance of the provision that helps pupils become the best they can possibly be. That must incorporate both the aspiration to succeed to the very highest levels and also an opportunity to find an activity within the school which gives all pupils the chance to excel. I have been overwhelmed at how many co-curricular opportunities are available in our school. The diversity and range of clubs and societies that take place weekly is outstanding and a true testament to the staff and pupils.

The virtue of a school does not depend entirely on its classrooms, the equipment in its laboratories, the number of its pupils, nor even the success of its exam results. There is an unseen influence that is exerted by buildings and surroundings that are beautiful and dignified. These are in keeping with fine honourable traditions and high ideals embedded at Kirkham Grammar School. We offer something that is intangible but very real, the atmosphere in which we dwell and the pervasive spirit which surrounds us, influences all of which we strive to achieve. Our most recent inspection confirmed what we all knew about Kirkham Grammar School; it is the best kept educational secret in Lancashire. However, we are delighted that it has been officially acknowledged against national criteria that we are working hard to ensure our pupils get the finest education. The inspection found that the quality of the pupils' academic and other achievements and the quality of the pupils' personal development is excellent. Pupils reflect the strong family ethos of the school and demonstrate excellent collaboration in and out of lessons.

Pupils develop excellent levels of confidence at all ages, supported by the strong PSHE (Personal, Social, Health and Educational) and enrichment programmes. Pupils show a clear respect for different faiths and diversity, demonstrating excellent levels of empathy and tolerance towards others. Pupils make informed choices, empowered and supported by their teachers.

The longer I spend at Kirkham Grammar School, the more I understand what clearly makes it such a unique school. We are about so much more than academic achievement and continue to thrive in a challenging market. The life of a school over a full academic year is a busy one. As Headmaster of Kirkham Grammar School, this experience continues to be filled with wonderful opportunities.

As the school motto clearly states, 'Ingredere Ut Proficias'.

For more information about Kirkham Grammar School, see page 180

I firmly believe from my years as a Headmaster that it is the breadth and balance of the provision that helps pupils become the best they can possibly be. That must incorporate both the aspiration to succeed to the very highest levels and also an opportunity to find an activity within the school which gives all pupils the chance to excel.

Boarding life: A round-the-clock learning experience

Staff at EF Academy discuss the benefits of boarding and ensuring every student thrives

Attending boarding school – living on campus and being part of a diverse community – intrinsically means that students have opportunities to learn at every moment of the day. From the moment they wake up to the time they turn out the lights, students at boarding schools are engaging their minds. John Gavlick, Director of Residential and Community Life at EF Academy New York, explains:

"Our students are in the early stages of forming their identities and we provide them with opportunities to flourish. Our goal is to build culturally competent individuals who understand the value of being a part of something much larger than themselves."

Extra support

One of the key benefits of boarding school is the relationship that students are able to build with their teachers. Smaller class sizes mean more individualized teaching and more personal support. Many teachers and advisors live on campus and are able to assist with homework or provide remedial tutoring after class or on the weekends. As teachers are able to dedicate a greater amount of time to each student, the relationship built is far stronger and a far better resource for students in need of support. Jenna Marcus, IGCSE Coordinator and IB English Literature Teacher, discusses her experience of this relationship:

"We're not just teachers, we're also this additional support. We need to be there just as someone they can talk to even if it's just someone who's listening to what they need to say – because we do serve as that emotional support for students. And I love making that connection with our students because they're not just receptacles of information, they're people and I want to help them grow as people as well as learners."

Many boarding schools also have dedicated pastoral teams or staff members whose role it is to ensure that all students are happy and thriving. This resource is particularly important at a boarding school where students are living away from home. At EF Academy New York, a student success team are committed to ensuring that every student's experience is the best that it can be. Pathway manager, Daniela Arcos, describes her role below:

"My role at EF Academy is to be available for students and help them with any difficulty they have, whether it's academic or personal in nature. I am in close contact with the student's teachers as well as residential team, so I am well aware of the student's overall wellbeing. I am also available for the parents with any concern they might have, communicating the information to the people that can help in more specific matters, or simply reaching out to the student and being present for them."

Personal growth

A round-the-clock learning experience also gives students a space to develop soft skills in addition to the academic subjects they study during the school day. These things are part of an important skill set that they will use for the rest of their lives.

For example, out of class access to science labs, music rooms and art studios allow students to cultivate their passions. Co-curricular activities, such as music or athletics, teach social skills such as collaboration, teamwork and leadership. Students also receive an education in how to be sensitive to cultural differences and how to navigate language barriers. They also learn independence as they live away from home and figure out how to navigate things like sharing space, doing laundry, and missing home. These kinds of skills are essential for future success. Meric Dunn,

Dean of Students at EF Academy New York, gives her perspective on boarding life:

"A boarding education is much more than a school. It's a way of life. It's the partnership among each and every community member. In this journey our goal is to provide a caring environment that inspires each student to excel and be internationally minded. Also, to not only be proud of their own culture, but also appreciate, respect and embrace all other cultures."

International immersion

Students at boarding school are constantly learning about their peers, themselves, and the wider world around them. Many of the students here at EF Academy even casually learn a second, third or fourth language just from engaging with their friends who speak different languages. For those who are learning new languages in the classroom, they always have a chance to practice their listening and speaking skills with native speakers.

The most beneficial thing about a 24-hour learning experience is that it's a great way for students to tailor their learning and living to their own needs. Because of the immersive environment, students at boarding school quickly find the learning methods that work best for them. Outside of the classroom, they have the freedom to choose how, when, and what they learn. No matter what passions they choose to pursue, they always have an excellent support system. Their peers, teachers and advisors are ready to help them discover their interests and keep their love of learning strong.

For more information about EF Academy, see pages 60, 302 and 304

Sixth Form – a time to be bold

Bill O'Brien-Blake, Head of Sixth Form at Burgess Hill Girls, explains a programme to prepare students for future demands

'A Levels', 'A Levels', 'A Levels'. Ask most parents of teenagers or the teenagers themselves about what happens in Years 12 and 13 and 'A Levels' will be the likely response. Now I don't want to demean A Levels and their results – they are the essential means of developing knowledge in distinct and valuable subject disciplines, future employers do consider them and university admissions are largely dependent on them – but a Sixth Form education should offer so much more.

Schools and colleges should be preparing students for the future of work as well as building strong platforms for their psychological and emotional wellbeing for the years and decades that follow. Adherence to academic demands, and ensuring the highest possible academic performance is a necessity, but it is no longer sufficient.

At Burgess Hill Girls we have created a unique programme, called the BOLD programme, to prepare our Sixth Formers for the evolving ever-changing demands of the world. It empowers our students with the skills necessary for them to thrive in their professional and personal lives. It ensures they leave Burgess Hill Girls equipped with not only exceptional academic qualifications, but with the social, interpersonal and leadership skills required to excel in every capacity in their future.

Our core academic offer ensures that girls can study three of the most valuable A levels to ensure they meet the demands of the most competitive academic degrees. Through the Extended Project, girls have the time and space to think innovatively and independently.

Around this, through tutorial sessions, assemblies, classroom-based training and real world experiences, we deliver The BOLD Programme.

Four key themes

The BOLD Programme is focused around four key themes; Beyond, Opportunities, Leadership and Development.

Going Beyond

Burgess Hill Girls Sixth Formers engage in informed and evidenced super-curricular activities, from reading and research to work experience and immersive opportunities. Tutors will advise and guide students through this additional engagement, ensuring that students take the lead in their own learning, developing their initiative and exploring their own interests to the fullest.

Exploring Opportunities

This is the necessary research and engagement that gives the girls the best understanding of the world beyond school, and how they will take their place in it. From thorough and comprehensive training on UCAS, to time given over for university visits and course research, our students are fully informed on all options that follow their A levels.

Taking Leadership

Students are supported in taking on opportunities to develop and practise leadership skills in preparation for life beyond school. It also includes a dedicated Leadership Training residential trip to Scotland in the weeks after GCSE exams.

Personal Development

Students enhance their personal attributes through community service, extra-curricular activities, and Sixth Form VIVAs, which allow for regular student evaluation against professionally and academically informed criteria.

Key features

The BOLD programme offers unique opportunities for all students at Burgess Hill Girls.

Leadership Training Scotland: A trip teaching the essential skills students need to take on the mantel of leadership within their school life and beyond.

BOLD VIVAs: These are a series of one-to-one interviews with Sixth Formers evaluated against professionally and academically informed criteria.

London Induction Day: Year 12 students fulfil an array of challenges, engaging with historical, social and cultural aspects of this global city, and further cementing the bonds between the girls.

Washington DC Residential: To ensure Sixth Formers are informed about the world and their place in it, this trip to the US capital allows for engagement with social, political, cultural, artistic and scientific institutions of international value.

Higher Education Research and Application: This process is embedded in the programme under the 'Exploring Opportunities' element, so every Sixth Former is well-supported in taking command of their own research.

Life Skills and Visiting Speaker Programme: Outside speakers enliven students' understanding, with a plethora of valid and valuable perspectives, and life skills classes cover topics essential for later success.

From the BOLD programme to Bold Girls

When students leave Burgess Hill Girls our unique curriculum ensures they have all the self-belief, determination, and life skills they need to fulfil their ambitions. They don't become Old Girls. They become Bold Girls.

For more information about Burgess Hill Girls see page 190

35

Developing character in our children

Pete Last, Headmaster of Kingsley School in Devon, considers the importance of character

Schools should develop children's character, not just their ability to pass exams. Is it more important for your child to get a large number of high quality GCSE and A level grades or is it more important for them to develop and sustain a good character?

I think this is a very interesting question for those of us who are parents to consider. My wife and I have been fortunate to have had three children, all of whom are now in their 20s and are entering the world of work. I cannot deny that their GCSE and A level results have played a part in the journeys they have followed and were, for example, a major factor in influencing what they studied at University and where they studied. As a Dad though, by far the most important thing for me is that my children are of good character; they are honest, reliable, determined, resilient, kind and respectful. This matters much more to me than their exam results ever did.

There is a lot of talk in many schools at the moment about the importance of character. Most people would probably agree with the assertion that it is important for us to "have a good character", even if they are not sure exactly what this might mean. So is good character something that can only be caught, or can it also be taught?

One of the most influential sources of useful research and information about character education is the Jubilee Centre for Character and Virtues, based in the School of Education at Birmingham University. Their website contains a wealth of research and practical information and materials for any individual or school wishing to develop how they teach character education. Reading their research it is clear that the Jubilee Centre strongly believe that good character can indeed be taught and that schools, colleges and universities have a key role to play in the development of character.

David Carr wrote in 2007: "it is often said that we remember teachers as much for the kinds of people they were than for anything they may have taught us."[1] Does this resonate with you? It certainly does with me; I cannot remember the actual taught content of many lessons I attended when I was at school but I can most definitely remember the teachers who made learning fun and who had a major impact on my developing personality. What

> As a school, we know that it is possible to teach character because we do it every day.

a privilege it is to be a teacher and what a responsibility teachers have to help shape the character development of the children they teach.

I am the Headmaster of Kingsley School in Bideford, North Devon and I have lots of conversations with prospective and current parents about their children and the dreams and aspirations that the parents have for them. For some parents, it would appear at first glance that exam success is the be all and end all of what they are wanting the school to provide, but it is usually only a matter of moments before the conversation has broadened out to include such important aspects of the children's development as their happiness, their integrity and their character. As a school, we know that it is possible to teach character because we do it every day.

We encourage our pupils to try to develop a growth mindset whereby their attitude towards things they are finding difficult is not "this is impossible, so I'm going to give up" but is rather "this is really hard but I'm going to persevere until I can do it". We see this in the classroom when students are struggling to master a tricky aspect of the subjects they are studying; we see it in our PE and games lessons when students are struggling to master a new technique or skill; we see it in our boarding houses when students are finding it difficult to be away from their families and settle in to new surroundings; we see it when we take pupils out on Duke of Edinburgh expeditions when the physical and mental challenges facing groups of young people can appear to be daunting. We see it every day in a myriad of ways throughout all age groups within the school, from our nursery children right through to our 6th form.

It is wonderful to watch students push themselves in such a wide variety of settings and, more often that not, surprise themselves with what they are capable of achieving. Even when they don't succeed, as a school we always endeavour to be there to pick them up, dust them down and set them on their way again, just as I remember doing so vividly when my own children were first learning to ride their bikes without stabilisers. Sometimes it hurts to fail, but the true test of character of whether you are strong enough to get back on your bike!

Endnote
1. Carr, D. (2007) 'Character in Teaching', *British Journal of Educational Studies*, 55(4): 369-389.

For more information about Kingsley School, see page 248

Supporting SEND students to high academic outcomes and personal success

Zoë Spilberg (pictured), Principal of Greene's Tutorial College in Oxford, on preparing students to succeed in life

For over 50 years, the ethos of Greene's Tutorial College has centred on treating each student as an individual. More than just an abstract principle, this is put into practice with the use of the tutorial method across all subjects and levels of study; students are taught either individually or in groups of 2-3 per tutor.

In the last decade, many studies have explored the unique learning benefits of the tutorial method. Whilst all students can benefit from such a focused approach, this highly-adaptable method truly comes into its own when teaching students with learning difficulties, disabilities, or chronic illnesses, or those who have had difficult experiences in mainstream education. With the benefit of individualised education and a dedicated Personal Tutor, Greene's students are supported in ways that are not possible in a typical school. With individual attention, children who have previously flown under the radar in a large classroom can have their teaching adapted to their strengths and abilities. Personal Tutors and subject tutors at Greene's work closely with our SENCo to ensure that students are not left to fail due to lack of appropriate support.

In addition to learning disabilities, there are many students with chronic illnesses and physical disabilities, and an increasing number of students with mental health conditions that can get in the way of success at school. For many students, the high-pressure and impersonal environment of a traditional school can have a significant impact on their health, sometimes to the point of hospitalisation. In these situations, students and their parents can feel they have missed the boat when it comes to education, however our Principal and Director of Studies work with the students' tutors to create a seamless support network and give the students the best possible chance at re-entering and completing their studies. With the right attention and preparation, we have seen students achieve both their academic and health goals and reach top universities such as Oxford and Cambridge, where they continue to thrive. A recent student, now at university, says of Greene's: "I feel so lucky to have come across Greene's, it gave me so many opportunities and kept me on the right track, and I don't think I'd have been able to [stay on track] anywhere else."

As part of ongoing efforts to provide a positive and supportive learning environment for all students, Greene's recently appointed an in-house Counsellor and Mental Health Lead, who meets with any student who would like to have an assessment and makes recommendations for how Greene's can help them in their studies, in addition to further clinical intervention if needed. The key advantage of an internal specialist is that, given the usual consent, they can confer directly with the students' tutors to advise of any accommodations that need to be made. In a small college like Greene's, with only a few full-time members of staff, there are additional advantages. Debbie, our current Mental Health Lead, says: "In a small staff team, you're more likely to have important conversations with each other," which prevents any concerns from slipping through the cracks.

Addressing disabilities and health conditions in an educational environment also means understanding that issues such as procrastination or poor attendance - frequently written off as 'laziness' - can be symptomatic of an underlying problem. In a typical school, SEND students are often overwhelmed or exhausted from the process of fitting into the classroom to the point where they are unable to process and manage the demands of their workload, and therefore fall behind in their work. Supporting high-performing SEND students can be difficult if they appear to be achieving above average grades, and in larger classes can only be discovered when a crisis causes a noticeable change in performance or behaviour. In a tutorial environment, on the other hand, it is almost impossible to miss early warning signs, and staff can intervene very quickly.

Greene's is proud of the flexibility we are able to offer students who come to us on EHCPs; for example, some students require exclusively one-to-one tuition, have needs that are frequently changing, or are unable to leave their homes, even for examinations. Due to our close work with both Oxfordshire County Council and the examining bodies, these students are still able to access the same academic opportunities as their peers. Exams can be a particular source of stress for SEND students, however our programme of frequent trial exams and our experience with a wide variety of access arrangements ensures these become second nature, and students are better able to demonstrate their true abilities.

Although non-selective, Greene's is an outcomes-driven college and we believe in helping each student achieve their best. This is of course not just about GCSE and A level grades; we are primarily committed to preparing young adults to succeed in life, and this should not be negatively affected by disability or illness. Greene's wants to support students academically and crucially also to stay well both physically and mentally during the process.

For more information on Greene's Tutorial College, see page 62

Help in finding the fees

Chris Procter, joint managing director of SFIA, outlines a planned approach to funding your child's school fees

Average school fee increases in the last year, according to the ISC census, were 3.7% There appears to have been a conscious effort by schools over the last 10 years to control fees. Since 2010 fee increases have averaged 3.9%. Between 2000 and 2010 they averaged 6.6%.

The latest Independent Schools Council (ISC) survey, completed by all 1,364 schools in UK membership indicate that there are now a record 536,109 pupils being educated privately, the highest number since records began in 1974, rising 0.1% since 2018. 65.3% of these were day school pupils, 34.7% were boarders. The share of girls and boys at ISC schools is very nearly equal, with boys representing 51% of all pupils.

The overall average boarding fee is £11,565 per term and the overall average day fee is £4,763 per term. However, fees charged by schools vary by region – for example the average boarding fee ranges from £9,438 per term in the North East to £13,331 per term in Greater London; the average day fee ranges from £3,581 per term in the North West to £5,759 term in Greater London.

The overall cost (including university fees) might seem daunting: the cost of educating one child privately could well be very similar to that of buying a house but, as with house buying, the school fees commitment for the majority of parents can be made possible by spreading it over a long period rather than funding it all from current resources.

It is vital that parents do their financial homework, plan ahead, start to save early and regularly. Grandparents who have access to capital could help out; by contributing to school fees they could also help to reduce any potential future inheritance tax liability.

Parents would be well-advised to consult a specialist financial adviser as early as possible, since a long-term plan for the payment of fees – possibly university as well – can prove very advantageous from a financial point of view and offer greater peace of mind. Funding fees is neither science, nor magic, nor is there any panacea. It is quite simply a question of planning and using whatever resources are available, such as income, capital, or tax reduction opportunities.

The fundamental point to recognise is that you, your circumstances and your wishes or ambitions, for your children, or grandchildren are unique. They might well be similar to those of other people but they will still be uniquely different. There will be no single solution to your problem. In fact, after a review of all your circumstances, there might not be a problem at all.

So, what are the reasons for seeking advice about education expenses?

- To reduce the overall cost?

- To get some tax benefit?

- To reduce your cash outflow?

- To invest capital to ensure that future fees are paid?

- To set aside money now for future fees?

- To provide protection for school fees?

- Or just to make sure that, as well as educating your children, you can still have a life?!

Any, some, or all of the above – or others not listed – could be on your agenda, the important thing is to develop a strategy.

At this stage, it really does not help to get hung up on which financial 'product' is the most suitable. The composition of a school fees plan will differ for each family depending on a number of factors. That is why there is no one school fees plan on offer.

The simplest strategy but in most cases, the most expensive option, is to write out a cheque for the whole bill when it arrives and post it back to the school. Like most simple plans, that can work well, if you have the money. Even if you do have the money, is that really the best way of doing things? Do you know that to fund £1,000 of school fees as a higher rate taxpayer paying 40% income tax, you currently need to earn £1,667, this rises to £1,818 if you are an additional rate taxpayer where the rate is 45%.

How then do you start to develop your strategy? As with most things in life, if you can define your objective, then you will know what you are aiming at. Your objective in this case will be to determine how much money is needed and when. You need to draw up a school fees schedule or what others may term a cash flow forecast. So, you need to identify:

- How many children?

- Which schools and therefore what are the fees? (or you could use an average school fee)

- When are they due?

- Any special educational needs?

- Inflation estimate

- Include university costs?

With this basic information, the school fees schedule/cash flow forecast can be prepared and you will have defined what it is you are trying to achieve. Remember though, that senior school fees are typically more than prep school fees – this needs to be factored in. Also, be aware that the cost of university is not restricted to the fees alone; there are a lot of maintenance and other costs involved: accommodation, books, food, to name a few. Don't forget to build in inflation, I refer you back to the data at the beginning of this article.

You now have one element of the equation, the relatively simple element. The other side is the resources you have available to achieve the objective. This also needs to be identified, but this is a much more difficult exercise. The reason that it is more difficult, of course, is that school fees are not the only drain on your resources. You probably have a mortgage, you want to have holidays, you need to buy food and clothes, you may be concerned that you should be funding a pension.

This is a key area of expertise, since your financial commitments are unique. A specialist in the area of school fees planning can help identify these commitments, to record them and help you to distribute your resources according to your priorities.

The options open to you as parents depend completely upon your adviser's knowledge of these complex personal financial issues. (Did I forget to mention your tax position, capital gains tax allowance, other tax allowances, including those of your children and a lower or zero rate tax paying spouse or partner? These could well be used to your advantage.)

A typical school fees plan can incorporate many elements to fund short, medium and long-term fees. Each plan is designed according to individual circumstances and usually there is a special emphasis on what parents are looking to achieve, for example, to maximise overall savings and to minimise the outflow of cash.

Additionally, it is possible to protect the payment of the fees in the event of unforeseen circumstances that could lead to a significant or total loss of earnings.

Short-term fees

Short-term fees are typically the termly amounts needed within five years: these are usually funded from such things as guaranteed investments, liquid capital, loan plans (if no savings are available) or maturing insurance policies, investments etc. Alternatively, they can be funded from disposable income.

Medium-term fees

Once the short-term plan expires, the medium-term funding is invoked to fund the education costs for a further five to ten years. Monthly amounts can be invested in a low-risk, regular premium investment ranging from a building society account to a friendly society savings plan to equity ISAs. It is important to understand the pattern of the future fees and to be aware of the timing of withdrawals.

Long-term fees

Longer term funding can incorporate a higher element of risk (as long as this is acceptable to the investor), which will offer higher potential returns. Investing in UK and overseas equities could be considered. Solutions may be the same as those for medium-term fees, but will have the flexibility to utilise investments that may have an increased 'equity based' content.

Finally, it is important to remember that most investments, or financial products either mature with a single payment, or provide for regular withdrawals; rarely do they provide timed termly payments.

Additionally, the overall risk profile of the portfolio should lean towards the side of caution (for obvious reasons).

There are any number of advisers in the country, but few who specialise in the area of planning to meet school and university fees. SFIA is the largest organisation specialising in school fees planning in the UK.

This article has been contributed by SFIA and edited by Chris Procter, Managing Director. Chris can be contacted at: SFIA, 29 High Street, Marlow, Buckinghamshire, SL7 1AU Tel: 01628 566777 Fax: 0333 444 1550 Email: enquiries@sfia.co.uk Web: www.schoolfeesadvice.org

The Independent Schools Council

The Independent Schools Council (ISC) works with its members to promote and preserve the quality, diversity and excellence of UK independent education both at home and abroad

What is the ISC?

The ISC brings together seven associations of independent schools, their heads, bursars and governors. Through our member associations we represent more than 1,350 independent schools in the UK and overseas. These schools are among the best in the world and educate more than half a million children each year.

The ISC's work is carried out by a small team of dedicated professionals in an office in central London. We are assisted by contributions from expert advisory groups in specialist areas. Our priorities are set by the board of directors led by our chairman, Barnaby Lenon. We are tasked by our members to protect and promote the sector in everything we do.

ISC schools

Schools in UK membership of the ISC's constituent associations offer a high quality, rounded education. Whilst our schools are very academically successful, their strength also lies in the extra-curricular activities offered – helping to nurture pupils' soft skills and encourage them to be self-disciplined, ambitious and curious. There are independent schools to suit every need, whether you want a day or boarding school, single sex or co-education, a large or a small school, or schools offering specialisms, such as in the arts.

Our schools are very diverse: some are selective and highly academic, while others have very strong drama or music departments full of creative opportunities in plays, orchestras and choirs. For children with special needs such as dyslexia or autism there are many outstanding independent schools that offer some of the best provision in the country.

Academic results

In 2019, 45.7% of Year 13 exam entries at independent schools were graded A*/A, compared to the national average of 25.5%. This year also saw 95.6% of Year 11 candidates at independent schools awarded a grade C/4 or higher, compared to the national average of 67.3%. This is especially impressive given the fact more than half of ISC schools are not academically selective. Figures recorded in 2019 also demonstrated more students are following different pathways post-GCSE. There was an increase in candidates taking the Extended Project Qualification, Pre-U and BTEC qualifications compared to 2018. The average points score for pupils taking the International Baccalaureate (IB) Diploma was 36, roughly equivalent to 4.5 As at A-level. In the IB, 51 pupils obtained 45 points - the highest mark - making up a quarter of all pupils worldwide who achieved this score.

Fee assistance

Schools take issues around affordability very seriously and are acutely aware of the sacrifices families make when choosing an independent education. Schools work hard to remain competitive whilst facing pressures on salaries, pensions and maintenance and utility costs. They are strongly committed to widening access and have made strenuous efforts to increase the amount they can offer in bursaries. This year more than £420m was provided in means-tested fee assistance for pupils at ISC schools. Currently a third of pupils at our schools benefit from reduced fees.

School partnerships

Independent and state schools have been engaged in partnership activity for many years, with the majority of ISC schools currently involved in important cross-sector initiatives. These collaborations involve the sharing of expertise, best practise and facilities, and unlock exciting new opportunities for all involved. To learn more about the partnership work taking place between state and independent schools, visit the Schools Together website: www.schoolstogether.org/

ISC Associations

There are seven member associations of the ISC, each with a distinctive ethos in their respective entrance criteria and quality assurance: Girls' Schools Association (GSA), Headmasters' and Headmistresses' Conference (HMC), Independent Association of Prep Schools (IAPS) Independent Schools Association (ISA), The Society of Heads, Association of Governing Bodies of Independent Schools (AGBIS), and the Independent Schools' Bursars Association (ISBA).

Further organisations who are affiliated to the ISC: Boarding Schools Association (BSA), Council of British International Schools (COBIS), Scottish Council of Independent Schools (SCIS) and Welsh Independent Schools Council (WISC).

The Independent Schools Council can be contacted at:
First Floor,
27 Queen Anne's Gate,
London,
SW1H 9BU
Telephone: 020 7766 7070
Website: www.isc.co.uk

independent
schools
council

Choosing a school initially

Educational institutions often belong to organisations that guarantee their standards. Here we give a brief alphabetical guide to what the initials mean

BSA

The Boarding Schools' Association

Since its foundation in 1965-66, the Boarding Schools' Association (BSA) has had the twin objectives of promoting boarding education and the development of quality boarding through high standards of pastoral care and boarding accommodation. Parents and prospective pupils choosing a boarding school can be assured that the 600 plus schools in the UK and internationally that make up the membership of the BSA are committed to providing the best possible boarding environment for their pupils. A UK boarding school can only be a full member of the BSA if it is also a member of one of the Independent Schools Council (ISC) constituent associations, or in membership of the BSA State Boarding Forum (SBF). These two bodies require member schools to be regularly inspected by the Independent Schools' Inspectorate (ISI) or Ofsted. Other boarding schools which are not members of these organisations can apply to be affiliate members. Similar arrangements are in place for overseas members. Boarding inspection of ISC-accredited independent schools has been conducted by ISI since September 2012, while Ofsted inspects boarding in state schools and non-association independent schools. Boarding inspections must be conducted every three years. Boarding in England and Wales is judged against the National Minimum Standards for Boarding Schools which were last revised for primary and secondary schools in England in 2015 and are set to be updated again soon.

Relationship with government

The BSA is in regular communication with several government departments, including the Department for Education (DfE), Home Office, Foreign and Commonwealth Office and Ministry of Defence. The Children Act (1989) and the Care Standards Act (2000) require boarding schools to conform to national legislation and the promotion of this legislation and the training required to carry it out are matters on which the BSA and the DfE work closely.

Boarding training

Through the BSA Academy (training school), the association maintains the high standards expected as a consequence of that support and from the BSA's Commitment to Care Charter – which all member schools must abide by. The BSA organises five conferences and more than 90 seminars a year for governors, Heads, deputies, housemasters and housemistresses, and matrons and medical staff where further training takes place in formal sessions and in sharing good practice. The BSA provides the following range of training and information:

- Professional qualifications for teaching and non-teaching staff in boarding schools. The BSA Academy has developed a host of courses including: Certificates of Professional Practice in Boarding Education, Certificate in International Boarding, Certificate in Professional Practice for Nurses and Matrons, and a Diploma for senior leaders. The certificates courses are the result of at least two years' study, and completion of the Diploma takes at least one year. A new MA in Residential Education was launched in conjunction with Buckingham University in September 2019. Courses run across the UK and worldwide.

- A rolling programme of day seminars on current boarding legislation and good practice.

- Bespoke training, INSET, and consultancy on best boarding practice, particularly with regard to safeguarding.

- The Accredited Boarding Practitioner scheme, where individuals working in boarding can have their service and experience accredited by BSA.

- Centre for Boarding Education Research (CEBER) which brings together a wide variety of articles and research on all matters related to boarding.

State Boarding Forum (SBF)

The BSA issues information regards its 40 state boarding school members and the BSA should be contacted for details of these schools. In these schools, parents pay for boarding but not for education tuition.

BSA Leadership Team

National Director: Robin Fletcher
Direction of Operations: Aileen Kane
International Director: Andrew Lewin
Head of Safeguarding ,Standards and Training: Dale Wilkins
Head of Member Services: Chris Ryan

4th Floor
134-136 Buckingham Palace Road
London SWIW 9SA
Tel: 020 7798 1580
Email: bsa@boarding.org.uk
Website: www.boarding.org.uk

GSA

The Girls' Schools Association, to which Heads of independent girls' schools belong

The Girls' Schools Association helps girls and their teachers to flourish. It represents the Heads of a diverse range of independent UK girls' schools (day & boarding), among which are some of the top-performing schools in the country.

The GSA encourages high standards of education and promotes the benefits of being taught in a largely girls-only environment. GSA schools are internationally respected and have a global reputation for excellence. Their innovative practice and academic rigour attract pupils from around the world. Students at GSA schools enjoy abundant extra- and co-curricular opportunities. Academically, they thrive in the humanities and do disproportionately well in 'difficult' modern languages and STEM (science, technology, engineering, maths) subjects. A high percentage – 96% – progress to higher education.

GSA schools share experience, specialisms, opportunities and facilities with state sector schools in a wide range of partnerships. Many also provide means-tested bursaries for families of limited financial means.

Twenty first century girls' schools come in many different shapes and sizes. Some cater for 100% girls, others provide a predominantly girls-only environment with boys in the nursery and/or sixth form. Some follow a diamond model, with equal numbers of boys but separate classrooms between the ages of 11 to 16. Educational provision across the Association offers a choice of day, boarding, weekly, and flexi-boarding education. Schools range in type from large urban schools of 1000 pupils to small rural schools of around 200. Many schools have junior and pre-prep departments, and can offer a complete education from age 3/4 to 18. Some also have religious affiliations. Heads of schools in the Girls' Day School Trust (GDST) are members of the GSA.

The Association aims to inform and influence national educational debate and is a powerful and well-respected voice within the educational establishment, advising and lobbying educational policy makers on core education issues as well as those relating to girls' schools and the education of girls. The Association liaises with the Department for Education, the Office for Standards in Education, the Qualifications and Curriculum Authority and other bodies.

The GSA also provides its members and their staff with professional development courses, conferences, advice and opportunities to debate and share best practice, ensuring that they have every opportunity to remain fully up-to-date with all aspects of their profession.

As the GSA is one of the constituent bodies that make up the Independent Schools' Council (ISC), its schools are required to undergo a regular cycle of inspections to ensure that these rigorous standards are being maintained. GSA schools must also belong to the Association of Governing Bodies of Independent Schools, and Heads must be in membership of the Association of School and College Leaders (ASCL).

The Association's secretariat is based in Leicester.

Suite 105, 108 New Walk, Leicester LE1 7EA
Tel: 0116 254 1619
Email: office@gsa.uk.com
Website: www.gsa.uk.com
Twitter: @GSAUK

President 2020: Jane Prescott, Portsmouth High School GDST
Chief Executive: Vivienne Durham

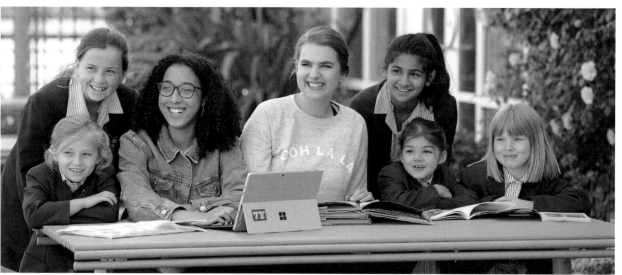

HMC

The Headmasters' and Headmistresses' Conference, to which the Heads of leading independent schools belong

Founded in 1869 the HMC exists to enable members to discuss matters of common interest and to influence important developments in education. It looks after the professional interests of members, central to which is their wish to provide the best possible educational opportunities for their pupils.

The Heads of some 296 leading independent schools are members of The Headmasters' and Headmistresses' Conference, whose membership now includes Heads of boys', girls' and coeducational schools. International membership includes the Heads of around 56 schools throughout the world.

The great variety of these schools is one of the strengths of HMC but all must exhibit high quality in the education provided. While day schools are the largest group, about a quarter of HMC schools consist mainly of boarders and others have a smaller boarding element including weekly and flexible boarders.

All schools are noted for their academic excellence and achieve good results, including those with pupils from a broad ability band. Members believe that good education consists of more than academic results and schools provide pupils with a wide range of educational co-curricular activities and with strong pastoral support.

Only those schools that meet with the rigorous membership criteria are admitted and this helps ensure that HMC is synonymous with high quality in education. There is a set of membership requirements and a Code of Practice to which members must subscribe. Those who want the intimate atmosphere of a small school will find some with around 350 pupils. Others who want a wide range of facilities and specialisations will find these offered in large day or boarding schools. Many have over 1000 pupils. 32 schools are for boys only, others are coeducational throughout or only in the sixth form. The first girls-only schools joined HMC in 2006. There are now 39 girls-only schools.

Within HMC there are schools with continuous histories as long as any in the world and many others trace their origins to Tudor times, but HMC continues to admit to membership recently-founded schools that have achieved great success. The facilities in all HMC schools will be good but some have magnificent buildings and grounds that are the result of the generosity of benefactors over many years. Some have attractive rural settings, others are sited in the centres of cities.

Pupils come from all sorts of backgrounds. Bursaries and scholarships provided by the schools give about a third of the 240,000 pupils in HMC schools help with their fees. These average about £35,000 per annum for boarding schools and £15,000 for day schools. About 190,000 are day pupils and 45,000 boarders.

Entry into some schools is highly selective but others are well-suited to a wide ability range. Senior boarding schools usually admit pupils after the Common Entrance examination taken when they are 13.

Most day schools select their pupils by 11+ examination. Many HMC schools have junior schools, some with nursery and pre-prep departments. The growing number of boarders from overseas is evidence of the high reputation of the schools worldwide.

The independent sector has always been fortunate in attracting very good teachers. Higher salary scales, excellent conditions of employment, exciting educational opportunities and good pupil/teacher ratios bring rewards commensurate with the demanding expectations. Schools expect teachers to have a good education culminating in a good honours degree and a professional qualification, though some do not insist on the latter especially if relevant experience is offered. Willingness to participate in the whole life of the school is essential.

Parents expect the school to provide not only good teaching that helps their children achieve the best possible examination results, but also the dedicated pastoral care and valuable educational experiences outside the classroom in music, drama, games, outdoor pursuits and community service. Over 89% of pupils go on to higher education, many of them winning places on the most highly-subscribed university courses.

All members attend the Annual Conference, usually held in a large conference centre in September/October. There are ten divisions covering England, Wales, Scotland and Ireland where members meet once a term on a regional basis, and a distinctive international division.

The chair and committee, with the advice of the general secretary and membership secretary, make decisions on matters referred by membership-led sub-committees, steering groups and working parties. Close links are maintained with other professional associations in membership of the Independent Schools Council and with the Association of School and College Leaders.

Membership Secretary: Ian Power
Tel: 01858 465260
General Secretary: Dr William Richardson
Tel: 01858 469059
12 The Point
Rockingham Road
Market Harborough
Leicestershire LE16 7QU
Email: gensec@hmc.org.uk
Website: www.hmc.org.uk

Leading Independent Schools

IAPS

The Independent Association of Prep Schools (IAPS) is a membership association representing leading headteachers and their prep schools in the UK and overseas

With around 670 members, IAPS schools represent a multi-billion pound enterprise, educating more than 160,000 children and employing more than 20,000 staff. As the voice of independent prep school education, IAPS actively defends and promotes the interests of its members.

IAPS schools must reach a very high standard to be eligible for membership, with strict criteria on teaching a broad curriculum, maintain excellent standards of pastoral care and keeping staff members' professional development training up-to-date. The head must be suitably qualified and schools must be accredited through a satisfactory inspection. IAPS offers its members and their staff a comprehensive and up-to-date programme of professional development courses to ensure that these high professional standards are maintained.

Member schools offer an all-round, values-led broad education which produces confident, adaptable, motivated children with a passion for learning. The targets of the National Curriculum are regarded as a basic foundation which is greatly extended by the wider programmes of study offered. Specialist teaching begins at an early age and pupils are offered a range of cultural and sporting opportunities.

IAPS organises a successful sports programme where member schools compete against each other in a variety of sports. In 2018-19, we ran 156 events for 22,000 competitors at 84 venues (including the London Aquatics Centre at the Queen Elizabeth Olympic Park in London).

Our schools are spread throughout cities, towns and the countryside and offer pupils the choice of day, boarding, weekly and flexible boarding, in both singe sex and co-educational schools. Most schools are charitable trusts, some are limited companies and a few are proprietary. There are also junior schools attached to senior schools, choir schools, those with a particular religious affiliation and those that offer specialist provision as well as some schools with an age range extending to age 16 or above.

Although each member school is independent and has its own ethos, they are all committed to delivering an excellent, well-rounded education to the pupils in their care, preparing them for their future.

IAPS
11 Waterloo Place
Leamington Spa
Warwickshire CV32 5LA
Tel: 01926 887833
Email: iaps@iaps.uk
Website: iaps.uk

Excellence in Education
The Independent Association of Prep Schools

ISA

The Independent Schools Association, with membership across all types of school

The Independent Schools Association (ISA), established in 1879, is one of the oldest of the Headteachers' associations of independent schools that make up the Independent Schools' Council (ISC). It began life as the Association of Principals of Private Schools, which was created to encourage high standards and foster friendliness and cooperation among Heads who had previously worked in isolation. In 1895 it was incorporated as The Private Schools Association and in 1927 the word 'private' was replaced by 'independent'. The recently published history of the

association, *Pro Liberis*, demonstrates the strong links ISA has with proprietorial schools, which is still the case today, even though boards of governors now run the majority of schools.

Membership is open to any Head or Proprietor, provided they meet the necessary accreditation criteria, including inspection of their school by a government-approved inspectorate. ISA's Executive Council is elected by members and supports all developments of the Association through its committee structure and the strong regional network of co-ordinators and area committees. Each of ISA's seven areas in turn supports members through regular training events and meetings.

ISA celebrates a wide-ranging membership, not confined to any one type of school, but including all: nursery, pre-preparatory, junior and senior, all-through schools, coeducational, single-sex, boarding, day and performing arts and special schools.

Promoting best practice and fellowship remains at the core of the ISA, as it did when it began 140 years ago. The association is growing, and its 521 members and their schools enjoy high quality national conferences and courses that foster excellence in independent education. ISA's central office also supports members and provides advice, and represents the views of its membership at national and governmental levels. Pupils in ISA schools enjoy a wide variety of competitions, in particular the wealth of sporting, artistic and academic activities at area and national level.

President: Lord Lexden
Chief Executive: Neil Roskilly, BA PGCE NPQH FRSA FRGS

ISA House, 5-7 Great Chesterford Court, Great Chesterford, Essex CB10 1PF
Tel: 01799 523619
Email: isa@isaschools.org.uk
Website: www.isaschools.org.uk

ISA | INDEPENDENT SCHOOLS ASSOCIATION

ISA celebrates a wide-ranging membership, not confined to any one type of school, but including all: nursery, pre-preparatory, junior and senior, all-through schools, coeducational, single-sex, boarding, day and performing arts and special schools

The Society of Heads

The Society of Heads represents the interests of independent secondary schools

The Society of Heads represents the interests of independent, secondary schools. The Society celebrated its 50th Anniversary in 2011. The Society has as its members 118 Heads of well-established secondary schools, many with a boarding element, meeting a wide range of educational needs. All member schools provide education up to 18, with sixth forms offering both A and AS levels and/or the International Baccalaureate. Also some offer vocational courses. Many have junior schools attached to their foundation. A number cater for pupils with special educational needs, whilst others offer places to gifted dancers and musicians. All the schools provide education appropriate to their pupils' individual requirements together with the best in pastoral care.

The average size of the schools is about 350, and all aim to provide small classes ensuring favourable pupil:teacher ratios. The majority are coeducational and offer facilities for both boarding and day pupils. Many of the schools are non-denominational, whilst others have specific religious foundations.

The Society believes that independent schools are an important part of Britain's national education system. Given their independence, the schools can either introduce new developments ahead of the maintained sector or offer certain courses specifically appropriate to the pupils in their schools. They are able to respond quickly to the needs of parents and pupils alike.

Schools are admitted to membership of the Society only after a strict inspection procedure carried out by the Independent Schools Inspectorate. Regular inspection visits thereafter ensure that standards are maintained.

The Society is a constituent member of the Independent Schools Council and every full member in the Society has been accredited to it. All the Society's Heads belong to the Association of School and College Leaders (ASCL) (or another recognised union for school leaders) and their schools are members of AGBIS.

The Society's policy is: to maintain high standards of education, acting as a guarantee of quality to parents who choose a Society school for their children; to ensure the genuine independence of member schools; to provide an opportunity for Heads to share ideas and common concerns for the benefit of the children in their care; to provide training opportunities for Heads and staff in order to keep them abreast of new educational initiatives; to promote links with higher and further education and the professions, so that pupils leaving the Society's schools are given the best advice and opportunities for their future careers; and to help Heads strengthen relations with their local communities.

The Society of Heads Office,
12 The Point, Rockingham Road, Market Harborough, Leicestershire LE16 7QU
Tel: 01858 433760
Email: info@thesocietyofheads.org.uk
Website: www.thesocietyofheads.org.uk

The average size of the schools is about 350, and all aim to provide small classes ensuring favourable pupil: teacher ratios. The majority are coeducational and offer facilities for both boarding and day pupils. Many of the schools are non-denominational, whilst others have specific religious foundations

School profiles

Channel Islands

St George's Preparatory School

Our School

St George's Prep and St George's Little Dragons Nursery boast some of the finest facilities in Jersey. The school is set in a stunning 35 acre site of woodland, grass playing fields, football pitches, adventure play, award winning sports hall, and an enviable swimming pool.

St George's is a non-selective school promoting a rich, varied and broad education. Our small class sizes and specialist teachers ensure our children are challenged and stimulated to strive for excellence in all they do. We assess all of our children before they join the school so that we are immediately able to offer whatever learning support they might need. We are quick to identify children with particular gifts and talents and set specific goals to challenge these children further. We also look to challenge children who excel at music, drama and sport.

Children are helped to understand themselves as individuals. We recognise that every child is an individual and aim to promote their happiness, self-confidence and well-being as members of a caring community.

Our idyllic walled garden for our younger children provides a secure and safe place for our children to play confidently with their friends. In the Manor house and stable block, there is a homely and safe environment where lessons take place in dedicated teaching rooms, by well-qualified specialist teachers.

The children enjoy freshly cooked healthy and nutritious lunches, prepared at school by our Chef, using locally grown produce. We are very fortunate to have an extremely active and well supported Parents Association. The GA organises a variety of events ranging from family quiz nights, film nights and the annual Family Bonfire Night. Although the main objective of the GA is to raise money for the school, we also ensure the events are very social, enabling parents throughout the school to feel part of the St George's family and many long term friendships are made here.

Curriculum

We choose to follow the Jersey Curriculum, which is based on the UK National Curriculum, to provide us with a comprehensive framework upon which to build. The freedom to augment, adapt and expand this curriculum, coupled with our small classes, use of specialist teachers and longer working days, helps to create the very best learning environment for our pupils and ensures they make the maximum progress, whether in the classroom, on the sports field or on the stage.

Such a tailor-made programme allows us to focus on each child as well as on the different expectations held by the many senior schools who welcome our pupils both at the Island colleges and mainland public schools.

Our excellent record of transfer testifies to the success of our unique set up. Importantly, we believe it is a set up that presents our pupils with a wider range of opportunities than those enjoyed by any other primary pupil in Jersey and promotes a balanced and well rounded outlook.

ST GEORGE'S
PREPARATORY SCHOOL

(Founded 1929)

La Hague Manor, Rue de la Hague, St Peter, Jersey JE3 7DB UK

Tel: 01534 481593

Fax: 01534 484304

Email: admin@stgeorgesprep.co.uk

Website: www.stgeorgesprep.co.uk

Headmaster: Mr Cormac Timothy

Appointed: April 2017

School type: Coeducational Day

Age range of pupils: 2–11

No. of pupils enrolled as at 01/09/2019: 244

Boys: 128 *Girls:* 116

Fees per annum as at 01/09/2019:

Day: £5,796–£15,495

Average class size: 14

Teacher/pupil ratio: 1:14

St Michael's Preparatory School

St. Michael's Preparatory School is situated in a unique educational setting on Jersey in the Channel Islands. A forward thinking IAPS prep school preparing pupils for the rigours of secondary school education both on and off island. We place great emphasis upon the traditional values of care, consideration and courtesy.

The staff and pupils are justifiably proud of the School, and work together to create and maintain a high-achieving, well-organised and friendly environment in which every child is encouraged to do 'a little bit better' than anyone thought possible.

The curriculum is designed to give all children a broad, balanced and relevant education, which enables them to develop as enthusiastic, active and competent learners acquiring the knowledge, skills and understanding to allow them to grow up in today's world leading a full and active life. The school's ethos places emphasis on the individual and aims to encourage development in academic, physical, spiritual, moral and cultural aspects of the 'whole child'.

The teaching is multi-sensory, allowing children of all abilities and learning styles to be able to make progress in their learning. Differentiation is integral to the curriculum and children with special needs are well supported, as are the gifted and talented, who go on to achieve scholarship success.

The schemes of work are based upon the National Curriculum, the Jersey Curriculum and the requirements of the ISEB Common Entrance and Scholarship syllabuses. The curriculum is enriched and enhanced by numerous trips and visits as Jersey has an array of museums, cultural sites of interest and environmental locations.

The school prepares children for Common Entrance and Scholarships to English boarding secondary schools as well as entry to local Jersey establishments. We also offer a Shell Year (pre-GCSE) specifically to provide a bridging opportunity for Year 10 entry to our island state schools. Classes are small and there is a very low pupil to teacher ratio. All expected subjects are taught and there are flourishing and well-equipped Art, Music, Science, Design Technology and ICT departments as well as a custom built Sports Hall, Dance/Drama Studio, Gymnasium and indoor Swimming Pool.

As well as providing a wide range of academic subjects, the school seeks to introduce each child to a large variety of sports, performing arts, activities and challenges enabling him or her to discover, through experience, hidden talents and preferences with a view to future specialisation.

I hope St. Michael's pupils will leave us having achieved the very best they are capable of, having found out what it is that they love and are good at, having learned to challenge themselves and to value other people.

I.S.I. Inspection (Oct 2017) Key findings:
- The quality of the pupils' learning and achievements is excellent
- The quality of the pupils' personal development is excellent

"St Michael's makes ordinary children special, and special children extra-ordinary." A parent quote.

ST MICHAEL'S
PREPARATORY SCHOOL

(Founded 1949)

La Rue de la Houguette, St Saviour, Jersey JE2 7UG UK

Tel: 01534 856904

Email: office@stmichaels.je

Website: www.stmichaels.je

Head of School: Mr Mike Rees

Appointed: 2014

School type: Coeducational Day

Age range of pupils: 3–14

No. of pupils enrolled as at 01/09/2019: 315

Boys: 169 **Girls:** 146

Fees per annum as at 01/09/2019:

Day: £10,230–£16,080

Average class size: 18 max

Teacher/pupil ratio: 1:9

Central & West

Dauntsey's School

Dauntsey's is a leading co-educational boarding and day school for 11-18 year olds. The school sits in an estate of one hundred and fifty acres of idyllic countryside in Wiltshire and offers some 800 pupils challenge and inspiration both inside and outside the classroom.

The Dauntsey's Experience

Academic excellence is at the heart of all that we do. However, education is much more than grades on a piece of paper. It's about developing the skills and characteristics, such as resilience, flexibility and a willingness to have a go, which we all need to have a successful, happy life. That's where our adventure, enrichment and extra-curricular activities have a crucial role to play. From drama, dance, music, sport and a huge range of clubs and societies, to our lecture series, adventure programmes and volunteering initiatives – there are opportunities to suit everyone.

The Dauntsey's Community

Community and collaboration underpin many aspects of Dauntsey's; it is a happy place with a strong family atmosphere, where friendship matters and where courteous informality between staff and pupils is highly valued.

Our pupils are expected to give of their best and to have a spirit of adventure. We aim to push them out of their comfort zone, both inside and outside the classroom, and we want them to arrive at the end of their time in the School saying: 'I did not think that I could do that, but I did.'

Our pupils, both boarding and day, come from many different schools and so arrive at Dauntsey's eager to make new friends. Both communities are fully integrated and boarding houses rapidly become home-from-home and fellow boarders become extended family. All pupils attend School six days a week with Saturday school compulsory for day and boarders alike, with a full academic programme for all year groups and sports matches every Saturday afternoon. A range of activities on Saturday evening and Sunday encourage friendship and a sense of community.

Houses in the Upper School (for pupils aged 14-18 years) are single sex. Lower School pupils (aged 11-14 years) board at the co-educational Manor, a fabulous Victorian mansion in extensive grounds, a short walk away from the main School campus.

"Coming back to the Manor at the end of the day feels like coming home. There is so much to do and so many people I like – I've certainly never felt lonely!" – Richard, Second Form Boarder at The Manor

Entry Requirements

At all stages, admission to Dauntsey's is via examination and interview. Pupils can join Dauntsey's aged 11, 13 or 16. We recommend that potential applicants and their families attend one of our open mornings, which offer an opportunity to see the School on a normal working day, to meet current pupils and talk to both teaching and admissions staff. We hold two open mornings a year in May and October. Individual appointments can be organised by contacting the Admissions Office at admissions@dauntseys.org.

For more information please visit our website which gives a real flavour of life at Dauntsey's – www.dauntseys.org

"...the school is highly successful in developing well-rounded, confident, skilled young people who are very well equipped for the next stage of their education." – ISI Inspection Report 2018

(Founded 1542)

High Street, West Lavington, Devizes, Wiltshire SN10 4HE UK

Tel: 01380 814500

Fax: 01380 814501

Email: admissions@dauntseys.org

Website: www.dauntseys.org

Head Master: Mr Mark Lascelles

Appointed: September 2012

School type: Coeducational Boarding & Day

Age range of pupils: 11–18

No. of pupils enrolled as at 01/09/2019: 820

Boys: 407 **Girls:** 413 **Sixth Form:** 270

No. of boarders: 298

Fees per annum as at 01/09/2019:

Day: £19,650

Full Boarding: £32,550

Average class size: 18; 12 in Sixth Form

Teacher/pupil ratio: 1:8

EF Academy Oxford

EF Academy International Boarding Schools prepare students for a global future with an exceptional high school education in the US or UK. At EF Academy, we believe in every student's ability to succeed. We empower them to do so through our renowned curricula, as well as quality one-on-one relationships with teachers and mentors alike. With a student body made up of 75 different nationalities, multilingualism and intercultural exchange are built into every course, which helps distinguish our students' academic credentials to both university admissions officers and future employers.

The Campus

Our private boarding school is situated in the city of Oxford, renowned for its scholastic tradition and rich cultural and architectural heritage. EF Academy students join Oxford's vibrant academic community, which attracts scholars from around the world.

On campus, students will find everything they need to focus and grow, including science laboratories and seminar-size classrooms, a bright and comfortable student lounge, a communal student kitchen, music room, drama studio, art studio, and outdoor spaces including a nature walk. Students also enjoy access to the library and sports center of nearby Oxford Brookes University.

Students live in on-campus residences with their classmates. House parents live in the residences and look after the students and ensure that they are safe and comfortable when they are not in class.

Academics

Education at EF Academy Oxford is highly personalized, creating an environment that stimulates an insatiable appetite for learning. Here, students are inspired to work hard, debate their views and actively take part in academic extension opportunities that propel students towards their goals.

Students follow the IB Diploma or A-Level programs and benefit from an enrichment program that includes visits to university math departments, science laboratories and lectures, ensuring students at EF Academy receive the ultimate pre-university experience.

University Placement

EF Academy Oxford graduates have gone on to attend universities such as the University of Oxford, Imperial College London, University of St Andrews, and Durham University. All of our students receive acceptance to university degree programs, many for highly competitive courses such as economics, engineering or medicine. Dedicated university advisors work together with students to help them prepare the best applications possible.

Extensive Support

At EF Academy Oxford, each student is assigned a personal tutor whose role is to monitor the student's academic progress and general welfare. They can turn to their tutor whenever they need support with homework and courses, or when they are experiencing homesickness.

Co-curricular Activities

Universities look for well-rounded students who get involved and extend their learning beyond the classroom. Students at EF Academy Oxford have access to a wide range of co-curricular activities. From subject-specific academic groups and competitions to sports and arts, there is an option for every student. The school's activities coordinator also arranges local excursions for students on the weekends.

EF ACADEMY

**International
Boarding Schools**

Pullens Lane, Headington, Oxfordshire OX3 0DT UK

Tel: +41 (0) 43 430 4095

Email: iaeurope@ef.com

Website: www.ef.com/academy

Head of School: Dr. Paul Ellis

School type: Coeducational Boarding

Age range of pupils: 16–19

No. of pupils enrolled as at 01/09/2019: 188

Fees per annum as at 01/09/2019:

IB Diploma/A-Levels: £30,750

Greene's Tutorial College

Greene's Tutorial College is the oldest tutorial college in Oxford. Based at our 17th-century premises in the heart of the city, we offer full- or part-time study programmes in an extensive range of A level and GCSE subjects.

Our academic courses are flexible and are uniquely customised to ensure that students' individual needs are recognised and catered for. At the heart of Greene's method of teaching is the tutorial method; a system of tuition used for centuries by the U.K.'s elite universities. This approach to education increases students' confidence and independence while consolidating concepts and knowledge through challenging discussion and presentations in one-to-one and small group tutorials.

Greene's offers this high-quality, personalised form of education to students of any age and background in a university-style environment. We combine academic tutorials with regular and systematic continual assessment: using online reports to provide feedback for every tutorial, in addition to running a robust series of trial examinations throughout the year. Feedback is also given to our students in weekly meetings with their dedicated Personal Tutor, as well as in discussions with our Director of Studies. Such rigorous assessment and close attention to students' progress has a significant positive impact on both their academic attainment and personal development, which students say proves invaluable when they begin their university studies.

Students come to Greene's for a variety of reasons: as an alternative to school or sixth form college, for supplementary or revision tuition, or to prepare for university. We help our students meet their specific university entry requirements – whether this is by improving their A level grades, taking specific aptitude or entrance tests, or by gaining experience in another subject area – and help them to acquire the intellectual curiosity and independence of thought to take them through college, university, and beyond.

The opportunity to develop skills outside of academic study is a key part of student life at Greene's. All students at Greene's join our highly successful Leadership Programme consisting of weekly seminars and workshops presented by internal staff and external speakers that encourage students to think critically, to be creative and adaptable, to present themselves persuasively, and to make effective and informed personal, academic, and career choices.

We are very happy to offer academic assessments, taster tutorials, and college tours at any time of the year to help students understand first-hand the advantages of the tutorial method at Greene's.

GREENE'S TUTORIAL COLLEGE

(Founded 1968)

45 Pembroke Street, Oxford, Oxfordshire OX1 1BP UK

Tel: 01865 664400

Email: enquiries@greenes.org.uk

Website: www.greenes.org.uk

Principal: Zoë Spilberg

Appointed: January 2019

School type: Coeducational Day & Boarding

No. of pupils enrolled as at 01/09/2019:

Sixth Form: 49

Fees per annum as at 01/09/2019:

£21,780 (one A level starts at £8,000)

Average class size: 1-3

Teacher/pupil ratio: 1:1

Headington School

Headington is a highly successful day and boarding school in Oxford for 800 girls aged 11-18 with a Preparatory School for 260 girls aged 3-11 occupying its own site just across the road. The School offers girls an unrivalled opportunity to pursue academic, sporting and artistic excellence in a caring and nurturing environment.

Founded in 1915 and set in 23 acres of playing fields and gardens, our superb facilities provide the perfect backdrop for teaching and learning that extends way beyond the classroom and curriculum. We encourage participation in all aspects of sport and culture, teamwork and leadership, challenging girls to discover and explore their own potential and achieve more than they thought possible.

Consistently in the premier league of academic schools in the UK, life at Headington is about much more than exam results. Through the sheer breadth of subjects and activities at Headington – and the option to study for the International Baccalaureate or A Levels – we aim to educate the complete individual, giving girls the confidence and self-awareness to compete, contribute and succeed at school, university and in their adult lives.

Facilities

Headington offers a superb range of facilities to support and enhance learning.

These include a state-of-the-art Music School complete with recording studio, 240-seat professional Theatre, light and airy Art School, Dance and Fitness Centre, Swimming Pool and award-winning Library. We recently completed an update to our Sixth Form Centre and a new Creativity and Innovation Centre will open in 2021.

Outside the classroom

Around 150 extra-curricular activities take place every week. A wide choice of subjects, sports, interests and hobbies and includes such diverse pastimes as Debating and Robotics, Cheerleading and CCF.

Headington offers a genuinely inclusive approach to sport and encourages each girl to enjoy sport at the level that suits her. Girls can choose from more than 30 different sporting activities, from Athletics to Zumba. The School enjoys national success in a wide range of sports including Fencing, Rowing, Cross Country, Swimming and Equestrian.

Around 450 individual music lessons take place each week while the School has four orchestras, three choirs and numerous ensembles.

There is a busy programme of productions in our Theatre each year and girls become involved in all aspects of theatre, from writing and producing their own plays, to lighting, costume and make up.

A huge range of dance options are on offer, from Ballet to Street Dance and Contemporary. As well as annual dance shows, the Headington Dance Company competes in local and national competitions.

Boarding

Headington has always been a boarding school and just over a quarter of the School board with us today. The five boarding houses provide the girls with a 'home from home' where, supported by a team of highly experienced staff, they develop into mature and independent young people. Many of boarders come from the UK and we are also very proud of our international boarding community, made up of more than 30 nationalities from all over the world. Girls can choose between full, weekly or half-weekly boarding.

(Founded 1915)

London Road, Oxford, Oxfordshire OX3 7TD UK

Tel: +44 (0)1865 759100

Fax: +44 (0)1865 760268

Email: admissions@headington.org

Website: www.headington.org

Headmistress: Mrs Caroline Jordan MA(Oxon)

School type: Girls' Day & Boarding

Age range of girls: 11–18

No. of pupils enrolled as at 01/09/2019:

Sixth Form: 250

Senior School: 800

Fees per term as at 01/09/2019:

Senior Day: £6,090 – £6,635 per term

Senior Boarding: £8,282 – £13,395 per term

Prep: £3,205 – £4,880 per term

Average class size: Depends on age

Teacher/pupil ratio: 1:8

Kingham Hill School

Kingham Hill School, surrounded by idyllic rural Cotswold beauty, offers a secondary school experience to girls and boys marked by nurturing pastoral care and academic rigour. The clear Christian foundation is central to its ethos in the 21st century, and it welcomes pupils of all backgrounds into family-style boarding and day houses. Although inclusive in intake, GCSE and A level results are well above the national average, with a high proportion of Upper Sixth leavers taking up places at Russell Group and other elite universities in the US and Europe. KHS is also unique in being a traditional British school with a US accreditation, through the Middle States Association (MSA). Around one in six pupils are American, who graduate with both A Level and AP qualifications, and the bespoke US college guidance programme is available to all pupils alongside UCAS. A similar proportion of pupils come from a diverse range of international backgrounds, and the 30 or so nationalities represented makes for a globally-minded and mature community.

The unofficial motto of KHS is, "Work hard, play hard, and serve well." Outside of the classroom, the daily extracurricular programme is compulsory, and includes a huge range of opportunities including sport, music, drama, CCF, Duke of Edinburgh's Award and a School Farm. Sports teams punch above their weight with full fixture lists at all levels, and the School is rightly proud of its Performing Arts Academy, which offers an annual series of concerts, plays, and musical theatre. A STEM programme gives pupils from Year 7 a hands-on experience of engineering, robotics, electronics, and aeromodelling, including a kart team which participates in the National Schools Karting Association (NatSKA) and the British Schools Karting Championship (BSKC). Service and leadership activities form an essential part of the weekly routine from Year 9, and in the Sixth Form, pupils are encouraged to spend time during the summer holidays at an orphanage in Zambia which has been supported by KHS for many years.

The School has a clear 15-year vision for its future, centred around seeking excellence in 10 strategic themes. This articulates the way KHS intends to remain faithful to its foundation, and to a small-school family home, whilst offering state-of-the-art facilities and a rounded education which prepares personable and engaging young men and women to face the challenges of higher education and a career. Most recently, the School has opened a new Maths and Science building and a new Library; a new Sports Hall is also currently under construction. True to its Founder's desire to see children with boarding need benefit from a KHS education, a recently launched Founder's Pupils initiative seeks to widen access to the opportunities and excellence on offer.

Transport links are excellent, and the School operates an extensive bus network for day pupils. For boarders, a mainline train station in Kingham allows a journey time of 25 minutes to Oxford, and 80 minutes to London Paddington. London Heathrow is just over an hour away, and the School arranges transport to the airport at the beginning and end of terms and half-terms.

The essence of a Kingham Hill education is rounded and servant-hearted personal development. The School prizes academic curiosity and a love of learning in the context of a classical liberal education, and promotes conservative family values. Above all is the belief that character is what really counts in life; the importance of resilience, courtesy, good manners, respect, hard work, adaptability, a sense of humour, and a willingness to make the best of every opportunity. To meet current pupils and see the ethos of KHS at first hand, please contact our Registrar, Mrs Helen Cope, at registrar@kinghamhill.org, to arrange a personal visit.

KINGHAM HILL SCHOOL

(Founded 1886)

Kingham, Chipping Norton, Oxfordshire OX7 6TH UK

Tel: 01608 658999

Fax: 01608 658658

Email: registrar@kinghamhill.org

Website: www.kinghamhill.org.uk

Head of School: Mr Nick Seward

Appointed: 2008

School type: Coeducational Boarding & Day

Religious Denomination: Christian

Age range of pupils: 11–18

No. of pupils enrolled as at 01/09/2019: 352

Boys: 210 **Girls:** 142

No. of boarders: 193

Fees per annum as at 01/09/2019:

Day: £17,895–£20,385

Weekly Boarding: £25,350–£31,305

Full Boarding: £26,160–£34,350

Average class size: 18

Teacher/pupil ratio: 1:8

Oxford Sixth Form College

Oxford Sixth Form College is a highly successful independent college specialising in A-level, BTEC and GCSE courses for students 15-19 in the heart of Oxford.

Established in 1988, the college has gained an excellent reputation for providing effective preparation for public examinations and university entry, achieved by thorough, exam-specific teaching and close attention to the needs of each individual student. We strongly believe that one size really does not fit all. We have a fantastic track record in helping students achieve their best, with many of our students being offered places at Russell Group and top 20 universities.

The Oxford Sixth Form College Experience

The college offers an environment quite different from that of a traditional school. The teaching approach is refreshingly interactive and informal. The emphasis on small group work enables a clear focus on individual needs and learning styles and a variation of pace and emphasis, which helps students to approach their work calmly and objectively. This 'tutorial method' is an extremely flexible teaching approach, which provides a dialogue between tutor and students and thus enables reinforcement of understanding and careful attention to areas of weakness.

The support provided by both subject tutors and each student's Senior Tutor is thoughtful and creative and students are encouraged at every stage to take an active part in the learning process through self-motivation, involvement, personal study and research. This is an important preparation for higher education. Various extra-curricular activities are offered enabling students to explore and develop the skills they will need in later life.

"I have found the quality of the teaching to be great and the enthusiasm teachers have for the subject inspiring."
– Lisha, A Level Student

Preparing students for University Life

The college has an inclusive ethos and a culture which encourages industry and a growing sense of responsibility. Students are encouraged at every stage to take an active part in the learning process.

There are no restrictions as to the choice of subjects or subject combinations, although students are helped to make choices appropriate to their degree course or vocational aim and directed towards subjects which engage their interest and fit in with their abilities and aptitudes.

The College

Our campus is a friendly, welcoming place and a home away from home for young people of many different cultures. There are plenty of social events throughout the year to let you get to know your fellow students better. We are very proud of what our students accomplish every year.

Our graduates go on to study at some of the UK's most prestigious universities and have stellar careers ahead of them thanks to the skills they learnt and choices they made while studying with us. They leave us equipped with essential qualifications, valuable life experience and English language skills that help them communicate confidently. But more than that, they also take away happy memories and lasting friendships.

Academic scholarships are available, please ask the College for further details.

It's a very exciting time for Oxford Sixth Form College, as it continues to make significant investment in improving its teaching building and boarding houses, with an increased focus on 2-year A-Levels and BTEC programmes.

OXFORD SIXTH FORM COLLEGE

(Founded 1988)

12-13 King Edward Street, Oxford, Oxfordshire OX1 4HT UK

Tel: +44 (0)1865 793233

Email: admissions@oxfordsixthformcollege.com

Website: www.oxfordsixthformcollege.com

Principal: Mr Mark Love

Appointed: 2017

School type: Co-educational Day & Boarding

Age range of pupils: 15–19

No. of pupils enrolled as at 01/09/2019: 197

Average class size: Av 4-8, Max 6-10

Radley College

At Radley we offer an environment for boys to grow in self-confidence, thrive academically, and make the most of the many opportunities we offer. We pride ourselves on the pursuit of excellence and on encouraging boys to develop their talents and discover new interests. Radley defines itself by its caring community where all are passionate about what they do, and dedicated to it.

A Radley education is about independent thought and learning with enthusiasm. It is about cultural awareness and the benefits of team sport. It is about academic ambition. It is about learning to live with others; it is about preparation for the world beyond its gates. Above all, it is about the core values that will underpin success in all its forms throughout a Radleian's life: as leaders, as citizens, as human beings.

Facilities
Radley College is a full-boarding single-sex environment, in beautiful rural surroundings with stunning facilities, four miles from the university city of Oxford: the perfect setting in which to provide the very best education.

Radley boasts a mix of both modern and traditional buildings set on a beautiful 800-acre estate. Chapel stands at the heart of the school allowing the College community to meet together daily for worship and reflection.

The outstanding sport facilities at Radley include three astro's, an 8-lane athletics track, a strength and conditioning centre and real tennis court. The rowing tank, which opened in 2015, offers a perfect facility for winter weather training and to correct technique.

Radley aims for excellence both in and out of the classroom, seeking to develop qualities of inquisitiveness, perseverance, humility and kindness.

Entry Requirements
Entry is in Year 6, via the ISEB Common Pre Test. There will also be an interview and a review of the current school report. For Sixth Form entry, assessment is in November of year 11. With a new Social (boarding house) opening in September 2020, we are particularly keen to hear from academically ambitious boys who would like to come in the Sixth Form.

Scholarships
Radley has Awards that can be worth up to 100% of the fees for talented boys at 11+ or 13+. We welcome applications for boys currently attending a maintained school who excel academically or at music, sport, art or drama. Radley will provide financial support for two years at a Prep school before continuing to Radley at 13 years of age.

To find out more please contact Admissions on 01235 543 174 or visit www.radley.org.uk

RADLEY

(Founded 1847)

Radley, Abingdon, Oxfordshire OX14 2HR UK

Tel: 01235 543106

Email: admissions@radley.org.uk

Website: www.radley.org.uk

The Warden: Mr J S Moule

Appointed: 2000

School type: Boys' Boarding

Religious Denomination: Church of England

Age range of boys: 13–18

No. of pupils enrolled as at 01/09/2019: 690

No. of boarders: 690

Fees per annum as at 01/09/2019:

Full Boarding: £38,325

Average class size: 20

Teacher/pupil ratio: 1:8

Shiplake College

Shiplake College is a thriving boarding and day school for boys aged 11-18, with girls joining in the Sixth Form. Overlooking the River Thames, two miles upstream of the famous Henley Royal Regatta stretch, students enjoy an inspirational 45-acre rural site. Flexi, weekly and full boarding is available from Year 7 (age 11).

Shiplake provides a friendly, supportive and structured environment to bring out the best in each and every pupil and aims to equip them with the skills they need to enter the next stage of their lives as confident, personable and talented young adults. Increasingly academically ambitious and renowned for outstanding pastoral care and personal development, the College welcomes pupils with wide-ranging skills and talents, who will make the most of the many opportunities offered to them.

Every pupil is placed at the heart of Shiplake life and the College's ethos is underpinned by the three Is – Inclusive, Individual and Inspirational. All pupils are valued regardless of academic prowess, artistic flair or sporting ability, with opportunities for all to join in and try new things.

We are a small community where every pupil becomes well-known to their House's pastoral team, especially the Housemaster, personal tutor and matron. Each pupil's best method of learning is identified and catered for by their teachers, with high-achieving pupils continually stretched while those requiring additional support can access it in a variety of ways. There is a wide range of A Level and BTEC subjects available, with all Sixth Formers also undertaking either the EPQ or CoPE as part of a bespoke PULSE (Personal Understanding, Learning Skills and Enrichment) programme.

Interpersonal skills, confidence and talents are also discovered outside the classroom. Two afternoons are reserved for an array of clubs and activities, including a comprehensive outdoor education programme, with pupils encouraged to extend their horizons and experience new challenges and responsibilities. Sports training takes place on three afternoons a week, with the majority of fixtures on Saturday mornings.

The College recruits highly motivated teaching staff with an ability and passion to inspire future generations and we ensure pupils have the best possible learning resources and facilities at their disposal. The environment we provide encourages pupils to take inspiration from their teachers, their surroundings, and each other.

2019 should see the College open a Sixth Form Centre, with a café where Year 12 and 13 girls and boys can socialise and work independently and some additional classrooms, and also a Boathouse and Multi-Activity Centre. This exciting facility will not only include storage for rowing boats and other watersports, mountain biking and outdoor education, CCF and DofE equipment, but will also incorporate an indoor archery/rifle range, a climbing wall, weights room and an ergo room, which transforms into a function room with a balcony overlooking the river.

Academic, Art, Music, Drama and Sport Scholarships, and means-tested bursaries, are available. The College is also offering one 100% All-Rounder scholarship to a boy currently at a state-maintained primary school who would be looking to join Year 7 in September 2020, who would not be able to attend Shiplake without substantial financial support.

Entry points are normally at Year 7 (11+), Year 9 (13+) and Year 12 (16+). Prospective families are encouraged to arrange an individual visit or attend an open morning, which take place in the Autumn Term and March each year. Please go to www.shiplake.org.uk to book your attendance, complete a registration form and explore the whole site, which includes details of admissions processes, fees, bus routes and answers to most academic, co-curricular and pastoral questions that prospective parents may have.

SHIPLAKE COLLEGE
HENLEY-ON-THAMES

(Founded 1959)

Henley-on-Thames, Oxfordshire RG9 4BW UK

Tel: +44 (0)1189 402455

Fax: +44 (0)1189 405204

Email: registrar@shiplake.org.uk

Website: www.shiplake.org.uk

Headmaster: Mr T G Howe MA, MSt, MBA

Appointed: 2019

School type:
Boys' Boarding & Day, Co-educational Sixth Form

Religious Denomination: Church of England

Age range of boys: 11–18

Age range of girls: 16–18

No. of pupils enrolled as at 01/09/2019: 475

Boys: 425 **Girls:** 50 **Sixth Form:** 195

No. of boarders: 135

Fees per annum as at 01/09/2019:

Day: £18,675–£23,460

Weekly Boarding: £26,175–£32,730

Full Boarding: £34,890

Flexi Boarding (2 nights per week): £22,050 – £26,820

Average class size: 16

Teacher/pupil ratio: 1:6

St Helen and St Katharine

Founded in 1903, St Helen and St Katharine is an independent day school for girls aged 9-18 in Abingdon, Oxfordshire. With an outstanding academic record which makes us one of the leading girls' schools in the country, our aim is to ensure that every student – from Junior Department through to Sixth Form – achieves success as she defines it, so that she can believe in herself, her talents and abilities, and feel prepared and equipped for life beyond school.

The Junior Department forms a unique bridge between primary and secondary education, with students taught in intentionally small classes by a team of dedicated primary specialists as well as senior school teachers in certain subjects. Throughout Lower and Middle School, stimulating and challenging teaching continues to reach beyond the curriculum, enabling students to become effective and independent learners. An extensive range of opportunities for academic enrichment beyond lessons is offered, such as attending lectures and conferences, visiting specialist speakers and discussion dinners.

Academic life in the Sixth Form is about learning beyond the ordinary business of a curriculum. Every student participates in a personalised programme of study that is aligned with her passions and ambitions. Success in A-levels enables leavers to secure places on their chosen courses at top UK universities, including a significant number who advance to Oxford and Cambridge. Our comprehensive HE and careers programmes aim to make the transition to the next educational stage as smooth as possible. Through the Kate Scheme, students are mentored by alumnae who offer their skills and advice to help them achieve their career aspirations.

Our broad and varied extracurricular programme of 100+ clubs and activities plays a central role within school life. Students are actively encouraged to give new things a go – they can participate purely for fun or follow their strengths and excel through teams and groups, music and drama productions. From fencing and photography to Mandarin as well as the Duke of Edinburgh's Award and Young Enterprise, there are always opportunities to extend interests, make friends across age groups and, through personal achievement, build confidence and self-belief.

Plans for the future include continuing to shape the best possible learning and social experience for Sixth Form; we have applied for planning permission to build a new Sixth Form Centre, providing nine classrooms, a lecture/performance space, a café, study areas and general social and work space. The guiding principle is to create a building which anticipates the feel of a university.

Students are admitted to St Helen's in Years 5, 6, 7, 9 and Sixth Form. It may be possible to admit students into other years – enquiries should be made to the Admissions Office.

Our scholarship and bursary provision seeks to recognise and support the core aims and traditions of the School. Scholarships are awarded to recognise excellence, ability and potential in one or more academic or extracurricular area while opening up access for young women who would not otherwise be able to attend the School through an extensive bursaries scheme has always been central to the St Helen's ethos. If a student has the ability, imagination and drive to grasp the opportunities on offer at St Helen's, we would like to give her that chance. The School offers means tested bursaries of up to 100% of fees, including subject-specific bursaries at A-level.

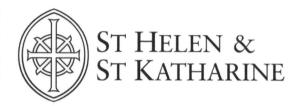

ST HELEN &
ST KATHARINE

(Founded 1903)

Faringdon Road, Abingdon, Oxfordshire OX14 1BE UK

Tel: 01235 520173

Email: info@shsk.org.uk

Website: www.shsk.org.uk

Headmistress: Mrs Rebecca Dougall BA MA

Appointed: January 2015

School type: Girls' Day

Age range of girls: 9–18

No. of pupils enrolled as at 01/09/2019: 730

Fees per term as at 01/09/2019:

Day: £5,665 per term

St Mary's Calne

St Mary's (founded in 1873) is an independent boarding and day school for girls aged 11-18, a happy, purposeful and flourishing community of around 365 pupils with an 80% to 20% boarding-to-day ratio. St Mary's welcomes cultural diversity and around 15% of the students come from overseas.

The school is located in the market town of Calne and amidst the Wiltshire Downs, an area of stunning natural beauty and historical significance. The school is within easy reach of the university towns of Bath, Bristol and Oxford and just over an hour by train from London. This ideal location means that the girls benefit from a huge range of curriculum-enhancing opportunities as well as extra-curricular ones.

Focus on the individual

Small by design, St Mary's provides exceptional all-round education in a warm, nurturing environment. It is the individualised approach to every aspect of school life that makes St Mary's Calne special.

The pastoral care is outstanding. Every girl has a Tutor to support her through aspects of school life, from organisational skills and subject choices through to university application.

High Achievers

St Mary's Calne has a well-deserved reputation for academic excellence. The school was the top achieving independent school in the South West, (The Sunday Times Schools Guide 2018) and is also the first independent school in the UK to be given the prestigious Platinum Science Mark Award.

In 2019, St Mary's Calne students went on to study at a range of leading universities including: Oxford, Cambridge, Birmingham, Bristol, Durham, Exeter, Leeds, LSE, Manchester, Newcastle, Nottingham, St Andrews and UCL. The girls will be studying a diverse range of subjects, ranging from Architecture, Biomedical Sciences, Classics, Economics, Geography and History to Medicine, Modern Languages, PPE and Zoology.

Outside the Classroom

Opportunities in sport, music, art and drama abound and the facilities are superb, including a £2.55 million sports complex and full-size astro, theatre, and a Sixth Form Centre with 120+ girls.

80% of girls play musical instruments and take part in a wide variety of ensembles. The girls perform at many events, both in the local community and further afield.

Drama productions in the purpose-built theatre are of the highest standard and have transferred to the London stage. The Drama Department has a unique relationship with RADA, offering a course in advanced communication skills and girls also perform annually at the Edinburgh Fringe.

The girls do exceptionally well in the Young Enterprise Programme, regularly progressing to the Regional Finals. Many pupils are talented artists and in 2019 accolades included three girls having their artwork selected for the first ever Young Artists' Summer Show (YASS) at the Royal Academy of Arts.

The girls excel at sport, and the school is represented at county level in several major sports, nationally in athletics and lacrosse, and internationally in horse riding, with all girls taking advantage of the superb sports facilities. The girls also enjoy many other sports, including tennis, hockey, fencing and ski racing.

Trips abound and in 2019 these included a Lacrosse Tour to the USA, a Geography Trip to Tenerife, a History of Art Trip to Florence and a Classics Trip to Crete.

For further information, or to book onto one of our Open Days, please visit: www.stmaryscalne.org

ST MARY'S CALNE

(Founded 1873)

Curzon Street, Calne, Wiltshire SN11 0DF UK

Tel: 01249 857200

Fax: 01249 857207

Email: office@stmaryscalne.org

Website: www.stmaryscalne.org

Headmistress: Dr Felicia Kirk BA(University of MD), MA, PhD(Brown University)

Appointed: January 2013

School type: Girls' Boarding & Day

Religious Denomination: Church of England

Age range of girls: 11–18

No. of pupils enrolled as at 01/09/2019: 365

Sixth Form: 121

No. of boarders: 290

Fees per annum as at 01/09/2019:

Day: £29,745

Full Boarding: £39,885

Average class size: Max 17, smaller in the Sixth Form

Teacher/pupil ratio: 1:5

Thornton College

Thornton College day and boarding school for girls, located between Milton Keynes and Buckingham, is set in 25 acres of beautiful grounds. The main school building is a manor house dating back to the 14th century and it became a school in 1917, founded by the Sisters of Jesus and Mary.

The school is very proud of its rich history, exceptional pastoral care for the individual and its strong emphasis on core Christian values, though it is also proud of the fact that it is a forward looking school, with exciting opportunities both in and outside the classroom, and where girls of all faiths and no faith are equally welcome. Thornton College is part of an international family of J&M schools in twenty eight countries around the world. This gives our students the best of opportunities for student international partnership programmes, celebrations, projects and exchanges, enabling a unique global outlook and cultural intelligence.

Boarding is 'upstairs' in our main manor house offering a home from home experience. The boarding bedrooms and common areas are bright and spacious. We offer flexi, weekly and termly boarding for domestic and international students with a dense programme of exciting evening activities and weekend trips.

Our academic results are comparable with high achieving competitive schools whilst having a varied ability intake. As a Forest School, girls at Thornton excel inside and outside the classroom with our prep school children enjoying our outdoor classroom in our woodlands and exploring and pond dipping in our eco habitat park. Students in senior and sixth form enjoy overseas sporting tours, World Challenges, Duke of Edinburgh (with sixth formers achieving their Gold Awards); EPQs; partnership work with our heritage link school St Columba's School for boys such as #STEM events, UCAS and careers events and debating. Thornton College is a pilot school and partner for ReachEdu leading the introduction of robotics into prep school curriculum.

Our one site school ensures that the transition from early years into our pre-prep, prep, senior and sixth form is smooth and our older girls are role models for our younger students ensuring plenty of opportunities for mixed age group activities. The Thornton co-educational nursery creates a sense of wonder making children's introduction to learning so exciting. Woodland walks, cookery, ballet, French, music and movement, library time and a host of other regular pursuits enhance the play and craft activities and excite their young minds. Our Sixth Form, which opened in 2016, offers a wide subject choice, small class sizes and individual attention with future pathway support. Sixth Form students undertake the Oxbridge programme, gain competitive apprenticeships, and apply and receive Russell Group offers.

At Thornton, EVERY GIRL is encouraged to develop her talents, not only in the classroom but through a broad co-curricular programme which makes use of our modern facilities and beautiful grounds.

Thornton College is non-selective, recognising, in line with its ethos, that children develop at different rates and stages of their lives and in each one there is potential to excel. A strong work ethic, exceptional teaching and excellent pastoral care provides the secure environment where each girl is known and encouraged to develop her strengths, her social skills and her ability to pursue, with confidence, the next stage of life.

THORNTON

(Founded 1917)

College Lane, Thornton, Buckinghamshire MK17 0HJ UK

Tel: 01280 812610

Email: admissions@thorntoncollege.com

Website: www.thorntoncollege.com

Headteacher: Mrs Val Holmes

Appointed: November 2018

School type: Girls' Day & Boarding

Age range of boys: 2½–4

Age range of girls: 2½–18

No. of pupils enrolled as at 01/09/2019: 437

No. of boarders: 57

Fees per annum as at 01/09/2019:

Day: £10,035–£16,005

Weekly Boarding: £17,310–£21,900

Full Boarding: £21,525–£26,700

Average class size: 14

Teacher/pupil ratio: 1:20

Wycombe Abbey

Wycombe Abbey is a global leader in outstanding education and modern boarding. The School is committed to creating tomorrow's women leaders and has a long tradition of academic excellence, it is consistently one of the country's top performing schools.

Our learning environment is supportive, yet challenging, with a sense that pupils and their teachers are on an educational journey together. We pride ourselves on the outstanding teaching provided by our specialists who communicate a genuine love of their subject and serve to inspire the girls they teach.

We believe that education should not simply be about delivering a curriculum and examination syllabus, but that real learning stems from stimulating intellectual curiosity and nurturing a love for the subjects being taught, which will stay with our girls throughout their lives.

In all we do, boarding is the key to our continued success. The School has a culture that inspires throughout the day, seven days a week, empowering girls to achieve their best, academically and socially. In our happy and close community, each girl is known, and cherished, as an individual. Consequently, every girl's potential, whatever that might be, is explored and fulfilled.

Girls learn to be independent, to value and support others, and to develop the skills needed for future challenges in a global workplace. Given the nature of boarding life, girls are able to enjoy a wealth of co-curricular opportunities. Each and every girl carves out a unique learning path according to her interests and has the space to thrive within our magnificent grounds. Our approach to boarding is also sympathetic to the needs of today's families and pupils have the opportunity to go home regularly and parents are actively involved in the numerous School events and activities.

The School is an oasis of calm, set in 170 acres of magnificent, conservation-listed grounds and woodland. Modern, state-of-the-art facilities include the Sports Centre, with a 25-metre indoor pool, the Performing Arts Centre with a theatre and recital hall, an atrium café, dance and fitness studios, and extensive sports pitches. Two brand new Boarding Houses opened in September 2017 and a refurbishment of all the boarding accommodation will follow.

Wycombe Abbey is easily accessible with excellent transport links. It is about 35 miles west of London and 30 miles east of Oxford. It is a 30-minute journey from Heathrow Airport and a 90-minute journey from Gatwick Airport by road.

To find out more about gaining a place at Wycombe Abbey, please visit our website at www.wycombeabbey.com or contact our Admissions Team on (+44) (0) 1494 897008 or by emailing registrar@wycombeabbey.com.

WYCOMBE ABBEY

(Founded 1896)

High Wycombe, Buckinghamshire HP11 1PE UK

Tel: +44 (0)1494 897008

Email: registrar@wycombeabbey.com

Website: www.wycombeabbey.com

Headmistress:
Mrs Jo Duncan MA (St Andrews), PGCE (Cantab)

Appointed: September 2019

School type: Girls' Day & Boarding

Religious Denomination: Church of England

Age range of girls: 11–18

No. of pupils enrolled as at 01/09/2019: 636

Fees per annum as at 01/09/2019:

Day: £30,270

Full Boarding: £40,350

East

Abbot's Hill School

Abbot's Hill School is a happy and thriving community in which pupils are encouraged to aim high, to grasp opportunities, enjoy learning and make lasting friendships.

The school offers an all-round education for girls aged 4-16 years, and the Day Nursery & Pre-School caters for girls and boys from 6 months. Our happy and united community gives each pupil the opportunity to shine.

The school is set within 76 acres of parkland on the outskirts of Hemel Hempstead, where our first-rate facilities provide space for outdoor sport and extra-curricular activities. Our Abbot's Hill's historic campus offers modern and extensive facilities in a magnificent country setting.

Abbot's Hill has a strong record of academic success. Throughout the school, pupils are taught in genuinely small classes. Excellent teaching and personalised support ensure that everyone is inspired to exceed their potential and to thrive.

The broad curriculum is enhanced by a wide range of trips and activities to stimulate learning. Extra-curricular clubs offer a lively balance of music, sports, languages, debating, drama and more. In short, there is something for everyone!

At Abbot's Hill, we pride ourselves on our pastoral care. We give individual attention to each girl so that she will develop as a person, but also to ensure she succeeds. The sense of being part of an extended family is frequently commented on by pupils, parents and staff alike.

The school's ethos is one which places the well-being and success of the individual child at its centre, and this is reflected in many aspects of school life.

In such a nurturing environment, pupils grow naturally in confidence, are happy to embrace new challenges and eagerly take on increasing responsibilities. Pupils leave Abbot's Hill fully equipped to take on the challenges and opportunities life has to offer.

Abbot's Hill girls progress seamlessly from one stage of education to the next. They become fully equipped to take on the challenges and opportunities life has to offer.

Our consistently excellent results at GCSE are testament to our ethos – that at Abbot's Hill, your daughter will achieve her very best because she is happy.

"I feel happy sending my daughter to school knowing that she is being given every opportunity to develop into a confident, well-rounded individual." – Prep School Parent

"There is a huge variety of things to do here and so many options. It really inspires you and helps you to spread your wings." – Senior School Pupil

(Founded 1912)

Bunkers Lane, Hemel Hempstead, Hertfordshire HP3 8RP UK

Tel: 01442 240333

Email: registrar@abbotshill.herts.sch.uk

Website: www.abbotshill.herts.sch.uk

Headmistress:
Mrs Kathryn Gorman BA (Hons), PGCE, MEd

Appointed: January 2020

School type: Girls' Day

Age range of girls: 4–16

No. of pupils enrolled as at 01/09/2019: 530

Boys: 20 *Girls:* 510

Prep School: 240

Senior School: 290

Fees per annum as at 01/09/2019:

Prep School: £11,142 – £14,049

Years 7–11: £19,185 – £19,302

Average class size: 12–18

Brentwood School

Brentwood School shines out as a beacon of excellence. Our students are happy individuals who thrive on the high standards which are expected of them. They benefit from state-of-the-art facilities, set in the heart of Brentwood in Essex, and surrounded by 75 acres of green playing fields and gardens.

Academically, we sit comfortably alongside the best day and boarding schools in the country, and we enjoy an unparalleled local reputation.

We celebrate a 463-year history and take our heritage seriously. We are a Christian School with a chapel and a chaplain, and our School values, encapsulated in our motto "Virtue, Learning and Manners", have as much resonance today as they did when written by English poet John Donne in 1622. Our pupils are expected to have self-respect, to exhibit pride in their appearance and embrace values such as courtesy, consideration for others, kindness, looking after each other, honour, courage, sportsmanship, duty and selflessness.

Brentwood School pupils achieve excellent academic standards that rank among some of the best in the country. Our track record of exam results shows consistent high grades are achieved by all our pupils. They work exceptionally hard and are supported by highly professional and inspiring teachers to achieve excellent results at both GCSE level and in Sixth Form, whether studying A levels or the IB Diploma. An average of eight students per year are offered places at Oxford or Cambridge and over 80% of offers are from Russell Group universities.

We offer both GCSEs and IGCSEs; A levels and the IB Diploma. More recent curriculum developments include the introduction of a Human Universe course in the Fourth and Fifth Year, which examines critical thinking and global issues.

Brentwood was the first school in Essex, and one of the first in the country, to adopt the Diamond Model: single-sex classes from the age of 11-16 within an overall mixed gender environment. We believe this model helps our teachers to tailor their teaching to the different learning styles of boys and girls and provides the best of single gender teaching within a coeducational environment.

From an early age, we encourage pupils to aim high, think creatively and develop independence, so by the time they leave Sixth Form, they are well prepared for the expected, but can also tackle the unknowns. A flourishing Old Brentwoods community keeps thousands of alumni connected across the globe.

Our vast and exciting co-curricular programme enjoys national prominence, and we focus on providing opportunities for all to participate, as well as the pursuit of excellence for the most able.

Our Combined Cadet Force is one of the oldest and largest in the country, we offer The Duke of Edinburgh's Award to pupils who want to satisfy their taste for adventure, and a Voluntary Service in Action Unit which raises tens of thousands of pounds every year to help specific charitable organisations.

Our sports centre houses a 25-metre swimming pool, glass-backed squash courts, fencing salle and dance studio and pupils achieve top sporting honours both nationally and internationally.

We are proud to be a Steinway School, enabling our pupils to learn on the very best-made pianos in the world, as well as some rare instruments otherwise unavailable to them.

Our musicians have played in the National Youth Orchestra, and our actors have gained places in the National Youth Theatre, RADA and other top Drama schools.

The lessons pupils learn at Brentwood will last for a lifetime. Integrity, initiative, a spirit of enterprise and an international mind-set help our pupils to thrive in the twenty-first century.

Brentwood School

(Founded 1557)

Middleton Hall Lane, Brentwood, Essex CM15 8EE UK

Tel: 01277 243243

Fax: 01277 243299

Email: headmaster@brentwood.essex.sch.uk

Website: www.brentwoodschool.co.uk

Headmaster: Mr Michael Bond

Appointed: September 2019

School type: Coeducational Day & Boarding

Religious Denomination: Church of England

Age range of pupils: 3–18

No. of pupils enrolled as at 01/09/2019: 1620

Boys: 917 **Girls:** 703

Fees per annum as at 01/09/2019:

Day: £19,800

Full Boarding: £38,799

Average class size: 18 in Prep & Senior; 8 in Sixth Form

Teacher/pupil ratio: 1:9

Felsted School

Felsted offers boys and girls aged four to eighteen a first class all round education, based on a safe, rural village campus in stunning North Essex, only one hour from London and Cambridge. We welcome students from all over the world to appreciate a British boarding school education. For our more local families we also offer day and a variety of boarding options, with daily bus routes from across the region.

A rounded, holistic approach

At Felsted, we value emotional and social development as much as academic and intellectual development. From the moment that your son or daughter joins Felsted's supportive and close knit community, he or she will be nurtured and challenged. We take pride in knowing and valuing every child as an individual, stretching them, encouraging them, and appreciating them for every contribution that they make to the community. Characteristics such as compassion towards one's peers or resilience through adversity are developed just as much as creative, academic or sporting prowess.

Pupils instantly become part of the Felsted family and quickly make new friends. They thrive in a School which cares for the individual and gives so many opportunities to excel both academically and in a wide range of activities. Away from the classroom, your child will become a valuable member of sporting teams (hockey, tennis, netball, cricket, rugby, squash, polo etc), involved in drama and music or many of the other clubs and activities available. The welcoming Boarding and Day Houses ensure that strong friendships are made, with an active weekend programme to ensure your child is happy and stimulated.

We believe that our rounded and holistic approach, supported by the global Round Square network to which we belong, is what will make a difference to your child's path through life. In return, we hope that your child will also develop into someone who seeks to make a difference to the lives of others at school and in the wider world. Leadership, Service, Charity and Internationalism are core values here at Felsted.

Felsted Highlights

- Leading British all round education for boys & girls aged 4 to 18, established in 1564
- Small class sizes, modern and dedicated facilities
- Top degree apprenticeships and university entry, including Oxbridge
- GCSEs, International Baccalaureate Diploma & A Levels. Top 5% in the UK for A Level Academic Progress
- Superb International induction course and Summer School
- Established international links and work education programme
- Outstanding co-curricular opportunities on site
- Excellence in sport: top quality coaches, facilities and fixtures
- West End quality drama and outstanding art facilities
- Unique partnership with the Junior Guildhall School of Music
- Scholarships, Awards and Bursaries available
- Rated 'Excellent' in every aspect, ISI Inspection
- A stunning village campus only one hour from London & Cambridge

"Felsted produces self-starting, entrepreneurial and independent spirits...a school that brings out the best in everyone."
The Good Schools Guide

Felsted

(Founded 1564)

Felsted, Great Dunmow, Essex CM6 3LL UK

Tel: 01371 822605

Email: intadmissions@felsted.org

Website: www.felsted.org

Headmaster: Mr Chris Townsend

Appointed: 2015

School type: Coeducational Day & Boarding

Age range of pupils: 13–18

No. of pupils enrolled as at 01/09/2019: 556

Boys: 324 *Girls:* 232 *Sixth Form:* 249

Fees per annum as at 01/09/2019:

Day: £24,495

Weekly Boarding: £34,725

Full Boarding: £37,485

Average class size: 18 (8/9 for IB classes)

Haileybury

Haileybury is an independent co-educational boarding school, located between London and Cambridge, in 500 acres of beautiful Hertfordshire countryside. Spectacular grounds are home to outstanding facilities, excellent teaching and superb pastoral care for its community of boarding and day pupils.

Founded in 1862, Haileybury is proud of its history, tradition and values, taking the best from the past whilst also looking to the future. Academic rigour and outstanding co-curricular provision are at the heart of the school, providing exceptional opportunities and a truly all-round education which enables pupils to discover enduring passions and talents. Haileyburians leave as leaders and life-long learners who can make a difference in the world beyond school.

Academic opportunity

The school offers a dedicated Lower School for Years 7 and 8, a wide range of GCSEs and IGCSEs and the choice of the IB Diploma or A levels in the Sixth Form. Haileybury is ranked Top 10 in The Times league table for co-ed independent schools which offer the IB.

Boarding and day

More than two thirds of pupils are boarders with school life centred around 12 boarding houses and Lower School benefitting from having their own house. Pupils join at 11+, 13+, 14+ or 16+ entry points. Flexi-boarding is available in Lower School, which means families do not have to commit to full boarding. From Year 9 onwards, there is the additional flexibility of pupils being able to return home after sports commitments on Saturday afternoons.

Exceptional opportunities

A key part of the school's philosophy is empowering each child to follow their passions and build self-confidence.

Pupils benefit from professional sports coaching and the school regularly hosts speakers and performers from the arts, sporting and academic worlds.

There is a packed co-curricular programme of more than 130 options, from scuba diving and African drumming to bee-keeping, Mandarin and survival skills.

The school's Model United Nations programme sees more than 700 international students invited to Haileybury each spring to debate global issues – one of the largest programmes of its kind in the UK. Throughout the year, there is an abundance of music concerts, drama productions and public performances while more than 30 visiting specialists teach hundreds of instrument lessons every week.

Supportive environment

At Haileybury, a caring environment is crucial to a pupil's happiness and fulfilment. There is an emphasis on pastoral care with round-the-clock support from housemasters and housemistresses, to the chaplain, tutors, and a resident doctor. The school is a home-from-home, with a warm and friendly feel. Every child is given the confidence to find their identity on a personal journey of discovery.

A warm welcome

There is a busy programme of open days and taster events which take place throughout the year. Families are warmly invited to discover what life at Haileybury has to offer and why its pupils flourish.

For further information, please contact head of admissions Michele Metcalfe, on admissions@haileybury.com

Haileybury

(Founded 1862)

Haileybury, Hertford, Hertfordshire SG13 7NU UK

Tel: +44 (0)1992 706200

Email: admissions@haileybury.com

Website: www.haileybury.com

The Master: Mr Martin Collier MA BA PGCE

Appointed: September 2017

School type: Coeducational Boarding & Day

Age range of pupils: 11–18

(entry at 11+, 13+ and 16+)

No. of pupils enrolled as at 01/09/2019: 889

Boys: 506 *Girls:* 383 *Sixth Form:* 348

No. of boarders: 590

Fees per annum as at 01/09/2019:

Day: £17,031–£25,620

Full Boarding: £21,837–£34,422

Teacher/pupil ratio: 1:7

Heath Mount School

Description: Heath Mount is a leading independent day and boarding school for boys and girls between the ages of 3 and 13. Our pupils are privileged to be educated at one of the oldest Prep school in the country, founded in 1796 and situated since 1934 in the Grade 1 listed mansion of the Woodhall Park Estate just outside Hertford.

Our idyllic woodland setting, dynamic teaching staff, family ethos and award-winning pastoral care provide a joyful and stimulating learning environment. We offer a broad curriculum that balances academic rigour with remarkable enrichment opportunities. Our pupils achieve outstanding results within a nurturing and supportive framework that puts happiness and mental wellbeing at the heart of all we do.

Facilities: We benefit from our own forest school and an all-weather Astro turf. A spacious central plateau houses rugby, football and cricket pitches, as well as our netball courts.

We have a well-equipped gymnasium, and our swimming pool offers the best of both worlds, with a retractable roof giving shelter in the winter and outdoor swimming in the warmer summer months, so our children really do have the opportunity to enjoy sport all year round.

Inside, all classrooms are equipped with the very latest in interactive technology. We have a dedicated ICT suite in the Pre-prep school and a newly refurbished ICT facility in the Prep school.

Our purpose-built Pre-prep is in the same grounds as the Prep school but separate from it. It has its own library, computer room, music room, dining room and hall in addition to a beautiful outdoor playground.

Pre-prep children also use many of the prep school's facilities such as the Sports Hall, Astroturf, Swimming Pool, Pottery Room and Chapel.

In September 2015 we opened our new classroom block for Year 3 and 4 pupils, in summer 2017 we opened our magnificent new performing arts centre and in summer 2019 we refurbished our Pre-prep building.

Feeder Schools: We feed to a wide range of senior schools including Eton, Harrow, Westminster, Radley, Oundle, Uppingham, Benenden, St Albans Boys, St Albans Girls, Haileybury, Bishop's Stortford College, Felsted, The Leys and Brighton College.

Exam results: In the academic year 2018-19, all of our Year 8 pupils gained entry to their first choice school and 40% were awarded one or more scholarships.

Entrance procedure: Prospective pupils may be registered with us from any time after birth and we welcome the majority of our children to our Nursery in the September following their third birthday. We are not a selective school and do not assess children starting at this stage though we do encourage early registration as places are limited and our Pre-prep is often oversubscribed.

We usually have a smaller number of spaces available for entry into Reception. We do not formally assess at this age, but will invite your child in to spend time with us to ensure that they have the social and developmental skills to access the Early Years Curriculum.

For entry into the Prep School for Year 3 and above, assessments in Maths, reading, writing and non-verbal reasoning will usually take place in addition to an observational assessment to ensure that your child is able to access our broad curriculum. References will also be sought from your child's current school. Provided we have space in our school we do accept children at any stage from Year 3 up to Year 8 entry.

Heath Mount School

(Founded 1796)

Woodhall Park, Watton-at-Stone, Hertford, Hertfordshire SG14 3NG UK

Tel: 01920 830230

Email: registrar@heathmount.org

Website: www.heathmount.org

Headmaster: Mr Chris Gillam BEd(Hons)

Appointed: September 2014

School type: Coeducational Day & Flexi-boarding

Age range of pupils: 3–13

No. of pupils enrolled as at 01/09/2019: 478

Boys: 255 **Girls:** 223

Fees per annum as at 01/09/2019:

Day: £11,955–£18,435

Flexi-boarding: £1,535 – £5,250

Average class size: 10-18

King's Ely

We know that if we could bottle the spirit of King's Ely we would be onto a real winner, but we would like you to come and experience it for yourself.

Nestled in the heart of the beautiful cathedral city of Ely in Cambridgeshire, King's Ely is an inspiringly visionary independent coeducational day and boarding school, yet one that is built on a fascinating history stretching back over 1,000 years.

We serve the academic and pastoral needs of around 1,000 boys and girls from the age of 2 through to 18, with boarders from 8 years old. King's Ely is located just 15 minutes north of Cambridge and a short walk from Ely train station, with a huge number of students taking advantage of Ely's direct rail links. We also have independently-run school buses which stop at key locations across the region.

The adventure of a King's Ely education enables pupils of all ages to flourish, from the children in King's Ely Acremont and Nursery to the young men and women in our Sixth Form; and whether a student shines in a classroom or lab, on a stage, on a pitch or on a mountainside, our school promises an abundance of opportunity for personal development, both academically and socially.

We empower our young people to challenge themselves, to push beyond the boundaries of their own expectations and to achieve more than they ever believed possible. King's Ely students achieve excellent GCSE and A Level results, with 98% gaining places in their first or insurance choice university. But our school is about much more than league tables.

Innovative approaches to teaching and learning are the hallmark of every section of King's Ely. Through a broad and balanced curriculum, pupils develop the self-knowledge and inner resilience that will enable them to face the challenges of an ever-changing world.

Music, drama, art and textiles are each embedded in the culture of King's Ely, with vast opportunities for pupils of all abilities and aspirations. All major sports are offered, along with an impressive array of other activities, helping every pupil to realise their sporting potential. Rowing, athletics, golf, cricket, hockey, tennis, rugby, netball, equestrian and football – the choices are endless. The working week, which no longer includes formal lessons on Saturdays, also enables pupils to participate fully in regional and national events.

King's Ely boasts some of the region's most historic buildings yet teaching facilities are modern and purpose-built. Our close links with Ely Cathedral make the perfect setting for concerts and performances, a daily extension to the school's workspace, the school chapel, and a place of outstanding beauty and spirituality.

Boarders, including the Ely Cathedral Boy and Girl Choristers, live in picturesque boarding houses, well led by caring housemasters and housemistresses. A strong pastoral structure where childhood is respected and cherished is a key feature.

From the high peaks of the Himalayas to the gushing torrents of the rivers in the Alps, our unique Ely Scheme also offers boundless opportunities for pupils to learn through outdoor education. We also give students the chance to undertake their Duke of Edinburgh Award at all three levels.

King's Ely is a family – a community that is vibrant, nurturing and inclusive. We are a school that can take each child on a seamless journey, travelling from one section to the next, whilst welcoming newcomers at key transition stages. Only by visiting King's Ely can you feel the energy and warmth of our community.

(Founded 973)

Ely, Cambridgeshire CB7 4EW UK

Tel: 01353 660707

Fax: 01353 667485

Email: admissions@kingsely.org

Website: www.kingsely.org

Principal: Mr John Attwater MA (Oxon)

Appointed: September 2019

School type: Coeducational Boarding & Day

Age range of pupils: 2–18

No. of pupils enrolled as at 01/09/2018: 1120

Fees per annum as at 01/09/2019:

Day: £10,470–£22,305

Full Boarding: £23,580–£32,280

Average class size: Max 20

Teacher/pupil ratio: 1:9

Mander Portman Woodward – Cambridge

Cambridge is where the MPW success story began. Some 44 years ago, three Cambridge graduates – Messieurs Mander, Portman and Woodward came together with an ambition to create a unique secondary education experience. They focused on several elements, based on their great Alma Mater, which they considered significant to the overall learning experience. Amongst these were the following: small class sizes, a strong tutorial system and superb teaching – and all of these within an informal atmosphere, which would allow creative minds to flourish.

Move the clock forward to the present day and these elements are still very much the hallmark of an MPW education. With fewer than 10 students per class for GCSE and A level, (though in fact the college average is closer to 6 in a class), the learning experience is truly personalised. As well as simulating the small class size at Oxbridge our students experience the privilege of being treated as an individual and not a number. Small classes mean our students know their questions will be answered and that they will have genuine contact time with their tutors in every lesson. With more than 30 A level subjects on offer and no restrictions on combinations, our students can choose subjects that suit them. Whilst Maths, Business, Economics and of course the Sciences remain popular choices, less well known subjects such as Ancient History and Classical Civilisation are also available.

With a current cohort of 60% British and 40% International, MPW Cambridge offers a world-class education to all. Education, however, is much more than what happens in the classroom. The preparation for life after secondary education is important too. Students need to be especially well-informed when they begin their UCAS application. The daily help by the personal tutors to each tutee is immense. From initial, informal discussion on determining the most suitable university course, through several drafts of the personal statement, often through BMAT or other entrance tests, for some even through daunting interview prospects, the MPW Personal Tutor is there. Their mandate is to 'hold the student's hand' throughout, providing encouragement and support.

We're also proud to assist those who might not have done so well the first time around. Our weekly assessments provide diagnostics where we can see which elements require further support. They also ensure that all of our students are fully prepared for the actual exam and properly understand critical success factors such as timing and weighting.

We'll leave the final words to Ofsted, taken from our college report: *'The college provides an outstanding quality of education. An outstanding curriculum supported by very well informed teaching enables students to reach standards of work that are well above average. The provision for the students' spiritual, moral, social and cultural development and their welfare, health and safety are outstanding. By the time the students leave they have developed into mature, thoughtful and responsible young people.'* Ofsted 2016.

M|P|W

Mander Portman Woodward

(Founded 1987)

3-4 Brookside, Cambridge, Cambridgeshire CB2 1JE UK

Tel: 01223 350158

Fax: 01223 366429

Email: cambridge@mpw.ac.uk

Website: www.mpw.ac.uk

Principal: Dr Markus Bernhardt

Appointed: September 2017

School type: Coeducational Day & Boarding

Age range of pupils: 15–19

Average class size: 6

Teacher/pupil ratio: 1:5

Orwell Park School

Developing a life-long love of learning in a magical setting...

Orwell Park, established in 1868, is a co-educational prep school for day pupils and boarders from 2 1/2 to 13. The outstanding beauty of the grounds and the historic 18th century buildings contribute to an inspiring experience which combines the legacy and the traditions of the past with the dynamism and energy of the present and future. Outstanding facilities include a working Victorian observatory, a walled garden with outdoor pool, a nine-hole golf course, floodlit sports facilities, a library in the mansion house, as well as a new, state of the art outstanding Pre-Prep facility, which was opened in 2013, set in the shadow of the main building among woods full of opportunities for outdoor learning.

Boys and girls are given every opportunity to be the best they can be, both in and outside the classroom. High expectations, and learning strategies tailored to the individual child, lead to high levels of attainment. Pupils progress to a wide range of senior schools both local and national and our leaving year group in 2018 achieved 31 scholarships in art, academic, music, DT, sport and all-rounder.

Whilst we value greatly the past, we also embrace technology and, as such, every child in Years 3-8 has their own ipad in order to enhance learning in the classroom and beyond. The ipads allow pupils to learn in a way that they are used to, fostering collaboration between pupils, whilst providing portability.

In addition to the traditional curricular subjects, Orwell Park pupils are involved in a comprehensive activity programme, including: orchestra and various ensembles, chess, community service, skiing, equestrianism, climbing on the bouldering wall, OPS Challenge (a two-year mini D of E course), camping and campfire fun in the School's woodlands, Art and DT clubs, Goldies and Blueys (boys'

and girls' clubs), as well as numerous large scale theatrical productions. The school achieves success in all the major sports and recently introduced cricket for all girls as the summer sport. In addition, Orwell Park is linked with Mayo College in Rajasthan, India and Year 7 pupils have the opportunity to visit India and sample the Taj Mahal, Jaipur and spend time at one of India's most famous boarding schools.

Boarding is extremely popular at Orwell Park and takes the form of flexible boarding, weekly boarding and full boarding, which incorporates a comprehensive programme of weekend activities. Pupils choose to board, driven by a desire to enjoy the company of friends once the normal school day is over. Dormitories are bright, spacious and clean and a dedicated team of boarding staff and school matrons are totally committed to the health and welfare of the boys and girls in their care.

Join us at an Open Morning to see for yourself what makes Orwell Park such a special and inspirational place to be.

For more information contact our Registrar on 01473 653224 or email admissions@orwellpark.org.

ORWELL PARK SCHOOL | *Celebrating* **150** Y E A R S

(Founded 1868)

Nacton, Ipswich, Suffolk IP10 0ER UK

Tel: 01473 659225

Fax: 01473 659822

Email: admissions@orwellpark.org

Website: www.orwellpark.co.uk

Headmaster: Mr Adrian Brown MA(Cantab)

Appointed: September 2011

School type: Coeducational Boarding & Day

Religious Denomination: Interdenominational

Age range of pupils: 2½–13

No. of pupils enrolled as at 01/09/2019: 283

Boys: 171 **Girls:** 112

No. of boarders: 109

Fees per annum as at 01/09/2019:

Pre-Prep Day: £2,794 – £3,974 per term

Prep Day: £5,762 – £6,386 per term

Prep Boarding: £7,715 – £9,200 per term

Average class size: 12-14

Teacher/pupil ratio: 1:12

St Cedd's School

St Cedd's School is a co-educational 3-11 IAPS Charitable Trust School offering pupils the opportunity to aspire and achieve in a caring environment that nurtures talent and supports individual endeavour. This is a school in which every child matters. We value and celebrate their many diverse talents and qualities and the grounded confidence the pupils develop results in great personal achievement.

Individual Pupil Progress

The progress of pupils, of all abilities, throughout the school is rapid. Our standardised assessment results and 11+ scores far exceed national averages and annually we celebrate an unrivalled success rate to selective grammar and independent senior schools with an impressive track record of scholarship awards. This level of achievement is significant given that we are academically non-selective. Assessments on entry are designed to capture the strengths and areas for development of each child so that the education is tailored to the needs of the individual.

Centre of Excellence

The Independent Schools Inspectorate (ISI) placed St Cedd's School at the top level in every category of inspection in February 2013 which places the school amongst the very best 3-11 preparatory schools in the country. The accolade confirms what we witness every day; high academic achievement, outstanding records of attainment in music, an inclusive sporting ethos and successes at national tournaments, a sense of purpose and ambition that shows itself in the attitude and actions of the pupils and staff, and a very effective pastoral care system.

In December 2018, the academic excellence of the school, and our provision for the most able, was recognised by the National Association for Able Children in Education in the awarding of the NACE Challenge Award.

Broad and Balanced Curriculum

With over 70 after-school activities to choose from, extra study opportunities are balanced with a firm focus on academic work. This synergy supports the development of confident self-assured pupils ready for the challenges ahead. PE, music, art, French and science are taught by specialists with the teaching of PE, music and French starting in the Pre-School. Acknowledging the breadth of talents of pupils is an important aspect of life at St Cedd's School. To this end, our baccalaureate-style Year 6 curriculum, HOLDFAST, leads to awards in recognition of 'Holistic Opportunities to Learn and Develop, Furthering Achievement, Service and Talent'.

As a member of the Choir Schools Association our Choristers sing in the Cathedral Choir and the Junior and Senior Chamber Choirs sing at Evensong in Chelmsford Cathedral.

Nurturing the Future

For more than 85 years, boys and girls at St Cedd's School have been enjoying a quality of education that is among the very best you will find. We provide the best start in our recently refurbished Pre-School where the children thrive in a colourful and nurturing environment that widens their horizons and instils in them a love of learning.

Breakfast Club operates from 7:30am-8:00am and a wrap-around care programme is open until 6:00pm. Fees include curriculum-linked extra-curricular activities, 1-1 learning support, lunch and the majority of after-school clubs.

To attend an open day, request a prospectus or to arrange an individual tour, please contact Mrs Abbott on 01245 392810 or email admissions@stcedds.org.uk.

St Cedd's School

(Founded 1931)

178a New London Road, Chelmsford, Essex CM2 0AR UK

Tel: 01245 392810

Email: info@stcedds.org.uk

Website: www.stcedds.org.uk

Head: Mr Matthew Clarke

Appointed: September 2018

School type: Co-educational Day

Age range of pupils: 3–11

No. of pupils enrolled as at 01/09/2019: 400

Boys: 200 *Girls:* 200

Fees per annum as at 01/09/2019:

Day: £8,550–£10,935

Class size: Average 23; Max 24

St Columba's College

St Columba's College is an independent catholic day school, established in the tradition of the Brothers' of the Sacred Heart, for boys, ages 4-18, in the lovely Cathedral city of St Albans, Hertfordshire. The school is open to boys from a wide variety of religious traditions, with learning underpinned by the Columban code of Courage, Courtesy and Compassion.

At each phase of education, Prep, Senior and Sixth Form, we are proud of our reputation for high academic achievement with first-rate pastoral care, small class sizes and a well-developed House system, forging positive relationships and encouraging healthy competition.

We aim to launch boys on their individual journeys to becoming well-rounded, socially aware young men who are equipped and confident for twenty-first century society. Every element of the curriculum and extended curriculum at St Columba's is regarded as equally important in our holistic aim of preparing young men 'not just to make a living, but to make a life'.

Our boys and their families are known and valued and our inspiring teachers challenge every pupil to achieve his own best standard. At St Columba's, we work closely with parents in a respectful partnership that benefits the boys and enriches our values.

Boys who enter our school are embraced by the Columban learning ethos of resilience, teamwork and a positive Growth Mindset. It begins in our Prep School, where the boys hone vital academic and social skills, in small expertly-staffed classes. Through engaging topic work and exciting challenges, they are encouraged to develop their own interests and learning styles, taking responsibility for themselves and developing the collaborative thinking that allows them to support others.

The Senior School curriculum is ambitious and varied. Our passionate and inspirational teachers provide pupils with high-quality learning opportunities, educating each student to the very best of his academic ability and offering support, challenge, and an individualised approach at every stage.

At Sixth Form, you will find a sanctuary of academic rigour and personal growth. There is a wide range of A level subjects and extra-curricular experiences available and our leadership opportunities enable students to emerge with skills, qualifications and attributes that make them ready for their next adventure, leaving behind a legacy of character and ambition.

There are Old Columbans forging successful and worthwhile lives in every field imaginable: we know, because they come back and tell us, passing on their experience, sharing their passions.

We offer an excellent extra extracurricular programme throughout the school including: numerous sports, such as rugby, basketball, athletics, football and cricket; choirs and music ensembles; lunch time and after-school clubs; the CCF (Combined Cadet Force) and the Duke of Edinburgh's Award Scheme.

In the Senior School and Sixth Form, academic and music scholarships are available and sport scholarships are available to those applying for the Sixth Form. Families can also apply for additional funding through our means-tested bursary scheme.

We hope that you share our vision of education and warmly invite you to visit the Prep School, Senior School or the Sixth Form to meet our staff and students and to experience our community first-hand.

Please contact Hilary Causer, Admissions Registrar, for further information on 01727 892040 or email admissions@stcolumbascollege.org

(Founded 1939)

King Harry Lane, St Albans, Hertfordshire AL3 4AW UK

Tel: 01727 892040 (admissions)

Email: admissions@stcolumbascollege.org

Website: www.stcolumbascollege.org

Head: Mr David Buxton

Appointed: 2008

School type: Boys' Day

Religious Denomination: Catholic

Age range of boys: 4–18

No. of pupils enrolled as at 01/09/2019: 820

Fees per annum as at 01/09/2019:

Reception, Prep 1, 2: £10,902

Prep 3: £12,783

Prep 4, 5, 6: £14,100

Senior: £16,326

Average class size: 6-24

St Faith's

Bright Beginnings – Exciting Futures

Judged UK Prep School of the Year in 2019 by the Times Educational Supplement, St Faith's is a Prep School for boys and girls aged 4-13 located in a green, spacious site in the heart of Cambridge.

We believe in providing a future-focused education, preparing our pupils for the needs of the modern world. Pupils need the skills of team work, an understanding of how a computer works and of the engineered world around them, and a strong grounding in Science and Maths, the Humanities and Languages as the foundation stones for virtually every path their future lives might take.

Across our curriculum each child is taught, developed and nurtured, to equip them well for life. Our teachers are passionate about sharing their knowledge, exploring new ideas, challenging the status quo and instilling a life-long passion for learning. Top-down excellence in all lessons ensures we continually stretch our pupils to achieve more than they thought possible. Owing to small class sizes, exceptional teachers and the above average ability of our children all subjects follow an accelerated curriculum and the vast majority of pupils work at a higher level commensurate with their age.

A leader in the early introduction of Computing to the curriculum, we now support over 25 schools in their development of Computing. In 2015 we became the first, and still only, Prep school to teach Engineering as a core curriculum subject for all children from age seven. Our curriculum explores all forms of engineering; chemical, mechanical, robotics, structural, civil, electrical and aeronautical. In 2018 The Times awarded us 'Strategic Education Initiative of the Year' for our introduction of Engineering to the curriculum. Furthermore, The Week Independent Schools Guide named us 'The Best of the Best' for STEM education in 2019.

Sport is a conduit for developing mental and physical fitness, team spirit and resilience. Twenty different individual and team sports are taught at St Faith's. Our 'Sport for All' culture ensures that all pupils, irrespective of ability, receive specialist sports teaching from the age of five. In 2018/19 11 team and 9 individual national titles were awarded to St Faith's in Gymnastics, Trampolining, Hockey and Athletics. Drama, Music and Art are tools not only for teaching children a life-long love of the arts but for promoting self-belief and confidence.

Our green and spacious 9-acre site, located in the heart of Cambridge, together with extensive playing fields a two-minute walk away, provide some of the best facilities of any prep school in the UK. The shelves in our library are crowded with over 12,000 works of fiction and non-fiction. Engineering suites provide access to tools and equipment beyond many inventor's wildest dreams. Fully-equipped science laboratories and computer suites are used by all year groups. The Hub provides flexible large indoor spaces for interdisciplinary projects, a roof-top night sky viewing platform and a virtual reality suite allows all children to explore the universe around them in the most exciting ways.

St Faith's pupils are confident, articulate, grounded and courteous, attributes which will stand them in good stead for their futures. On average 28 scholarships are awarded to our Year 8 pupils as they move to senior schools, with over 90% of leavers gaining a place at their first choice school.

St Faith's
CAMBRIDGE

(Founded 1884)

Trumpington Road, Cambridge, Cambridgeshire CB2 8AG UK

Tel: 01223 352073

Email: admissions@stfaiths.co.uk

Website: www.stfaiths.co.uk

Headmaster: Mr N L Helliwell

Appointed: September 2011

School type: Coeducational Day

Age range of pupils: 4–13

No. of pupils enrolled as at 01/09/2019: 540

Boys: 305 **Girls:** 235

Fees per annum as at 01/09/2019:

Day: £13,170–£16,590

Average class size: 16-18

St Margaret's School, Bushey

St Margaret's School in Bushey, Hertfordshire, is an independent day and boarding school for pupils aged 3 to 18. Founded in 1749, we are one of the oldest independent schools in the UK. As well as day places for all ages, we offer a range of flexible boarding options for both UK and international pupils from the age of 11.

We are a school with a proven record of academic success in public examinations and our pupils move onto competitive courses at leading universities and institutions both here in the UK and around the world. In 2019, 70% of our A-Level results were A*-B grades, with 62% of all GCSE results at 9-7 (A*-A) grades.

Our outward looking ethos aims to encourage a genuine enthusiasm for learning and an ability to independently explore subjects beyond the classroom. Our curriculum addresses a rapidly changing world filled with complex challenges as well as exciting new possibilities.

From January 2020, we will begin our transition to co-education, where St Margaret's School will journey from being an all girls school to providing education to both girls and boys.

The pastoral care at St Margaret's is the central pillar upon which the success of the school is based and we are proud of the quality of care and opportunity given to every one of our pupils no matter what stage of their education. We offer a rich programme of extra-curricular activities and pupils are encouraged to find their talent whatever that may be.

There is no typical St Margaret's pupil; all are valued individually by our qualified and committed staff. However, they are all dedicated young people who strive to succeed in all that they do and are passionate about topics facing them today. The quality of care at St Margaret's School enables pupils to grow in an atmosphere of tolerance and understanding and leave equipped with the confidence, aptitude and skills they need for life and for work.

Our beautiful 60 acre site boasts a combination of superbly resourced historic and modern buildings and we are easily accessible from both London, the Home Counties and all the major London airports. If you have not yet visited us, please do and we will show you the love of learning, culture of achievement and relish of challenge that is the essence of St Margaret's.

St Margaret's School

(Founded 1749)

Merry Hill Road, Bushey, Hertfordshire WD23 1DT UK

Tel: 020 8416 4400

Email: schooloffice@smbushey.com

Website: www.stmargaretsbushey.co.uk

Acting Headmistress: Miss Julie Chatkiewicz

Appointed: September 2019

School type: Day & Boarding. Co-ed from 2020

Age range of girls: 3–18 years

No. of pupils enrolled as at 01/09/2019: 465

Fees per term as at 01/09/2019:

Senior School Day Fees: £5,832 per term

Senior School Boarding Fees: £10,992 per term

Junior School Day Fees: £4,886 per term

Average class size: 20

The Leys School

Founded in 1875 The Leys School is Cambridge's only co-educational boarding school for children aged 11 – 18. Unusually for a city school, it is situated within a leafy 50 acre campus, close to the banks of the River Cam, yet only a 10 minute walk from the buzz of the city centre. Our ethos is simple – to provide an excellent, all-round education for our pupils, combining the traditional values of tolerance, respect and decency with a forward-looking and collaborative approach to teaching and learning.

Our Unique Location; the Cambridge Experience

The university of Cambridge provides the kind of enrichment opportunities most schools can only dream of. Links with the University are strong and we take full advantage of this; we host world-renowned speakers in our Great Hall and attend academic lectures within university departments. Our Chapel Choir regularly joins forces with the College choirs, singing in some of the most stunning College Chapels in the world. We share our award-winning Boathouse with 3 university colleges and compete in many of their sporting fixtures. Our superb location truly does offer a world of exceptional opportunities.

Academic Life

Through the provision of a broad and balanced curriculum Leys pupils develop into articulate, confident and well-rounded individuals. Their timetables are tailored to their aptitudes, needs and interests. As pupils move up through the school they take on increased responsibility for planning their workloads, with support from a coordinated tutorial system. Class sizes are small and the school's academic results reflect the expertise, vitality and enthusiasm of its teachers.

Beyond the Classroom

Pupils at The Leys are encouraged to take part in as many wider-curricular activities as they can realistically manage. Over 100 clubs, societies and groups take place every week. 26 sports are offered from Athletics to Water Polo, alongside CCF, Duke of Edinburgh and Community Service groups. The opportunities for outdoor pursuits are endless and, combined with first class performance facilities, the school exudes an air of purposefulness and busyness.

Support and Wellbeing

The Leys is a close-knit community, based on mutual respect and shared values. Its backbone is the House system where our pupils are assured of a supportive and caring environment. Their wellbeing is at the heart of what The Leys stands for; it is a happy, inspiring and unique place.

Joining The Leys

Girls and boys join The Leys in Years 7, 9 and 12 and may either sit the school's own tests, obtain places via pre-assessment in Year 7 or apply for one of a range of scholarships, bursaries or exhibitions. To find out what makes The Leys such a special place contact the Admissions Team to arrange a visit.

THE **Leys**

C A M B R I D G E

(Founded 1875)

Trumpington Road, Cambridge, Cambridgeshire CB2 7AD UK

Tel: 01223 508900

Fax: 01223 505303

Email: admissions@theleys.net

Website: www.theleys.net

Headmaster: Mr Martin Priestley

Appointed: September 2014

School type: Coeducational Boarding & Day

Age range of pupils: 11–18

No. of pupils enrolled as at 01/09/2019: 572

Fees per annum as at 01/09/2019:

Day: £16,545–£22,920

Full Boarding: £24,960–£34,245

Average class size: 15-20

Teacher/pupil ratio: 1:8

The Peterborough School

The Peterborough School is the city's only independent day school for boys and girls from Nursery to Sixth Form.

Situated on one beautiful, leafy campus in the heart of Peterborough, the Nursery, Prep and Senior Schools enjoy excellent transport links and shared facilities.

The combined campus means the School is a vibrant place with small classes providing boys and girls with the individual attention, opportunities, confidence and ability to exploit fully their natural potential within a happy, caring and friendly community.

The 56-place Nursery has been rated Outstanding in its last two ISI Inspections. It enjoys an excellent location in a separate building on the School site, with ample gardens and outside spaces, and is close enough to Peterborough station, with its high-speed train services to London, to make it highly attractive for working families.

In the Preparatory School (4 to 11 years), the children are encouraged to be independent and inquisitive learners and develop many important skills through the extended curriculum and many extra curricular clubs and activities available.

In the Senior School and Sixth Form, students' unique talents are identified and developed, whether they are in the classroom, in the creative arts or on the sports field. Closely monitored academic performance means students usually achieve levels higher than those originally expected.

The Sixth Form is going from strength to strength with consistently impressive A Level results and is an area of focus for development, with a new bespoke Sixth Form block now in place. This facility has a large, wi-fi enabled Study Room, including a student meeting space, offices and a large, well-facilitated Common Room with kitchen. This development has also created a new state-of-the art Senior Library.

Our pastoral support is extremely strong and we passionately believe that children cannot learn well unless they are happy.

Headmaster, Adrian Meadows, is proud that the long-standing traditions of the school, which was founded in 1895, remain but at the same time it is a forward-looking, progressive place where children continually surprise and delight him. *"I have seen students winning a national STEM award on the same day that the Reception Classes and Pre-schoolers enjoyed a Teddy Bear's Picnic. Being amongst children of such a wide age range is fascinating, entertaining and always interesting but overall it is incredibly rewarding and humbling to be part of such an amazing school and community."*

Visitors to the School and Nursery are very welcome. We have Open Days on Saturdays in September and May each year when appointments are not necessary. There is also a Sixth Form Open Evening in October. Alternatively, visits can be booked by calling the School on 01733 343357 or completing the Request A Visit form on our website www.thepeterboroughschool.co.uk.

(Founded 1895)

Thorpe Road, Peterborough, Cambridgeshire PE3 6AP UK

Tel: 01733 343357

Fax: 01733 355710

Email: office@tpsch.co.uk

Website: www.thepeterboroughschool.co.uk

Headmaster: Mr A D Meadows BSc(Hons)

Appointed: September 2007

School type: Coeducational Day

Age range of pupils: 6 weeks–18 years

No. of pupils enrolled as at 01/09/2019: 440

Fees per annum as at 01/09/2019:

Day: £10,467–£15,642

Average class size: 15

Tring Park School for the Performing Arts

Tring Park School for the Performing Arts is unique amongst specialist schools in the UK. At Tring Park talented young people from 8–19 specialise in Dance, Acting, Musical Theatre or Commercial Music, while also having the opportunity to study for GCSEs and up to 23 A Level subjects. Entrance is via audition and scholarships are available for Dance via the Government's Music and Dance Scheme. School scholarships and bursaries are available for Drama and Musical Theatre.

Pupils perform regularly both in Tring Park's Markova Theatre as well as in London, throughout the UK and Europe. Our graduating dance students perform in 'Encore Dance', Tring Park's touring company which, this year, performed 11 shows in England and Wales culminating in a London performance at the Sadler's Wells Lilian Baylis Studio. Musical Theatre students have a regular season at the Pizza Express Pheasantry in Chelsea. Tring Park provides ballet dancers annually to perform in the Christmas production of *Nutcracker* with English National Ballet at the London Coliseum. Six pupils have played the part of Billy in *Billy Elliot* in the West End and on tour, The Tring Park Chamber Choir "The Sixteen" has won the 2019 BBC Songs of Praise Senior Choir of the Year – the second time in four years and recently came third in the highly competitive International Eisteddfod.

During the Summer Tring Park runs highly sought-after boarding and day courses in Dance, Musical Theatre and Acting.

Our new four-storey boarding house and teaching block opens in September 2019. The building includes six academic and vocational teaching spaces, a theatre workshop and 70 beds for our boarders. Stage two will include an art department and 6th Form Study Centre and the final phase will create a 450 seat theatre.

Alumni success

Daisy Ridley – Rey in *Star Wars* and *Murder on the Orient Express*

Lily James – *Mamma Mia! Here we go again*

Nafisa Baba – winner BBC Young Dancer of the Year 2017

Kit Esuruoso – played Tina Turner's son in the West End show *Tina*. Soon to star in Australian film *Akoni*.

Drew McOnie – Director of the Musical *King Kong* on Broadway

Max Westwell & Will Bozier – 'lead Swan' in Matthew Bourne's New Adventures new production of *Swan Lake*.

Testament to Tring Park's academic provision, students have left to read Medicine, Law, Physics and Engineering whilst others have careers in stage management and other performance-related industries.

Please check the website for upcoming Open Days.
To apply online: www.tringpark.com/opendays
Registrar: Adélia Wood-Smith
registrar@tringpark.com
Registered charity No. 1040330

(Founded 1919)

Tring Park, Tring, Hertfordshire HP23 5LX UK

Tel: 01442 824255

Fax: 01442 891069

Email: info@tringpark.com

Website: www.tringpark.com

Principal: Mr Stefan Anderson MA, ARCM, ARCT

Appointed: September 2002

School type: Co-educational Boarding & Day

Religious Denomination: Non-denominational

Age range of pupils: 8–19

No. of pupils enrolled as at 01/09/2019: 354

Boys: 103 **Girls:** 251 **Sixth Form:** 150

No. of boarders: 220

Fees per annum as at 01/09/2019:

Day: £15,405–£24,510

Full Boarding: £26,190–£37,050

East Midlands

Oakham School

The possibilities for learning really are limitless at Oakham. As a large co-educational boarding and day school we are proud to be able to offer a truly staggering range of experiences, activities and opportunities.

Whilst academic excellence lies at the heart of everything we do, our focus goes far beyond just encouraging our students to achieve outstanding results in their examinations. Our genuinely holistic approach to education means that students leave Oakham as intellectually ambitious thinkers, who are effective and independent learners, well equipped with the skills and habits of mind to thrive in tomorrow's world.

At Oakham, learning is never just confined to the four walls of a classroom. Hundreds of students take part in the Arts – there are five major drama productions every year, we teach over 500 individual music lessons each week, and our award-winning Art & Design Department is a hive of creative activity. Oakham also has a national reputation for Sport, offering 30 different sports to students of all levels – from enthusiasts to elite athletes. Activities are also an integral part of life beyond the classroom, with students able to choose from over 125 activities to take part in each week, to discover and develop their interests and talents, and provide service to others. In addition to Duke of Edinburgh, CCF, and Voluntary Action, options range from dance to robotics, e-textiles to sailing – there really is something for everyone!

Oakham is an exceptionally caring community and we nurture all aspects of our pupils' well-being during every stage of their Oakham journey. Our unique House structure ensures students have an age-appropriate space to develop and grow, surrounded by staff who are expertly trained to both support their needs and to challenge them to become independent, thoughtful, and responsible young adults.

Students also benefit from the School's location close to Rutland Water, in the heart of rural England. They are able to enjoy the safety of living and working in a beautifully green campus just a few minutes' walk from Oakham's historic town centre and amenities, yet at the same time Oakham's excellent road and rail links mean that London, Birmingham and Cambridge are all within easy reach.

Oakham is well known and loved for being a friendly and unpretentious school. Whilst we are proud of our 400-year heritage, our priority is always to be at the forefront of educational developments: in short, to be educational innovators. We were one of the first independent schools to move to co-education in 1971 and we were also one of the first schools to introduce the IB Diploma, alongside A-levels. We continue to look to the future and our focus now, in today's digital world, is on effectively teaching students Information Literacy.

By the time they leave us, Oakhamians are well rounded and confident young adults, equipped to ask the right questions, to know how to find the answers for themselves, and in doing so, to be able to make a difference in the world.

"This is a clear-eyed, energetic, forward-thinking school." The Good Schools Guide

(Founded 1584)

Chapel Close, Oakham, Rutland LE15 6DT UK

Tel: 01572 758500

Email: admissions@oakham.rutland.sch.uk

Website: www.oakham.rutland.sch.uk

Headmaster: Mr Henry Price

Appointed: September 2019

School type: Coeducational Boarding & Day

Religious Denomination: Church of England

Age range of pupils: 10–18

No. of pupils enrolled as at 01/09/2019:

Boys: 549 *Girls:* 495 *Sixth Form:* 392

No. of boarders: 558

Fees per annum as at 01/09/2019:

Day: £17,250–£21,360

Full Boarding: £26,115–£35,010

Flexi Boarding (2-5 nights): £20,550 – £33,255

Average class size: 18 (10-16); 10 (16-18)

Teacher/pupil ratio: 1:7

Greater London

Breaside Preparatory School

One only has to meet our children to understand what it is that makes Breaside Preparatory School the unique place that it is.

Our children are:

Inspired

The Breaside curriculum offers a wide range of academic subjects designed to motivate and challenge every child to be the best that they can be. Using evidenced research and the views of the pupils themselves, teaching and learning is constantly evolving with innovative 'flipped' teaching models successfully running alongside more traditional methods. Our children love to be challenged and through the personalised approach to learning that we have adopted, all of our children can excel and thrive. We are incredibly proud to be accredited with the prestigious NACE Challenge Award and placed within just 1.6% of schools across the UK. Our programme of extra-curricular clubs is hugely popular, with children right the way from Kindergarten to Year Six engaging in instrumental lessons, language learning and creative arts. Such is the variety that if you walk through the school at any given time you could be met with Reception children conversing in Mandarin, Year 6 pupils teaching others the intricacies of Coding, Year 4 avidly engrossed in a Philosophy discussion or Kindergarten practising the gate pose in Yoga.

Successful

Academic success is at the heart of a Breaside education. Our children continuously set their sights high and strive to achieve. Their outstanding results speak for themselves, being significantly above national expectations, and our list of leavers destinations grows wider and more distinguished year upon year. No matter what the destination, we are incredibly proud that our children move on to a school that is perfect for them. We have recently been ranked 11th in the Sunday Times Parent Power Top 100 Prep Schools list – a testament to the wonderful hard work of our children and staff.

Resilient

Fostering independence and resilience is key to our ethos. We actively encourage risk taking and prepare the children for the future through a broad spectrum of experiences both in and out of the classroom. Residential trips this year so far have taken the children 'off grid' at Bushcraft, swinging through the high ropes at PGL in Osmington Bay and to a chateau in Normandy to immerse themselves in French culture. Forest School is a highlight of the children's week and the life skills that they are developing from this are clear to see. Our newly created outdoor gym and trim trail complements the focus on our children's health and well-being and a well developed PSHE programme places a focus on keeping healthy both physically and mentally.

Happy

Friendship, security, challenge, FUN! Time and time again these words appear on our annual student survey and can indeed be seen from the second the gates open in the morning. The Breaside buzz is palpable, just ask any of the students, parents or staff. The joy that comes from being part of the Breaside family is immense and underpins the rich learning experience that is on offer. Here students have a voice. They are the ones shaping how and what they learn, striving for excellence and growing into global citizens of the future.

For more information or a personal tour of the School and Kindergarten please call 020 8460 0916, info@breaside. co.uk, www.breaside.co.uk

(Founded 1950)

41-43 Orchard Road, Bromley, Kent BR1 2PR UK

Tel: 020 8460 0916

Fax: 020 8466 5664

Email: info@breaside.co.uk

Website: www.breaside.co.uk

Executive Principal:
Mrs Karen A Nicholson B.Ed, NPQH, Dip EYs

Appointed: 2008

School type: Coeducational Day

Age range of pupils: 2½–11

No. of pupils enrolled as at 01/09/2019: 376

Boys: 185 **Girls:** 191

Fees per annum as at 01/09/2019:

Day: £11,580–£13,494

Kew College

Set in leafy South-West London, Kew College is a gem of a school. In terms of education, it is a centre of excellence providing a rich, relevant and varied curriculum, but it is much more than that.

The minute you walk through the door, the ethos of the school is apparent; it is a friendly and caring environment which is relaxed but purposeful. The relationship between staff and pupils is warm and open and there is a tangible buzz of creativity in the air. The children are respectful, responsible, hard-working, and fun-loving individuals who thrive given opportunities to take risks in their learning and set challenges for themselves.

The results of entrance exams to secondary schools at Year 6 are excellent year on year, with numerous scholarships attained. Set this against the school's non-selective background and it is testimony to the quality of education that it provides. The children display an overwhelming desire to achieve and are inspired by staff who work with boundless energy, dedication and determination. No stone is left unturned as they strive to support and nurture every child to achieve to their full potential.

Education at Kew College is also about helping the pupils to develop their intellectual character. The children have a concrete sense of their own strengths and a confidence that goes hand in hand with that self-belief. This is coupled with a gracious sense of humility and open-mindedness, the realisation that the way forward in tomorrow's world is through co-operation and team work. This strong moral value system is embedded from an early age so that, by the time the pupils leave Kew College, they are able to think independently and critically. They are inquisitive, reflective and well-rounded; true individuals who are prepared for the rigours of secondary school and for the changing world in which they live.

"Both of our boys joined the school in the Nursery and have flourished in the nurturing and caring environment the school provides. The children are all confident, articulate, well-mannered, and thoroughly nice kids who are comfortable in the company of adults. Our boys have thrived at Kew College and always raced enthusiastically into school each day. The teaching and school philosophy is very much focused on helping each child to achieve their best in a happy environment. As parents, we really couldn't ask for more." **The Stewart family**

"We chose Kew College for our four daughters for its warm atmosphere and its happy, friendly, and well-mannered pupils. We feel fortunate to have also found a school which fulfils its promise of educating our children to their highest potential. We have children with differing abilities and personalities but Kew College has provided support and education for all of them. Every child at this school is unique, but one thing that every child here has in common is that they will leave strengthened by their experience." **The Ahmed Family**

Registrar: Mwarburton@kewcollege.com

(Founded 1927)

24-26 Cumberland Road, Kew, Surrey TW9 3HQ UK

Tel: 020 8940 2039

Fax: 020 8332 9945

Email: enquiries@kewcollege.com

Website: www.kewcollege.com

Head:
Mrs Marianne Austin BSc(Hons), MA(Hons), ACA, PGCE

School type: Coeducational Day

Age range of pupils: 3–11

No. of pupils enrolled as at 01/09/2019: 296

Boys: 148 **Girls:** 148

Fees per annum as at 01/09/2019:

Nursery: £7,350

Kindergarten – Year 6: £12,750

Average class size: 20

Laleham Lea School

At Laleham Lea we firmly believe in putting the child at the centre of everything we do. From the warm welcome as you walk through the door in the morning to the playground where all ages play, run and socialise together as one happy family.

Bright, light filled classrooms and enthusiastic, experienced teachers engage young minds' thirst for knowledge, helping each developing individual to reach their full potential and ultimately move on to the school of their choice.

Our pupils become happy, confident, fulfilled young people through both academic and extra-curricular activities. Every child takes part in team sports and every child is involved in school productions and concerts. Our greatest pleasure is to watch a once shy child blossom into the confident soloist, take a leading role in school assembly or simply help a fellow pupil through a challenging moment.

A high standard of teaching and learning is central to our success. Your son or daughter will be taught in well-equipped classrooms and our teachers hold specialist qualifications and have experience in specific areas of the curriculum such as Science, Modern Languages, Computer Studies (ICT), Art, Music and Sports.

As a Catholic school we put our Christian values at the forefront of our daily routine and welcome children of all faiths who are sympathetic to our Catholic ethos. We encourage a high standard of behaviour based on values of love, respect, and a positive work ethic. We regularly celebrate Mass together either in our own Long Room or in the calm serenity of the John Fisher School Chapel.

Recognising that Gospel values are central to the life of the school, we at Laleham Lea aim to create a loving, welcoming environment in which our children may grow intellectually, socially and emotionally; an environment in which their talents are recognised and fostered and their weaknesses treated with compassion; an environment which provides quality teaching and learning within a balanced curriculum framework and which helps every child to reach their true potential.

Together with parents, who are the first educators, we aim to lead our children towards tolerance, understanding and sensitivity to the needs of others so that they may grow up as well balanced individuals with a strong sense of personal identity and an awareness of God's love.

Through our close relationship with other schools in the area, we benefit from the use of the extensive sports field, stage and Chapel of the neighbouring John Fisher School and our children enjoy weekly swimming lessons at Waddon Swimming Pool.

Our outstanding pastoral care provides for a happy, caring community for all and we invite you to come and visit Laleham Lea; we can assure you of a very warm welcome.

Contact Mrs Edwards in the School Office to book your tour and secure your child's place for 2020/21 and beyond. 0208 660 3351. www.lalehamlea.co.uk.

(Founded 1965)

29 Peaks Hill, Purley, Surrey CR8 3JJ UK

Tel: 020 8660 3351

Email: secretary@lalehamlea.co.uk

Website: www.lalehamlea.co.uk

Headteacher: Ms K Barry

School type: Coeducational Day

Age range of pupils: 3–11

No. of pupils enrolled as at 01/09/2019: 112

Fees per annum as at 01/09/2019:

Day: £8,940

Average class size: 14

St Catherine's School

St. Catherine's is a vibrant and caring Catholic school that welcomes girls of all faiths and backgrounds. Our friendly community helps each pupil develop confidence as she explores her gifts and talents, and is inspired to meet challenges creatively. The School proudly combines excellent pastoral care with over 100 years' experience of independent education and a modern curriculum that prepares girls for the 21st century.

Our recent excellent inspection reports from the Independent Schools Inspectorate and the Diocese of Westminster note that '*teaching at St. Catherine's is more than the sum of its classroom parts...pupils have a wrap-around experience that leads them to learn exceptionally well*' and that '*pupils flourish because of the secure, caring ethos of the School*'. We see these features in the achievements of our girls and in their readiness to learn.

In the Prep Department, which takes girls from 3 to 11 years of age, an emphasis on curiosity and discovery establishes firm foundations which later allow pupils to excel in the Senior School and Sixth Form. All girls enjoy the wide range of subjects and benefit from teaching staff who are passionate about giving each of them the opportunity to thrive. Teachers and tutors know the girls individually, and so offer support and challenge at all stages, and are in regular contact with parents.

The girls certainly rise to the challenges posed by public examinations. St Catherine's is proud of the value that is added to their achievements as they progress through the School and we enjoy seeing so many young women go on to university courses and careers of their choice, and to bright futures.

Those who visit St. Catherine's often remark on the warm and genuine enthusiasm of our pupils. The school's Christian ethos and emphasis on values helps girls to engage with the world around them, while open discussion, time for reflection, pupil-led committees and a wide range of creative opportunities create a lively environment where they can feel a sense of belonging. Our emphasis on character, and on the deeper values of compassion, integrity and resilience, is also developed through a comprehensive extra-curricular programme.

St Catherine's is committed to developing its facilities and over recent years we have been pleased to see girls enjoying new buildings and refurbishments, like the Science Block and Sixth Form Centre, which are designed to enhance their curriculum and social experiences. We also provide exciting trips, competitions and school events throughout the year; whether it is a trip to Costa Rica, regional athletics finals or a part in the latest school musical, there are plenty of opportunities for girls to develop their skills and their friendships within the school community.

Information about public examination results, extra-curricular opportunities and wrap-around care can all be found on the school website: www.stcatherineschool.co.uk

(Founded 1914)

Cross Deep, Twickenham, Middlesex TW1 4QJ UK

Tel: 020 8891 2898

Fax: 020 8744 9629

Email: info@stcatherineschool.co.uk

Website: www.stcatherineschool.co.uk

Headmistress: Mrs Johneen McPherson MA

Appointed: September 2018

School type: Girls' Day

Age range of girls: 3–18

No. of pupils enrolled as at 01/09/2019: 440

Fees per annum as at 01/09/2019:

Day: £11,205–£15,585

Average class size: 15-20

Teacher/pupil ratio: 1:11

St Helen's College

Nestled on the edge of Court Park in a quiet corner of Hillingdon, St. Helen's College is a family-run independent school for boys and girls aged 3 to 11, with a separate, thriving Kindergarten for boys and girls aged 2-3.

The school has a real family feel and has been described by inspectors as a 'haven of harmony'. Indeed, the most recent ISI quality inspection judged St. Helen's College outstanding, the quality of teaching excellent, the pupils' personal development outstanding and pupils' achievements, both academic and extra-curricular, excellent.

The report said: *'Pupils achieve high standards in academic work and a wide range of other activities. They are extremely successful in all aspects of learning…this is reflected in their success in entrance examinations both to maintained grammar and independent schools'.*

The school's values and ethos set it apart. Led by the Head, Shirley Drummond, staff create a harmonious, loving environment, nurture the individual qualities of every pupil and ensure that children develop a lifelong love of learning, find out where their talents and interests lie, and leave school with traditional values and strength of character, ready to face the challenges of adult life with confidence, resilience and joy!

The children enjoy lessons taught by highly qualified specialist teachers right from the start, allowing them to study at a high level led by teachers with a real passion for their subject. There is also an extremely wide-ranging and quite unique range of 70+ co-curricular activities available, with superb music, drama and sports provision and clubs including cookery, gardening, yoga, taekwondo, ceramics, dance and many, many more.

The school benefits from specialist modern facilities and is strongly rooted in its local community, enjoying links with local churches, Brunel University and local theatres.

The safe, loving, encouraging environment at St. Helen's College fosters excellent academic achievement and well-rounded, confident pupils. Inspectors noted, *'Pupils' personal development is outstanding, well supported by excellent pastoral care. The overall feeling is of a warm, friendly community where everyone knows each other and feels safe and secure'.*

St. Helen's College operates a flexible year-round extended care provision, with Breakfast Club from 7.30 a.m. and after school care until 6 p.m. daily during term time, and Holiday Club running during school holidays to assist working parents.

Parents may register children for entry to the school at 2+ (Kindergarten) or 3+ (Nursery). This is an extremely popular school and early registration is advisable. Prospective parents may register online using the online registration form or by contacting the school using the details below.

'School at work' open mornings are held in October and April each year, at which current pupils conduct tours of the school and answer questions for prospective parents. The Head, Head of Lower School and Director of Admissions are available to answer questions and take registrations at these events.

Alternatively, prospective parents may book an individual tour one morning during term time by telephoning 01895 234371 or emailing info@sthelenscollege.com.

(Founded 1924)

Parkway, Hillingdon, Uxbridge, Middlesex UB10 9JX UK

Tel: 01895 234371

Email: info@sthelenscollege.com

Website: www.sthelenscollege.com

Head: Mrs. Shirley Drummond BA, PGCert, MLDP, FCCT

Appointed: 2016

School type: Coeducational Day

Age range of pupils: 2–11

No. of pupils enrolled as at 01/09/2019: 383

Boys: 193 *Girls:* 190

Fees per annum as at 01/09/2019:

Day: £9,900–£12,240

Average class size: 22

Teacher/pupil ratio: varies

The John Lyon School

John Lyon is an academically selective independent boys' day school, based in Harrow-on-the-Hill in North West London.

Academic excellence is at the very heart of what the School achieves for the 600 boys who study here and the curriculum is at the very heart of everything we do.

Pupils gain a good grounding in all the major academic subjects. Dedicated teachers work to develop learning skills, creativity and the ability to apply learning in all areas of life. Building on this platform, boys perform well from the point they join – whether at age 11, 13 or 16 – and achieve excellent results in public examinations at GCSE and A-Level.

Most students gain places at leading UK universities and then move on into the workplace in a huge and varied range of valued professions.

A John Lyon boy also gains from his time outside the classroom. In particular, there is a strong and growing reputation for Music, Art, Drama and Sport. Add to this an exciting Co-Curricular timetable focusing on each boy's sense of community, achievement and wellbeing, a range of more than 70 extra-curricular activities, and pastoral care that is second to none, John Lyon is a school designed to nurture high-achieving and happy boys.

Pupils typically join John Lyon from the London Boroughs of Harrow, Ealing, Brent, Hillingdon, Barnet, Camden, Hammersmith & Fulham and Kensington & Chelsea, as well as other parts of Middlesex, Berkshire, Buckinghamshire and Hertfordshire. The school is well-connected on the London Underground (Metropolitan and Piccadilly lines), as well as by Chiltern Railway services between Marylebone and Aylesbury / High Wycombe.

Admissions

John Lyon offers a broad education to pupils who aspire to achieve excellence in all they do.

As such, the admissions process at John Lyon tests each boy's academic ability, as well as containing elements we use to learn about his character and to give us an insight into potential and 'teachability'.

We look to offer places to able young pupils who have a great attitude to learning combined with a desire to be the best that they can be.

Entry is based on a combination of examination and interview (for Years 7 and 9) and on GCSE results and interview for Year 12. Our tests do not contain 'trick' questions and we aim to create a level playing field to allow future John Lyon pupils to shine.

We understand that choosing a school can be a difficult process for both parents and pupils. At John Lyon we pride ourselves in our welcoming and helpful approach to admissions.

Bursaries and Scholarships

John Lyon is committed to widening access, enabling the children of those who could not otherwise afford the fees to benefit from our all-round independent school. This corresponds to the original intention of John Lyon, who, when he founded Harrow School in 1572, stated that he wished to provide an education for children in the parish. Each year, the School makes available a number of means-tested bursaries to pupils who demonstrate exceptional talent and potential.

All pupils who take the 11+ or 13+ examination in January will be considered for an Academic Scholarship. Their performance in the examination, their school reference and their interview will all be taken into consideration. Sixth Form Scholarships are awarded dependent on GCSE results. We also award a small number of Scholarships to candidates of outstanding ability and potential in Drama, Music and Sport.

(Founded 1876)

Middle Road, Harrow on the Hill, Middlesex HA2 0HN UK

Tel: 020 8515 9400

Email: admissions@johnlyon.org

Website: www.johnlyon.org

Head: Miss Katherine Haynes BA, MEd, NPQH

Appointed: September 2009

School type: Boys' Day

Religious Denomination: Non-denominational

Age range of boys: 11–18

No. of pupils enrolled as at 01/09/2019: 600

Fees per term as at 01/09/2019:

Years 7-11: £6,411 per term (including lunch costs)

Sixth Form: £6,175 per term (excluding lunch costs)

Average class size: 18

Teacher/pupil ratio: 1:10

Whitgift School

Whitgift is one of Britain's finest independent day and boarding schools, offering a friendly, challenging and inclusive environment for 10-18 year old boys. Our core purpose is to educate bright and talented young men to become independent learners and thinkers, to achieve beyond what they believed they could, and to leave the School ready to give back to the society in which they will be leaders.

The School offers a variety of pathways to qualifications, including the A Levels, Pre U and the International Baccalaureate, where it is the top performing boys school in the UK. Alongside exceptional academic standards, the co-curricular activities feature more than 80 clubs & societies, more than 40 sports and an Outdoor Education programme that travels worldwide. A packed Performing Arts programme performs regularly, staging first-class musicals and plays. Orchestras and choirs tour internationally, and play at major venues, including the Royal Albert Hall, Cadogan Hall and Goodwood House.

The School's Boarding House, opened in 2013, is superbly-equipped and offers full, weekly and flexi-boarding to boys aged 13-18. This option allows boys to make the most of their time at Whitgift without distractions or a lengthy commute. Structured homework and free time sessions, as well as organised evening and weekend activities ensure that boarders build a strong balance between their academic studies and their co-curricular interests. For those who live further afield, there are 11 dedicated bus routes covering a wide radius.

Whitgift takes pride in being a diverse student body and global citizenship and digital literacy are key areas of focus for the entire school community. Over 43 languages are spoken by boarders alone. Pastoral support is at the foundation of our provision, with each pupil and his parents guaranteed a friendly face to turn to for advice and guidance. The latest ISI Report states, *"The quality of pastoral care is outstanding…a calm courteous approach pervades the School, indicated by highly civilised and positive relationships between staff and pupils."*

Whitgift offers generous scholarships and bursaries and more information can be found on our website.

Open Events

We encourage you to come and visit us on one of our Open Events to get a true feel for our inspiring school community.

Open Afternoons appointments to visit can be made via our website or by contacting the Admissions Team (see contact information below).

Whitgift 13+ entry and Boarding Pre-Test

Alongside our general entry process, we are pleased to announce that Whitgift will be undertaking a 13+ entry Day and Boarding Pre-Test for boys who will be in Year 6 in the Academic Year 2019/20. The process will open in mid-August and families that are interested can apply/register for the Pre-Test to Whitgift via the Admissions Section of our website www.whitgift.co.uk, by downloading an Application Form or by contacting the Admissions Office to request an Application Form. These completed forms should be returned to the Admissions Office by 25 October 2019.

If you have any questions regarding our admissions process or the 13+ Day and Boarding Pre-Test, please do not hesitate to contact our Admissions Office.

Contact the Whitgift Admissions Team

T: 0208 633 9935
E: admissions@whitgift.co.uk

WHITGIFT

(Founded 1596)

Haling Park, South Croydon, Surrey CR2 6YT UK

Tel: +44 20 8633 9935

Email: admissions@whitgift.co.uk

Website: www.whitgift.co.uk

Headmaster: Mr Christopher Ramsey

Appointed: September 2017

School type: Boys' Day & Boarding

Religious Denomination: Accepting of all faiths

Age range of boys: 10–18

No. of pupils enrolled as at 01/09/2019: 1490

Fees per annum as at 01/09/2019:

Day: £20,640

Weekly Boarding: £33,081

Full Boarding: £40,140

Average class size: 20

Teacher/pupil ratio: 1:7

London

Bassett House School

At Bassett House, we believe that all children deserve to learn to fly and achieve their very best. The school was founded in 1947 by Sylvia Rentoul who recognised children as individuals, and encouraged them to express themselves, helping to grow their achievements and self-confidence. Our teaching techniques and apparatus are continually updated but our ethos remains constant.

Our children's energy, exuberance and curiosity for learning stand out. These have been engendered by our whole school commitment to adopting a growth mindset. Mention you cannot do something at Bassett House and any child will roar back at you "I can't do it YET!"

Focused attention remains our hallmark. We believe tailor-made teaching opens up young minds to endless possibilities, encouraging them to think creatively. We start by ensuring high staff-to-pupil ratios and many specialist teaching staff. Our teachers know every child in their care inside out and use great teaching supported by our excellent equipment (including cutting-edge technology) to bring lessons to life for each child.

Our 'sport for all' ethos encourages all our children to think of themselves as athletes, while allowing our sporting stars to shine. We offer football, netball, tag rugby, hockey, tennis, rounders, athletics, gymnastics and eurhythmics as part of the core curriculum and clubs in swimming, fencing, volleyball, yoga and dance.

We don't stop there. Vibrant music and drama give our children a passion for participation and performance, fostering a sense of achievement and boosting self-confidence. Our children first take to the stage from age 3 and have many opportunities to shine throughout life at Bassett House, whether in whole-school assemblies, stage shows or concerts. We have choirs, musical ensembles and an orchestra and provide individual instrumental music lessons from specialist music teachers.

Our extra-curricular clubs, together with our weekly enrichment hour, expand our children's horizons beyond the core curriculum. Each term children can choose to add a variety of activities to the school day, be it Lego modelling, computer coding, Scottish dancing, origami, chess, geography, cookery, arts and crafts or debating.

Residential trips from year 3 onwards create a sense of adventure and build self-reliance. The glow of a 7-year-old's face recounting a night-time bug-hunting expedition, a 9-year-old's thrill at working with a friend to sail a dinghy, a 10-year-old embracing the challenge of sleeping out under a self-made shelter: we create these memorable moments, knowing that their positive effects will last a lifetime.

All of this makes not only for well-rounded individuals, it translates into excellent academic results. When they leave aged 11, Bassett House children are ready to thrive at London's best senior schools. And they do: our children win places to the cream of London's senior schools. For those who want to board, Bassett House prepares them well for life at leading boarding schools.

We collaborate closely with our sister schools, Orchard House and Prospect House, sparking off new ideas to promote ever more successful teaching practices. The three schools share a common ethos but each retains its unique personality.

The schools (brought together under the umbrella of House Schools Group) are proudly non-selective. True to our belief, children are not tested and judged at the tender age of 3 or 4 years. Our outstanding results repeatedly show all children can fulfil their potential, regardless of early learning ability. We encourage our high-flyers to skyrocket, whilst children who need a little extra help are given the support they need to reach their fullest potential.

Our last full ISI inspection awarded us 'excellent' and 'outstanding' in all areas and we flew through our 2016 compliance inspection.

BASSETT
HOUSE SCHOOL

(Founded 1947)

60 Bassett Road, London, W10 6JP UK

Tel: 020 8969 0313

Email: info@bassetths.org.uk

Website: www.bassetths.org.uk

Headmistress:
Mrs Philippa Cawthorne MA (Soton) PGCE Mont Cert

Appointed: January 2014

School type: Co-educational Day

Age range of pupils: 3–11

No. of pupils enrolled as at 01/09/2019: 190

Fees per annum as at 01/09/2019:

Day: £5,499–£19,200

Average class size: 20

Teacher/pupil ratio: 1:7

Cameron House

The curriculum
'An excellent curriculum provides all pupils… with opportunities to achieve high standards in a wide range of subjects and activities… within a creative, stimulating environment where all pupils are treated as individuals and encouraged to do their best. The quality of the pupils' achievements and learning is excellent.' (ISI Inspection 2016) Pupils of all abilities are prepared broadly and deeply for the full gamut of 11+ examinations within a rich and dynamic academic curriculum, using high quality resources and a broad range of ICT. We encourage children to research, reflect, ask questions, listen well and problem-solve – and to develop positive learning habits for life around the 'Five Cs of Cameron House': curiosity, collaboration, creativity, critical thinking and courage.

Setup and atmosphere
'Across the school the quality of the pupils' personal development is excellent… All pupils display excellent moral development, have a firm sense of right and wrong, and are extremely courteous.' (ISI Inspection 2016) We aim to be a vibrant, warm and high-energy school, to which pupils are proud to belong and to which they contribute by growing their own skills, character and personal relationships. Our dedicated and highly qualified teachers know every pupil and every family, aiming to care for each with wisdom, professionalism and kindness.

Games and the arts
'Pupils develop excellent physical skills at all ages through the busy and demanding range of activities and… achieve significant success in competitive sports in relation to the size of the school.' (ISI Inspection 2016) Sport is integral to the rhythm of school life both within the timetable, and within the extra-curricular programme, with our team sports including touch rugby, netball, football and hockey, and individual sports such as fencing and karate offered as well. We are passionate about the arts, and provide a wealth of creative activities in art, design and technology, music and drama – through timetabled specialist teaching, after-school clubs, themed days, cultural visits and opportunities to train and perform in the school's arts programme, as well as local and national events.

Pastoral care
'Pastoral care makes an excellent contribution to pupils' personal development. Strong personal relationships reflect the friendly, family atmosphere. Staff know their pupils very well and… the school maintains very close links with parents.' (ISI Inspection 2016) We are a relaxed but respectful community, working together for the common good within a culture of praise and mutual respect, aiming to develop self-respect, self-discipline and empathy in our relationships, strong spiritual awareness and a deep appreciation of the beauty of the natural world. We want to embody our motto – 'Da Mihi Sapientiam' (Give Me Wisdom) – by growing wisdom in our pupils in thought, word and deed.

Outstanding characteristics
Cameron House has been led by the same Director-Principal for 37 years, providing seamless, detailed and passionate oversight and care. 'The quality of governance is excellent. Dynamic and energetic leadership across the school is highly effective in enabling the school to successfully fulfil its aim to create a happy and warm family atmosphere in which pupils are treated as individuals and are motivated to work and play to the best of their ability. Senior and middle managers provide clear educational direction and this is demonstrated in the excellent quality of pupils' achievements and in their outstanding personal development' (ISI Inspection 2016)

(Founded 1980)

4 The Vale, Chelsea, London, SW3 6AH UK

Tel: 020 7352 4040

Fax: 020 7352 2349

Email: laura@cameronhouseschool.org

Website: www.cameronhouseschool.org

Headmistress: Mrs Dina Mallett

Principal:
Miss Josie Cameron Ashcroft BSc(Hons), DipEd, CertT

School type: Coeducational Day

Religious Denomination:
Church of England, all denominations welcome

Age range of pupils: 4–11

Fees per annum as at 01/09/2019:

Day: £19,305

City of London School
A rounded education in the Square Mile

There is no such thing as a typical CLS boy. What characterises the education offered is a true preparation for life.

City of London School is a truly unique independent school, not least because of its unrivalled location on the banks of the Thames, between St. Paul's Cathedral and the Tate Modern. We are at the heart of the capital and our pupils benefit enormously from all that is on offer on our doorstep. Our location allows us to attract the very best outside speakers, offer top-class work shadowing placements and visit the many places of interest in this world-class city. We are a modern and forward-looking institution drawing on clever boys from all social, economic and ethnic backgrounds and, in so doing, truly reflect the diversity of the capital in the 21st century. Boys come from a huge number of both state primary and independent preparatory schools and, once here, receive an academic yet liberal education. Our central location allows boys to travel to City from all over London, encouraging resourcefulness and self-reliance in their journey to school, and in their wider life.

Our examination results are excellent, but, more importantly, boys leave us ready for life beyond school, with a sense of identity and an independence of thought and action which are rare among leavers from independent schools; it is significant that the vast majority of boys go on to their first choice of university, with a large number attending Oxford and Cambridge universities, and various medical schools. Facilities are outstanding (the school moved downstream to its new buildings in 1986) and are continually updated. The state-of-the-art Winterflood Theatre and refurbished Science laboratories provide a first-rate environment in which our pupils learn and thrive. We are generously endowed with academic, music and sports scholarships and, in addition, the bursary campaign has raised significant funding for a number of full-fee places to be awarded each year to those who could not otherwise afford even a proportion of fees. In this way, the school seeks to maintain the socio-economic mix which has always been its tradition and strength. Admission at 10+, 11+, 13+ and 16+ is by entrance examinations, followed by interviews for those candidates who complete their examination papers to a satisfactory standard.

For dates and to book onto one of our open days please visit our website.
Tel: 020 3680 6300
Email: admissions@cityoflondonschool.org.uk

City of London School

(Founded 1442)
Queen Victoria Street, London, EC4V 3AL UK
Tel: 020 3680 6300
Email: admissions@cityoflondonschool.org.uk
Website: www.cityoflondonschool.org.uk
Head: Mr A R Bird MSc
Appointed: January 2018
School type: Boys' Day
Age range of boys: 10–18
No. of pupils enrolled as at 01/09/2019: 950
Sixth Form: 250
Fees per annum as at 01/09/2019:
Day: £18,939

Devonshire House Preparatory School

Academic and leisure facilities

The school is situated in fine premises in the heart of Hampstead with its own walled grounds. The aim is to achieve high academic standards whilst developing enthusiasm and initiative throughout a wide range of interests. It is considered essential to encourage pupils to develop their own individual interests and a good sense of personal responsibility.

Curriculum

Early literacy and numeracy are very important and the traditional academic subjects form the core curriculum. The younger children all have a class teacher and classroom assistant and their day consists of a mixture of formal lessons and learning through play. Whilst children of all ages continue to have a form teacher, as they grow older an increasing part of the curriculum is delivered by subject specialists. The combined sciences form an increasingly important part of the timetable as the children mature. The use of computers is introduced from an early stage, both as its own skill and as an integrated part of the pupils' education.

Expression in all forms of communication is encouraged, with classes having lessons in art, music and drama, and French. Physical exercise and games also play a key part of the curriculum. Much encouragement is given to pupils to help widen their horizons and broaden their interests. The school fosters a sense of responsibility amongst the pupils, and individuality and personal attention for each pupil is considered essential to make progress in the modern world.

The principal areas of the National Curriculum are covered, though subjects may be taken at a higher level, or at a quicker pace. For the girls approaching the 11+ senior schools' entry examinations, special emphasis is given to the requirements for these, and in the top two years for the boys, Common Entrance curriculum is taught. The pupils achieve great success in these examinations and a number also sit successfully for senior school scholarships.

The school has its own nursery, The Oak Tree Nursery, which takes children from two-and-a-half years of age.

Entry requirements

The Oak Tree Nursery: For children entering the Oak Tree Nursery, places are offered on the basis on an informal assessment made at the nursery. Children in The Oak Tree Nursery transfer directly to the Junior School.

The Junior School: For children entering the junior school from the ages of three to five, places are offered on the basis of assessment made at the school. From the age of six, places are usually subject to a written test taken at school. At eight, children transfer directly into the upper school. Parents and their children are welcome to visit for interview and to see around the school.

The Upper School: Entry to the upper school is principally from the junior school. For pupils seeking to join the school from elsewhere places are normally subject to a written entrance test.

(Founded 1989)

2 Arkwright Road, Hampstead, London, NW3 6AE UK

Tel: 020 7435 1916

Email: enquiries@devonshirehouseprepschool.co.uk

Website: www.devonshirehouseschool.co.uk

Headmistress: Mrs S. Piper BA(Hons)

School type:
Preparatory, Pre-preparatory & Nursery Day School

Religious Denomination: Non-denominational

Age range of boys: 2½–13

Age range of girls: 2½–11

No. of pupils enrolled as at 01/09/2019: 650

Boys: 350 **Girls:** 300

Fees per annum as at 01/09/2019:

Day: £10,545–£19,470

Heathside School

Heathside School has been established for over 25 years. During that time, we have grown from a small, single form entry prep school in Hampstead village to a larger school which caters for children up to the end of Year 9 and provides boarding from Year 5 upwards. We are proudly co-educational, non-denominational and non-selective.

Heathside is a friendly, inclusive and academic school. Our community is positive, kind and mutually supportive, which provides the right environment for pupils to learn well and grow.

The school maintains an informal and relaxed atmosphere while fostering a high level of compassion, individual responsibility, self-motivation and achievement. We look to develop thoughtful and caring individuals with a well-rounded understanding of the world and a strong sense of respect for both themselves and others.

Our vision at Heathside is to empower students to acquire, demonstrate, articulate and value knowledge and skills that will support them, as independent lifelong learners, to make a positive difference to the world they will inherit. The values of the school are respect, tolerance, inclusion and personal excellence.

We encourage the development of the whole person and, as a result, Heathside is a happy place and academic standards are high. We have a proud tradition of tailoring our teaching so that every child gets the best from a lesson – a high staff-to-student ratio, a focus on small group work and individual attention allow us to offer challenge and support as appropriate. We prepare children for the 11+ and 13+ examinations and have an outstanding track record of gaining scholarships and entry into many highly respected independent schools although many children continue their learning at our Upper School.

Our curriculum builds on strong foundations in literacy and numeracy, scientific understanding and creative thinking. We produce highly able mathematics and lifelong readers and writers. Art, music and drama are particular strengths; children perform in several productions each year and every child in school learns French from a native speaker. We play a wide range of sports to high standards and we have been national chess champions many times. Extra-curricular activities range from capoeira and Chinese to fencing and philosophy clubs.

Most children join us in the Nursery, which can take children from two years of age; we do have occasional places in other years. It is never too early to register for a place which you can do on our website. At the right time, your child will be invited to spend a morning with us to ensure the right fit between Heathside and your child.

In July 2019, Heathside was acquired by Dukes Education. Dukes Education's schools are chosen for their consistent excellence in the provision of learning and development for young people. Each has a unique and precious character. Dukes preserves this by ensuring Heads lead on all decisions regarding their schools and add to this the power of the collective: bringing together best practice, training, and opportunities to invest in their schools through the security of a group.

(Founded 1993)

84-86 West Heath Road, London, NW3 7UN UK

Tel: +44 (0)20 3058 4011

Email: admissions@heathside.net

Website: www.heathsideprep.co.uk

Headteacher: Katherine Vintiner

School type: Coeducational Day & Boarding

Age range of pupils: 2–14

No. of pupils enrolled as at 01/01/2019: 500

Fees per annum as at 01/09/2019:

Day: £15,000–£18,300

James Allen's Girls' School
Including James Allen's Preparatory School

'When you begin your life as a JAGS girl you join a community which combines extraordinary tradition with a forward-looking approach. The oldest girls' school in London, we strive for excellence in all we do, developing scholarly young women who gain top academic results and places at top institutions. But there is nothing pompous or old fashioned about a JAGS education. Come and visit us and you will meet future doctors and engineers in our labs, Oxbridge scholars in our library and the next generation of politicians and diplomats in our lecture theatre. But these same girls will also be volunteers in charity placements at the weekends, will sing loudly in the gospel choir or tap dance across our stage.

The portrait of our founder, James Allen, hangs on the main school corridor. The same man who had the vision to educate young women back in 1741, proudly declares beneath the painting that he was 'Six feet high, skilful as a Skaiter, a Jumper, athletic and humane'. We love the fact that James could skate – a true advocate of a full extra-curricular programme. But it's his humanity we most admire and most seek to uphold.

Celebrating a grounded approach and founded on a long standing tradition of diversity and access, JAGS is a genuine reflection of modern, south London life.'

Sally-Anne Huang, Headmistress

James Allen's Girls' School provides first class education to girls aged 4-18 in South London with a with character and social conscience, developing their personal and professional skills to prepare them for adulthood.

Key to our success is the ability attract a diverse mix of intellectually curious and dynamic pupils, with a means tested bursary scheme making the school accessible to girls from all economic backgrounds. Academic scholarships are also available alongside scholarships in music, sport and art.

JAGS is consistently ranked highly in national A-level results tables and students go on to study the top institutions in the UK and abroad.

Every girl is encouraged to explore a wide range of subjects when they join, covering all key areas and including several language options and creative disciplines. As they mature and choose to focus on subject specialisms, our teachers will help them gain qualifications at the highest level as well as develop research skills and become independent learners.

Our facilities include 22 acres of playing fields and a sports complex that includes a swimming pool, climbing wall and astro pitches. A professionally designed theatre gives girls a chance to learn about performing arts whilst a vibrant music department holds performances throughout the year in our new Community Music Centre with its 500 seat auditorium and 15 practice rooms.

School trips in the UK and around the world provide further opportunities to enhance academic learning and broaden life skills. Recent trips include volunteering at a school in Uganda, an art trip to New York and performing concerts during a music tour of Italy.

At JAGS we care that your daughter is happy and have a strong pastoral care team to give them support should they need it. The school has two School Nurses who are available to deal with medical and personal problems. Students can also talk to CAMHS counsellor and our School Chaplain.

For more information, visit our website www.jags.org.uk and follow us on Twitter and Facebook (@JAGSSchool).

James Allen's Girls' School

jags

(Founded 1741)

144 East Dulwich Grove, Dulwich, London, SE22 8TE UK

Tel: 020 8693 1181

Email: enquiries@jags.org.uk

Website: www.jags.org.uk

Head of School: Mrs Sally-Anne Huang MA, MSc

Appointed: September 2015

School type: Girls' Day

Religious Denomination: Church of England

Age range of girls: 4–18

No. of pupils enrolled as at 01/09/2019: 1075

Fees per term as at 01/09/2019:

Pre-Prep & Prep: £5,679 per term

Senior School: £6,267 per term

Average class size: 18-28

Teacher/pupil ratio: 1:9

Lloyd Williamson Schools

Introduction

The Lloyd Williamson Schools have grown in both size and reputation to become the established schools they are today. The main departments are: three Nurseries, a Transition School for 5-7 year olds, a Senior School for 7-11 year olds and an Upper School for 11-16 year olds. We plan to expand the age range to 18 taking one extra year group per year from 2021.

The names *Lloyd* and *Williamson* are family names that belong to the proprietor. We believe they convey one of the main points of ethos at the school: that we are a *family* – and a strong one at that!

We have built an excellent reputation for strong academic standards and personalised, holistic learning for individual children.

We are based in W10 and W8 in the Borough of Kensington and Chelsea, with small classes to a maximum of 16 in Primary and 18 in Secondary. The schools have extended opening hours, competitive, realistic fees and all-year-round provision, including Holiday Clubs.

Mission Statement and Ethos:

- We celebrate childhood and nurture each child to be the best they can be in a challenging and inspiring environment that ignites a passion for life and learning – we are not a one-size-fits-all school
- Teachers build positive relationships, working with each child to be curious, intellectual and creative – we all like to think outside the box – fear of failure is banished!
- Equality and diversity permeate the fabric of our school – we are a family where everyone belongs, based on empathy and respect
- We encourage partnership and dialogue with parents and children thrive academically without losing their childhood – we cherish each child's self-esteem

- A blend of traditional and forward thinking teaching prepares our children for their next school and for life

Admissions

Parents are invited to meet the Co-Principals for personal and individual tours of the school during school hours in order to gain a real flavour of how the school operates on a daily basis.

The school supports requests for places from families with a diverse range of backgrounds; the binding quality is motivation! We do not compare children with one another; we challenge them against their own goals and next steps. This allows children to feel safe, be creative and curious instead of managing anxiety about 'not keeping up'! Our children are happy, confident students available to learn – they develop a rich and positive sense of who they are and can be.

The school is open from 7:30am-6:00pm (main school hours from 8:30am-3:30pm). This means that working parents can drop off their children and get to work knowing their children are safe and without the additional cost of nannies.

As a small school, everyone knows everyone from the babies up to our oldest member of staff!

We cherish individuality and self-confidence and our aim is that every child will develop an organic and strong positive sense of self. We enable this through the development of positive relationships so that all our children can learn to be strong and independent.

Contact Information

www.lws.org.uk
Admissions: admin@lws.org.uk
Main School and W10 Nursery: 020 8962 0345
W8 Nurseries: 020 7243 3331

LLOYD WILLIAMSON
——— SCHOOLS ———

(Founded 1999)

12 Telford Road, London, W10 5SH UK

Tel: 020 8962 0345

Fax: 020 8962 0345

Email: admin@lws.org.uk

Website: www.lloydwilliamson.co.uk

Co-Principals: Ms Lucy Meyer & Mr Aaron Williams

Appointed: December 1999

School type: Coeducational Day

Age range of pupils: 4 months–16 years

Fees per annum as at 01/09/2019:

Day: £14,400

Nursery: £79 – £99.50 per 10.5 hours day

Average class size: 12-16

Teacher/pupil ratio: 1:12

Newton Prep

In a London landscape crowded with prep schools, Newton Prep stands out for its unbeatable combination of vibrant size and eclecticism, its extraordinary facilities and outside spaces and its position at the heart of Central London's most burgeoning community: including the rapidly growing Battersea Power Station development, where Apple (the holder of the OTHER famous apple logo) will have their Europe HQ from 2021.

There's an electricity in the air and it's important that we are a part of that buzz. It is also key to our ethos: to ensure that Newton children are well-educated, curious, kind and articulate but, above all, in this modern world, to encourage them to think for, and be, themselves.

At Newton Prep, we provide a liberal environment in which children are equipped with a sense of self, resilience and hopefulness, beyond the obvious need to excel academically. We encourage children to think beyond the curriculum and they hoover it up. Whether it's piano lessons, judo or Boggle, children need ways of engaging. We aim for our Newton Prep children to enter adolescence feeling that they already have more to contribute than just academic achievements. Yes, we need to get them into the right schools but not at the expense of their well-being.

We encourage all our children to reflect on school life, not just power through it. Delegates from throughout the school take part in both Pupil Parliaments. Here children can express their views and make suggestions about how we might improve the school. Each child is therefore encouraged to embrace the notion of using their voice to influence things for the good of the many.

Despite the excellence of their education, Newton Prep children are notable for their lack of arrogance and entitlement. The kindness and generosity shown by the pupils towards their peers is remarkable and we are particularly proud of the engagement between the older children and the little ones. This spirit of community is also built into the Newton Diploma, our revolutionary humanities curriculum for our Years 7 and 8, now into its second year. This is a cross-curricular, rigorous and exciting programme that scraps the creaky arts syllabi of Common Entrance and allows pupils to exploit links between subjects, extend initiatives for service and leadership and breathe real fire into their intellectual curiosity. Last winter, for example, our Year 7 children raised over £13,000 for Centrepoint by enlisting celebrity and Twitter-fuelled support for their cardboard city sleep-out overnight.

Luckily, our extensive resources enable such personal growth, in whichever direction a child wants. With a huge all-weather pitch capable of supporting four fixtures at a time, a state-of-the-art, 120-seat recital hall, a music technology suite, recording studio, 300 seat auditorium, three gymnasiums, bustling art studios, dance studios, a library and collegiate-style science labs, children are encouraged to "do" as well as "learn". We even have an oasis of a garden: where our children perform Shakespeare, hunt for mini-beasts and conduct scientific experiments.

We are not a blazers-and-boaters kind of school. We don't have to look to the past and can focus all our present energies on ensuring a bright future for our children. One parent who sent her five children through Newton, commented, "Newton combines a quirky nature and knowledge of families with great space and facilities... All the teachers understood my (very different) children, the management is open to fresh ideas and the school is large enough to accommodate variety."

Above all, we want Newton Prep children to enjoy their precious childhood years.

(Founded 1991)

149 Battersea Park Road, London, SW8 4BX UK

Tel: 020 7720 4091

Fax: 020 7498 9052

Email: enquiries@newtonprep.co.uk

Website: www.newtonprepschool.co.uk

Headmistress: Mrs Alison Fleming BA, MA Ed, PGCE

Appointed: September 2013

School type:
Coeducational Pre-Preparatory & Preparatory Day

Age range of pupils: 3–13

No. of pupils enrolled as at 01/09/2019: 631

Boys: 311 **Girls:** 320

Fees per annum as at 01/09/2019:

Day: £9,600–£20,340

Average class size: 20 (smaller in Years 7 & 8)

North Bridge House

North Bridge House prides itself on providing an individually tailored education for boys and girls, aged from 2 to 18 years. We know, support and inspire every pupil to achieve their full potential and provide a solid foundation for a successful academic career and adult life.

Pupils can join us from Nursery and stay until Sixth Form or benefit from first-class preparation for other top senior schools. We work closely with parents to choose the right educational environment for their child, ensuring that every individual thrives and helping them to gain many sought after scholarship places.

Our high-achieving Senior Schools and Sixth Form prepare pupils for university life and the world of work with careers events, industry speakers and UCAS support, and celebrate top GCSE results. 2019 saw NBH Senior Hampstead achieve 31% 8 and 9 grades at GCSE and NBH Senior Canonbury gain 32% A*/A grades at A Level.

At the heart of each school is a highly qualified and inspirational team of teachers who deliver a rich and varied range of academic and extra-curricular activities, tailor-made to challenge, stimulate and reward our pupils. This, together with our outstanding pastoral support, allows them to grow in confidence and independence. At our Senior and Sixth Form, the progressive teaching team also refer to research into teen development to further understand and maximize the potential of their pupils. For example, Sixth Formers start their lessons later in the day as studies have shown that their sleeping patterns make them less likely to absorb teaching early in the morning.

Through PE and games we develop the individual's physical and emotional wellbeing, as well as essential team working skills. The latter are then further enhanced in the senior years through the Duke of Edinburgh Awards, civic engagements and leadership programmes.

At North Bridge House we nurture each individual to exceed their expectations – and pave the way to success and the top universities. To find out more, please do join us at an open day or book a guided tour at northbridgehouse. com/open.

School locations:
North Bridge House Nursery School
33 Fitzjohn's Avenue, Hampstead, London NW3 5JY
North Bridge House Pre-Prep School
8 Netherhall Gardens, Hampstead, London NW3 5RR
North Bridge House Prep School
1 Gloucester Avenue, Regent's Park, London NW1 7AB
North Bridge House Senior Hampstead
65 Rosslyn Hill, Hampstead, London NW3 5UD
North Bridge House Senior School & Sixth Form Canonbury
6-9 Canonbury Place, Islington, London N1 2NQ

North Bridge House

(Founded 1939)
65 Rosslyn Hill, London, NW3 5UD UK
Tel: 020 7428 1520
Email: admissionsenquiries@northbridgehouse.com
Website: www.northbridgehouse.com
Head of Senior Hampstead: Mr. Brendan Pavey
Head of Nursery & Pre-Prep Schools:
Mrs. Christine McLelland
Head of Prep School: Mr. James Stenning
Head of Senior Canonbury: Mr. Brendan Pavey
Head of Senior Hampstead: Mr. Brendan Pavey
School type: Co-educational Day
Age range of pupils: 2–18 years
No. of pupils enrolled as at 01/09/2019: 1375
Fees per annum as at 01/09/2019:
Day: £7,635–£20,400
Average class size: 20

Orchard House School

At Orchard House School, children are loved first and taught second. Our Pupil Pastoral Plan monitors the well-being of each child and was recently shortlisted for a TES (Times Educational Supplement) national award for educational innovation. This emphasis on a nurturing environment is not, however, at the cost of academic excellence. In fact, our outstanding results show how creating the right environment enables every child to thrive academically and emotionally. We believe learning should be exciting and fun, and the children should positively want to come to Orchard House every day. And they do: we harness the exuberance and energy of every child in our care, and instil within them a lifelong love of learning.

Orchard House's diverse curriculum creates a sense of adventure, developing the children's appetite for risk. This feeds into greater academic and creative achievements. Whether it's a whole-school skipping day, a project with Jaguar to enable our 10- and 11-year-old mathematicians to engineer performance cars or learning archery in Normandy (taught solely in French), Orchard House children embrace novel tasks throughout their time with us. By the time they sit 11+ exams, they are past masters at tackling new challenges with verve: this shows in our stellar results.

Sport at Orchard House encourages a respectful, competitive attitude, teaching children the value of camaraderie and the buzz of going for gold, or goal. We offer football, netball, rugby, hockey, lacrosse, cross country, tennis, athletics, triathlon, cricket, rounders, swimming and gymnastics and arrange regular team-sport fixtures against other schools, often lifting the trophy but always relishing the match.

Similarly, music and drama build confidence and self-esteem, as well as many opportunities for every child to perform. Visiting music teachers offer individual instrumental tuition on a variety of instruments. We have a school orchestra, Pippin choir, chamber choir, senior and junior choir and a parent and staff choir. There are many other instrumental groups including a pupil-led rock band.

We collaborate closely with our sister schools, Bassett House and Prospect House, sparking off new ideas to promote ever more successful teaching practices. The three schools share a common ethos but each retains its unique personality. The schools (brought together under the umbrella of House Schools Group) are proudly non-selective. True to our belief, children are not tested and judged at the tender age of 3 or 4 years. Our educational success shows all children can fulfil their potential, regardless of early learning ability.

The Independent Schools Inspectorate awarded Orchard House the highest accolades of 'excellent' in all areas and 'exceptional' in achievements and learning in its last full inspection and we flew through our 2018 compliance inspection. The top-notch education we provide leads to our first-class academic results and the scholarships our pupils win to their next schools.

ORCHARD
HOUSE SCHOOL

(Founded 1993)

16 Newton Grove, Bedford Park, London, W4 1LB UK

Tel: 020 8742 8544

Email: info@orchardhs.org.uk

Website: www.orchardhs.org.uk

Headmistress:
Mrs Maria Edwards BEd(Beds) PGCE(Man) Mont Cert

Appointed: September 2015

School type: Co-educational Day

Age range of pupils: 3–11

No. of pupils enrolled as at 01/09/2019: 290

Fees per annum as at 01/09/2019:

Day: £9,210–£19,200

Average class size: 20

Teacher/pupil ratio: 1:7

Prospect House School

At Prospect House School, we focus on making each child feel valued and secure and on making their educational experience both challenging and fun. This allows us to develop every child to their fullest potential, as our outstanding results demonstrate. Our most recent full Independent Schools Inspectorate inspection, in 2013, rated us 'excellent' against all the inspectors' criteria and we flew through our 2017 regulatory compliance inspection.

Prospect House's superb teachers provide a supportive and encouraging academic environment in which children excel. The sound of laughter is never far away, as Prospect House children discover their aptitude for sport, music, art, computing, drama or a whole host of other opportunities both within the curriculum or before or after school. Whether taking up the trombone, building a go-cart or orienteering on Putney Heath, our children relish each new challenge and emerge better able to face the next challenge that comes their way.

Music is an important part of life at Prospect House. We have over 200 individual music lessons taking place each week and a school orchestra, chamber choir and senior and junior choirs, as well as a number of ensembles. All children act in assemblies, school plays, musical productions and concerts throughout the year. Children in Years 1 to 6 enjoy drama lessons and our high-quality staging, lighting, sound and props give every production a professional feel.

Physical activity promotes wellbeing, so we offer a busy sports programme. This includes football, netball, hockey, running, cross country, tennis, athletics, cricket, rounders, swimming, dance and gymnastics. Our approach to fixtures and tournaments successfully balances participation for everyone with letting our sports stars shine.

Residential trips thrill the children with the sense of adventure, encouraging risk-taking and building self-reliance, whether on a history expedition, a bushcraft adventure or a week in Normandy immersed in the French language and culture.

We encourage our children to think for themselves, to be confident and to develop a sense of responsibility for the world in which they live. By the time they leave us aged 11, Prospect House children are ready to thrive at London's best senior schools. This is reflected in our impressive 11+ results. Every year, a notable proportion of our children win scholarships to leading senior schools.

We collaborate closely with our sister schools, Bassett House and Orchard House, sparking off new ideas to promote ever more successful teaching practices. The three schools share a common ethos but each retains its unique personality.

The schools (brought together under the umbrella of House Schools Group) are proudly non-selective. True to our belief, children are not tested and judged at the tender age of 3 or 4 years. Our stellar results repeatedly show all children can fulfil their potential, regardless of early learning ability. We encourage our high-flyers to soar, whilst children who need a little extra help are given the support they need to reach their fullest potential. At Prospect House, every child is helped to achieve a personal best.

PROSPECT
HOUSE SCHOOL

(Founded 1991)

75 Putney Hill, London, SW15 3NT UK

Tel: 020 8246 4897

Email: info@prospecths.org.uk

Website: www.prospecths.org.uk

Headmaster: Mr Michael Hodge BPED(Rhodes) QTS

Appointed: September 2017

School type: Co-educational Day

Age range of pupils: 3–11

No. of pupils enrolled as at 01/09/2019: 316

Fees per annum as at 01/09/2019:

Day: £9,210–£19,200

Average class size: 20

Teacher/pupil ratio: 1:7

Queen's Gate School

Queen's Gate School is an independent day school for girls between the ages of 4 and 18 years. Established in 1891, the school is an Educational Trust situated in five large Victorian Houses within easy walking distance of Kensington Gardens, Hyde Park, and the South Kensington museums.

The School offers an education for life in a challenging environment where sound values and individuality are nurtured within a supportive atmosphere. Our aim is to create a secure, happy, yet stimulating environment in which each girl can realise their academic and personal potential and make full use of individual interests and talents. We encourage the development of self-discipline and create an atmosphere where freedom of thought and ideas can flourish.

The Principal, Mrs Rosalynd Kamaryc, has been in post since 2006 and has built on the existing strengths of the School, whilst enabling girls to enjoy new opportunities in and out of the classroom.

Girls follow as wide a curriculum as possible and generally take GCSEs in ten subjects that must include English, Mathematics, a science and a modern language. A full range of A Level subjects is offered. In the Lower Sixth girls normally take four subjects, reducing to three in the Upper Sixth. The girls are offered excellent careers advice to assist in their UCAS and US applications.

Sport is highly valued at Queen's Gate with two compulsory sessions for all girls each week. We have many sports available at other times during the School day including netball, athletics, basketball, hockey, fencing, swimming, rowing, cross-country, biathlon and dance. Girls achieve much success, with some earning national and international status.

Co-curricular activities at Queen's Gate see girls taking part in Model United Nations meets throughout the year, become part of clubs including horticultural society, STEM club and Cosmetics club and experience trips around the UK and abroad to enhance their learning experience.

Music plays a large role in the School life, with concerts and mini recitals throughout the School year both in school and at local venues, and Drama productions across both schools see girls performing at venues including RADA and the Chelsea Theatre.

The Junior School is situated just a few yards down the road from the Senior School at 125 and 126 Queen's Gate. The beautifully restored buildings boast spacious form rooms, three fully equipped laboratories, a state-of-the-art STEAM (Science, Technology, Engineering, Art and Mathematics) Room and an elegant Assembly Hall. Junior pupils also use Senior School facilities and benefit from specialist subject teaching from Senior School staff. Senior girls often visit the Junior School to assist with activities, thus reinforcing the continuity of education from 4-18 available at the School.

Admission is by test and interview in the Junior School. Entrance to the Senior School is by the London 11+ Consortium entrance examination. Applicants for the Sixth Form must achieve six GCSEs at Grade 7 or above with Grade 8 or 9 (or their equivalent) required in those subjects they wish to pursue at A level.

In addition to the Open Events that are run by the Senior and Junior Schools throughout the year, parents are always welcome to make a private visit to see the schools at work. Appointments can be made by contacting the Registrar on 0207 594 4982 or by email registrar@queensgate.org.uk.

Queen's Gate

(Founded 1891)

133 Queen's Gate, London, SW7 5LE UK

Tel: 020 7589 3587

Fax: 020 7584 7691

Email: registrar@queensgate.org.uk

Website: www.queensgate.org.uk

Principal: Mrs R M Kamaryc BA, MSc, PGCE

Appointed: January 2006

School type: Girls' Day

Age range of girls: 4–18

No. of pupils enrolled as at 01/09/2019: 538

Sixth Form: 95

Junior School: 146

Senior School: 392

Fees per annum as at 01/09/2019:

Junior School: £19,500

Senior School & Sixth Form: £21,600

Average class size: 23

Teacher/pupil ratio: 1:10

St Joseph's Convent School For Girls

'No work can be so productive of good to society as the careful instruction of women'.
Catherine McAuley 1841 foundress.

St Joseph's is a longstanding and established Independent school set within the leafy oasis of Wanstead.

It was established over 100 years ago to drive and firmly establish the importance of a powerful education for girls where they could thrive and realise their potential within the safe and guiding hands of experienced and specialist teachers.

The school has continued successfully through the intervening years preparing a whole host of young girls for the wider world.

St Joseph's has refreshed and strengthened its core values to ensure it meets the needs of the 21st century whilst retaining the exemplary aspects of its tradition.

A highly qualified team of staff who are deeply committed drive the ethos and mission of the school. We recognise the importance of academic rigour but also the vital requirement of nurturing the whole child including, physical, spiritual, mental, musical, artistic and emotional needs. St Joseph's girls are happy, vibrant and articulate with a self-confidence which exudes powerfully in the way they conduct themselves. They have a huge appetite for learning across the curriculum and especially love challenge. They are given several opportunities throughout their time at St Joseph's to fully realise these attributes. Our annual residential trip for Preps is one such occasion. The girls are problem solvers, team players, risk takers and consequently resilient.

We foster in them a love of learning which drives their appetite to be successful and aspirational. As a result, our girls blossom under the tutelage of our experienced team where the girls' wellbeing is centred. Due to small class ratios, we get to know our girls extremely well and foster excellent relationships which allow them to thrive. However, we acknowledge parents as the first teachers of their children and, through continuous reflection and purposeful communication, we work in partnership for the best outcomes for the girls. After their time at St Joseph's, girls transition to a number of highly sought after senior schools with several being awarded a range of scholarships.

The head teacher is a warm and energetic leader who is passionate about achieving the best outcomes for the girls, welcoming all members of the school community each day. The school exudes an atmosphere of happiness which displays itself throughout as a harmonious oasis of excellence.

'St Joseph's is a school that is transitioning to ensure that it meets the challenges of 21st century education and nurtures girls who will be the leaders of tomorrow.'.

(Founded 1918)

59 Cambridge Park, Wanstead, London, E11 2PR UK

Tel: 020 8989 4700

Email: enquiries@stjosephsconventschool.co.uk

Website: www.stjosephsconventschool.co.uk

Headteacher: Sheila Birtles (interim)

School type: Girls' Day

Religious Denomination: Catholic

Age range of girls: 3–11

Fees per term as at 01/09/2019:

Day: £2,486–£2,700

St Paul's Cathedral School

Governed by the Dean and Chapter and seven lay governors, the original residential choir school, which can date its history back to the 12th century, has, since the 1980s, included non-chorister day boys and girls aged 4-13. The number of pupils is currently 250.

In its 2017 inspection, the ISI awarded the School its highest accolade of 'Excellent' in both educational attainment and pupil progress.

A broad curriculum prepares all pupils for 11+ and 13+ examinations including scholarship and Common Entrance examinations. The school has an excellent record in placing pupils in outstanding senior schools, many with scholarships. With its unique and central location, the school is able to make the most of what London can offer culturally and artistically in particular. A wide variety of sports and musical instrument tuition is offered: the school has an exceptional record in preparing pupils for ABRSM exams. Choristers receive an outstanding choral training as members of the renowned St Paul's Cathedral Choir.

The life of the school is based on the following aims and principles:

St Paul's Cathedral School is a Christian, co-educational community which holds to the values of love, justice, tolerance, respect, honesty, service and trust in its life and practice, to promote positive relationships throughout the school community and where the safety, welfare and emotional well-being of each child is of the utmost importance.

The school aims to instil a love of learning through a broad curriculum. It aims to give each pupil the opportunity to develop intellectually, socially, personally, physically, culturally and spiritually. All pupils are encouraged to work to the best of their ability and to achieve standards of excellence in all of their endeavours.

Through the corporate life of the school, and through good pastoral care, the school encourages the independence of the individual as well as mutual responsibility. It aims to make its pupils aware of the wider community, espouses the democratic process and encourages a close working relationship with parents and guardians.

Facilities: the school is situated on one site to the east of St Paul's Cathedral. It has a separate Pre-Prep department, excellent Science lab and ICT room. It has two outside play areas and a hall. There are plans to provide new boarding facilities for the choristers.

Entry is at 4+ and 7+ years. 4+ entry is held in the November preceding the September a child will enter the school and 7+ entry is held in the January preceding the September a child will enter the school. At 7+, pupils are given a short test and spend a day in school. Chorister voice trials are held throughout the year for boys between 6 and 8 years old. Occasional places in other year groups sometimes become available and, at 11+, the school now offers scholarship awards in music, the arts, sport and academics. Further information can be found on the school's website www.spcslondon.com

St Paul's Cathedral School is a registered charity (No. 312718), which exists to provide education for the choristers of St Paul's Cathedral and for children living in the local area.

ST PAUL'S CATHEDRAL SCHOOL

(Founded 12th Century or earlier)

2 New Change, London, EC4M 9AD UK

Tel: 020 7248 5156

Fax: 020 7329 6568

Email: admissions@spcs.london.sch.uk

Website: www.spcslondon.com

Headmaster: Simon Larter-Evans BA (Hons), PGCE, FRSA

Appointed: September 2016

School type: Coeducational Pre-Prep, Day Prep & Boarding Choir School

Religious Denomination: Church of England, admits pupils of all faiths

Age range of pupils: 4–13

No. of pupils enrolled as at 01/09/2019: 260

Boys: 149 **Girls:** 111

Fees per term as at 01/09/2019:

Day: £4,911–£5,287 per term

Full Boarding: £2,970 per term

Average class size: 15-20

Teacher/pupil ratio: 1:10

The Merlin School

Choosing a school for your child at 4 years old, is an important decision and a significant first opportunity to inspire a little learner and prepare them for the next stage. At Merlin School we specialise in these precious early years. The Merlin School, established in 1986, is a creative and nurturing co-educational pre-prep school, which does not assess on entry. You'll find us in the heart of Putney, in a beautiful Victorian house. We offer a warm and homely atmosphere where all staff take time to engage with our children, supporting the development of their independence and confidence. Creative and practical activities enhance learning and stimulate their imagination.

Our school motto is 'have a go' and our main area of focus is to evoke a thirst for learning, encouraging curiosity in the world around us. Whilst Maths and English underpin our syllabus, we very much delight in the breadth and depth of subjects taught here. Pupils relish the challenge of their first formal sports lessons, learning about team work and sportsmanship, alongside their specific sports skills, gearing them up to find their own sporting pathway. Our children bounce in to Science lessons wondering what practical activity awaits, they master thinking in their computing lessons and build confidence with presentations, assemblies and innovative drama productions which are written specifically for them.

We believe that losing sight of the importance of the broad spectrum of subjects and cramming children in one or two areas only, can result in denying pupils crucial and exciting opportunities. It is about the child enjoying their childhood and 'doing!'.

Over half of our timetable is taught by specialist teachers including Science, Drama, Music, Art/DT, Computing, French and PE/Games with both our Deputy and Head being actively involved in the teaching of all year groups. Our Topic work is both vibrant and stimulating; a wander around our classrooms will take you on a journey through various topics from Gods and Monsters to The Seven Wonders of The World.

At the end of their educational journey with us we send our pupils off to their next schools with the confidence to build new relationships, the enthusiasm to learn and a positive attitude to new challenges. Despite being a non-selective school Merlin children make excellent progress, from their individual starting points, and go on to a range of prestigious Prep Schools.

At Merlin School we are immensely proud of our recent Ofsted inspection (November 2017), where we were graded 'Outstanding' in all five areas. Ofsted described our curriculum as being 'planned carefully to captivate pupils' interests'. Merlin children were described as 'resilient and independent learners who set about every activity with enthusiasm... they display excellent communication skills and are confident learners'. Our EYFS provision was reported as Outstanding, highlighting the strong and sustained progress the children make in all areas of learning.

Please do book an appointment to come and see for yourself – we look forward to welcoming you!

(Founded 1986)

4 Carlton Drive, London, SW15 2BZ UK

Tel: 020 8788 2769

Email: admissionenquiries@merlinschool.net

Website: www.merlinschool.net

Principal: Mrs Kate Prest

Appointed: March 2003

School type: Co-educational Pre-Prep

Age range of pupils: 4–8

No. of pupils enrolled as at 01/09/2019: 175

Fees per annum as at 01/09/2019:

Day: £5,041 (Inclusive)

Average class size: 15

The Mulberry House School

First experiences are so important – early educational experiences will set the tone for the rest of a child's life. For The Mulberry House School, making each child's first important experience of a school a secure and happy one is paramount. The school prides itself on working in partnership with parents to ensure that school is a place where children arrive eagerly each day and depart with a sense of achievement and pleasure.

The Mulberry House School was established to provide children between the ages of 2 and 7+ years with the highest standard of education and care. The school's ethos is that a well-rounded education is one that nurtures the individual and offers an environment in which pupils learn without limits.

For the earliest years, a broad and balanced curriculum in line with the Early Years Foundation Stage is offered from the First School site.

Then, when the children move to the Second School site for pre-reception, reception, year one and two, these firm foundations are built upon, guided always by the National Curriculum.

A range of specialist teachers – including PE, Music, Dance, Drama, Mandarin and Art – are employed to further enrich the curriculum. All children are encouraged to develop as critical, independent thinkers and natural problem solvers, ultimately equipping them with the skills to be life-long learners.

The school constantly strives to produce well-rounded children capable of communicating effectively with confidence and eloquence. With this in mind, they provide children with a wide range of experiences to develop their interests and enrich their learning opportunities through first hand experiences.

Visits to museums, galleries, wildlife centres and theaters are organised to complement curriculum topics and the children's interests. Visitors to the school also provide interesting specialist knowledge to further extend learning.

Children are invited to join a wide range of clubs throughout their time at the school. These have included Engineering, Coding, Animation, Netball, Spanish and Arts clubs. Enrichment opportunities beyond the curriculum encourage problem solving, creative thinking and higher order thinking skills.

Additionally, an outdoor classroom at the local nature reserve, Westbere Copse has enabled pupils to explore the natural environment first hand; building on their resilience, confidence and self-esteem. Each class visits the nature reserve weekly and this enables each child to develop problem solving skills, giving them the ability to risk assess, enhancing creativity and encouraging a connection with nature.

Outdoor sessions have included pond dipping, minibeast hunts, creating bird feeders, den building, making nature presses and creating clay sculptures. Through such sessions the children have the opportunity to build relationships and use teamwork outside. These are vital life skills, essential in helping to create independent learners.

Through all of this, The Mulberry House School is able to successfully prepare children for the next stage of their education, helping them to secure places at some of the top prep schools. As a non-selective school, this is very much thanks to the hard work of an extremely professional team of staff, and equally determined and enthusiastic children.

Come and experience The Mulberry House School by visiting us at one of our Open Evenings (Register at www.mulberryhouseschool.com for an Open Evening).

THE MULBERRY HOUSE SCHOOL

(Founded 1989)

7 Minster Road, West Hampstead, London, NW2 3SD

Tel: 020 8452 7340

Email: admissions@mulberryhouseschool.com

Website: www.mulberryhouseschool.com

Headteacher: Victoria Playford (BA Hons, QTS)

Appointed: January 2017

School type: Coeducational Nursery & Pre-Prep

Age range of pupils: 2–7

No. of pupils enrolled as at 01/09/2019: 190

Fees per term:

£3,976–£7,364

Teacher/pupil ratios: EYFS (2–3 years) 1:4, EYFS (3–4) 1:8, Prep class (Reception, Year 1 & Year 2) 1:10

University College School

University College School (UCS) was founded in 1830 by University College London (UCL) to promote the principles of intellectual curiosity, breadth of study and independence of mind. Such attributes combine to achieve academic excellence, and UCS is one of the highest achieving schools in the UK. UCS now comprises three schools all situated within a mile of each other:

- Pre-Prep for boys aged 4-7
- Junior Branch for boys aged 7-11
- Senior School for boys aged 11-18 and girls aged 16-18

There is so much more to an outstanding education than examination grades but pupils leave UCS with exceptional grades at GCSE and A-Level. In 2018, 31% of A-Level exams taken at UCS were graded at A* and 70% were either A* or A. In 2017, the school was ranked 10th amongst independent co-educational sixth forms in England for A-Levels and 7th amongst independent boys' schools for GCSE. UCS's track record of supporting university applications to both UK and overseas institutions is first class and is facilitated by knowledgeable and caring staff. It is expected that at least 20 offers per annum are received from either Oxford or Cambridge and an increasingly large number of pupils now head to prestigious universities in the USA. Recent leavers have accepted places at Harvard, Stanford, MIT, Duke and Columbia.

The curriculum throughout the UCS Foundation is broad and is designed to match the educational needs of pupils at all stages of their development. At the Senior School, "Dialectics" lessons in the first two years invite children to inquire into the philosophy of learning, and lessons in all subjects place a strong emphasis on the value of discussion. Pupils thrive in this dynamic learning environment and lessons are finely tuned to enable pupils to increase their problem-solving skills, their sense of curiosity and their love of learning for learning's sake. The extensive co-curricular programme permits a vast number of pupils to participate in performing arts and every pupil participates fully in the games programme.

UCS is renowned for providing outstanding pastoral care and much of this is based on developing strong and open relationships with parents as well as pupils. Approachable, experienced staff, that are warm and engaging, nurture relationships with pupils and guide them through their schooling. The support for pupils is as comprehensive as it can be. Their well-being is the highest priority.

UCS is a united community of individuals, and pupils develop diversity, lateral-thinking and confidence. The coupling of independence of mind with academic excellence not only makes UCS one of England's leading schools, it makes UCS truly distinctive. Selecting children with no regard to race or creed, UCS fosters in them a sense of society alongside a respect for the individual. Pupils are taught humanity, understanding and empathy which enables them to contribute to and lead in so many areas of 21st century life. By offering the fullest range of opportunities for personal and for group endeavour, pupils learn the value of commitment and the joy of achievement. UCS is a place of study, but also of self-discovery and self-expression; a school that places equal value on learning with others as on learning from others.

(Founded 1830)

Frognal, Hampstead, London, NW3 6XH UK

Tel: 020 7435 2215

Email: seniorschool@ucs.org.uk

Website: www.ucs.org.uk

Headteacher: Mr Mark J Beard

Appointed: September 2013

School type: Boys' Day, Co-educational Sixth Form

Age range of boys: 4–18

Age range of girls: 16–18

No. of pupils enrolled as at 01/09/2019:

Senior School: 875

Junior Branch: 255

Fees per annum as at 01/09/2019:

Senior School: £7,030

Junior Branch: £6,498

Pre Prep: £5,817

North-East

Argyle House School

Nestled in Ashbrooke – the leafy suburb of Sunderland, lies an educational establishment of repute. Argyle House School is the North East's only family owned independent school. The school was established in 1884 by Mr. Hanna M A. In 1968, Mr. Jeff Johnson, a student of the school and later a teacher there, bought the school from Mr. Hanna's family. In 2002, Jeff Johnson handed over the reins of Argyle House School to his two sons, Chris and Neil. After taking over as Headteacher, Mr. Chris Johnson has since developed the school into a place of nurture by providing an environment for children to enjoy learning whilst instilling in them strong family values; the core values upon which the school was built.

The strengths of the school lie on many levels. It is a school where children come willingly to learn. Studying and learning are two different things. The willingness to learn comes from the kind of environment that a school has. When they are happy, they are more receptive to learn. Argyle House School provides such an environment. Also, this is not a school with 1000 children! Class numbers are small and there is merit in this structure. This enables our teachers to focus on a child's strength, his or her interests and then guide them accordingly. When a child is known individually to a teacher, this makes a tremendous difference in their development. Our teachers know each and every one of them. We never look upon a child as a student of the school. They are always looked upon as sons and daughters. When they come to school, they're coming home. A place where they are loved and respected.

We emphasise the importance of values, of honesty, of respect, of kindness, of being responsible citizens, of humanity and above all, the value of hardwork and the importance of being a good human being. What we lay down as a foundation today will enable our children to build their future with confidence. We stress the importance of what we call 'The R-Principle' where

we encourage our children to be; resourceful, resilient, respectful, responsible, reflective and to possess the ability to reason. Our teachers take on different roles apart from teaching such as being mentors and guides; a friend who listens and comforts; a father or mother who is stern but loving as well. When a school has such an environment, happiness takes over.

We are of the opinion that education must be enjoyed and it must give the child the chance to develop not just academically, but also physically, socially and emotionally too. Extra-curricular activities are crucial here. In fact, our clubs and activities are far ranging and we have close to 30 clubs for children to utilise. We've attained the highest possible rating by ISI in our most recent inspection.

Our facilities are updated regularly and we've increased our wider partnership links. We've also devised new curriculums with our pupils in mind, which feature extra GCSE subjects. The environment of the school not only creates well-rounded individuals but also academic achievers. Government statistics have once again named Argyle House School as number one for GCSE results in Sunderland. To ensure a healthy body and mind, children are encouraged to participate in Sport, Music, Drama and Arts. From a student accomplishment perspective, we are proud to have a number of children who have excelled in their sporting endeavours. Two brothers claimed gold in European Gymnastics and one child represented Great Britain in Karate.

We consider the happiness of children to be the key factor to both academic and social success. With no airs or graces, our down to earth approach to education and development allows children to achieve to the maximum of their abilities. Outstanding facilities, backed by dedicated teachers, a comfortable environment and deep rooted values make Argyle House School truly exceptional.

ARGYLE HOUSE SCHOOL SUNDERLAND

(Founded 1884)

19-20 Thornhill Park, Sunderland, Tyne & Wear SR2 7LA UK

Tel: 0191 5100726

Email: info@argylehouseschool.co.uk

Website: www.argylehouseschool.co.uk

Headteacher: Mr. Chris Johnson

School type: Co-educational Day

Age range of pupils: 3–16

No. of pupils enrolled as at 01/09/2019: 233

Fees per annum as at 01/09/2019: Please enquire

Average class size: 17

Teacher/pupil ratio: 1:6

North-West

Chetham's School of Music

The thriving creative community at Chetham's includes around 300 students aged 8-18, whose common passion is music. Entry to the School is based solely on musical ability and potential, never on background or ability to pay; 90% of students receive bursaries up to full fees through the Government's Music and Dance Scheme. This common bond of musical passion makes for a truly inspirational place which transforms the lives of all who are part of it.

There are many different qualities that permeate the fabric of Chetham's: the warm and welcoming atmosphere, the constant creative buzz, admirable academic standards, Chetham's history and heritage, superb teaching and performance spaces, the cosmopolitan city of Manchester, diverse backgrounds and personalities – and of course, the music. Chetham's is the largest specialist Music School in the UK and the only one based in the north of England. The School is also a national and international resource for music education – welcoming teachers, professional players, composers and conductors, community groups, school children and other young musicians, both experienced and novices, to come together and make music. Chetham's Fit to Perform programme takes an innovative new approach to wellbeing, promoting mental and physical fitness designed specifically with young musicians in mind.

Based in the heart of Manchester, Chetham's is housed in a state-of-the-art new School building, with its onsite concert hall, The Stoller Hall, offering a world-class acoustic for student performances and visiting artists from around the world. Excellent academic results are achieved through small class sizes, a dedicated teaching team, and a community which values success. Ongoing investment into boarding accommodation, and a cross-departmental team helping students to balance music and academic study with time to socialise, explore and grow, ensure that students finish school as well-developed, ambitious and curious young people. Our network of partnerships with professional orchestras and organisations extends across the music industry, encompassing performance, outreach and leadership, and creating vital connections for students' professional futures.

Chetham's is one of the highest achieving non academically-selective school in Manchester, and every year students progress to leading music conservatoires and universities across the world. We take as much pride in those who move on to careers in engineering, medicine or law as in those playing leading roles on the concert platform; in DJs, jazz pianists and folk singers as in classical conductors and soloists. What unites every member of the Chetham's community is their passion for music; a passion that, whatever their future direction, will forever enrich their lives.

Admissions to Chetham's

Open Days:
Saturday 5 October 2019
Saturday 11 January 2020
Summer Open Days in May and June
Chetham's holds regular whole-school Open Days in October and January each year, when prospective students can meet staff and students, hear ensembles in rehearsals, and discover more about a specialist music education. Further Open sessions in May and June support students planning entry in 2021 onwards, and specifically target Juniors, Secondary Phase, and Sixth Form applicants.

Admission is by musical audition only. There are no academic requirements, and means-tested Government funding provides up to full support with school fees. Many students benefit from Advice Auditions, a chance to receive guidance on your musical progression before making a full application to the School.

Auditions and Advice Auditions run throughout the year.

Chetham's
School of Music

(Founded 1969)

Long Millgate, Manchester,
Greater Manchester M3 1SB UK

Tel: 0161 834 9644

Fax: 0161 839 3609

Email: hello@chethams.com

Website: www.chethams.com

Head of School: Mr Alun Jones

Appointed: September 2016

Chair of Governors: Mr Malcolm Edge

School type: Coeducational Boarding & Day

Age range of pupils: 8–18

No. of pupils enrolled as at 01/09/2019: 306

Fees per annum as at 01/09/2019:

Day: £25,821 (overseas £27,300)

Full Boarding: £33,324 (overseas £35,697)

Average class size: 20

Teacher/pupil ratio: 1:10

Highfield Priory School

Highfield Priory School is an Independent Co-educational Day School for children from the age of 18 months to 11 years. It is situated in the Fulwood area of Preston, within easy distance of the M6 which makes it handy for parents on their daily commute. The school is a real haven of tranquillity amidst the hustle and bustle of the busy city. It enjoys nine acres of grounds, including a conservation area and outdoor classroom.

The Nursery School is situated on the school site and benefits from the best of both worlds. Whilst retaining an intimate home-from-home atmosphere in the Bungalow, it has access to all the school facilities and the children are able to enjoy walks (including babies in prams and pushchairs) around the school nature reserve: Highfield Haven; visits to the school library; dance lessons in the Performing Arts Studio and PE and Games in the Sports Hall and on the sports field.

Ten Reasons Why You Should Choose Highfield Priory School For Your Child

- We have a long reputation of academic excellence. This is our eighth year running in the top 30 of The Sunday Times Top 100 Preparatory Schools in England and we are the National Winners of the ISA's Junior and Prep. School Award for Excellence and Innovation (ISA 2017-2018).
- In 2019, we achieved the highest grading possible from the Independent Schools Inspectorate for our School and Nursery: 'Outstanding' (EYFS) and 'Excellent' across all areas (School).
- We have been awarded Three Star Gold Membership for our work with Gifted and Talented pupils.
- We 'Aim High' for our children and prepare them academically, socially, physically and emotionally for the Grammar, Independent or State Secondary School of their choice.

- We have Specialist Teachers and Facilities in Science, Modern Languages, Music, ICT, Drama, Sport, Elocution and Art.
- We encourage our children to develop a love and appreciation of the great outdoors through Orienteering and Team Building exercises, a Residential Trip to Shropshire and in our outdoor classroom, Highfield Haven.
- Our children discover and develop new talents through our extensive Extra-Curricular Activity Programme.
- We hold a firm belief in inclusion: all children are given regular opportunities to build confidence in competitive sporting fixtures and performing on stage in front of an audience.
- We have a long history and a strong sense of tradition and traditional teaching methods; we do not allow government policy to cause us to deviate from giving our pupils a firm and confident grounding in Reading, Writing and Arithmetic.
- We work hard to help our pupils to be the best that they can be, but we also work hard for their parents. We know modern life is hectic and unpredictable and we understand the importance of establishing trust and confidence as well as Extended Care to allow for the demands of the working parent.

Highfield Priory School was originally created circa 1936 to educate the children of local business men and women who were looking for an excellent academic environment for the education of their children. This history of the pursuit of academic excellence, a strong work ethic and good manners continues to this day. Visitors to Highfield regularly comment on the children's elocution, self-confidence and courteous behaviour. Its current Headmaster, Mr Jeremy Duke, has been in the post since 2010.

(Founded 1940)

Fulwood Row, Fulwood, Preston, Lancashire PR2 5RW UK

Tel: 01772 709624

Email: schooloffice@highfieldpriory.co.uk

Website: www.highfieldpriory.co.uk

Headmaster: Mr Jeremy Duke BSc (Hons)

Appointed: September 2010

School type: Coeducational Day

Religious Denomination: Christian

Age range of pupils: 18 months–11 years

No. of pupils enrolled as at 01/09/2019: 273

Fees per annum as at 01/09/2019:

Day: £7,850

Nursery: £51 per day (open 51 weeks of the year)

Average class size: 16

Kirkham Grammar School

At Kirkham Grammar School, we believe in the values of a traditional education alongside a drive towards modern ambition. It is our intention to continue to build upon our history as a recognised centre of excellence for academic attainment and the holistic development of the learner. We believe everyone has a place in our community including our parents, pupils, staff, governors and alumni alike; we all have a part to play in the drive for continued excellence.

Kirkham Grammar School is an Independent Co-educational Day and Boarding School for pupils aged 3-18. The school prides itself on its warm family atmosphere. Academic success remains at the heart of the school's aims.

The Senior School has undergone a transformation over the last decade and boasts a host of magnificent new facilities. In addition, we have completed phase one of a planned four phase development programme. This included the refurbishment of the Summerlee Hall, a multi-purpose space available for use by the whole foundation; a new psychology classroom; a new conference room and an upgrade to the rugby pitches and sports facilities. The teaching provision includes twelve interactive classrooms and a science block designed to meet the needs of the large number of pupils who pursue studies in this area. Sporting facilities are outstanding with a floodlit all weather surface and Lawrence House Pavilion.

The Junior School is situated opposite the Senior School and has a roll of 250 pupils aged from 3-11 years. As well as enjoying its own on-site state of the art facilities, it also has access to the Senior School facilities, including an Astroturf pitch and multi-purpose hall.

Our newly designed Pre-School has now fully opened. The setting has been thoughtfully designed to meet the needs and requirements of children from rising 3s to 4 years old. The Pre-School offers a wide range of exciting activities and resources, which promote each child's learning across all areas of the Early Years Foundation Stage framework. The setting is a welcoming 'home-from-home' where children feel relaxed and happy, while being guided and nurtured by our dedicated Pre-School team. As always at Kirkham Grammar Junior School, our fundamental aim is to offer the best possible environment in which children can flourish and naturally love learning forever.

Our most recent inspection, recognised the school as, 'excellent across all areas', the highest grading possible within the independent sector. During the inspection, over 60 lessons were observed, meetings undertaken and every aspect of the school's infrastructure and life inspected. The inspection found that the quality of the pupils' academic and other achievements is excellent, saying: *"Pupils are articulate and display excellent verbal and communication skills."* The report added: *"Pupils are ambitious learners, eager to respond to challenging opportunities in lessons and clear target setting in marking."* The quality of the pupils' personal development was also deemed excellent: *"Pupils reflect the strong family ethos of the school and demonstrate excellent collaboration in and out of lessons."* Following the inspection, Headmaster Mr Berry said: *"The inspection confirmed what was already known; Kirkham Grammar School is the best kept educational secret in Lancashire. However, it was pleasing for everyone that it has been officially acknowledged against national criteria that we are working hard to ensure our pupils receive the finest education."*

We believe Kirkham Grammar School exists for our children and therefore they must have the best! This is reflected in the school remaining full in all year groups for September 2019.

KIRKHAM
GRAMMAR SCHOOL

(Founded 1549)

Ribby Road, Kirkham, Preston, Lancashire PR4 2BH UK

Tel: 01772 684264

Fax: 01772 672747

Email: info@kirkhamgrammar.co.uk

Website: www.kirkhamgrammar.co.uk

Headmaster: Mr Daniel Berry

Appointed: 2016

Head of Junior School: Mrs Kirsten O'Donoghue

School type: Co-educational Boarding & Day

Age range of pupils: 3–18 years

No. of pupils enrolled as at 01/09/2019: 870

Boys: 455 **Girls:** 415 **Sixth Form:** 180

No. of boarders: 70

Fees per term as at 01/09/2019:

Junior School (4–11 years) Day: £2,996 per term

Senior School (11-18 years) Day: £4,010 per term

Senior School (11-18 years) Boarding: £3,605 per term (in addition to the Day fee)

Pre-School (3-4 years): £258 (Full week)– £52.80 (Full day)

Average class size: 15

Teacher/pupil ratio: 1:9

Lime House School

Finding the right school for your child is one of the most important decisions you will make. A good education can make all the difference to a child's future.

Lime House School [www.limehouseschool.co.uk], just south of Carlisle on the edge of the Lake District National Park, is an independent, co-educational boarding and day school which welcomes pupils, aged seven to 18, from all over the world.

Lime House School offers a rigorous academic and intellectual education which will challenge and engage your child. Supportive and nurturing in approach, the school empowers pupils to establish secure foundations for independent learning from which to launch their futures in tertiary education, and the careers of their choice.

The school has a wide and varied curriculum at both Primary and Secondary levels, with a dynamic range of subjects offered to Sixth Form. Pupils of all abilities are welcome, those with Special Education Needs are supported by a dedicated team of professionals.

Headteacher, Mary Robertson-Barnett, MA (Oxon), PGCE, says: *"It is a privilege to lead a school of such vibrancy. The academic programme is rich and fulfilling, with pupils benefiting from tailored programmes, delivered by subject specialists, who enthuse our learners with their passion. The super-curricular opportunities inform the academic life of the school with a range of cultural, performance, and sporting activities.*

"Pupils are guided in their growth as future global citizens and custodians, by their personal development tutors, and are encouraged to explore their dreams and define their path. Lime House School is a joyous and enriching place for all who are involved in our community."

The school's ethos is that learning should be integrated and fun, extending beyond the classroom and informing all we do.

The activities programme includes: sporting; music; art; photography; debating; environmental and strategic thinking. The school garden – a new initiative to support the school's ecological work – is thriving under the tender care of pupils who engage wholeheartedly with their beautiful surroundings. Weekends are structured, with pupils exploring diverse educational, cultural and fun filled experiences.

Lime House is a school of outstanding potential, its vibrancy and tolerance reflected in each of its pupils. Why not arrange a visit to see what we can offer your child?

(Founded 1899)

Holm Hill, Dalston, Carlisle, Cumbria CA5 7BX UK

Tel: 01228 710225

Fax: 01228 710508

Email: office@limehouseschool.co.uk

Website: www.limehouseschool.co.uk

Headteacher:
Mrs Mary Robertson-Barnett MA(Oxon), PGCE

Appointed: September 2017

School type: Coeducational Day & Boarding

Age range of pupils: 7–18

No. of pupils enrolled as at 01/09/2019: 165

Fees per annum as at 01/09/2019:
£9,750

Average class size: 15

Teacher/pupil ratio: 1:20

Rossall School

For many, a childhood by the sea is a dream; at Rossall, that dream becomes a reality. Rossall is an exceptional school, rooted in its heritage yet innately dynamic, brimming with personality and excited about the future.

We are shaped by our coastal location and somehow infused with the sense of anticipation, curiosity and adventure that early explorers must have felt – where can we go? What will we find? How can we get there?

We are shaped by the wonderful architecture which creates a safe haven within its Cambridge-like quads, by the vast dining hall, atmospheric Chapel and beautiful rooms.

We are shaped by our expansive site and make full use of our 160 acres, particularly for outdoor activities and sport, from cross country running and CCF field exercises to golf practice and Ross-hockey on the beach. Our ponds, trees, marsh, grassland and dunes also provide unending scope for outdoor learning and discovery.

But above all, we are shaped by the great people, both staff and students, who live and work at Rossall. There is an indelible Rossall spirit that is cultivated here – warmth, courage, humour, empathy, resilience, curiosity and the ability to talk to anyone are some of its most prominent features! It is a compelling mix.

Our teachers provide a brilliant balance of inspiration, care and deep subject knowledge to fire the imagination and ensure that our students have all the building blocks they need for success, not only at school and not only in the classroom, but also later on in life. We are proud of our students' academic achievements and delighted that they achieve consistently above national and world averages in their examinations.

We deliver a broad and balanced curriculum with the principles of the International Baccalaureate learner profile at its heart. In the Nursery, we follow the Early Years Foundation Stage (EYFS) learning goals. From the age of 2 to 11, we offer the IB Primary Years Programme (PYP). At age 16, students sit GCSE and iGCSE examinations, then students choose between the IB or A Level route in the Sixth Form. The IB principles run through our teaching and learning in every phase of the school and underpin a dynamic and enjoyable yet rigorous learning experience.

With nearly forty different nationalities living and learning together at Rossall, we truly are a global village. The combination of UK day students and students from right across the world creates an exciting international dimension and an appreciation of diverse culture, religions and politics.

Whether joining Rossall as a day or boarding pupil, you will be coming to a vibrant and happy community. All the basic needs are catered for, but in a most generous way – food is plentiful and delicious, we have an on-site Medical Centre, our houses are beautifully appointed and our houseparents and tutors are amazing – adept, knowledgeable and attuned to the needs of the young people in their care.

To come and experience the School first hand, you can arrange a private tour to fit in with your commitments.

Scholarships: To enable a wide range of children to join Rossall, we offer a number of scholarships each year. We offer academic, music, drama and sports scholarships to children in Years 7, 9 and 12.

EXPANDING HORIZONS

(Founded 1844)

Broadway, Fleetwood, Lancashire FY7 8JW UK

Tel: +44 (0)1253 774201

Email: admissions@rossall.org.uk

Website: www.rossall.org.uk

Head: Mr Jeremy Quartermain

Appointed: August 2018

School type: Co-educational Boarding & Day

Religious Denomination: Church of England but accept all religions

Age range of pupils: 2–18

No. of pupils enrolled as at 01/09/2019: 640

Boys: 340 **Girls:** 300 **Sixth Form:** 190

No. of boarders: 250

Fees per annum as at 01/09/2019:

Day: £8,445–£13,740

Full Boarding: £21,645–£39,210

Average class size: 16

Teacher/pupil ratio: 1:11

South-East

Bethany School

Set on a 60 acre rural campus in the beautiful Kent countryside, Bethany School is a flourishing co-educational day and boarding school that provides a welcoming and caring environment for pupils between the ages of 11 and 18.

Bethany enjoys a reputation as a particularly friendly and happy community. It is a strong, thriving school with an enviable building programme, including recent and regular upgrading of boarding school facilities; a fantastic new six lane 25m indoor swimming pool, state-of-the-art fitness suite and a new Sixth Form centre with excellent facilities.

Location
Situated in Kent's 'Garden of England', Bethany has an idyllic location with easy accessibility. London is less than an hour by train, Gatwick Airport one hour by taxi and Heathrow an hour and a half. The Eurostar terminal at Ashford International is just 30 minutes away.

The curriculum and information technology
As a mainstream school, Bethany prides itself on nurturing academic excellence while catering for pupils with a broad range of abilities. The School offers a wide variety of subjects in modern classrooms with specialist facilities, including our Science Centre with modern laboratories.

The entire campus is served by a wireless network and all pupils have their own laptop. Much of the curriculum is delivered through ICT and pupils gain important digital skills. Almost all of our Sixth Formers progress on to university courses, leaving Bethany with a mature self-confidence and clear direction.

CReSTeD registered since 1994, Bethany's Learning Support department enjoys an international reputation for its success in giving specialist help to dyslexic pupils within the mainstream curriculum. In addition, for those pupils who require it, we offer support for English as an Additional Language.

Boarding life and overseas pupils
We offer boarding in full, weekly and flexi arrangements across five boarding houses, and our boarding community brings great diversity to Bethany. We are a small school and yet we have boarders coming from 22 different countries, enriching our education with a variety of experiences and backgrounds.

We aim to inspire individual excellence in every pupil and this approach underlies everything we do at Bethany. Its success is evidenced by the excellent transition from School to university made by our pupils each year. Sixth Form boarders benefit from single bedrooms with en suite bathrooms, all with easy access to kitchens and laundry rooms. This experience, combined with our Body for Life programme, is designed to be a stepping stone to life at university, all within the supportive environment of the School.

Outside the classroom
At Bethany, we believe that pursuits outside the classroom are very important in developing pupils' personalities. Everyone takes part in sport at least three times a week, and chooses from a huge array of extra-curricular activities including horse riding, chef school, golf, fishing, clay pigeon shooting, archery, orchestra and country pursuits. The Duke of Edinburgh's Award is hugely popular and very successful at Bethany.

Throughout the School there are opportunities to perform in drama, music and dance. Our Art department is particularly strong and many pupils join us to take advantage of our 'mini art college'.

The Headmaster firmly believes that school should be enjoyed rather than endured and it is the atmosphere of positive nurturing and encouragement, focused on the potential of each individual, that helps makes Bethany 'refreshingly different'.

Bethany since 1866

(Founded 1866)
Curtisden Green, Goudhurst, Cranbrook, Kent TN17 1LB UK

Tel: 01580 211273

Fax: 01580 211151

Email: admissions@bethanyschool.org.uk

Website: www.bethanyschool.org.uk

Headmaster: Mr Francie Healy BSc, HDipEd, NPQH

Appointed: 2010

School type: Co-educational Boarding & Day

Age range of pupils: 11–18 years

No. of pupils enrolled as at 01/09/2019: 333

Boys: 232 **Girls:** 101 **Sixth Form:** 98

No. of boarders: 106

Fees per annum as at 01/09/2019:

Day: £17,310–£19,110

Weekly Boarding: £26,865–£29,670

Full Boarding: £28,965–£32,610

Average class size: 15-17

Teacher/pupil ratio: 1:8

Burgess Hill Girls

"The community at Burgess Hill Girls is very special. The way we bond with our teachers is not something you come across every day. I feel very lucky to be a part of this school."
Laura, Year 10, Burgess Hill Girls

A transformative education
Burgess Hill Girls is an Excellent rated independent school in Sussex for girls aged 2 to 18 years of age.

Whatever the stage at which your daughter joins Burgess Hill Girls you can be confident of two things: that she will be known for who she is as an individual and she will be provided with an outstanding, transformative education of the whole person.

I am, I can, I should, I will
Our school motto, 'I am, I can, I should, I will', conveys and underpins our whole approach, identifying and realising the potential of your daughter as she proceeds, giving her the very best possible opportunities to become a successful women of the future.

As parents, success will be having a happy and healthy daughter who loves going to school, loves to learn, loves participating, and is able to make friends for life. For the girls, success may be doing well in lessons and tests, being part of a team, playing a musical instrument and having fun with friends. At Burgess Hill Girls we pride ourselves on unlocking the academic talent that is found within our girls and strongly believe each individual will thrive in our high-achieving environment. Whilst Burgess Hill Girls aims to provide the very best opportunities for everyone to excel, we believe that success is more than obtaining the highest marks and grades. We recognise just as much all those fantastic qualities that are not materialistic or target driven. Success at our school is when we produce bright, confident and independent young women who have and will continue to achieve great things.

Perfectly located
Burgess Hill Girls stands in 14 acres of beautiful grounds within a conservation area close to Burgess Hill's town centre in the centre of Sussex. All aspects of the school are located on this one campus; Nursery, Junior, Senior, Sixth Form and Boarding Houses. The school is only a five minute walk from the railway station (on the London to Brighton line) and close to excellent road networks (10 miles from Brighton and only 20 miles from Gatwick); the school is easily accessible for local and international students. A flexible, daily minibus service is provided for girls across Sussex and beyond.

Visit Burgess Hill Girls
We would be very pleased to meet you, put a name to a face and show you round our school. Please get in touch to arrange a visit.

BURGESS HILL
— GIRLS —
Tomorrow's Women

(Founded 1906)

Keymer Road, Burgess Hill, West Sussex RH15 0EG UK

Tel: 01444 241050

Email: admissions@burgesshillgirls.com

Website: burgesshillgirls.com

Head of School: Liz Laybourn

Appointed: 2017

School type: Girls' Day & Boarding

Religious Denomination: Interdenominational

Age range of boys: 2.5–4

Age range of girls: 2.5–18

No. of pupils enrolled as at 01/09/2019: 505

Boys: 29 **Girls:** 476 **Sixth Form:** 70

No. of boarders: 50

Fees per annum as at 01/09/2019:

Day: £8,100–£20,100

Full Boarding: £31,050–£35,850

Average class size: Max 20

Teacher/pupil ratio: 1:11

Churcher's College

Churcher's College is an Independent day school for boys and girls from 3-18 years of age offering Nursery, Junior, Senior and Sixth Form education. With around 865 pupils in the Senior School and 225 pupils in the Junior School (not including the Nursery) of approximately equal numbers of boys and girls, Churcher's College enjoys recognition as one of the most accomplished independent, co-educational day schools in the country.

The school is hosted on two sites in Hampshire which enables the Junior School and Nursery pupils to flourish in their own beautiful grounds in Liphook, whilst maintaining close links to the Senior School and Sixth Form located in nearby Petersfield. Both sites offer extensive on-site playing fields and unrivalled facilities, providing the comfort and opportunities of an open, healthy environment.

Churcher's College offers the widest range of experiences and the opportunity to be the best. The school has received independent acknowledgement for its academic success, creative and performing arts, adventurous activities and sporting achievements. Churcher's is an inclusive school where parents, children, staff and friends all contribute to the rich and broad education provided. We aim to nurture children into educated informed, socially responsible and respectful citizens ready to succeed in life.

"I am hugely impressed with the number of opportunities that have been made available to me throughout my time at Churcher's. I have taken part in the Biology, Chemistry, and Physics Olympiads and completed an EPQ on human evolution. I have also been very fortunate to receive an offer to study Natural Sciences at Cambridge where I hope to continue my education in Chemistry, Cell Biology and Maths. As for extra-curricular opportunities I have thoroughly enjoyed the adventurous activities available.

These have included the Devizes to Westminster kayak marathon and completions of the Ten Tors and the Welsh 3000's events. However, my highlight has been going on expedition to the Galapagos for 5 weeks. The last seven years have been incredibly busy and even more enjoyable due to the huge array of opportunities available in all areas of school life." **Pupil**

"Thank you … we are very proud of her … she is absolutely over the moon to be going to her first choice of university. We wanted to say what a wonderful two years she has had at Churcher's – she has never been so happy at school and has done amazingly well in all areas as well as creating a great friendship group – we couldn't have asked for more!" **Sixth form parent**

"Our family feel hugely privileged to have discovered Churcher's and its team."
Senior school parent

"By the time the pupils leave the school they are well balanced, thoughtful and considerate individuals with an excellent standard of personal development."
"Teachers have strong knowledge which they present enthusiastically to their pupils; this acts as a stimulus for increasingly sophisticated thinking."
"The extra-curricular provision is excellent."
ISI Inspection 2015

"Value added is impressive: one whole grade at A level higher than ALIS value added expectation."
"The school achieves balance very well … those happy keeping busy in a lively environment will enjoy life at Churcher's College."
The Good Schools Guide Inspection 2017

CHURCHER'S COLLEGE
NURSERY • JUNIOR • SENIOR • SIXTH FORM

(Founded 1722)

Petersfield, Hampshire GU31 4AS UK

Tel: 01730 263033

Email: admissions@churcherscollege.com

Website: www.churcherscollege.com

Headmaster: Mr Simon Williams MA, BSc

Appointed: September 2004

School type: Co-educational Independent Day

Age range of pupils: 3–18 years

No. of pupils enrolled as at 01/09/2019:

Senior School: 865

Junior School: 225

Fees per annum as at 01/09/2019:

Day: £10,320–£16,035

Average class size: 22

Teacher/pupil ratio: 1:12

Cranleigh School

Cranleigh is Surrey's leading co-educational independent school offering both day and boarding education for children aged 7-18, enabling siblings to be educated together.

Set on adjacent hills, the Preparatory School and the Senior School enjoy a spectacular 280-acre rural setting on the Surrey/West Sussex border, by the Surrey Hills, an Area of Outstanding Natural Beauty; yet they are conveniently situated close to the mainline city of Guildford, roughly equidistant between Gatwick and Heathrow, and only an hour's drive from London, where Cranleigh pupils regularly visit professional exhibitions and performances.

Both the Prep and the Senior Schools are proud of their excellent academic track records, culminating in outstanding performances at Common Entrance, GCSE and A-level. 99% of pupils go on to Higher Education, and Cranleigh also has a consistently strong Oxbridge contingent.

Such academic excellence does not come at the expense of co-curricular success at Cranleigh and the Schools currently boast national and county level representatives in a wide range of sports, including kayaking, cricket, riding, hockey, rugby and swimming. The School is currently rated third best school in the country for sports.

Pupil participation in sport, music and drama is actively encouraged at all levels; most Saturdays see every pupil playing sport for the school. More than 10 dramatic productions each academic year provide acting opportunities for all and the hugely popular Technical Theatre encourages the development of backstage skills.

Around 40 per cent of pupils play at least one musical instrument. Many take the opportunity to perform in more than 30 concerts a year, with over 10 musical groups, including symphony orchestra, wind band, chapel choir, big band, strings, trios, quartets and several other choirs.

The Schools offer outstanding facilities alongside new academic blocks. Sports facilities enjoyed by both the Prep and the Senior School include a double-sized indoor sports centre, four artificial playing surfaces, full equestrian centre, two expansive hard court areas for netball and tennis, a generous array of rugby and cricket pitches, a three-par, nine-hole golf course and an indoor pool. Equally outstanding sports staff includes former England players, a former Davis Cup player, an England national coach and an Olympic Gold Medallist (Hockey).

The Schools also boast professional-standard theatre facilities, rehearsal rooms, beautiful art studio spaces and a modern design centre fully equipped with 3D printers. The students have the opportunity to showcase their work in professional exhibitions several times a year.

Most importantly, Cranleigh prides itself on providing a happy, nurturing environment, founded upon an extremely supportive pastoral system (every pupil has their own tutor) and a high staff to pupil ratio, underscored by an invariably passionate House spirit. In such an environment, pupils can flourish into the well-rounded, self-motivated and confident individuals Cranleighans are famed for becoming, well prepared for life after school and invariably blessed with a circle of lifelong friends.

Pupils enter Cranleigh following a process of holistic review, at the main entry points of 13 and 16, and in other years where places are available. Regular small groups open mornings are held and a wide range of academic and non-academic Scholarships are available.

CRANLEIGH
EX CULTU ROBUR

(Founded 1865)

Horseshoe Lane, Cranleigh, Surrey GU6 8QQ UK

Tel: +44 (0) 1483 273666

Fax: +44 (0) 1483 267398

Email: admissions@cranleigh.org

Website: www.cranleigh.org

Headmaster: Mr Martin Reader MA, MPhil, MBA

Appointed: September 2014

School type: Co-educational Boarding & Day

Age range of pupils: 7–18 (including Prep School)

No. of pupils enrolled as at 01/09/2019: 654

Boys: 402 **Girls:** 252 **Sixth Form:** 240

No. of boarders: 467

Fees per annum as at 01/09/2019:

Day: £32,370

Full Boarding: £39,330

Average class size: 20 (9 in Sixth Form)

Teacher/pupil ratio: 1:7

Durlston Court

At Durlston Court Prep School our purpose is to provide a first class Prep School education for every child. Whenever your son or daughter joins us you can be sure that we will help them to develop into a happy, confident and successful child who will flourish and thrive in a nurturing and inspiring environment. Your child will be excited by the limitless learning opportunities and will relish the individualised challenges that we provide. There is a real magic at Durlston; the children who come here are inspired to become the best that they can be; children that parents can be proud of.

"Pupils develop high levels of self understanding, growing into confident, resilient young people who are prepared to take risks, and have huge determination to succeed." ISI

We look forward to welcoming your family into our Durlston Family – at any point. From first steps in Kindergarten to magical days in Pre-Prep, your child will be nurtured through the start of their educational journey. Our Middle School will support and guide your child offering a wealth of new and exciting challenges and when your child reaches our Senior School they will embody what it means to be a Durlstonian – confident, kind, hard-working and not afraid to challenge themselves. This applies across all areas – in the classroom, on the sports field and performing to a large audience.

Excellent teaching and learning underpins all that we do. Working in small class sizes with specialist teachers and facilities will give your child an educational journey that is right for them. They will be encouraged to try new challenges and find out what they love. As a result, they will make huge progress in their learning.

Durlston Court offers Limitless Opportunities to discover, create and explore:

STEM lessons and clubs provide limitless opportunities to: experiment in the Science Lab – a place to inspire curiosity; explore innovative projects using soldering, sewing, coding and laser cutting in our Design and Technology Centre; plan, build and refine – from a Greenpower race car to a coracle; grow in confidence, solving mathematical problems in fun situations.

Everybody learns to play at least one musical instrument and are given regular opportunities to perform, helping them to develop their confidence. Our impressive drama productions showcase talent but also provide opportunities for all to be involved in a spectacular show including being part of the back stage technical team. Your child will also develop their creativity and explore new techniques in our wonderful Art and Ceramics Studios.

From Year 3 your child will have at least one hour of sport with daily lessons and weekly opportunities to compete in fixtures. Furthermore, specialist coaching and sports clubs from tennis to rowing take place before school and after.

"Pupils demonstrate high levels of success... in an extremely wide variety of activities including in the creative and performing arts and sport." ISI

We are committed to promoting an all-round education and fully preparing our pupils for Senior School. We are proud of our academic record and our limitless opportunities ensure pupils leave Durlston as well-rounded, independent and confident young people, equipped and prepared to engage and to succeed in the world of today and tomorrow.

DURLSTON COURT
Preparatory School

(Founded 1903)

Becton Lane, Barton-on-Sea, New Milton, Hampshire BH25 7AQ UK

Tel: 01425 610010

Email: registrar@durlstoncourt.co.uk

Website: www.durlstoncourt.co.uk

Head of School: Mr Richard May

Appointed: September 2015

School type: Coeducational Day

Age range of pupils: 2–13

No. of pupils enrolled as at 01/09/2019: 296

Boys: 165 **Girls:** 131

Fees per annum as at 01/09/2019:

Day: £3,540–£15,390

Average class size: 12-15

Teacher/pupil ratio: 1:4-1:15

Learning
Without Limits

Eagle House School

Eagle House is a coeducational, boarding and day Prep, Pre-Prep and Nursery located in Berkshire that celebrates its 200th anniversary in 2020. The school's superb grounds and excellent facilities are the background to an experience where success, confidence and happiness are paramount. The school is proud of its academic record, preparing children for a host of top independent schools and boasting a diverse and robust curriculum.

Younger pupils follow the International Primary Curriculum and our older children have embarked on a new 'Curriculum 200', specially created for Years 5 to 8 that links subjects through topics and themes. Great teaching, new technology and a focus on the basics mean that children make good progress and love to be in the classroom. Independent learning is a focus for all children and our Extended Project programme helps drive inquisitive minds.

We unashamedly offer lots as part of our Golden Eagle activities experience. Children benefit from a huge range of opportunities in sport, music, drama, art, outward bound and community programmes. Busy children are happy and fulfilled children and we like to think that all pupils are Learning for Life.

Learning for Life means that children benefit from the best all-round education. They can feel confident in the classroom, on the games field, on stage, in the concert hall and in the community. Everyone is given the chance to stretch themselves in every area. Challenge is an important part of growing up and at Eagle House we learn that success and failure are both positive experiences.

Bright learning environments, outdoor learning areas and wonderful sporting facilities are important but it is the community that shapes a young person. Through the excellent pastoral care and tutor system, coupled with a buddy structure, ensuring children have an older pupil to support them, Eagle House seeks to develop wellbeing from the youngest to the oldest.

Recognising how to be a positive influence within a community is also part of the Eagle House journey. Our wonderful Learning for Life programme teaches children about themselves and the wider community. We were recently recognised by The Week Magazine as a great Prep School for Community Service and we aim to make all our pupils responsible and independent as well as able to show empathy and understanding towards others. Time for reflection in chapel and assemblies also improves the way we look at the world and mindfulness sessions help us all take stock.

Boarding is a popular option and allows children to experience a varied evening programme of activities as well as being part of a vibrant and caring community. Boarding encourages independence but it is also great fun and whether full, weekly or flexi, boarders have the most wonderful time.

We often say that Eagle House children have the time of their lives and we firmly believe this. Learning for Life at Eagle House opens the doors to all sorts of opportunities and this results in children who are highly motivated and enthusiastic in all they do.

Eagle House buzzes with achievement and laughter – not a bad way to grow up!

Eagle House is a registered charity (No 309093) for the furtherance of education.

(Founded 1820)

Sandhurst, Berkshire GU47 8PH UK

Tel: 01344 772134

Email: info@eaglehouseschool.com

Website: www.eaglehouseschool.com

Headmaster: Mr A P N Barnard BA(Hons), PGCE

Appointed: September 2006

School type: Coeducational Day & Boarding

Age range of pupils: 3–13

No. of pupils enrolled as at 01/09/2019: 380

Boys: 200 **Girls:** 180

No. of boarders: 50

Fees per annum as at 01/09/2019:

Day: £12,030–£18,810

Full Boarding: £25,275

Average class size: 18

Teacher/pupil ratio: 1:8

Feltonfleet School

Feltonfleet is a community where 'individuals really matter' – a core belief which shapes all we say and do.

We know the most enjoyable personal growth comes from developing a child's natural talents and skills. In nurturing this potential within a sharing community, with a strong sense of family, children are able to discover their gifts and grow in self-confidence, independence and compassion.

Our ethos is based upon positive learning, living and leading, alongside core values of kindness, honesty, respect and responsibility. The overriding sense of happiness and laughter is palpable in the classrooms, on the playing fields and in the Boarding House. Our unique blend of day and boarding pupils creates a real buzz around school. Feltonfleet children are optimistic and inquisitive, with a thirst for life and learning. They thrive here.

The combination of talented and dedicated staff, an inspiring curriculum and 25 acres of beautiful grounds with exceptional facilities, encourages children to use their imagination, to think creatively, to explore the world around them and to strive to excel.

In 2015 a brand new Performing Arts Centre opened to complement the Drama, Music and Dance departments. The new, award nominated space, which includes the Ashbee Theatre and Dance Studio, is linked to the original building via an impressive glass corridor which houses the Main Reception. The theatre has retractable seating for up to 400 and advanced sound and light systems, providing a wonderful performance space and event venue.

In addition to a well-equipped sports hall, extensive playing fields and hard surface tennis courts, Feltonfleet boasts a 15m indoor swimming pool, floodlit all-weather Astroturf pitch and climbing wall. The school has its own rifle ranges for both air-rifle and .22 shooting. Beyond the playing fields a band of woodland is home to the eco-pond and a wilderness area for play and Science study.

High standards and expectations are grounded in the conviction that academic excellence and enjoyment of childhood go hand in hand. Unusually for a prep school, we have 'time to stop & think' lessons to nourish emotional wellbeing and to develop resilience and strategies for lasting mental health.

The Feltonfleet journey falls into four stages and reflects our belief that success and achievement happen in a happy, optimistic environment where children travel at different speeds along their bespoke academic and personal pathway.

Throughout the curriculum we seek to equip each child with the core academic skills and learning attributes so that they can take pride and responsibility for their own learning. Children gradually progress from being dependent learners to inter-dependent learners, developing the self-esteem and the confidence in themselves to 'risk' learning and acquiring new skills. Each stage in the journey is linked by our core values and strong sense of community.

As our pupils complete the four stages of their Feltonfleet journey, graduating after Common Entrance, they secure places and scholarships to leading independent senior schools in a range of academic, sporting, musical and all-round disciplines. They are well prepared for the next stage of their journey.

Come and see what makes Feltonfleet a wonderful school for your child's preparatory education. We would be delighted to show you around.

Feltonfleet
PREPARATORY SCHOOL

(Founded 1903)

Cobham, Surrey KT11 1DR UK

Tel: 01932 862264

Email: office@feltonfleet.co.uk

Website: www.feltonfleet.co.uk

Head of School: Mrs S Lance

Appointed: January 2018

School type: Coeducational Day & Weekly Boarding

Age range of pupils: 3–13

No. of pupils enrolled as at 01/09/2019: 435

Fees per annum as at 01/09/2019:

Day: £12,315–£18,090

Weekly Boarding: £18,090

Nursery: £6,600

Average class size: 18

Teacher/pupil ratio: 1:7

Gordon's School

Gordon's – The Most Unique School in England

Built by public subscription over a century ago at the insistence of Queen Victoria, Gordon's School is the national monument to General Charles Gordon of Khartoum and is listed as one of Britain's outstanding schools by Her Majesty's Chief Inspector.

A non-selective, co-educational residential and day boarding school, the School's academic record outstrips many selective schools. The progress made by students over the past three years has put Gordon's in the top one per cent of schools in England and Wales for progress at A Level.

But while Gordon's School embraces modern ideas, General Gordon's legacy of traditional values remains. The School's ethos is that high performance without good character is not true success.

To this end, it's not just in the classrooms where students excel. Successes are achieved in drama and the arts; debating and public speaking; dance and sport. The School also boasts an enviable record in attaining Duke of Edinburgh awards.

While the individual is celebrated, the whole School unites for parades. Since its inception, students have marched and there has always been a Pipes and Drums band. Dressed in their Blues uniform, the students parade around eight times a year and the school is the only one permitted to march along Whitehall – an annual tradition in remembrance of General Gordon.

Set in over 50 acres of beautiful Surrey countryside within easy access of major airports and roads, the School is home to some 800 students and offers Day and Residential (weekly and termly) Boarding from only £2,665 per term.

Each Student is assigned to one of the ten Houses – four residential boarding and six day boarding. Recently opened has been a dedicated Year 7 Residential Boarding House for our youngest students. Inter-House competitions are fiercely contested!

Spiritual guidance and support is given through chapel services and informal worship. And House Parents provide a 'home from home', lending special atmosphere to each Boarding House and ensuring that free time off for students is fun, with numerous activities.

There are three main admission points – at 11 years old; 13 years old and for Sixth Form. Scholarships are offered for those coming into the Sixth Form. As well as reduced fees, the scholarships enable those awarded to benefit from a programme to enhance their development and give them wider opportunities to progress in their field. Bursaries are also available.

The real judgement of Gordon's is the students. All who visit are struck by the friendliness, discipline and vibrancy throughout the school and by the family atmosphere, exemplified by the special rapport between staff and students. This is borne from a community that strives to live with integrity, to be courteous, enthusiastic and diligent, even in adversity.

Gordon's School is unique. Please book a visit and find out why.

(Founded 1885)

West End, Woking, Surrey GU24 9PT UK

Tel: 01276 858084

Fax: 01276 855335

Email: registrar@gordons.school

Website: www.gordons.school

Head Teacher: Andrew Moss MEd

Appointed: September 2010

School type: Co-educational Day & Boarding

Age range of pupils: 11–18

No. of pupils enrolled as at 01/09/2019: 836

Boys: 447 **Girls:** 389 **Sixth Form:** 239

Fees per annum as at 01/09/2019:

Day: from 5,994

Weekly Boarding: from £16,698

Full Boarding: from £17,838

Average class size: 22

Teacher/pupil ratio: 1:12

Hampton Court House

Hampton Court House is an independent, co-educational day school in South West London. The school was founded in 2001 and offers places for children from the age of 3 to 18 years old. The school is situated in its own private parkland and is 35 minutes from Central London.

Hampton Court House pupils are truly made to feel a part of the school. They offer their own ideas and opinions and many school activities are pupil-led.

Pupils as young as 3 years of age have a weekly ballet lesson with a Royal Academy of Dance Ballet teacher as well as Forest School lessons in the grounds or in neighbouring Bushy Park with a qualified Forest School teacher.

The school follows the National Curriculum, the teaching staff are subject specialists who teach year groups across the school. In addition to the many subjects taught at Hampton Court House, languages such as French, Latin, Spanish and Mandarin are highly valued. Pupils have daily French lessons in the early years of the school and in Years 1 to 4 they are taught in a French/English immersion programme. Latin and Mandarin are introduced to pupils from Year 5, Spanish is also introduced in Year 9, giving pupils a breadth of languages to study in GCSE and A level years.

Students are encouraged to take part in co-curricular activities, clubs, and school trips. Many of the pupils are involved in charitable fundraising including a recent sponsored run for a Syrian refugee camp in France. In addition to sports on the timetable for all pupils from Pre-Nursery to Year 11 the pupils can take part in lunchtime and after school clubs and activities. The sports programme at Hampton Court House is tailor-made for its size and location with sports such as rowing, athletics and Olympic lifting offered to all pupils from Year 7 upwards.

Hampton Court House promotes an active engagement in media and current affairs, believing that it is important to have an opinion on the events and decisions which shape our world. A sense of humour and an understanding of the opinions and feelings of others encourages pupils to feel supported and nurtured. Every member of Hampton Court House strives to be honest, considerate, compassionate and generous.

Hampton Court House is a school which places an emphasis on kindness and values but also encourages pupils to strive for academic excellence. The trend of ever improving GCSE results has continued with a higher proportion than ever before getting A grades or equivalent. 78% of the GCSE results were 7, 8 or 9 on the new scale (where 7 is an A) and 46% were 8 or 9 (A*). Nationally, only 20.6% of grades were 7 or better and only 11.4% were 8 or 9.

In recent years Hampton Court House has been recognised by UNESCO for their commitment to transcending cultural boundaries. The school has received two TES Independent School nominations, two Good Schools Guide Awards, and a Computing in Schools: Network of Excellence award.

If you would like to find out more about Hampton Court House contact the school on: 020 8614 0857; alternatively visit www.hamptoncourthouse.co.uk.

HAMPTON COURT HOUSE
FORTITER IN RE SUAVITER IN MODO

(Founded 2000)

Hampton Court Road, East Molesey, Surrey KT8 9BS UK

Tel: 020 8614 0857

Fax: 020 8977 5357

Email: admissions@hchnet.co.uk

Website: www.hamptoncourthouse.co.uk

Headmaster: Mr Guy Holloway

Appointed: 2013

School type: Coeducational Day

Age range of pupils: 3–18

Average class size: Approx 20

Teacher/pupil ratio: 1:10

Highfield Preparatory School

Who wouldn't want their daughter to skip happily into school, make really good friends and discover all her talents, where she can become the best she possibly can be? This is our aim for every girl here and it is what makes Highfield so wonderful.

Highfield Preparatory School is the leading independent girls' school in Maidenhead, offering a great start to the life of learning. In the Nursery and Reception class right through to Year 6, the girls are taught to love learning and are inspired to achieve their very best. We genuinely want every girl to have the opportunity to shine and be proud, to learn who they are, and have the confidence to have a go with the belief that they can succeed. The girls are encouraged to take risks in order to develop resilience. When mistakes are made it is often when the best learning takes place.

We are passionate about education in the fullest sense and provide a balance of academic achievement, enjoyment and activity, making us a beacon of excellence in all that we do.

Highfield girls are bright and inquisitive, each with their own unique abilities, interests and aspirations. Curiosity and imagination is encouraged at every stage and provides the foundations for a love of learning and life in the important formative years. Every talent is nurtured; every girl is unique.

Our girls value the school's diversity and learn from each other in a spirit of celebration of difference. We welcome their enthusiasm and encourage their interest in good citizenship. Being at Highfield means being part of a vibrant community in which we expect the girls to question, to take on responsibility and to care for others.

We believe, that in the important primary years, girls learn best in girls' schools. They learn by doing, listening, exploring and experimenting. The girls are given daily opportunities to explore, question, try, investigate, discover, apply and have fun! This all starts in the Nursery where the girls learn to develop confidence and independence.

We are proud of our reputation as a school with a strong ethos and nurturing pastoral care coupled with academic excellence. Our girls achieve well beyond national expectations and move on to some of the best schools in the area at 11+, often achieving academic, sports and music scholarships.

The atmosphere at Highfield is one of warmth and enthusiasm and there is a genuine desire for the girls to strive for the very best for themselves, intellectually and personally. To achieve this we offer wonderful resources in a happy, secure and stimulating environment where all girls learn and develop at their own pace.

From Nursery to Year 6 we offer wraparound care from 7.45am to 6pm and have an onsite all-year round holiday club, as well as offering a wide range of after school clubs. We pride ourselves on offering excellence and a superb education at a competitive price, providing exceptionally good value to our families.

Come and see for yourself why Highfield Prep can offer your daughter a First Class Education.

(Founded 1918)

2 West Road, Maidenhead, Berkshire SL6 1PD UK

Tel: 01628 624918

Fax: 01628 635747

Email: office@highfieldprep.org

Website: www.highfieldprep.org

Headteacher: Mrs Joanna Leach

Appointed: March 2015

Chairman of Governors: Mr W Bradley

School type: Girls' Day

Age range of boys: 3–5 (Siblings)

Age range of girls: 3–11

No. of pupils enrolled as at 01/09/2019: 107

Fees per annum as at 01/09/2019:

Day: £1,119–£12,675

Average class size: 17

Kent College, Canterbury

Kent College is an outstanding day and boarding school that celebrates both its 130 years of history and tradition, and its forward-looking, innovative approach to education. It has a reputation as a friendly school and is most definitely a place where teachers really get to know the pupils, with the time and space to give individual attention, both academically and pastorally. Music, drama and sport all play central roles in the life of the school, and many pupils also enjoy the opportunities provided by the school's Farm and Riding Centre.

Location
The school's location, on the outskirts of the historic city of Canterbury, provides a safe, healthy and beautiful environment for pupils to grow up. The school sits in 80 acres (32 hectares) of land with 26 acres of sports fields, grazing for the farm and ancient woodland for walking and cross country running. Yet the centre of Canterbury, with its wide selection of shops, restaurants, theatres, cinemas and world-heritage site, within which sits Canterbury Cathedral, is just a short walk away. A high-speed train service links Canterbury to London in under an hour and the school is within 100 minutes drive of Gatwick, Heathrow, Stansted and City of London airports.

Academic profile
Kent College prides itself on offering personalised academic programmes, small class sizes and exceptionally well-qualified and experienced teaching staff. Our mission is always pupil-centred and to focus on enabling every child to become the best they can be. All students are provided with a MacBook laptop when they start at the school. Pupils achieve excellent academic results at GCSE, A level, and in the International Baccalaureate (IB). An average point score of 37 in the IB consistently places Kent College in the top 10 IB schools in the UK. The school also offers a wide range of additional support for pupils, including access to a dyslexia unit and specialist English language teaching for overseas students in the International Study Centre.

Boarding
Kent College has a long history of welcoming boarding pupils from abroad, as well as from British families resident in the UK or working overseas. Boarders make up around one-third of pupils in the Senior School and there are over 40 countries represented in the boarding community. The five friendly and comfortable Senior boarding houses truly become a 'home away from home'. The school also offers weekly and occasional boarding.

Beyond the classroom
The performing arts are a particular strength at Kent College, with an impressive line-up of vocal and instrumental ensembles, and many opportunities to perform for all ages and abilities. An exciting new development is the construction of the Great Hall, a state-of-the-art 600-seat auditorium, opened in Summer 2019. The Hall will provide cutting-edge facilities for worship, concerts and the performing arts for the school's highly regarded Drama and Music departments. In sport, the aim is to provide something for every pupil, from recreational sport and promoting fitness to top-level coaching for our elite players. Hockey and cricket are particular strengths, with regular representation by Kent College pupils in the county and national squads. There is also a wide-ranging list of activities and clubs on offer for all pupils, including a full Duke of Edinburgh programme, and the opportunity to work on the school farm and up to 60 clubs and activities including archery, debating, photography, fencing and rowing.

(Founded 1885)

Whitstable Road, Canterbury, Kent CT2 9DT UK

Tel: +44 (0)1227 763 231

Email: admissions@kentcollege.co.uk

Website: www.kentcollege.com

Executive Head: Dr David Lamper

Senior School Head: Mr Phil Wise

Junior School Head: Mr Andy Carter

School type: Coeducational Day & Boarding

Religious Denomination: Methodist

Age range of pupils: 0–18 years (Boarding from 8)

No. of pupils enrolled as at 01/09/2019:

Sixth Form: 200

Senior School: 590

Junior School: 200

No. of boarders: 225

Fees per annum as at 01/09/2019:

Day: £10,191–£18,864

Full Boarding: £26,244–£35,628

Average class size: 15, max 18

King Edward VI School

King Edward VI School, Southampton, has been at the heart of the city for over 460 years and is one of the UK's leading independent 11-18 co-educational day schools.

With a reputation for academic excellence, the School boasts a thriving Sixth Form that produces consistently excellent A Level examination results ensuring students continue on to a range of competitive institutions, most to one of the UK's top 25 universities and, on average, approximately 10% of students proceed to Oxford or Cambridge. Results at GCSE and IGCSE are equally outstanding.

Outside of the academic, King Edward's also aims to foster a sense of personal worth in every pupil through a wide range of co-curricular activities, particularly with an active engagement in community work, so that every individual emerges as a fully responsible member of society. In the last year alone the student Charities Commission has raised over £27,000 for local and national charitable causes.

Each year students can be found taking part in excursions to worldwide destinations. A yearly charitable trip to South Africa allows Sixth Formers to work with disadvantaged children living in rural poverty, whilst other recent destinations have included a technology trip to Tokyo, a biology field trip to Ecuador and the Galapagos Islands, a cultural exchange with a school in North Carolina, and a trekking expedition in Vietnam. Language students regularly participate in the exchange programmes on offer to Germany, France and Spain as well as in cultural visits to schools in the USA and Prague. Closer to home the School also organises an annual summer camp to Swanage for local young carers, run by our Sixth Formers.

Sport and the arts are an integral part of school life. Students are given the opportunity to represent the School across the major team games as well as individual sports. Overseas tours, regular fixtures, tournaments and school events offer a competitive sporting environment and King Edward's boasts 33 acres of sports ground, a fully equipped gym and multiple all weather pitches. The Creative Arts Faculty offers an amazing array of facilities from recital rooms, a recording studio and music technology suite to a custom-built dance studio. The state-of-the-art Dobson Theatre has a capacity for 400 seats and provides a superb venue for our talented dramatists and musicians. An array of public performances throughout the year allow King Edward's performers to showcase their talents, whatever their ability level.

Students are actively encouraged to become involved in fund-raising and community work and take part in some of the 150 clubs and societies that are available outside of lesson time. King Edward's also runs a well-established Duke of Edinburgh's Award Scheme that makes use of the school's Rural Studies Centre in Dartmoor.

King Edward's strives to ensure that all pupils reach and fulfil their full potential. A happy atmosphere amongst first-class teaching facilities provide exceptional academic stimulus alongside an extraordinary breadth of co-curricular opportunities. Seventeen bus routes extend throughout south Hampshire, allowing students from the New Forest, Salisbury, Winchester and east of Southampton easy and direct access to the School.

(Founded 1553)

Wilton Road, Southampton, Hampshire SO15 5UQ UK

Tel: 023 8070 4561

Fax: 023 8070 5937

Email: registrar@kes.hants.sch.uk

Website: www.kes.hants.sch.uk

Head Master: Mr N T Parker

Appointed: August 2019

School type: Coeducational Day

Age range of pupils: 11–18

No. of pupils enrolled as at 01/09/2019: 960

Fees per annum as at 01/09/2019:

Day: £16,605

Average class size: 22

Teacher/pupil ratio: 1:10

King's Rochester

King's is a remarkable school with a rich and diverse heritage; people have been educated here for over 1,400 years under the watchful gaze of Rochester Cathedral and Rochester Castle. Founded in 604AD, King's is the second oldest school in the world and the world's oldest Cathedral Choir School.

While a sense of place is bound to have an impact on the development of the children learning here, it is the skills, experiences and opportunities provided to them, both within and outside the classroom, that will enable them to thrive in an uncertain and fast-changing world.

At King's, we believe in preparing children for the 21st Century through educating the whole child. Our priority, though, is ensuring that happy children perform to their best and the school is an exceptionally happy and friendly place where moral values, self-discipline, emotional intelligence and a Christian spirit underpin our family community.

Our academic results are excellent at all levels but we believe that building a love of learning and developing independent thinking skills are just as important as achieving the best grades. To achieve this, we keep our class sizes small so that teachers know their pupils as individuals and can help each of them shine. We are a school where all are cared for as individuals and where links between home and school are a real strength.

We offer, and encourage pupils to take part in, a huge range of co-curricular opportunities to ignite and nurture their interests, providing experiences which will develop confidence in them for life. Sport, Music, Drama, Outdoor Pursuits, CCF and a range of clubs and societies are integral to the school's commitment to provide a broad educational experience.

Music is a huge strength and we are privileged to use Rochester Cathedral as our chapel. We hold seasonal concerts throughout the year in the Nave and the Cathedral Choristers are educated in our Preparatory School. Music Scholars go on to leading international conservatoires.

Under the refurbished Vines Church is our Drama studio, equipped with digital sound and lighting. We are a proud Royal Shakespeare Company Associate School and our pupils have staged productions across Kent. King's has a strong reputation for exceptional drama performances and recent productions of "Into The Wood's" and "Titanic the Musical" have been in comparison with the West End.

Our coaches and many of our pupils play at County, National and International level. The King's Rochester Sports Centre provides pupils with extensive facilities to train, in addition to playing fields, a heated indoor swimming pool and boat house situated on the bank of the River Medway, while the Paddock is regarded as one of the finest cricket fields in the country.

The boarding community at King's reflects the personal approach of the school. Boarding starts from age 11 and we have 60 beds across our two Boarding Houses, "St Margaret's House" for girls and "School House" for boys. The small boarding community ensures a real boutique feel to both Houses which are comprised of both British and international students.

We offer co-education from 3 to 18 and our structure of Pre-Prep, Prep and Senior Schools enables us to offer a tailor-made experience for each age group while giving access to the excellent facilities of the whole school.

King's Rochester is truly a community which enables individuals to flourish.

(Founded 604 AD)

Satis House, Boley Hill, Rochester, Kent ME1 1TE UK

Tel: 01634 888555

Fax: 01634 888505

Email: admissions@kings-rochester.co.uk

Website: www.kings-rochester.co.uk

Principal: Mr B Charles

Appointed: 2019

School type: Coeducational Day & Boarding

Age range of pupils: 13–18

No. of pupils enrolled as at 01/09/2019: 600

Sixth Form: 95

No. of boarders: 50

Fees per annum as at 01/09/2019:

Day: £7,440–£20,190

Full Boarding: £22,950–£33,015

Average class size: 16

Teacher/pupil ratio: 1:16

Maltman's Green School

Our Approach

At Maltman's Green we believe in the pursuit of excellence whilst maintaining a sense of enjoyment. Girls are inspired to do their best inside and outside of the classroom through an exceptional academic curriculum and extensive extra-curricular opportunities. We prepare girls for the modern world through a relevant, adaptable and innovative approach that is supported by a foundation of traditional values. Our girls are given every opportunity to succeed across multiple disciplines, fostering confidence and self-belief, and empowering them for whatever future awaits.

We believe that the emotional, social and physical wellbeing of our girls is paramount. By providing a personalised learning experience in an encouraging and nurturing environment, we ensure our girls feel happy, confident and valued – a perfect foundation from which children can flourish. This ethos has been recognised by the ISI who applauded our "outstanding" pastoral care.

Games and The Arts

Our sports provision is an outstanding feature of the School, with dedicated facilities and daily lessons. All girls enjoy friendly tournaments between houses and within year groups where those with the talent and inclination can progress to squad level to compete locally, regionally or nationally with exceptional results.

Music is a very important part of life at Maltman's Green. Specialist teaching, incredible facilities and lots of choice give our girls plenty of opportunity to explore and showcase their musical talents. Over 100 girls participate in our various choirs and we have nine different musical instrument lessons available as well as a variety of instrumental ensemble groups to join. Drama too has a big part to play in school life where regular performances and workshops give girls a strong sense of confidence and creative expression. Our dedicated performance space with high-quality staging, lighting, costumes and props give our shows a professional feel.

Achievements

Our girls are encouraged to be independent thinkers, to challenge themselves and to always try their best. Maltman's Green provides a firm foundation, preparing girls to face senior school and beyond with confidence, determination and a lifelong love of learning. This is reflected in our impressive 11+ results and a record number of scholarships awarded to Independent Senior Schools. This, combined with our girls' impressive achievements across sport, music and drama affirm our position as one of the foremost prep schools in the country.

Outstanding Characteristics

2018 marked our 100th Anniversary and, since the School was founded in 1918, we have seen numerous developments and upgrades to our facilities, including dedicated subject classrooms, a 6-lane, 25-metre indoor swimming pool, an IT suite, Music wing, Art & DT suite, Science laboratory, a multi-use gymnasium, a state-of-the art theatre space and a dedicated 2-3yr olds day-care centre. We have an in-house Forest School practitioner and place great importance on outdoor learning. Our woodlands, discovery garden and landscaped grounds offer a secluded, peaceful and nurturing environment. This excellent suite of facilities is complemented by our highly committed, well-qualified and experienced body of staff who enable us to provide an outstanding and unique breadth of challenging opportunities for our girls.

MALTMAN'S GREEN
SCHOOL

(Founded 1918)

Maltman's Lane, Gerrards Cross, Buckinghamshire SL9 8RR UK

Tel: 01753 883022

Email: registrar@maltmansgreen.com

Website: www.maltmansgreen.com

Headmistress:
Mrs Joanna Pardon MA, BSc(Hons), PGCE

Appointed: 2005

School type: Girls' Day

Age range of girls: 2–11

No. of pupils enrolled as at 01/09/2019: approx 365

Fees per term as at 01/09/2019:

Day: £1,925–£5,275 per term

Manor House School, Bookham

Founded in 1920 and soon to be celebrating its Centenary Year, Manor House School can be found nestled amidst seventeen acres of gardens, woodland and sports fields in Bookham, Surrey. The School provides an excellent all-rounded approach to education in a happy, friendly and caring school environment. An individual approach to teaching and learning enables each pupil at the School to achieve their personal best, both academically and personally. The aim is to develop happy young women who love coming to school and believe in their abilities to learn and succeed.

There is an extensive co-curricular enrichment programme with up to 50 extra-curricular clubs and activities operating across the school each term. Girls are encouraged to seek out new experiences and try something new.

Manor House achieves excellent Key Stage 2 and GCSE results. For more information on their recent results, visit www.manorhouseschool.org/academic-results/gcse-results.

Seven school values form the foundations of school life and the school motto 'To Love is to Live' was chosen in 1921 by the Bishop of Plymouth. Dr. Masterman, who was a close friend of one of the school's original founders.

The School has recently appointed a new Head of PE and Manor House girls are increasingly enjoying high levels of success in all areas of Sport boasting some future world class soccer players, cyclists, triathletes and tennis stars in its midst.

There is a new and popular Senior Scholarships Programme from Year 7 (application in Year 6) offering Major and Minor Academic Scholarships at 50% and 40% of the basic annual tuition fee and up to 30% for an Art, Drama or Music award. Additionally, a new Year 3 scholarship, for Academic and Music entries, effective in September 2020, will be launched in September 2019 for Year 2 applicants.

The school has been voted in the top ten most beautiful schools in the country in recent years. Facilities include an award-winning Nursery, new Well-Being Centre, Forest School, indoor sports hall which transforms into a seated theatre space for professional productions, outdoor swimming pool, a Tennis Academy, tennis and netball courts and purpose-built science blocks. Girls enjoy many opportunities in the creative and expressive arts, with additional music, singing and drama lessons a popular choice.

The School was shortlisted for an Independent Schools Award in the Creative and Expressive Arts in 2018 and again, in 2019, for Marketing.

The day operates from 7.45am to 6pm to accommodate working and/or busy parents. Fees include a daily hot lunch and afternoon tea is available as an optional extra each day at 4pm.

The School operates a minibus service in the mornings and afternoons and a late bus to the local train station which is serviced by good rail connections. The School bus routes service Ashtead, Dorking, Claygate, Cobham, Epsom, Esher, Fetcham, Hinchley Wood, Guildford, Kingswood, Walton-on-Thames, Weybridge, Wimbledon/Kingston, West Byfleet and surrounding areas.

For more information visit www.manorhouseschool. org.

There are three main Open Morning events per year in October, February and May. For more information, contact: admissions@manorhouseschool.org.

(Founded 1920)

Manor House Lane, Little Bookham, Leatherhead, Surrey KT23 4EN UK

Tel: 01372 457077

Email: admin@manorhouseschool.org

Website: www.manorhouseschool.org

Headteacher: Ms Tracey Fantham BA (Hons) MA NPQH

School type:
Girls' Day School with Co-educational Nursery

Age range of boys: 2–4

Age range of girls: 2–16

No. of pupils enrolled as at 01/09/2018: 300

Fees per annum as at 01/09/2018:

Day: £9,555–£17,955

Average class size: 15-20

Northbourne Park School

Northbourne Park School is a co-educational independent day and boarding school for children between the ages of Nursery and 13. Set in over 100 acres of beautiful park and woodland in rural Kent, the school is within easy reach from central London, Eurostar and Gatwick Airport. Northbourne Park School provides children with a first-class education focussing on the individual needs of every child, inspiring them to succeed across a wide range of learning experiences. We are a school that offers each child freedom and space, together with countless opportunities to grow in confidence and succeed.

Academic

From the Nursery and Pre-Prep right through to the Prep School, Northbourne Park School is an environment where each and every child can flourish. Pupils gain confidence in their learning and through inspirational teaching from dedicated staff, and adapt well to an engaging and stimulating curriculum with a real sense of achievement. We focus on individual needs and consistently achieve academic excellence, with many of our pupils gaining scholarships to prestigious Senior Schools. The school's unique Language Programme helps every child develop foreign languages in an integrated learning environment. The result is a clear advantage when they move on to Senior Schools.

Sport

We are passionate about sport and through an excellent sports programme the pupils develop key skills and learn the importance of teamwork and leadership. There are many opportunities to try a variety of sports from traditional sports to the more diverse such as archery and trampolining.

Creative Arts

We nurture a love for all the Arts. Many pupils learn one or more instruments in our purpose-built Music suite. They have the opportunity to take part in the choir, band, orchestra, string and brass groups performing regularly within the school and in the local area. Other opportunities include LAMDA lessons, regular drama productions and Public Speaking that ensure the pupils are articulate and confident in their performances. Artistic talents are encouraged through a range of media including sculpture, costume design, film-making on iMacs and pottery.

Community

Pupils are provided with a first-class level of pastoral care in a safe and nurturing environment with a real family atmosphere. Our welcoming boarding community provides a home-from-home environment and a continuous boarding service at weekends throughout the term. Boarders enjoy regular excursions and activities, and the accompanied services to London and Paris provide opportunities for weekends at home. Northbourne Park School holds Tier 4 Status for non-European pupils requiring visas under the UK Visa and Immigration Service scheme.

Extra Curricular

We provide the pupils with a fun and extensive programme of afternoon clubs that help develop their interests and skills in hobbies that can endure long into adult life. Love of the outdoors and respect for the environment begins in the Pre-Prep and develops through into the Prep School with fun physical adventures. Whether they are playing in the woods, camping out overnight or following our pioneering Outdoor Education Programme, children love Northbourne Park life.

The children are at the heart of everything we do and it is important to us that they learn with confidence and enjoy each and every day at school. All prospective pupils are welcome and we offer a wide range of scholarships.

Every day is an Open Day at Northbourne Park School, come and visit us!

(Founded 1936)

Betteshanger, Deal, Kent CT14 0NW UK

Tel: 01304 611215/218

Fax: 01304 619020

Email: admissions@northbournepark.com

Website: www.northbournepark.com

Headmaster: Mr Sebastian Rees BA(Hons), PGCE, NPQH

Appointed: September 2015

School type: Coeducational Day & Boarding

Age range of pupils: 3–13

No. of pupils enrolled as at 01/09/2019: 181

Boys: 95 **Girls:** 86

No. of boarders: 53

Fees per annum as at 01/09/2019:

Day: £7,632–£17,007

Weekly Boarding: £21,405

Full Boarding: £24,786

Average class size: 15

Teacher/pupil ratio: 1:9

Seaford College

Seaford College is a coeducational independent day and boarding school for pupils aged 6 to 18, situated amid 400 acres of picturesque parkland in West Sussex. The College, with its excellent amenities and outstanding panoramic views, offers an inspirational environment that nurtures academic excellence, sporting success and creative talent.

The college uses its resources to provide and enhance educational, cultural, spiritual and social opportunities so that students leave school as confident, articulate and well-rounded individuals.

Pupils in the Preparatory School at Seaford College share the superb facilities with the Senior School and enjoy a seamless education from 6 to 18. The Prep School prides itself on its friendly atmosphere.

Boarding is offered to students from the age of 10 and many pupils elect to board in order to take full advantage of the social, sporting and extracurricular activities on offer. The College offers full boarding, weekly and flexible boarding in order to meet the needs of pupils and their parents.

A new boys' boarding house, has individual and twin bedrooms opened in 2011. Girls board in the historic Mansion house. Recent developments include a new music suite, which consists of individual teaching and practice rooms, a computer and keyboard room, a sound-proofed band practice room and outdoor concert arena.

A state-of-the-art maths and science block offers the latest technologies and facilities, while the College has long been recognised as a centre of excellence for art and design. A large exhibition gallery is incorporated into the purpose-built arts faculty.

Seaford College offers outstanding sports facilities, including an all-weather water-based Astroturf hockey pitch, golf course and driving range. Students regularly play at county level. A state-of-the-art sports centre was opened in 2017.

Overseas students are expected to study English as a foreign language and study for the International Language Testing System, which is a requirement for UK university entrance.

Seaford opened an impressive Sixth Form centre in September 2019. They have their own social areas, study areas and cafe. Seaford sees its Sixth Form very much as a transitional stage. They have their own social centre, which has facilities for individual study, a lounge area and several classrooms where subjects such as Economics, Business Studies and Media Studies are taught.

Sixth Form boarders have study bedrooms, as well as their own common room. Students are divided into small tutor groups, but most commonly meet on a 1-to-1 basis with their tutors to discuss aspects of their work and progress.

Many of Seaford's Sixth Formers go on to university or higher education – all are equipped with self-confidence, as well as a passion for life and a willingness to succeed.

Entry to the College is by test and Trial Day and, although intake is non-selective, expectations are high. If your child is talented and enthusiastic, the College offers a range of scholarships at 11+, 13+ and Sixth Form, including Academic Studies, Music, Art and Sport.

The college has its own dedicated learning support unit, catering for pupils with dyslexia, dyscalculia and dyspraxia.

Whatever their chosen path, Seaford College seeks to prepare young people for adult life so that they have the personal skills and confidence to make it a success. The school allows its pupils to achieve their potential and beyond, inspiring personal ambition and success so that personal ambitions are achieved inside and outside the classroom.

(Founded 1884)

Lavington Park, Petworth, West Sussex GU28 0NB UK

Tel: 01798 867392

Fax: 01798 867606

Email: headmasterpa@seaford.org

Website: www.seaford.org

Headmaster: J P Green MA BA

School type: Coeducational Boarding & Day

Age range of pupils: 6–18

No. of pupils enrolled as at 01/09/2019: 842

Boys: 539 **Girls:** 303 **Sixth Form:** 230

No. of boarders: 188

Fees per annum as at 01/09/2019:

Day: £10,725–£22,230

Weekly Boarding: £22,350–£30,120

Full Boarding: £34,380

Average class size: 15-20

Teacher/pupil ratio: 1:9

Sherfield School

Sherfield school is a leading co-educational independent day and boarding school for children from 3 months to 18 years. It offers an outstanding, all-round academic, active and creative environment where children of all ages have the opportunity to thrive and flourish as they experience the excitement and enjoyment of learning.

Set in 76 acres of idyllic parkland in Hampshire, the 12th Century manor house is at the heart of Sherfield school and boasts a wealth of history linked to the local community. Sherfield School lies nestled in beautiful countryside between Reading and Basingstoke. With good public transport links and its own minibus service, Sherfield is set in a safe, semi-rural setting, yet within close proximity to London.

Pupils at Sherfield benefit from rich and diverse learning experiences, both within and outside the classroom. There are a range of high quality facilities including indoor sports hall, drama studio, two synthetic all-weather surfaces, fitness suite, recording studio and extensive woodland. The state of the art boarding house offers full, weekly and flexi boarding options, in a vibrant and engaging environment offered to domestic and international pupils.

The co-curricular provision is extensive, with provision from 7.30am to 6pm for day pupils and evening and weekend activities for boarders. A new enrichment programme enables pupils to develop a wide range of skills for the future, leading to an Ad Vitam Paramus diploma, unique to Sherfield. Outdoor learning is embedded in the ethos of the school, providing opportunities for pupils to learn in different contexts and develop a blend of academic and non-academic experiences.

At Sherfield, we strongly believe in a holistic approach to learning, and one that results in continued development, unleashing the true potential of passionate and creative problem solvers that make up this vibrant school. Children are ready to continue their journey long after leaving Sherfield and contribute to an everchanging global society.

An education at Sherfield is unique, as every pupil receives personalised support and guidance, identifying their individual talents and nurturing their potential. The Sherfield experience enables young people to thrive and flourish as they experience the excitement and enjoyment of learning. Pupils at Sherfield are ambitious, enterprising, inventive, thoughtful, inquisitive and supportive of each other. As a close knit community, they develop the confidence and desire to be the best they can possibly be as they take control of their futures. In an ever changing and evolving society, Sherfield pupils are adept at developing the necessary skills, qualities and experiences to meet the challenges of the future.

At Sherfield great academic results are just a by-product of something even bigger, a brilliant, well-rounded education that identifies and celebrates every child's strengths, and teaches them how to become the best version of themselves. As our Latin motto 'Ad Vitam Paramus' suggests, Sherfield prepares children for life.

South Drive, Sherfield-on-Loddon,
Hook, Hampshire RG27 0HU UK

Tel: 01256 884800

Email: admissions@sherfieldschool.co.uk

Website: www.sherfieldschool.co.uk

Headmaster: Mr Nick Brain BA(Hons), PGCE, MA, NPQH

Appointed: September 2018

School type: Coeducational Day & Boarding

Age range of pupils: 3 months–18 years

No. of pupils enrolled as at 01/09/2019: 385

No. of boarders: 45

Fees per annum as at 01/09/2019:

Day: £10,320–£17,085

Weekly Boarding: £18,960–£26,130

Full Boarding: £22,125–£30,495

Sir William Perkins's School

Building Confidence, Integrity and Excellence

Sir William Perkins's School aims to build confidence, integrity and excellence in a caring, innovative and happy community so that each student leaves with the best possible chance of achieving their full potential and ready to make their mark on the world.

As shown through regular excellent exam results, academic success is certainly a priority, but education is about more than just achieving top grades. SWPS strives to educate the whole person and produce confident and well-rounded young people ready to face any challenges they take on.

Students are encouraged to get involved in the numerous co-curricular activities on offer and to take every opportunity they can to develop their interests and creativity, as well as strong interpersonal, teamwork and leadership skills while also reading into the wider community.

At SWPS, financial and honorary Academic scholarships are offered, and candidates have the opportunity to apply for Arts and Music Scholarships as well as Perkins Bursaries. The additional opportunity to apply for Sport Scholarships is available upon entry to the Sixth Form.

SWPS has convenient transport links and is easily reachable by train or car, as well as offering school coach services to a wide area. The school sits on twelve acres of Surrey greenbelt land and boasts two all-weather pitches as well as a large secluded sports field.

Due to the range of subjects taught, the School features several purpose-built departments with continuously updated contemporary equipment and technologies to stay at the forefront of education. Facilities such as a Sports centre, complete with dedicated IT suite, sprung-floored dance studio and specialist strength and conditioning gallery; the Design Technology department, offering Product Design workshops, 3D printer, laser cutter, nutrition kitchen and textiles workshop; the Art and Design department: with photography darkroom, print-making tools and ceramics kiln; or the Drama, Theatre and Digital Video Editing departments with fully equipped production decks and editing equipment.

Further afield, the SWPS Boat House sits on Laleham reach (a 5 minutes journey from the school) which hosts the SWPS Boat Club. SWPSBC includes over a third of SWPS students and have built upon their success since their founding, and over the last couple of years have qualified and competed in finals at Henley Royal Regatta.

As well as the Senior School, SWPS hosts their Sixth Form. Based out of the 'penthouse' Sixth Form centre complete with wrap-around terrace, SWPS Sixth Formers can enjoy all of the facilities at SWPS while studying their chosen further education curriculum. Students are provided careers and subject guidance before making their A Level selections to ensure they're making the best choice for them, to arm them with the tools they'll need in the future. As well as the academic side, a full and varied enrichment programme is offered building on their leadership skills and breadth of knowledge, as well as ensuring they continue to receive a well-rounded education that's not all about exam results and grades.

The only way to really experience all of this is to visit SWPS. The school offers numerous Information Mornings (for both parents and pupils) where you'll get to meet the warm and friendly staff, get a tour of the fantastic facilities from current students, as well as ask any questions you want answered, all while (most importantly) enjoying the delicious refreshments!

Dates and bookings available on the SWPS website at www.swps.org.uk.

(Founded 1725)

Guildford Road, Chertsey, Surrey KT16 9BN UK

Tel: 01932 574900

Fax: 01932 574901

Email: office@swps.org.uk

Website: www.swps.org.uk

Head: Mr C C Muller

Appointed: September 2014

School type: Girls' Day

Age range of girls: 11–18 years

No. of pupils enrolled as at 01/09/2019: 600

Fees per term as at 01/09/2019:

Day: £5,618 per term

Average class size: Senior School: 24, Sixth Form: 10

Teacher/pupil ratio: 1:8

St Catherine's, Bramley

Founded as both a boarding and day school for girls in 1885, we believe that the successful blending of these two aspects of school life into one happily integrated community is part of what makes St Catherine's. Everyone, boarder or day girl, feels part of the whole. Boarding fosters a strong respect and care for others and gives girls the confidence to develop their independence and their own sense of style.

Academic results place us comfortably within the most prestigious girls' independent boarding schools in the UK. The curriculum is designed to ensure it has breadth and variety. Our very impressive Destinations of Leavers' data is testament to the excellent outcomes at A Level, enabling our Sixth Formers to go to their chosen universities, in the UK and worldwide, and feel well prepared to take on new challenges.

Bramley village is set in the heart of attractive Surrey countryside with acres of opportunity for outside activities. Being under an hour from Heathrow and Gatwick means no long journeys at the start and end of terms. Regular trains to London from nearby Guildford, make a day in the capital city very easy to organise. On Fridays/Sundays a return bus service into SW London runs for weekly boarders.

St Catherine's weekend boarding programme is carefully thought-out and has been singled out on a number of occasions for particular praise; from cultural excursions to theatres, museums and galleries to theme parks, the seaside, Christmas Markets and culturally interesting cities: Bath, Winchester, Windsor, Portsmouth etc. London's cultural and entertainment attractions are just an hour away, whilst the historic county town of Guildford is on our doorstep which offers theatres, a multiplex cinema and shopping opportunities.

The Anniversary Halls sports and performing arts complex houses a multi-function sports hall and professional dance studio as well as a superb auditorium for concerts and theatrical productions. Girls can choose from around 15 different sports which they can commit to and enjoy at their own level. Numerous choirs, Wind Band, String Orchestra, Symphony Orchestra, Concert Band, Jazz Band, and Brass Ensemble represent some of the musical groups girls enjoy. Musicians benefit from superb acoustics and a full orchestra pit. Girls can master skills in stage design, lighting and sound under the guidance of our Technical Director. They enjoy learning ballet, jazz, tap and modern dance in St Catherine's own professional dance school. Art, Chess, Debating, Sailing, Equestrianism, Young Enterprise, community projects, Charity fund-raising and The Duke of Edinburgh's Award Scheme feature in a long list of extra-curricular activities.

St Catherine's is unequivocally for girls. It is a school where girls grow and develop at their own pace, not one dictated by others. The advantages of girls' schools are legion – not only do girls achieve better examination results, they also have more opportunities for leadership. Girls do particularly well in Science, Technology, Engineering, and Mathematics and are more likely to continue these subjects at A level and into university. We educate girls to see themselves as future leaders in society, movers and shakers, politicians, thinkers, creators and industrialists. The St Catherine's Association, comprising thousands of alumnae, parents, and friends of the School gives the girls access to invaluable careers' advice, global networks and opportunities for work experience/internships and sponsorships.

St Catherine's offers an unforgettable education for every girl. A warm welcome awaits you.

(Founded 1885)

Station Road, Bramley, Guildford, Surrey GU5 0DF UK

Tel: 01483 899609

Email: admissions@stcatherines.info

Website: www.stcatherines.info

Headmistress: Alice Phillips

Headmistress of Preparatory School: Miss Naomi Bartholomew

School type: Girls' Day & Boarding

Religious Denomination: Church of England

Age range of girls: 4–18

No. of pupils enrolled as at 01/09/2019:

Prep School: 255

Senior School: 655

Fees per annum as at 01/01/2020:

Day: £9,240–£18,885

Full Boarding: £30,285

Average class size: 18

Teacher/pupil ratio: 1:8/9

St Neot's School

St Neot's, founded in 1888 is a co-educational day school for children aged 2 – 13 years, where the number one priority is to prepare children for successful, happy and purposeful lives. The school is situated on the border of Hampshire and Berkshire and is set in 70 acres of beautiful grounds and woodland.

Staff are inspired to awaken intellectual curiosity and encourage children to challenge themselves in a supportive and happy environment. Each individual is motivated to achieve their full academic potential, to discover their talents and to develop the passion to pursue them. They are given the tools to embrace opportunities, think creatively, develop self-confidence and foster empathy towards others, preparing them both intellectually and emotionally for success in the 21st Century.

We aim to provide the highest standards in teaching and learning within a well rounded educational experience and St Neot's has a very strong record of success in achieving Scholarships and Awards to numerous Senior Schools.

St Neot's is committed to providing a World of Opportunity in every aspect of school life. Stimulating learning environments ensure that engaged pupils work towards the highest academic standards, whilst also enjoying a breadth of experience in sport, music, art, drama and dance.

Forest School, Outdoor Learning and Leadership Days encourage the children to venture outside their comfort zones, to take risks and develop the purpose and drive to make the most of their talents in life beyond school. The St Neot's journey culminates in the Years 7 and 8 leadership programme, which draws together a mix of skills through the Pre Senior Baccalaureate (PSB).

Physical Education is a strength of the school and our sports complex, comprising sports hall, 25m indoor swimming pool, all-weather astro, cricket nets, hard tennis and netball courts, significantly supplement our extensive playing fields. There is also an on-site mountain bike track and a traversing wall. Judo, dance, tennis and swimming are taught by specialist coaches and there are many after school clubs and activities covering a wide range of interests. Holiday Clubs run in all school breaks and offer a wealth of opportunities, both sporting and creative.

St Neot's holds a Gold Artsmark award, giving recognition to our achievements in art, music, drama and dance. A number of plays, concerts and recitals take place throughout the school year for all age groups, either in the school grounds or the Performing Arts Centre.

Open Mornings take place termly and details of these can be found on the school website – www.stneotsprep.co.uk. We would also be delighted to arrange an individual tour and a meeting with the Head. Please contact Admissions on 0118 9739650 – e-mail – admissions@stneotsprep.co.uk

ST NEOT'S
PREPARATORY SCHOOL

(Founded 1888)

St Neot's Road, Eversley, Hampshire RG27 0PN UK

Tel: 0118 9739650

Email: admissions@stneotsprep.co.uk

Website: www.stneotsprep.co.uk

Head of School: Deborah Henderson

Appointed: September 2015

School type: Co-educational Day, Preparatory

Age range of pupils: 2–13 years

No. of pupils enrolled as at 01/09/2019: 306

Fees per annum as at 01/09/2019:

Day: £4,828–£16,224

Average class size: 18

Teacher/pupil ratio: 1:8

St Swithun's School

Compassion, integrity, and a quiet sense of self-confidence
St Swithun's School is a renowned independent day, weekly and full-boarding school for girls set in 45 acres overlooking the Hampshire Downs on the outskirts of Winchester, yet only 50 minutes by train from central London. It offers excellent teaching, sporting and recreational facilities.

The school has a long-standing reputation for academic rigour and success. Girls are prepared for public examinations and higher education in a stimulating environment in which they develop intellectual curiosity, independence of mind and the ability to take responsibility for their own learning. They achieve almost one grade higher at GCSE than their already significant baseline ability would suggest, and approximately half a grade higher at A level. St Swithun's offers a comprehensive careers and higher education support service throughout the school years. Its Oxbridge preparation is part of a whole-school academic enrichment programme providing additional challenge and stimulation.

St Swithun's describes itself as an 'appropriately academic' school, celebrating intellectual curiosity and the life of the mind, but not to the exclusion of all else. They expect their pupils to develop individual passions and through them to acquire a range of skills and characteristics. These characteristics will include a willingness to take risks, to question and to debate, and to persevere in the face of difficulty. In the words of Samuel Beckett: *"Ever tried. Ever failed. No matter. Try again. Fail again. Fail better."*

Whilst achieving academic excellence, girls also have the opportunity to do 'something else'. There is an extensive co-curricular programme of over 100 weekly and 50 weekend activities to choose from.

As well as academic classrooms and science laboratories, there is a magnificent performing arts centre with a 600-seat auditorium, a music school, an art and technology block, a sports hall and a full-size indoor swimming pool. There is an impressive library and ICT facility. The grounds are spacious and encompass sports fields, tennis courts and gardens.

With kindness and tolerance at the heart of its community, St Swithun's provides a civilised and caring environment in which all girls are valued for their individual gifts. By the time a girl leaves she will be courageous, compassionate, committed and self-confident with a love of learning, a moral compass and a sense of humour.

Open days provide an excellent introduction to the school and include a student-led tour, an opportunity to meet the staff and a presentation from the head giving an overview of the unique atmosphere and opportunities at St Swithun's. To book a place on an open day, or to arrange an individual visit at a more convenient time, please contact Kate Cairns on 01962 835703 or email registrar@stswithuns.com. Keep up to date with latest news by visiting www.stswithuns.com, or on Twitter @StSwithunsGirls.

St Swithun's
WINCHESTER

(Founded 1884)

Alresford Road, Winchester, Hampshire SO21 1HA UK

Tel: 01962 835700

Fax: 01962 835779

Email: office@stswithuns.com

Website: www.stswithuns.com

Head of School: Jane Gandee MA(Cantab)

Appointed: 2010

School type: Girls' Boarding & Day

Age range of girls: 11–18

No. of pupils enrolled as at 01/09/2019: 500

Sixth Form: 140

No. of boarders: 225

Fees per annum as at 01/09/2019:

Day: £20,976

Full Boarding: £34,776

St. Andrew's School

St. Andrew's School was founded in 1937 and is a respected and thriving coeducational prep school, of around 300 children. Set in 11 acres of grounds approximately half a mile from Woking town centre, the School seeks to create a nurturing and happy environment of trust and support in which all pupils are encouraged and enabled to develop their skills, talents, interests and potential to the full – intellectually, physically and spiritually.

At St. Andrew's children feel secure and confident and are highly motivated to perform to the best of their ability in all aspects of school life. They are competitive without losing sight of their responsibility to share and they are justifiably proud of their school and their own personal achievements. We also place great emphasis on consideration for others. Courtesy and mutual respect underpins the behaviour policy at St. Andrew's and we aim to teach children about patience, empathy and unselfishness, whilst encouraging them to use their time wisely in an independent and self-reliant manner.

St. Andrew's School prides itself in providing a broad based curriculum that focuses on enabling our children to enjoy a full range of subjects. Educating the whole child is central to our ethos and, whilst academic standards are high, there are also real opportunities to develop their skills in art, music and sport together with a fantastic programme of after school activities. This is supported by specialist teaching facilities for all subjects including science, ICT, music and art. In our latest ISI inspection (Jan 2016) the school was rated 'excellent' in all areas and, with the benefit of individual attention and specialist teachers in all areas of the curriculum, the children are able to reach their full potential in a happy, caring and supportive environment.

When it is time to move on to senior schools at the end of Year 8, the children are prepared for entrance and scholarship exams to a wide range of independent senior schools and the school provides guidance and advice to parents on the senior school choices that best suit each individual child.

St. Andrew's is very proud of its excellent on-site facilities including a brand new theatre, food tech room, classrooms, library and changing rooms together with excellent sports pitches, all weather sports surface, tennis courts, cricket nets and a swimming pool. We are very fortunate to enjoy the benefits of carefully designed school grounds that meet the needs of the children's physical and social development. Main school games are football, hockey, cricket, netball and rounders. Other activities include cross-country running, swimming, tennis and athletics.

Children can be supervised at school from 8am and, through our extensive after-school activities programme for Year 3 and above, until 6-6.30pm most evenings during the week. An after-school club is available from 4.15pm to 6pm (chargeable) for Pre-Prep, Year 3 and Year 4 children.

Children are assessed for entry into Year 2 and above. The school has a number of scholarships and bursaries available.

Don't just take our word for it, come and visit the school to see for yourself! We have three open days, one per term, but you are also welcome to visit the school at other times. Please contact the Headmaster's PA (Registrar) for more information and to arrange a visit. We look forward to welcoming you.

ST. ANDREW'S

SCHOOL · WOKING

(Founded 1937)

Church Hill House, Horsell, Woking, Surrey GU21 4QW UK

Tel: 01483 760943

Email: admin@st-andrews.woking.sch.uk

Website: www.st-andrews.woking.sch.uk

Headmaster: Mr A Perks

Appointed: 2008

School type: Coeducational Day Preparatory

Age range of pupils: 3–13

No. of pupils enrolled as at 01/09/2019: 315

Fees per annum as at 01/09/2019:

Day: £6,555–£15,495

Teacher/pupil ratio: 1:10

Stroud School

Stroud School is an exciting, independent preparatory school where boys and girls aged 3 to 13 years old thrive in its unique family environment. In May 2012, it became the preparatory school for King Edward VI School, Southampton, bringing together two highly successful academic Hampshire independent schools.

Highwood House is a beautiful Victorian building standing in 22 acres of beautiful rural countryside. With only five former Heads since its foundation in 1926, Stroud has always been a school that values the family ethos. It is a school with a strong academic record, fantastic sports facilities and links to strong academic secondary schools. Stroud's curriculum achieves the highest academic standard without compromising the key skills its children need to be successful in the workplace and generally in life.

All pupils learn in a relaxed and fun environment. Inside the classroom, Stroud offers academic excellence with a keen grasp on individualised learning. The breadth of co-curricular activities and after school clubs allows every student to find and feed their passion. The School's values: 'Honesty, Respect, and Happiness' underpins all activities at Stroud and the School sees these values reflected in its pupils' behaviour every day. As a result, Stroud fosters a culture in which the children have a genuine desire to achieve success.

Taking lessons outside of the classroom, with expansive grounds at its disposal, forms an integral part of learning and Stroud has recently been awarded the 'Council for Learning Outside the Classroom' (CLOtC) Silver Award, a national accreditation that has been endorsed by the Department for Education. This award sits perfectly alongside the School's 'Eco Schools Green Flag', which it has maintained for the past six years.

A large body of research shows that outdoor learning improves children's health, increases their enjoyment and engagement with learning and leads to a greater connection with nature. Stroud offers an extended programme of 'Learning Outside the Classroom' for this very reason. From week long overseas trips to day visits to local country parks, to Forest and Beach School. Forest School has been an integrated part of Pre-Prep education at Stroud for many years and the Beach School has been a hugely popular and rewarding addition to the curriculum.

Extra-curricular activities also enhance its core curricular programme. It is the School's responsibility to build the whole child and encourage growth and independence whilst introducing new opportunities, allowing children to explore different roads they wouldn't normally venture down. All clubs at Stroud lead to this; whether it's solving a maths equation in Maths Club, holding a conversation in German Club or perfecting a tackle at rugby practice. Extra clubs help build confidence and the School has seen a huge benefit to pupils' well-being and a greater sense of achievement and resilience.

Stroud regularly uses the pitches at Wellington Sports Ground, the Outward Bound Centre in the Dartmoor National Park, and is looking forward to its pupils performing in the new multi-million pound theatre at King Edward VI School. New development plans allow for new facilities that will keep pace with a 21st Century educational need. What has not changed at Stroud, however, is the opportunities that it provides for its pupils.

To find out more about life at Stroud or to arrange a visit, call 01794 513231 or email registrar@stroud-kes.org.uk.

www.stroud-kes.org.uk

Stroud School, Romsey
King Edward VI Preparatory School

(Founded 1926)

Highwood House, Highwood Lane, Romsey, Hampshire SO51 9ZH UK

Tel: 01794 513231

Email: registrar@stroud-kes.org.uk

Website: www.stroud-kes.org.uk

Head: Mr Joel Worrall

School type: Coeducational Day

Age range of pupils: 3–13

Average class size: 16-18

The Granville School

The Granville School is a non-selective school for girls aged 3-11 and boys from 3-4. It is set in delightful grounds surrounded by woodlands. It is situated in a quiet residential area north of Sevenoaks within a 5 minute walk of Sevenoaks mainline station. While keeping its traditional values, The Granville is committed to providing the children with an educational experience which enhances their learning and delivers results. The current site of the school has been altered, adapted and extended over the years and it boasts specialist teaching areas, large airy and bright classrooms and excellent sporting facilities including an indoor swimming pool. Our specialist facilities include a Science Laboratory, Music and Drama studio, Art and Design studio, Computer Suite and three well stocked libraries. All of our classrooms are equipped with state of the art interactive white boards and many lessons make use of the class sets of iPads that the School has available.

These are complemented with a Sports Hall – also used for assemblies and drama productions, Tennis Courts and Outdoor Play Areas and indoor heated swimming pool. This year the Granville will be opening a Forest School enabling pupils to benefit from the rich educational environment offered by our wooded grounds, supported by specially trained teachers in learning outside the classroom.

There are on-site catering facilities, offering a fresh (nut free), home cooked and nutritional menu every day. The governors are constantly assessing the buildings and land which we own in order to ensure that our pupils enjoy a high quality environment in which they can flourish.

The Granville girls have an excellent record of achievement and accomplish exceptional results at the 11+ stage. Many gain Scholarships and Exhibitions to a variety of independent schools. Girls are prepared for entry into both independent schools and state grammar schools. Staff work in close partnership with parents to help guide them and their daughters through the various different procedures for a wide range of schools. This ensures that the girls fulfil their potential and achieve places in schools where they will thrive. The results achieved by our Year 6 girls speak for themselves:

2019 Offers and Scholarships
16 Kent 11+ Grammar Schools
11 Sevenoaks (3 scholarships – Academic)
10 Walthamstow Hall (4 scholarships 2 Academic, 1 Music, 1 Sport)
7 Woldingham (2 Scholarships 1 Sport, 1 Allround)
5 Caterham (3 scholarships, Music, Drama and Sport)
2 Kent College (1 scholarship Academic)
2 Cobham Hall (1 scholarship Drama)
1 St George's Ascot (1 scholarship Academic)
1 Benenden
1 Beechwood
1 Christ's Hospital
1 Tormead
1 Wycombe Abbey

We would be delighted to meet you and show how the School would benefit your daughter on one of our Open Mornings which are held on the following dates:
Friday 15 November 2019
Friday 31 January 2020
Friday 28 February 2020
Friday 1 May 2020
Friday 5 June 2020

Please contact us on 01732 453039 or email registrar@granvilleschool.org

(Founded 1945)
2 Bradbourne Park Road, Sevenoaks, Kent TN13 3LJ UK
Tel: 01732 453039
Email: secretary@granvilleschool.org
Website: www.granvilleschool.org
Headmistress: Mrs Louise Lawrance B. Prim. Ed. (Hons)
School type: Girls' Day, Coed Nursery
Age range of boys: 3–4
Age range of girls: 3–11

Upton House School

Upton House is a progressive and highly regarded Nursery, Pre-Prep and Prep school educating boys and girls from aged 2 – 11 years. Located in the heart of Windsor, Upton boasts excellent academic standards, high calibre staff and a warm and nurturing environment where children blossom and are prepared with confidence for the very best senior schools. Individual talent is developed, and a progressive curriculum offers a balanced education ensuring children are equipped with vital life skills for the future.

"Our children progress to their next schools as confident, successful and independent individuals. We were delighted to be awarded 'Excellent' in all areas in our recent Independent Schools Inspection Report." Rhian Thornton, Headmistress

Although non-selective, 30% of pupils in the past 3 years have achieved one or more scholarships to their chosen senior school. Details of scholarships and next schools can be found on the website.

Little Upton Pre-Nursery and Nursery is a very special environment where children begin their Upton journey from as young as age 2. Little Upton is open a flexible 48 weeks a year should parents require and benefits from being in a beautiful whole school setting. Staff are highly qualified, experienced practitioners and engage the children in stimulating, challenging and exciting activities that enable them to develop their love of learning within the Early Years Foundation Stage. Specialist subjects include French from 2 years old and Mandarin from 3 years old as well as regular PE and music lessons.

Facilities in the Pre-Prep and Prep departments at Upton House include a newly opened arts block housing music rooms, an art and DT studio and a media room with green screen filming facilities. A modern and vibrant computer suite is equipped for a progressive computing curriculum including coding and robotics. All classrooms are furnished with interactive white boards and iPads are used daily by pupils to support learning throughout the school. Facilities also include a kitchen for Food Technology lessons, a drama and dance studio, gymnasium, two libraries and a delightful Nursery music room. Diverse sporting activities include netball, rugby, hockey, cricket and athletics as well as rowing, judo, fencing and ballet. A wide range of individual musical instrument lessons are also available.

Children at Upton House enjoy breakfast club from 7.45am, healthy meals prepared on site and a wide range of after school extra-curricular activities until 6pm. Holiday clubs are run on site during the holidays.

We would be delighted to welcome you to our next whole school open morning on Wednesday 16th October 9.30am for a chance to see the school in action and meet our staff. To book for open morning, or arrange a personal tour of the school, please register online or contact Miss Rachel Atkins registrar@uptonhouse.org.uk

We look forward to welcoming you!

(Founded 1936)

115 St Leonard's Road, Windsor, Berkshire SL4 3DF UK

Tel: 01753 862610

Email: registrar@uptonhouse.org.uk

Website: www.uptonhouse.org.uk

Head: Mrs Rhian Thornton BA (Hons) NPQH LLE PGCE

Appointed: September 2016

School type: Co-educational Prep, Pre-prep & Nursery

Age range of pupils: 2–11 years

No. of pupils enrolled as at 01/09/2019: 245

Boys: 60 **Girls:** 185

Fees per term as at 01/09/2019:

Day: £3,143–£5,225 per term

Average class size: 16

Vinehall

Overview

Children come first at Vinehall. We believe that in providing a wide range of opportunities we can allow our children to achieve success, instilling in them a strong sense of purpose and self-confidence. Our staff and parents work together to create a warm and thriving community, where kindness and tolerance towards others are leading values. The School's ethos is encapsulated in our motto, 'to do our best for the benefit of others'.

Idyllic Setting: Within an unrivalled setting of 49 acres in the East Sussex countryside, our children enjoy much freedom to explore our expansive grounds, to benefit from the simply outstanding facilities and to discover life for themselves. Our facilities include a full-size sports hall, a 250-seat theatre, an indoor heated pool, an all-weather astro turf, six tennis courts and a nine-hole golf course.

Outstanding education, academic innovation: At Vinehall, we want to foster a love of learning for its own sake by encouraging our children to ask questions and think for themselves. We want our children to develop the necessary skills to work productively as part of a group and to become resilient, resourceful and reflective learners, unafraid of trying something new or making mistakes.

Alongside the established curriculum subjects, pupils at Vinehall have Life Skills lessons; the content of these lessons is broad, ranging from study skills and financial literacy to global citizenship, mental health and well-being. STEM (Science, Technology, Engineering and Maths) is also taught as a curriculum subject from Year 5, providing pupils with the opportunity to 'think like an engineer' and to develop practical problem-solving skills.

After two years of planning, September 2019 will see the introduction of a bespoke programme of study for pupils in Years 7 and 8, focusing on a thematic approach to learning. As part of a rigorous academic curriculum that we hope will give children a more relevant and stimulating learning experience, our focus will be on ensuring that our children have the skills and dispositions that will mean they leave Vinehall as independent, engaged learners.

"All pupils are successful at gaining entry to senior schools of their choice and many regularly gain academic scholarships and music, performing arts and sports awards." ISI inspection Report January 2018

Full, weekly and flexible boarding: Vinehall has a well-established boarding community of boys and girls. We offer full, weekly or flexible boarding open to all. For full boarders there are regular exeat weekend breaks every two or three weeks. Most boarders describe the weekends at Vinehall as the highlight of their week, with a wide range of trips and activities on offer. Weekly boarding is available for those wishing to spend weekends with their families. Flexible boarding is on offer to provide a helping hand to day pupils. The Vinehall Express offers accompanied train travel to and from Charing Cross.

"Boarders say that the boarding experience increases their independence and personal skills in readiness for full-time boarding in their future senior schools." ISI Inspection report January 2018.

"Pupils at Vinehall have excellent attitudes towards learning, nurtured by high expectations and the mutually supportive, inclusive and enabling culture of the school." Independent Schools Inspectorate Report January 2018

(Founded 1938)

Robertsbridge, East Sussex TN32 5JL UK

Tel: 01580 880413

Fax: 01580 882119

Email: admissions@vinehallschool.com

Website: www.vinehallschool.com

Headmaster: Joff Powis

Appointed: September 2017

School type: Co-educational Day & Boarding

Age range of pupils: 2–13

No. of pupils enrolled as at 01/09/2019: 235

Fees per annum as at 01/09/2019:

Day: £9,948–£18,543

Weekly Boarding: £21,765–£22,227

Full Boarding: £23,559–£24,147

Average class size: 14

Teacher/pupil ratio: 1:6.5

Wellington College

Wellington College, founded in 1853, is a vibrant, inspiring and challenging coeducational boarding and day school set in 400 acres of parkland, 40 minutes from Heathrow. Its pupils develop a unique identity inspired by intellectual curiosity, true independence, a generous and far-reaching inclusivity and the courage to be properly and unselfishly individual.

The College is celebrated for its achievements both in and out of the classroom and its sporting, artistic and dramatic provision are second to none. Stellar examination results, outstanding provision across all co-curricular areas, and a raft of national accolades contribute to the College's national and international reputation.

Wellingtonians study GCSEs, followed by the IB Diploma or A-levels and, whichever route they take, results are superb: in 2019, the average A-level outcome was AAA, and the College's incredible IB average of 40.0 yet again made Wellington one of the UK's highest achieving boarding schools to offer the IB Diploma. 60% achieved 40 points or above and seven students achieved the maximum 45 points. On average 9% of the cohort gain places at Oxford or Cambridge every year and, in 2019, 39 students went on to US universities, many to Ivy League institutions.

The College has an outstanding reputation in sport for both boys and girls across 31 different activities in terms of both participation and performance levels. National team success this year came in Cross Country, Equestrian, Fencing, Golf, Gymnastics, Hockey, Rackets, Real Tennis, Rugby, Skiing, Swimming and Shooting. In addition to this team success, a staggering number of individuals gained National or International honours across 18 different sports and even included a World Champion in Real Tennis. 2019 also saw the opening of the College's new sports centre housing two indoor tennis and netball courts and four cricket lanes.

Performing Arts are equally strong. Music and Drama are stunning, with nearly two-thirds of pupils taking lessons in musical instruments or LAMDA. Recent activities have included a trip to Geneva for the Yehudi Menuhin International Violin Competition, a choir tour to Spain, an annual musical (this year was *West Side Story*), contemporary Shakespeare productions and imaginative and inclusive junior plays. Dance enjoys a purpose-designed studio and two spectacular shows each year play to packed houses. The G.W. Annenberg Performing Arts Centre, Wellington's new 900-seater performing arts venue, opened in September 2018. It was no surprise that Wellington was awarded Artsmark Gold by the Arts Council.

Leadership and service to others are central to the College's core values: co-curricular activities include CCF, Duke of Edinburgh, and its outward-facing Global Social Leaders programme, in which pupils learn to create and run innovative social action projects, tackling local and global issues. Over 70 clubs and societies provide some unique opportunities, from WTV (Wellington's own television company) to the pupil-run radio station, DukeBox, which broadcasts 24 hours a day, seven days a week, reaching listeners in 41 countries across the globe. Wellington's family of schools includes its prep school, Eagle House, six schools in China, one in Thailand and sponsored Primary and Secondary Academies in Wiltshire. Wellington was the first HMC school to be accredited as a Teaching School and now partners 18 local state schools. All of this provides pupils and staff with meaningful opportunities for partnership and service within the national and international communities.

Further information including details about Visitors' Days can be found on the website and the Admissions Office can be contacted on +44 (0)1344 444013.

WELLINGTON COLLEGE

(Founded 1853)

Duke's Ride, Crowthorne, Berkshire RG45 7PU UK

Tel: +44 (0)1344 444000

Email: admissions@wellingtoncollege.org.uk

Website: www.wellingtoncollege.org.uk

Master: Mr James Dahl

Appointed: September 2019

Director of IB: Mr Richard Atherton

School type: Coeducational Boarding & Day

Religious Denomination: Church of England

Age range of pupils: 13–18

No. of pupils enrolled as at 01/09/2019: 1060

Boys: 635 **Girls:** 425 **Sixth Form:** 465

No. of boarders: 850

Fees per annum as at 01/09/2019:

Day: £30,375–£34,890

Full Boarding: £41,580

Average class size:
Lower + Middle = 20 Upper School = 12

Teacher/pupil ratio: 1:7

South-West

Exeter Cathedral School

Exeter Cathedral School is a leading independent day and boarding Prep School for girls and boys aged 2 ½ – 13.

Founded in the 12th century as a choir school, ECS now educates approximately 250 pupils. 36 of these are the boy and girl Choristers of Exeter Cathedral. We offer a fully-rounded Prep School education to pupils from a variety of backgrounds and with a range of talents and interests, whether they be sporting, academic, artistic or musical.

We have an enviable location (right in the heart of the city and yet nestled safely in the lee of the Cathedral); small class sizes, allowing us to really know each and every pupil as an individual; a proven track record of securing places and scholarships (academic, art, music, performing arts, sport) to a range of leading senior schools; and a firm commitment to being a forward-thinking Prep School with traditional values. We aim to offer an outstanding Prep School experience and are proud of our commitment to educating the 'whole child': we seek to do this by providing a nurturing, purposeful, exciting and gently-Christian environment in which each child is known as an individual, and in which each child is mindful of, and grateful for, those around them, and aware of the part that they and others play in building their community.

Our purpose-built Nursery building was opened in 2015 and is housed in our Pre-Prep Department in the Cathedral Close. Run by our specialist Head of Nursery and a team of Key Workers, the ECS Nursery offers a first-rate Nursery Education which encourages children to explore, to question, to discover and to build confidence. Children spend 2 years in our Nursery before moving across the playground into our Reception classes.

Our Pre-Prep is housed in a former Canonry in the Cathedral Close. Children transfer across the playground into Reception, before moving up to Year 1 and then Year 2. Our dedicated and highly-qualified staff, led by our Head of Pre-Prep, work with the children (c15 per class) and families to build independence, enquiry, curiosity and a genuine love of learning.

Our Prep School is located right next to the Cathedral. In the younger years, the core subjects are taught by Form Teachers and our creative curriculum is delivered by in-house specialists. Our senior pupils receive Common Entrance preparation from experienced subject specialists. At 13, pupils move on to a range of leading Senior Schools, many with scholarships and awards: in 2019, 81% of Year 8 pupils secured a scholarship at their first-choice senior school.

We expect high standards from our pupils and our staff, and we share a commitment to rigorous academic endeavour; outstanding pastoral care and individualized attention; an exciting range of extra-curricular opportunities; a world-class musical heritage; and to working with families to help each child flourish and thrive. In May 2019, ECS was delighted to receive a glowing Independent School Inspectorate (ISI) report, praising the School for the pupils' academic and personal development. ECS was awarded 'Excellent' in all areas – the best result possible for any independent school in an ISI Inspection.

Above all, we are a school where people matter, and where staff and families work in partnership to help children acquire the right habits for life.

UT VOCE ITA VITA

EXETER CATHEDRAL SCHOOL

Nursery | Pre-Prep | Prep

(Founded 1179)

The Chantry, Palace Gate, Exeter, Devon EX1 1HX UK

Tel: 01392 255298

Email: admissions@exetercs.org

Website: www.exetercathedralschool.co.uk

Headmaster: James Featherstone

Appointed: January 2016

School type: Co-educational Day & Boarding

Age range of pupils: 2½–13

No. of pupils enrolled as at 01/09/2019: 255

Boys: 140 **Girls:** 115

No. of boarders: 10

Fees per annum as at 01/09/2019:

Day: £7,338–£12,234

Full Boarding: £18,768–£19,866

Average class size: 15

Kingsley School

Welcome to Kingsley School

There are many reasons students could fall in love with Kingsley School, an independent co-educational boarding and day school located in Bideford on the banks of the River Torridge in North Devon.

One reason could be location – Kingsley is set in 25 acres of playfields and woodland, surrounded by stunning countryside, and just five minutes from popular surfing beaches. And another reason could be the school's strong academic tradition – at Kingsley every sixth form student typically goes on to university, including top-tier higher education institutes like Oxford and Cambridge.

But ultimately our students rate the opportunity to find their place, the exceptional support they receive and the welcome as the prime reasons they just can't see themselves going anywhere else but Kingsley.

Kingsley students are happily celebrating their exceptional A-Level and BTEC Summer 2019 results. 51% of all grades awarded are A* and A at Kingsley this year, putting Kingsley's results at double the 25.5% national average for achievement at this level. The average UCAS score per pupil was 148 (equivalent to more than 3A grades at A level).

Kingsley School is an inclusive day and boarding school where every child is important and is treated with dignity and respect. As a relatively small school of around 400 boys and girls, Kingsley's atmosphere is like that of a large family where everybody knows each other well.

The school's philosophy encourages personal qualities such as courage, generosity, honesty, imagination, tolerance and kindness. In addition, we develop the students' wider interests and skills in sport, music, art, and drama. Kingsley also has a national reputation for its Learning Development Centre which provides additional support for students with moderate learning needs. Overall, a Kingsley education develops the individual character and talents of each and every student both inside and outside the classroom.

Becoming part of the family: The boarding houses at Kingsley help form part of the family atmosphere at the school. Students live in three comfortable and well-equipped houses in the school's grounds; two for boys and one for girls. Each house has 30-40 students who are supervised by two teachers and their families who live in the houses as well.

Sport and Clubs: Sport includes traditional sports plus judo, handball and gymnastics squads competing at a National level. As part of the National Theatre Connections programme, the school drama cast performed at the Theatre Royal, Plymouth and the National Theatre, London this year. Popular extra-curricular clubs include the Duke of Edinburgh's Award Scheme, orchestra, computing, art, film making, choir and surfing.

Transport: we run an accompanied coach service to and from Heathrow Airport and Bristol Airport at the beginning and end of each term. Weekly boarding options with transport to London and the South East.

Headmaster Pete Last said: "As a parent, I know that choosing the right school can be daunting, but Kingsley is a place which really does recognise that each child has individual needs, with their own set of skills and talents that deserve to be developed. Smaller, more attentive classes with caring and supportive teachers gives the school a familial feel. I am proud of each and every student, their progress, support of one another and their outstanding personal achievements."

Do follow us on social media

Facebook: Kingsley School Bideford
Instagram: Kingsley School
Twitter: @KSBideford
YouTube: Kingsley School Bideford
www.kingsleyschoolbideford.co.uk

(Founded 1884)

Northdown Road, Bideford, Devon EX39 3LY UK

Tel: 01237 426200

Fax: 01237 425981

Email: admissions@kingsleyschoolbideford.co.uk

Website: www.kingsleyschoolbideford.co.uk

Headmaster: Mr Pete Last

Appointed: January 2017

Head of the Prep School: Mr Andrew Trythall

School type: Coeducational Day & Boarding

Age range of pupils: 0–18

No. of pupils enrolled as at 01/09/2018: 395

No. of boarders: 100

Fees per term as at 01/09/2019:

Day: from £2,020 per term

Weekly Boarding: from £5,695 per term

Full Boarding: from £7,685 per term

Average class size: 14

Teacher/pupil ratio: 1:9

West Midlands

Denstone College

Achievement, confidence and happiness are central to the College philosophy, with pupils always encouraged to aim high and reach their full potential.

We offer a rounded education, where proper emphasis is placed on academic achievement, but where a wide range of other opportunities ensures that every individual finds and develops his or her own talents. Denstonians emerge with a degree of self-esteem and confidence that is only possible after years of opportunity and challenge, both academic and extracurricular. The College site of over 100 acres is located in magnificent countryside, yet is well served by road, rail and air. We welcome parents and their children to visit us and experience a taste of the Denstone education.

Three-school structure

At the heart of our approach to educating young people is the 'three-school structure'. Unusual in traditional independent schools, this is a structure that allows our three different age groups to live, work and socialise in their own unique areas. It is based on the fact that 18-year-olds and the under-13s have very different needs. The traditional house system runs happily alongside this structure, and all its best features remain. House loyalty and spirit are as strong as ever in competitions, sport, music and drama.

Facilities

Over the past decade the College has benefited from a £10m development programme, with a new Music School and additional classrooms opened in September 2010. Further extensive classroom facilities, and the Adamson's sports complex, were completed and opened in June 2012. Then in September 2013, the doors opened to a beautiful library which is at the heart of teaching and learning at Denstone. In addition, work was completed in June 2017 on a brand new classroom block to house Maths and Modern Foreign Languages, which has the latest in teaching technology. The day and boarding accommodation undergoes regular improvement and redecoration with an extension to girls boarding with beautiful en suite facilities eighteen months ago. Impressive language and IT teaching facilities have been developed, and there have been many general classroom refurbishments to a high standard. A large sports hall allows for a wide range of minority and unusual sports. Other recent improvements include an additional Astroturf, and all weather cricket facilities.

Academic focus

Pupils are given every support and opportunity to realise their full academic potential, with progress being monitored closely through a highly developed system of tutors, reports and grade sheets. We provide a purposeful environment with skilled teachers, where high standards are expected and pupil/teacher ratios are very favourable.

Opportunities

A Denstone education gives students more choices and greater opportunities to expand their horizons. Frequent trips are a feature of our calendar, and a programme of more than 40 activities and an excellent record in the Duke of Edinburgh's Award Scheme also help to ensure that Denstonians are always busy. Our sporting history is outstanding, with College teams regularly successful at regional or national levels. We have a modern sports hall, swimming pool, two all-weather AstroTurfs, fives courts and an English Golf Union (EGU)-affiliated golf course.

"Being a Denstonian gives you more chances in life… there's no limit to what you can do." Sixth-former

(Founded 1868)
Uttoxeter, Staffordshire ST14 5HN UK
Tel: 01889 590484
Fax: 01889 590744
Email: admissions@denstonecollege.net
Website: www.denstonecollege.org
Headmaster: Mr Miles Norris MA (Oxon)
Appointed: September 2018
School type: Coeducational Boarding & Day
Age range of pupils: 11–18
No. of pupils enrolled as at 01/09/2019: 614
Boys: 369 *Girls:* 245 *Sixth Form:* 198
No. of boarders: 171
Fees per annum as at 01/09/2019:
Day: £13,596–£16,434
Weekly Boarding: £19,698–£22,152
Full Boarding: £19,698–£28,617
Average class size: Less than 20
Teacher/pupil ratio: 1:11

Ellesmere College

Founded in 1884, Ellesmere is a co-educational boarding and day school which offers students between the ages of seven and 18 a platform for academic success and personal development. A wide ranging academic curriculum and extensive activities programme allows each student the opportunity to advance in a range of disciplines, whether in the Arts, Music, Drama, Sport, or to develop leadership and entrepreneurial skills. Ellesmere College treats every pupil as an individual and where success is 'doing the very best you can'; a philosophy that all parents, pupils and staff recognise and support wholeheartedly.

The Lower School (7-13) provides an environment which focuses on individual needs, and helps children grow into happy, secure young people, with the confidence to tackle new challenges and understand the world around them.

Students joining the Middle School (13-16) enjoy a stimulating environment with an extensive academic programme and an even wider range of curricular and co-curricular opportunities. Ellesmere students consistently celebrate excellent GCSE results – where over a third of all grades were in the top A*/A, and more than half of all grades awarded were in the A*/B.

Music is a key element of Ellesmere life and there is something for everyone – from the Chapel Choir to National Finalists in the Barnardo's Choir of the Year Competition and Songs of Praise Young Choir of the Year 2018. The standard of drama is also very high and Ellesmere is the only UK independent school to hold the Arts Council's Arts Mark Platinum Award.

For sports enthusiasts, Ellesmere is one of only nine schools in the world to be an accredited Athlete Friendly Education Centre (AFEC) by the World Academy of Sport (WAoS), which provides greater flexibility to students allowing them to balance their studies with heavy training and competition schedules. With the nationally renowned Titans Swimming team, 7 sporting academies, and incredible state of the art facilities, pupils can train in every Olympic discipline.

Following GCSEs, students have a choice of A-levels, BTEC or the International Baccalaureate Diploma. The College takes the preparation of students for Oxbridge and the USA very seriously and the academic enrichment programme offers extension activities in all subjects. With 82 per cent of applications gaining offers from the top 50 Universities in the world and an exclusive careers partnership programme which finds opportunities for sixth form pupils to experience the real world; preparation for life is central to the development of the individual.

What makes a successful school? A committed leadership team, an excellent set of professional teachers, a globally recognised set of qualifications and a broad approach to pupil development via an expansive academic and co-curricular programme.

At Ellesmere we believe that developing the whole pupil is much more than just passing examinations; a philosophy which is paramount to the continued success of nurturing our students.

Come and experience this unique environment for yourself by booking a visit or join us on one of our Open Days throughout the year – visit our website for more details: www.ellesmere.com

 Ellesmere

(Founded 1884)

Ellesmere, Shropshire SY12 9AB UK

Tel: 01691 622321

Fax: 01691 623286

Email: registrar@ellesmere.com

Website: www.ellesmere.com

Head of School: Mr Brendan Wignall MA, FRSA, MCMI

School type: Coeducational Day & Boarding

Age range of pupils: 7–18

No. of pupils enrolled as at 01/09/2019: 550

Fees per term as at 01/09/2019:

Day: £6,330 per term

Weekly Boarding: £8,217 per term

Full Boarding: £11,511 per term

Teacher/pupil ratio: 1:8

Hallfield School

Happy. Secure. Purposeful.

Hallfield School is a select-entry independent school in Edgbaston, Birmingham, educating children from the age of three months to eleven years.

We have a superb academic track record and a focus on supporting our pupils to become confident, well-rounded individuals equipped in every way to succeed. Each of our five hundred and fifty pupils matter to us as individuals.

We are proud of our outstanding reputation for preparing children for entry into the highly selective Local Authority Grammar and Independent schools across the West Midlands. From our hugely successful chess players to our athletics, cricket and rugby teams, we aim to enhance every aspect of our pupils' lives.

Celebrating our One-hundred-and-fortieth year in 2019, Hallfield School displays its strength today with a long and successful history; this is a testament to our heritage – but also to how the school has constantly changed to ensure its standards remain amongst the highest in the independent sector.

Our distinguished past is matched by our ambitions for the future, to offer the pupils who come here a world-class prep school education. Our pupils enjoy unrivalled academic success due to our excellent teaching environment, partnership with the child and parents and small class sizes.

However, a Hallfield education is so much more besides academic excellence. Here at Hallfield we nurture the whole child and encourage them to become the very best versions of themselves. Our nurturing approach enables this success and powers the co-curricular activities such as chess, drama, music and languages that we consider central to life at Hallfield. This is crucial to helping our pupils become confident, rounded individuals equipped for the next chapter of their education. We enable our pupils to give more than they ever imagined possible.

Our job at Hallfield is to inspire ambition in our children, balanced with the humility, respect and consideration that is interwoven into our ethos as a school with a Christian foundation. We aim to create global citizens, aware of their own responsibilities and impact on the world in which we all live. We are a world-class school on your doorstep.

Our philosophy is that happy children are successful children. We are committed to Hallfield remaining the leading preparatory school in the Midlands, and one of the more prominent nationwide, by continuing in the future to be committed to our pupils' welfare and well-being. Creating secure, self-reliant learners is our principal aim.

We also believe in adding value. Your child's attainment will be immeasurably enhanced by their time at Hallfield, even our most reluctant learners achieve above national-average results. In addition, they will be encouraged to develop personally, acquiring the "soft" study and social skills that will power their achievements in the future and their community.

The future at Hallfield is extremely bright and that's thanks to the wonderful children who come to be part of our exciting and supportive community. Here's to sharing that future together.

If you would like to visit Hallfield School, our open mornings provide a snapshot of how we work at Hallfield School – and offer parents the opportunity to meet staff, as well as take a guided tour around our twenty-acre site. We look forward very much to meeting you in the not too distant future. You will be assured of a very warm welcome here at Hallfield School.

Please come and visit us on our Open Mornings:
Tuesday, November 5 – 8.30am–10.30am
Tuesday, November 19 – 8.30am–10.30am

HALLFIELD SCHOOL

(Founded 1879)

Church Road, Edgbaston, Birmingham, West Midlands B15 3SJ UK

Tel: 0121 454 1496

Fax: 0121 454 9182

Email: office@hallfieldschool.co.uk

Website: www.hallfieldschool.co.uk

Headmaster: Mr Keith Morrow

Appointed: September 2012

School type: Coeducational Day

Age range of pupils: 3 months–13

Average class size: 18

Teacher/pupil ratio: 1:6.5

Lucton School

Small classes, talented and committed teachers, a friendly atmosphere and a wonderful rural location combine to provide an outstanding, all-round educational experience at Lucton.

An Oxford University admissions tutor commented that the typical thing about Lucton students is that there is no typical student – they are very much individuals! What they do have in common is that they leave us confident in their abilities and strengths, ready to embrace opportunities and play their part.

They also achieve excellent results at A-level and GCSE and secure an impressive range of university places. The School is justly proud of its remarkable added-value scores and its ability to draw out the full potential of every individual.

A safe and secure location

Founded in 1708, the School is set in a safe, rural location in 55 acres of beautiful Herefordshire countryside. There is a good mix of day pupils, weekly boarders and full boarders. Many team and individual sports are offered and boarders enjoy a wealth of weekend activities – sporting, cultural, social and just good fun – all included in the fees. Senior boarders have individual rooms – although some younger ones prefer to share – and pastoral care at Lucton is second to none. Overseas students may use the School's free airport buses at the beginning and end of term.

Strong academic record

Offering a wide range of GCSE and A-level subjects, Lucton has a strong academic record and an established tradition of getting the best possible results from each pupil. We accept mixed ability students, yet over the last two years A-level results have averaged over 80% A-C. In 2019 the A-level results were 30% A* to A grades with nearly 60%

A* to B and all leavers gained places at their first choice universities.

A unique feature is Lucton's 'Access to A-level' course, which also serves as a one-year GCSE or Pre-IB course, designed to provide overseas students with a grounding in a range of subjects and incorporating accelerated learning of English – ultimately preparing them for entry to the best courses at the best universities.

Excellent facilities

Facilities include junior and senior libraries, science laboratories, ICT rooms, a design and technology workshop, sports hall, tennis courts, indoor swimming pool, many games fields and Equestrian Centre. Senior students enjoy their own sixth-form centre, including library, IT suite, comfortable common room and quiet study area.

Admission can take place at any time of year by interview and assessment. The School offers discounts to Forces families.

In a previous boarding inspection, Lucton School was awarded 'Outstanding' for Equality and Diversity, an excellent reflection of how well boarders from all backgrounds are made welcome at Lucton. In the latest whole school inspection, along with many other categories, boarding was rated as 'Excellent'.

(Founded 1708)

Lucton, Herefordshire HR6 9PN UK

Tel: 01568 782000

Email: admissions@luctonschool.org

Website: www.luctonschool.org

Headmistress: Mrs Gill Thorne MA

Appointed: 2003

School type: Coeducational Day & Boarding

Religious Denomination: Christian

Age range of pupils: 1–18

No. of pupils enrolled as at 01/09/2019: 350

No. of boarders: 80

Fees per term as at 01/09/2019:

Day: £2,450–£4,750 per term

Weekly Boarding: £7,800–£9,200 per term

Full Boarding: £9,295–£11,260 per term

Teacher/pupil ratio: 1:8

Malvern St James Girls' School

"…full of girls who are going to change the world". Good Schools Guide

MSJ is a leading independent school for girls set at the foot of the majestic Malvern Hills. What helps to make us distinct and refreshing, is our recognition and active support for the individual talents, interests and passions of girls, and the liberating and inclusive ethos the school embraces.

We nurture a freedom of spirit, respect for others and support of every member of our school community. Our staff are innovative and passionate about their work and constantly evolve new ways to inspire learning and exploration of their subjects, often beyond the curriculum. We actively encourage debate and open discussion. We explore the world around us, at home and across the globe. We believe in maintaining truth and transparency as a school community.

The Prep Department, Senior School and dedicated Sixth Form Centre sit together on the main school site, whilst Boarding houses are a stone's throw away, and a short walk from the town of Great Malvern where girls can go to shop, have coffee, or to see a film or play as they grow older and more independent. As well as full or weekly boarding, girls can flexi-board one, two or three nights per week.

MSJ is a refreshing and inspiring school for girls. A school that helps girls to truly develop their thinking skills, to explore who they are and to develop the courage and self-belief to go out into the world and be true to who they are.

Location

The School benefits from being positioned in the small but culturally lively town of Great Malvern, on direct rail routes from London Paddington and Birmingham. The M5 and M50 are nearby and London, Birmingham, Bristol and Manchester airports are within easy reach. Great Malvern Railway Station is directly opposite the school and just a 30-second walk from the Main Building.

Curriculum

MSJ doesn't produce a 'type' of girl. We achieve excellent academic results but we are not an exam factory. Our ethos is one of inclusion and respect. Girls can pursue their passions and interests in the field of their choice – all routes are equal. It may be horse riding, engineering, politics, the environment or climbing. We recognise the importance of allowing each individual to grow and flourish. We find ways to support girls to achieve their passions.

The curriculum also supports pupils who need special provision including very able pupils, and those for whom English is an additional language. Those who have specific areas of expertise have adapted timetables to allow them to focus on their specialism, giving time to practise and train, with personalised coaching and mentoring sessions.

Our 'Russell Up' provides preparation for the most competitive UK and international universities and career pathways.

Scholarships

Academic, Drama, Music, Art, Riding, Flexi-Boarding, Technology and Sport Scholarships are available and our Founders' Awards bursary programme enables outstanding girls applying for Sixth Form to access the excellent educational opportunities offered at MSJ. We also offer generous bursaries.

Armed Forces families pay only 10% of the Malvern St James Girls' School boarding fees – as long as they are eligible for the Continuity of Education Allowance and can provide evidence of this.

MALVERN ST JAMES
Girls' School

(Founded 1893)

15 Avenue Road, Great Malvern, Worcestershire WR14 3BA UK

Tel: 01684 892288

Fax: 01684 566204

Email: admissions@malvernstjames.co.uk

Website: www.malvernstjames.co.uk

Headteacher: Mrs Olivera Raraty BA PGCE

Appointed: 2016

School type: Girls' Boarding & Day

Age range of girls: 4–18

No. of pupils enrolled as at 01/09/2019: 410

No. of boarders: 200

Fees per annum as at 01/09/2019:

Day: £7,170–£19,875

Weekly Boarding: £20,520–£34,620

Full Boarding: £22,905–£38,190

Teacher/pupil ratio: 1:8

Mander Portman Woodward – Birmingham

MPW Birmingham was founded in 1980 with the goal of ensuring that students experience an education based on the Oxford and Cambridge tutorial system. This means that lessons are more relaxed and informal than a typical school, but are also academically stimulating and demanding. With fewer than ten students in any class, lessons are intensive but rewarding with plenty of opportunity for individual attention and personalised teaching.

MPW Birmingham guides students in their learning by encouraging them to focus on our model of success: aspiration, attitude, attendance, application and achievement. We help students obtain results that all too often they never thought were possible. With almost 30 subjects to choose from at A level and many at GCSE, MPW Birmingham provides a breadth of study opportunity that is unique for a small college. MPW helps students demystify the examination process and develop both the technical skills and academic knowledge needed to perform well under timed conditions. We offer all of our students the opportunity to sit weekly assessments enabling students to perfect examination technique.

We run a university support programme that values every student in equal measure regardless of aspiration; we treat all students as though they are elite. We prepare students for a range of courses including medicine, dentistry and Oxbridge and ensure that they are well equipped to cope with the demands of university life.

Students benefit from outstanding pastoral care with each student being allocated a Personal Tutor. This builds upon our core values of diligence, respect, tolerance and care. We expect our students to work hard but we also expect to provide more support to our students than they would receive at other schools. Our culture is one based on high expectations but one that is both nurturing and unpretentious. We run a non-compulsory enrichment programme in which many students participate, developing both sporting and cultural interests. There is no glass ceiling in MPW Birmingham and we strive to enable all students to reach their potential and use their talents without inhibition.

Our mission is to be one of the leading colleges of its type within the country, enabling students to develop confidence, maturity, knowledge and skills, turning academic aspirations into reality. MPW helps build the character of students enabling them to develop good self-discipline regarding work, intellectual curiosity and a sense of duty regarding community. Our best ambassadors are our students and we are rightly proud of what they achieve with us and what they go on to achieve afterwards. We change lives for the better and help bring about progress and success. Irrespective of where a student is starting from, MPW helps young people achieve special things.

Mander Portman Woodward

(Founded 1980)

17-18 Greenfield Crescent, Edgbaston, Birmingham, West Midlands B15 3AU UK

Tel: 0121 454 9637

Fax: 0121 454 6433

Email: birmingham@mpw.ac.uk

Website: www.mpw.ac.uk

Principal: Mr Mark Shingleton

School type: Coeducational Day

Age range of pupils: 14–19

Average class size: 8

Shrewsbury School

Located on a beautiful 110-acre site, perched above the historic town of Shrewsbury and the banks of the River Severn, Shrewsbury School has a world-class reputation for all-round excellence. Fully co-educational, with a seven-day boarding heartbeat and an integral day community, we deliver a dynamic education that develops the abilities and enthusiasms of every individual girl and boy.

School should be serious fun. Learning and enjoyment go hand in hand: in the classroom, through a vibrant co-curricular programme and in the communal life of the School. At Shrewsbury, we aim to provide the most diverse, challenging and supportive environment in which all our children can thrive and exceed their own expectations.

A good education opens doors. This means getting the best possible examination results and qualifications. Academic excellence is achieved through a wide-ranging curriculum that uncovers and encourages a genuine love of learning, alongside inspirational teaching that challenges each pupil to strive for her or his personal best.

Our 2019 leavers achieved another excellent set of A Level results, with 73% of the exams awarded at the top A*, A or B grades, and more than 18% of all exams gaining the top A* grade. Our pupils also celebrated a strong set of GCSE results, with 65% of the exams awarded an A* or A grade and 40% of results achieving the top A* grade.

However, examination certificates are just one product of education. Many skills, values and aptitudes do not come with a piece of paper, but they are nonetheless vital for happy and purposeful living. A great education nurtures character; and it lasts a lifetime.

We want all our pupils to enjoy their life beyond the classroom and Shrewsbury has a long-standing reputation for musical, dramatic and sporting excellence. We compete internationally in cricket and rowing and, on a national level, we are one of the strongest schools for football, cross-country and fives. Facilities and coaching are first-rate across each of these sports, as well as a host of others, including rugby, hockey, netball, lacrosse, fencing, swimming and tennis.

The breadth and quality of drama and music-making at Shrewsbury is remarkable. Shrewsbury School plays and musicals have regularly drawn praise at the Edinburgh Fringe Festival and each year our pupils have the opportunity to perform at prestigious venues, such as London's Cadogan Hall and Birmingham Town Hall. A number of our pupils win places at top music colleges year-on-year.

Shrewsbury pupils also enjoy an extraordinary variety of clubs, societies and co-curricular activities, many of which take place on a dedicated weekly basis. Surrounded by glorious unspoilt countryside, the School makes the most of its close proximity to the Shropshire hills and Snowdonia.

The Shrewsbury School motto gets to the heart of our vision: *Intus Si Recte Ne Labora* – 'if all is right within, trouble not'. Ours is not a superficial, skin-deep education but one that seeks to develop the whole person. If our values are true, and we live by them with honesty and conviction; if we look beyond the surface of things to question and champion independence of mind; and if we learn deeply in order to lead lives of meaning, generosity and purpose, then we will see the full fruits of a Shrewsbury education.

Shrewsbury School

(Founded 1552)

The Schools, Shrewsbury, Shropshire SY3 7BA UK

Tel: 01743 280552

Fax: 01743 243107

Email: admissions@shrewsbury.org.uk

Website: www.shrewsbury.org.uk

Headmaster: Mr. Leo Winkley

Appointed: 2018

School type: Coeducational Day & Boarding

Religious Denomination: Anglican

Age range of pupils: 13–18

No. of pupils enrolled as at 01/09/2019: 807

Boys: 544 **Girls:** 263

No. of boarders: 612

Fees per annum as at 01/09/2019:

Day: £25,770

Full Boarding: £37,560

Average class size: GCSE: 18; A level: 8

Teacher/pupil ratio: 1:9

Tettenhall College

With a history dating back to 1863, Tettenhall College has played a significant role in educating young people from across the region and today provides a stimulating learning environment for boys and girls, boarders and day pupils, from the age of 2-18.

The emphasis at Tettenhall College is on a personalised education that develops the whole person, both in and beyond the classroom with exceptional extra-curricular opportunities that complement the rigorous academic environment. The School ensures that everyone will find their niche and grow in confidence.

Life skills and preparation for life beyond school are important elements of the educational offering here and this permeates from Nursery through to Sixth Form. In the Preparatory School, the unique enrichment programme aims to deepen and widen the experiences of pupils with subjects ranging from Latin to Mandarin, and Philosophy to Engineering. English, reading and mathematics remain at the heart of the curriculum and are taught daily. Science classes, taught in the modern laboratory, now include an engineering focus.

Academic success is a major focus across the whole School, with consistently high GCSE and A Level grades above national averages. In 2019, 25% of pupils achieved A*, A or B in all of their subjects, with the majority of our pupils gaining places at their first choice of university, including some of the top institutions in the country.

However, for a non-selective school, an equally important measure of success is 'value-added', which compares pupils' predicted grades at entry to the School with actual grades achieved at 16. On this measure, Tettenhall College is also above many of the highly selective state and independent schools in the country. Our small class sizes ensure that the most able pupils receive the necessary stretch to flourish whilst those requiring support are given this – at no extra cost.

Recent developments have transformed many areas of the School site, with major new facilities now on offer. Multi-purpose sports pitches, squash courts and study facilities plus a new Sixth Form Centre and a vibrant Library all add to the new face of Tettenhall College in 2019.

The School has come a long way since its foundation over 150 years ago, yet the traditional values and the wonderful historic setting remain the same. Please contact our Registrar and come and take a closer look. admissions@tettcoll.co.uk or 01902 751119. www.tettenhallcollege.co.uk

Tettenhall College

AN INDEPENDENT SCHOOL FOR AGES 2 TO 18

(Founded 1863)

Wood Road, Tettenhall, Wolverhampton, West Midlands WV6 8QX UK

Tel: 01902 751119

Email: admissions@tettcoll.co.uk

Website: www.tettenhallcollege.co.uk

Headteacher: Mr David Williams (to be replaced by Mr Christopher McAllister, January 2020)

Appointed: January 2014

School type: Coeducational Day & Boarding

Age range of pupils: 2–18

No. of pupils enrolled as at 01/09/2019: 420

Fees per term as at 01/09/2019:

Full Boarding: £10,279–£11,166 per term

Nursery (age 2+): £768 – £2,760 per term

Pre-School: £670 – £2,350 per term

Reception – Year 13: £1,374 – £4,858 per term

Average class size: 16

Teacher/pupil ratio: 1:10

The Royal School Wolverhampton

The building works continue! After opening as a Free school/ State Boarding School in 2016, and following the ambitious and successful growth programme in pupil numbers over the past three years, The Royal School's exciting building programme is now well under way to develop first class teaching facilities for pupils from five to 19. Phase one of the school's development plan saw a new Sixth Form Centre and refurbished classrooms. Phase two starts in the summer with new labs and more classrooms coming on line.

At the centre of all that we do is our inclusive community where students study, play and live together harmoniously. The Royal is a small, cohesive community with a friendly atmosphere for both day pupils and boarders alike. Our strong academic tradition is based upon individual attention and encouragement, as well as excellent pastoral care founded on respect, tolerance and understanding of others. Students achieve their full academic potential, whilst a wide range of extended-day activities is available to develop character and leadership. We prepare pupils for Oxbridge and other top universities while also catering to pupils of all abilities. The School regularly achieves high standards in both A-Level and G.C.S.E. results, particularly in STEM subjects of mathematics and the sciences. The Royal combines traditional values with a modern outlook and a 'real-world' attitude. At the Royal, education is about developing the whole individual.

Developing the 'whole person' in sport, drama, music and adventurous activity, young people at The Royal are also better placed to make the best of their opportunities to become well-rounded individuals with confidence and empathy for those around them.

The Royal School
Wolverhampton

Penn Road, Wolverhampton, West Midlands WV3 0EG UK

Tel: +44 (0)1902 341230

Email: info@theroyal.school

Website: www.theroyalschool.co.uk

Head of School: Mark Heywood

School type: Co-educational Day & Boarding

Age range of pupils: 4–19

Boarding: 11–19

No. of pupils enrolled as at 01/09/2019: 1328

Fees per annum as at 01/09/2019:

Full Boarding: £12,300

Average class size: 25

West House School

Situated in the leafy oasis of the Calthorpe Estate, West House School has occupied the same site since its foundation in 1895. Since that time, the school has evolved significantly to become an independent preparatory school for boys aged 4-11 years, with a co-educational Early Years Department offering care and education for children aged from 12 months. West House is a member of The Independent Association of Preparatory Schools and, as such, upholds the requirement to provide a 'world class education'.

Set within five acres of beautiful grounds, less than two miles from Birmingham city centre, the school lies at the heart of a thriving community. Pupils of all ages benefit from two all-weather playing surfaces, a nature reserve and the multi-functional Duce Hall, providing indoor sporting and theatrical facilities. The school is also surrounded by many outstanding cultural and recreational amenities which enrich the lives of all pupils and allow them to explore and extend their talents in numerous curricular and extra-curricular pursuits.

West House is a non-denominational school, guided by Christian principles. It is divided into three departments – Prep (Years 3-6), Pre-Prep (Years 1 & 2) and the Early Years Foundation Stage (Nursery – Reception). From their earliest years, children are encouraged to adopt the core values of the school which are actively promoted throughout the working day and frequently form the focus of assemblies and PSHE lessons.

The school continues to boast a unique family atmosphere of which founding Headmaster, Arthur Perrott Cary Field, would have been proud. In the spirit of combining the best of its traditions with an education that prepares pupils for life in the middle part of the twenty first century, it remains determined to be at the forefront of innovation.

This is reflected in the delivery of an ambitious curriculum which complements academic rigour with significant opportunities for pupils to explore personal interests in sport, art, music and drama.

Employing 45 full-time and part-time academic staff, many of whom are subject specialists, West House has grown considerably during the last five years to accommodate approximately 330 pupils, with 130 attending the EYFS Department.

Pupils are prepared for a wide range of senior schools, and standards at 11+ are consistently high, with most Year 6 boys transferring to local grammar schools, King Edward's School, Birmingham and Solihull School. A number of pupils are awarded academic and sporting scholarships and the school also enjoys outstanding success in academic challenges, quizzes and competitions at regional and national level.

Further details about the school can be found at www.westhouseprep.com

(Founded 1895)

24 St James's Road, Edgbaston, Birmingham, West Midlands B15 2NX UK

Tel: 0121 440 4097

Fax: 0121 440 5839

Email: secretary@westhouseprep.com

Website: www.westhouseprep.com

Headmaster:
Mr Alistair M J Lyttle BA(Hons), PGCE, NPQH

School type: Boys' Day

Age range of boys: 1–11

Age range of girls: 1–4

No. of pupils enrolled as at 01/09/2019: 350

Fees per term as at 01/09/2019:

Day: £1,466–£4,083 per term

Average class size: 17 (two form entry)

Teacher/pupil ratio: 1:12

Yorkshire & Humberside

Pocklington School

Pocklington School – inspired for life

Pocklington is an inclusive, family focussed and academic school that offers incredible experiences inside and outside the classroom. We believe in encouraging pupils to seize opportunities from the broad range of activities on offer. Along with our approach to teaching and learning, these help to form the bedrock of our young Pocklingtonians' character and grow the qualities that support our values. Our sense of community, care for each other and pride in the school is tangible. This is no more evident than in our outstanding boarding provision. At the heart of this ethos lie our Values and Virtues. They drive all that we do at Pocklington and mean our pupils leave with a deep sense of social responsibility and the ability to shape their own future.

Pocklington School lies 12 miles east of York in a safe, rural setting on the edge of a small, friendly market town, on a 50-acre campus with good public transport links and its own minibus pick-up service. The School was founded in 1514 and has retained its strong tradition of encouraging pupils to have the courage to take chances with learning and always remain true to themselves.

Numerous co-curricular activities for day and boarding pupils take place every day until 5pm, and each pupil is encouraged to pursue their own interests to help develop the depth of character and self-awareness to tackle life's challenges on their own terms. Extensive facilities include a 300-seat theatre, an indoor sports hall, conditioning room and swimming pool, plus 21 acres of grass sports pitches and two full-sized synthetic pitches. Full, flexible and casual boarding options are available, in boarding houses which create a home from home for both domestic and international students.

Right through from Prep School, with its emphasis on nurturing children's natural curiosity, imagination and enthusiasm for learning, to the Sixth Form where independent thought is prized, our pupils are encouraged to be resilient, resourceful learners. Lessons are planned around giving pupils the opportunity to develop their independence and character, rather than simply acquiring and retaining facts. We employ the best educational tools and appropriate new technology facilities to ensure youngsters are enthused and inspired by the world of knowledge available to them. Flexible learning platforms and an individual approach allows each pupil to progress at his or her pace, boosting their confidence and self-esteem so they often exceed their expectations.

Our new £3m Art and Design Technology Centre, which opened in Autumn 2017, has every facility to encourage the pursuit of traditional arts and crafts, as well as provide cutting-edge equipment for digital and computer design, and manufacturing technology. The innovation and cross fertilisation of ideas the Centre promotes are increasingly valued in society today.

Sixth Form facilities include spacious communal areas, a study centre, and comprehensive library. Students are encouraged to work both collaboratively and independently as they begin to make the transition to university study and/or workplace success.

Recent former pupils who retain links with the school include Davis Cup winner Kyle Edmund, England rugby star Rob Webber and world-renowned concert pianist Alexandra Dariescu.

We aim to instil the Pocklington Values and Virtues into all of our pupils, to engage with our families and support them in raising the Pocklingtonians of tomorrow and to be open to innovation, conscious of tradition and so secure our Foundation's future.

POCKLINGTON SCHOOL

Ages 3 to 18

(Founded 1514)

West Green, Pocklington, York, North Yorkshire YO42 2NJ UK

Tel: 01759 321200

Fax: 01759 306366

Email: enquiry@pocklingtonschool.com

Website: www.pocklingtonschool.com

Headmaster: Mr Toby Seth MA (Cantab)

Appointed: January 2019

School type: Coeducational Day & Boarding

Religious Denomination:
Christian ethos welcoming all faiths and none

Age range of pupils: 3–18

No. of pupils enrolled as at 01/09/2019: 759

Boys: 408 **Girls:** 351 **Sixth Form:** 155

No. of boarders: 100

Fees per annum as at 01/09/2019:

Day: £15,057

Weekly Boarding: £26,991

Full Boarding: £29,346

Queen Ethelburga's Collegiate Foundation

Students and staff at Queen Ethelburga's College and Faculty are celebrating another successful year, following the publishing of the 2019 A level and BTEC examination results. Students in the Faculty, which offers a wide range of academic, creative and vocational courses, achieved 70% A*/A at A Level (93% A*/B) and 82% D*/D in Level 3 BTECs, (equivalent in UCAS university points to A*/A at A Level).The Faculty students are also celebrating notable success with an outstanding range of first choice university places, including Economics at the University of Cambridge and Veterinary Medicine at the University of Nottingham. Students in the academically-focused College achieved 80% A*/A at A Level (92% A*/B) and 94% D*/D in the small number of BTECs taken to enrich the A-level programmes, again with a strong range of first choice places achieved at Oxford, Cambridge, and other excellent UK and worldwide universities. *"This is a great achievement across the board and I am sure our students are as delighted with their efforts as we are,"* said Steven Jandrell, Collegiate Principal. As seen in national league tables, the A level results for both the College and the Faculty have been in the top 20 schools in the country over last few years.

QE also places great emphasis on our students growing into resilient, caring, compassionate and confident adults, who develop independence and initiative, and who can take responsibility for their own learning and futures. We provide opportunities for students to take part in a range of wider enrichment and extra-curricular activities to help them to gain skills in leadership, teamwork and collaboration, and decision making.

Students at QE have access to an impressive 150 sports and activities each week, including popular sports such as rugby, hockey, football, netball, cricket, swimming, basketball, rounders, tennis, dance, gymnastics, trampolining, climbing, athletics, badminton, and volleyball. Our team of sports staff cater for all abilities and encourage each student to make the most of all the fantastic opportunities on offer during their time here. We have a well-honed mix of physical education teachers and specialist sports coaches, many of whom are ex-professional sportspeople themselves. This means there really is no limit to the level our students can train to. Health and fitness is so central to school life for students that many continue with sport and exercise, either recreationally or as a route of study, that it continues to be a key part of their lives long after they have left us for the next step in their education or career.

What enables us to deliver all of this sporting activity so successfully of course is the outstanding range of high quality facilities on campus. We're pretty unique in that we have a dedicated Sports Village, completed in 2016, to which all students have access to inside and outside of formal school hours. The Village is home to a 25-metre swimming pool, triple court sports hall, 100 station fitness suite and free weights centre. Outside we have a four-lane synthetic cushioned running track and over 30 acres of both grass and artificial 3G pitches. We also have a number of specialist studios used for; martial arts, wrestling, dance, gymnastics, table tennis, cycling, archery, fencing and boxing.

In addition to all this, the students can make use of an eight-metre climbing wall at the campus activity centre, which also houses an assault course, BMX track and additional tennis courts.

There really is something for everyone and for all abilities.

All of Queen Ethelburga's students follow a sports programme with the values of fair play, honesty and determination at its heart. Our motto of 'be the best that I can, with the gifts that I have' is never more evident than through the work we do as TEAM QE.

(Founded 1912)

Thorpe Underwood Hall, Ouseburn, York, North Yorkshire YO26 9SS UK

Tel: 01423 33 33 30

Email: info@qe.org

Website: www.qe.org

Principal: Steven Jandrell BA

Appointed: September 2006

School type: Coeducational Day & Boarding

Religious Denomination: Multi-Denominational

Age range of pupils: 3–19

No. of pupils enrolled as at 01/09/2019: 1545

Boys: 808 *Girls:* 737 *Sixth Form:* 605

No. of boarders: 1177

Average class size: 18

Teacher/pupil ratio: 1:10

The Froebelian School

The Froebelian School in Horsforth is a thriving and dynamic independent prep school, which places children at the very heart of all it strives to achieve. From the age of three, we seek to equip our boys and girls with a lifelong thirst for and love of learning and the school continually achieves impressive levels of academic success; preparing our children for the next stage in their educational journey.

The children and staff work harmoniously together creating a special place, with a uniquely happy atmosphere.

Our aim is to provide a first class all-round education and committed pastoral care in which the unique needs, abilities, interests and aspirations of our bright, inquisitive children are met and their talents can flourish in a caring, structured and secure environment. This enables us to develop the whole child and we work hard to build solid foundations, which balance both the co-curricular and academic spheres of school life and honour our school motto – 'Giving a flying start to the citizens of tomorrow.' As a result, our children regularly secure a place at their first choice senior school and we enjoy an excellent scholarship success rate.

We are delighted that Froebelian children are happy and want to come to school every day and are passionate that all children enjoy a positive experience. Throughout the year extensive learning opportunities are balanced by a wide range of co-curricular activities in sport, music, art and technology and events. We foster our children's curiosity and imagination at every stage of school life and the children are nurtured and supported by an excellent staff:pupil ratio of 1:10.

Welcoming over 180 pupils between the ages of 3 and 11, we set the highest standards and expectations and The Froebelian School is acknowledged as one of the North's leading Independent prep schools.

The latest Independent Schools Inspectorate report judged The Froebelian School as 'excellent' for the quality of the pupils' achievements and the quality of pupils' personal development – this is the highest judgement available from the Independent Schools Inspectorate.

"The pupils' attitudes to learning are exceptional" **ISI Inspectorate 2017**

Awarded 'Outstanding' by Ofsted, our private day nursery, First-Steps at Froebelian, follows the school's ethos closely and offers younger children the opportunity to start realising their full potential at an earlier age.

"The leadership and management are inspirational" **Ofsted**

Situated in Horsforth, a pleasant and vibrant suburb of Leeds near to the ring road, the school is easily accessible from most areas of Leeds, Bradford and Harrogate. Our site is very secure with a wooded area offering delightful views over the Aire valley.

The school is an educational charity where ultimate responsibility rests with a School Council (governors). The day-to-day running of the school is delegated to the Headteacher, supported by a Senior Leadership Team.

Our children adore their school and are justly proud of all they do. They love learning and there is a true sense of fun. We would love you to experience the warmth and politeness of our children for yourselves – please do come and meet them!

Visit www.froebelian.com to find out more.

THE FROEBELIAN SCHOOL
GIVING A FLYING START TO THE CITIZENS OF TOMORROW

(Founded 1913)

Clarence Road, Horsforth, Leeds, West Yorkshire LS18 4LB UK

Tel: 0113 2583047

Fax: 0113 2580173

Email: office@froebelian.co.uk

Website: www.froebelian.com

Head Teacher: Mrs Catherine Dodds BEd (Hons), PGCE

Appointed: 2015

School type: Coeducational Day

Age range of pupils: 3–11

No. of pupils enrolled as at 02/07/2019: 188

Boys: 96 **Girls:** 92

Fees per annum as at 01/09/2019:

Day: £5,220–£7,785

Teacher/pupil ratio: 1:10

Scotland

Edinburgh Steiner School

Educating the Hands, Heart & Head – A Holistic Curriculum for the 21st Century

Edinburgh Steiner School sits within three acres of conservation area, comprising mature grounds, C-listed buildings and an emphasis on child-friendly architecture.

Celebrating 80 years of providing an important alternative to mainstream independent education for up to 360 children aged 3.5 to 18 years, the School became an educational flagship with the introduction of Curriculum for Excellence in Scotland, owing to its breadth of subjects.

Delivered through the Waldorf Main Lesson Programme, the precursors to creative thinking are developed throughout a pupil's school career, encouraging imagination, creativity and flexible thinking – skills highly prized in today's society.

Nowhere is this more evident than in the four years of the Upper School. At a time where most young people become specialised as a result of their exam choices, pupils at Edinburgh Steiner School continue to study a broad spectrum of arts, sciences, crafts and humanities in addition to their national exam subjects.

"The school has successfully maintained high standards of academic achievement over recent years" Education Scotland report, May 2019

Pupils of Edinburgh Steiner School are known to be enquiring, confident and adaptable with a global and environmental awareness, who understand how to make connections, to interpret information and to innovate.

Steiner Education: Waldorf Steiner education, now in its 100th year, is the largest and fastest growing independent school system in the world and continues to gain relevance in modern times.

With a deep understanding of the physical, emotional, intellectual and spiritual needs of the developing human being, pupils are treated as individuals.

This comprehensive education encompasses everyone regardless of social or religious background. This is perhaps why it has such a diverse international community of pupils, with a recent survey showing there are 33 languages spoken in the small school community.

What makes us unique? Marking this milestone year, Edinburgh Steiner is now a centre for the delivery of Integrated Education – a suite of portfolio-based qualifications for 14-18 year olds that develop a spectrum of creative thinking skills.

From Kindergarten to the final year, subject matter is linked to a child's developmental stage and their education flows naturally from previous learning. Two modern languages are taught from the age of six; with computer-based learning delayed until the teenage years.

Creative Arts play an integral part in the curriculum, nurturing imagination, confidence, technical skills and an emotional connection to learning from an early age. The love for learning developed by this approach is evident, with 92% of pupils continuing on to further education at their first choice of course.

An above average number of pupils engage with entrepreneurial activities – reflecting the success of the education in cultivating responsible, free-thinking young people who can contribute to society with initiative and purpose.

(Founded 1939)

60-64 Spylaw Road, Edinburgh, EH10 5BR UK

Tel: 0131 337 3410

Fax: 0131 337 6066

Email: info@edinburghsteinerschool.org.uk

Website: www.edinburghsteinerschool.org.uk

School type: Coeducational Day

Age range of pupils: 3.5–18

No. of pupils enrolled as at 01/09/2019: 300 (School and Kindergarten)

Fees per annum as at 01/09/2019:

Kindergarten: Sliding scale from £4,299

Class 9-12 (Age 14-18-years-old): £9,716

Average class size: 20

Teacher/pupil ratio: 1:8.5

Gordonstoun

As well as preparing students for exams, Gordonstoun prepares them for life.

The school's uniquely broad curriculum encourages every individual to fulfil their potential academically, but it does more than that. It encourages students to fulfil their potential as human beings. The school motto is 'Plus est en vous' – There is more in you. At Gordonstoun, this sense of possibility is presented to its students, every single day.

"It wasn't until we saw the curriculum and the schedule of what they would be doing each day that we truly understood the difference between Gordonstoun and other schools." Current parent.

Although Gordonstoun is within striking distance of two international airports, the school's remarkable location on a 200 acre woodland estate by the Moray Coast in the North of Scotland provides the background for its world beating outdoor education programme. Gordonstoun was the birth place of both the Outward Bound Movement and the Duke of Edinburgh's Award, and expeditions to the Scottish Highlands or sail training on the School's 80ft Sailboat are an integral part of the school's day to day life. Students gain invaluable experience in being both leaders and team players and in having compassion and understanding for their fellows – and of themselves. Their outlook is broadened, their ability to consider the needs of others developed, and they gain resilience – life skills which can only complement the school's commitment to, and realisation of, academic excellence.

Active engagement in service to the local community also comprises a core part of Gordonstoun's 'working week', further expanding the students' sense of personal and social responsibility and building self-esteem. From Year 11 each student commits to one of the school's twelve services. These range from the Fire Service and Coastguards to Community Service and Technical support.

Gordonstoun follows the English GCSE and A level curriculum. With a staff/pupil ratio of 1:7 and every student's progress carefully overseen by their tutor, they go on Universities, Colleges and Art Schools all over the world – from Oxford and Cambridge, to Central St Martins, MIT or the Northern School of Music – to study a diverse range of subjects, from Latin to aeronautical engineering, from physics to drama and performance.

The students at Gordonstoun inhabit a community which is both balanced and internationally dynamic. Pupils aged 7-18 live and learn alongside fellow students from across the social, cultural and geographical board. And because Gordonstoun is one of the few remaining full boarding schools, it has a seven day programme which ensures that students are happily integrated and engaged. It also affords the opportunity to make full use of the comprehensive facilities on offer – which include an expansive sports centre, a drama and dance centre and music studios.

The uniquely all-round education on offer at Gordonstoun provides its students with the chance to develop intellectually, emotionally, physically and spiritually because Gordonstoun understands that the broader the experience the broader the mind.

In the words of a current parent:

"I send my children to Gordonstoun because I want them to have an excellent academic education. But I want them to have more than that. I want them to enter the ever changing world with a sense of possibility and optimism about themselves and their options. Gordonstoun's uniquely broad curriculum gives them the best possible chance of achieving that."

(Founded 1934)

Elgin, Moray IV30 5RF UK

Tel: 01343 837829

Fax: 01343 837808

Email: admissions@gordonstoun.org.uk

Website: www.gordonstoun.org.uk

Principal: Ms Lisa Kerr BA

Appointed: 2017

School type: Coeducational Boarding & Day

Age range of pupils: 4½–18

No. of pupils enrolled as at 01/09/2019: 542

Boys: 313 **Girls:** 229 **Sixth Form:** 189

Senior: 429 **Junior:** 113

No. of boarders: 392

Fees per term as at 01/09/2019:

Day: £5,350–£9,950 per term

Weekly Boarding: £8,650 per term

Full Boarding: £8,650–£13,750 per term

Average class size: 12

Teacher/pupil ratio: 1:7

Strathallan School

Our mission is to provide an outstanding education that gives opportunities for all pupils to perform to the very best of their abilities. Each individual, no matter their passion or interest, is supported and inspired to shine during their time at school. Our pupils excel academically, compete in sports at national and international levels, succeed in scholastic championships and play as part of nationwide orchestras and ensembles. In the 2018-19 academic year, 60 of our pupils played as part of a national sporting team and we became British and Scottish Champions across six sports.

Our aim is to send pupils out into the world with close friends and the ability to make new ones, with the knowledge and skills to succeed at university and beyond. We will be delighted to welcome you and discuss how your child or children might join the Strathallan family and benefit from the opportunities on offer for them here.

Academic excellence

Academically, we strive for excellence and our ambition is to inspire a lifelong enjoyment of learning for learning's sake. Our flexible curriculum and innovative teaching means we can support every pupil, whatever their ambitions and style of learning. In 2019, Strathallan students achieved their best A Level results in almost a decade, with a quarter of all A Level students awarded straight A* or A grades. Our leavers go on to Oxbridge and Russell Group universities, international study, work placements, the Armed Forces and professional sporting careers.

Global community

Strathallan is a friendly, welcoming place with a strong sense of community. In 2019 The Care Inspectorate rated Strathallan a Grade 6 (Sector Leading) Excellent for the Quality of care and support. It's an outstanding environment in which to learn and each pupil is encouraged to explore their talents and to realise their potential academically, in the arts, in sport and in a host of interests and activities. We make the most of our self-contained, rural location every day, but at our core, we are a truly international community with pupils and alumni around the globe. This diversity of community and experience means Strathallians leave our school with the maturity and cultural intelligence to succeed, wherever they go.

Opportunities for all to excel

Our pupils find confidence in themselves at Strathallan. They have the freedom and space to develop their own skills in an idyllic environment with the support of a close, caring community. We believe that learning outside the classroom bolsters success inside the classroom, and it's this holistic approach to education that leads to a rich diversity of pupil experience and consistently exceptional achievements. We ensure there is something for every one of our pupils, and any parent choosing Strathallan will quickly realise that their child will be known here – for who they are, for their individual abilities and for their potential. Young people leave Strathallan with the skills and knowledge to succeed in their chosen career, and the confidence to make their mark on the world.

"I look back at my time at Strathallan with fondness. The quality of education in the classroom, in the creative arts and on the sports field was of the highest possible level. With Strathallan on my CV there are no doors that are not open to me."
Former pupil

STRATHALLAN SCHOOL

Opportunities for *all* to excel

(Founded 1913)

Forgandenny, Perth, Perth & Kinross PH2 9EG UK

Tel: 01738 812546

Fax: 01738 812549

Email: admissions@strathallan.co.uk

Website: www.strathallan.co.uk

Headmaster: Mr Mark Lauder MA Hons

Appointed: 2017

School type: Coeducational Boarding & Day

Age range of pupils: 9–18

No. of pupils enrolled as at 01/09/2019: 520

Fees per annum as at 01/09/2019:

Day: £15,435–£23,532

Full Boarding: £24,729–£34,650

Average class size: 14

Teacher/pupil ratio: 1:7

Wales

Llandovery College

MAKING A DIFFERENCE TO YOUR CHILD'S FUTURE

What Makes Llandovery College Special?

Llandovery College is a vibrant, forward-thinking day and boarding school for boys and girls from 4-18 years old, providing first class teaching in small class sizes and offering a wide range of opportunities for intellectual, social and physical development. Our broad ability and inclusive school ensures that the learning needs of every pupil are catered for enabling them to reach and exceed their individual potential.

A Llandovery College education excels in the values and attitudes it fosters in its young men and women. Compassion, tolerance, kindness, integrity, generosity of spirit and good citizenship underpin a dedication to academic excellence.

Stunning setting and strong sense of community

Set within 45 acres of stunning grounds in the picturesque Towy Valley there is a tangible sense of community and common purpose within the College. The House system brings boarders and day pupils together, promoting a strong sense of belonging and loyalty whilst forging deep bonds of friendship. Our pupils are well known by teachers and staff and we consider ourselves one large family.

Academic success

The College boasts an enviable university entrance record with Oxbridge successes and with many pupils moving on to Russell Group universities. In addition, our pupils achieve an exceptionally high rate of acceptance to their first choice university. Pupils leave equipped with the skills and confidence to lead successful, happy and fulfilling lives.

Outstanding opportunities

The College is renowned for its outstanding rugby heritage and achievements, producing world class rugby players such as Internationals and British & Irish Lions George North and Alun Wyn Jones. Girls rugby is also flourishing with former pupil Carys Phillips captaining the Wales women's national rugby union team.

The College's passion for sport is unrivalled and pupils have competed at regional, national and international levels in no less than 17 sports. Facilities include a 9-hole golf course, fully equipped gym and extensive pitches.

Music and the performing arts also have an enviable reputation with the orchestra and choir performing to an exceptionally high standard both at home and overseas.

Co-curricular activities

An extensive co-curricular programme offers pupils the opportunity to explore new interests as well as develop expertise in existing passions. The College has a thriving Combined Cadet Force and a wide range of outdoor activities, clubs, societies and pursuits to cater for all interests.

Scholarships

Academic and special talent scholarships are available from Year 7 onwards.

"The pupils achieve excellent levels of personal development, feeling secure, safe and valued in the friendly, mutually trusting ethos which prevails throughout the school" – ISI Report

Contact

For more information or to visit Llandovery College please contact 01550 723 005 or admissions@llandoverycollege.com

Llandovery College

(Founded 1847)

Queensway, Llandovery, Carmarthenshire SA20 0EE UK

Tel: +44 (0)1550 723005

Email: admissions@llandoverycollege.com

Website: www.llandoverycollege.com

Warden: Dominic Findlay

Appointed: September 2019

School type: Co-educational Boarding & Day

Religious Denomination: Church in Wales

Age range of pupils: 4–18 years

No. of pupils enrolled as at 01/09/2019: 250

No. of boarders: 110

Fees per annum as at 01/09/2019:

Day: £6,165–£18,225

Full Boarding: £18,450–£27,525

Average class size: 12

Teacher/pupil ratio: 1:9

St David's College

Founding Ethos

St David's College was founded in 1965 with a vision that was ahead of its time. That vision was to create a school that nurtured every aspect of a pupil's academic, physical and social/emotional/spiritual wellbeing. This very vision still informs our purpose and mission as a school. Today it is known as a Three Peak education and is designed to prepare our pupils to leave school with unique personalities and individual strengths, and a deep resilience ready for life beyond school.

Learning at St David's

Our small class sizes and highly trained staff enable us to create a learning environment in which teaching can be tailored to the learning style of each individual. Upon entry to St David's each pupil is assessed so that we can develop a learning plan to help that individual achieve their academic potential. We are proud to have a highly regarded specialist provision to support pupils with Dyslexia and additional learning barriers. This provision is co-ordinated through our Cadogan Learning Support Centre, a department that is staffed by around 20 dedicated learning support teachers, teaching small group and one to one lessons. St David's College is a mainstream academic school and our approach to teaching can also nurture pupils who are more able and talented and stretch those who are academically strong. Class sizes are small throughout the school, averaging around 8 pupils per class, with no class more than about 12 pupils as a maximum.

On offer is a good range of academic and vocational qualifications, again we want to offer an education that each pupil can tailor to their learning style and of course their aspirations. Pupils achieve an average Value Added score of 0.75, in many cases achieving much higher grades than those predicted for them before joining St David's. For our latest examination results please contact us.

Extra Curricular

An important aspect of a St David's College Three Peak Education is the experiences our pupils have outside of the classroom. Our national award winning Extra-Curricular programme is delivered through diverse activity programme and our industry leading Outdoor Education department. Around 5 expeditions leave site each week as part of a true outdoor education, with opportunities for every pupil to experience. From sailing, kayaking and climbing to caving and much, much more. Opportunities abound every week for pupils to expand their leadership and teamwork skills and further strengthen their confidence. The many international expeditions our pupils go on are documented online and worth discovering. This year alone saw 10 of our pupils awarded their Gold Duke of Edinburgh's award at Buckingham Palace, illustrating how adventurous our pupils are.

Location

There is no more awe-inspiring location to learn than Gloddaeth Hall, home to St David's College, with its beautiful surroundings. The campus is flanked by the stunning North Wales coastline to one side and the dramatic peaks of Snowdonia on the other. But with London just 3 hours away from the local train station, Manchester and Liverpool airport just over 1 hour away and great road links our location is very convenient. We're not as far away as you think!

(Founded 1965)

Gloddaeth Hall, Llandudno, Clwyd LL30 1RD UK

Tel: 01492 875974

Email: admissions@stdavidscollege.co.uk

Website: www.stdavidscollege.co.uk

Headmaster: Mr Andrew Russell

Appointed: August 2017

Chairman of Governors: Mr Pete Gaskell

School type: Co-educational Boarding & Day

Age range of pupils: 9–19

No. of pupils enrolled as at 01/09/2019: 254

Fees per term as at 01/09/2019:

Day: £3,930–£6,230 per term

Full Boarding: £8,120–£11,630 per term

Average class size: Max 12

Teacher/pupil ratio: 1:5

Westbourne School

1st in the UK League Tables for 5 consecutive years and awarded The Sunday Times Schools Guide, IB School of the Year 2019, Westbourne School is one of the UK's leading academic schools. Established in 1896, Westbourne develops well-rounded students, equipped with the skills, knowledge, confidence and character to become leaders of the future in their chosen field.

Nationally recognised excellence

- 1st in the UK League Tables for the past 5 years (Daily Telegraph/Best-Schools; smaller schools)
- IB School of the Year 2019 (Sunday Times Schools Guide)
- 1st IB Sixth Form (Sunday Times Schools Guide)
- 3rd Overall in the UK (Sunday Times Schools Guide)
- Awarded 'excellent' in all 5 inspection categories (Estyn National Inspectorate 2018)

"Its sixth form results last summer were beaten by just two schools in England, Wales and Northern Ireland. Students achieved A*-B equivalent A-level grades of 97.9% in their Higher Level IB papers, the best results of any school offering only the IB in the sixth form." Alistair McCall, Editor, The Sunday Times Schools Guide

Gold standard programmes

IB Diploma: Internationally recognized and widely respected for its breadth of programme. 2/3rd of Westbourne Higher Level grades are consistently 7s and 6s (A*/A equivalent). 2/3rd of students received a Bilingual Diploma.

GCSE/IGCSE: Full course and 1 year GCSE/IGCSE programmes: 40% of GCSE grades are A* equivalent; (20% Grade 9 | 20% Grade 8s), 5 times the UK national average.

Pre-IB: One year, Pre-Diploma foundation course for international students, specifically designed for 15-16 year.

Certainty of university entry

90% Russell Group University average. Westbourne graduates progress to study highly competitive courses including Medicine, Engineering, Economics, Computer Science, Business and Law.

Outstanding teachers and unparalleled support

Offering individualised academic excellence, Westbourne has a warm and highly supportive culture. Small class sizes, an 8:1 pupil-to-teacher ratio and a tutorial style ensures every student excels.

More than 50% of teachers at Westbourne have a PhD or Masters and more than 50% have taught internationally, so can quickly relate with local and international students alike.

Boarding environment

Located in the safe seaside town of Penarth, ranked as one of the Top 10 best places to live in the UK, also just minutes from the vibrant capital city of Cardiff, Westbourne is a resoundingly British school. A student body of 72% British students, complemented by 16% European, 12% Asian students drawn from 24 different countries; no one nationality dominates.

Boarding students live within 2 minutes-walk of the main school building, in a modern fully-equipped boarding house, supported by live in, caring and professional House Parents.

Co-curricular activities and world-class facilities

Westbourne runs an expansive co-curricular programme, enriched with opportunities for students to test themselves through competitions, Olympiads and Duke of Edinburgh Awards.

WESTBOURNE SCHOOL
academic excellence for the modern world

(Founded 1896)

Hickman Road, Penarth, Glamorgan CF64 2AJ UK

Tel: 029 2070 5705

Email: enquiries@westbourneschool.com

Website: www.westbourneschool.com

Headteacher: Dr GW Griffiths BSc, PhD, ARCS, PGCE

School type: Co-educational Day & Boarding

Age range of pupils: 2–18

No. of pupils enrolled as at 01/09/2019: 220

Fees per annum as at 01/09/2019:

Day: £8,100–£14,010

Full Boarding: £32,750–£35,850

Average class size: 16

Teacher/pupil ratio: 1:8

Overseas

École Jeannine Manuel – Lille

École Jeannine Manuel Lille is a non-profit pre-K-12 coeducational school founded in 1992. As the sister school of École Jeannine Manuel Paris, they have the same educational project and the same mission: promote international understanding through bilingual (French/English) education. An associated UNESCO school, École Jeannine Manuel Lille is the only non-denominational independent school in Nord-Pas-de-Calais, with over 800 pupils representing 40 nationalities and every major cultural tradition. The school's academic excellence matches its diversity: École Jeannine Manuel Lille achieves excellent performances, both at the French Baccalaureate and the International Baccalaureate. The school is accredited by the French Ministry of Education, the International Baccalaureate Organization (IBO), the Council of International Schools (CIS) and the New England Association of Schools and Colleges (NEASC).

The campus of school extends over 3.5 hectares and includes a boarding house, a restaurant, two football fields, a multi-sport room, and high standard sports facilities and equipment. The boarding house welcomes this year 111 pupils from 6th to 12th grades.

Each year, École Jeannine Manuel Lille welcomes non-French speaking students. Over the years École Jeannine Manuel has developed a program to suit the needs of these students, for whom the emotional challenge of relocation is often as great than its academic challenge. Thanks to their French teachers and their methods, the students will be fluent in French in a few months.

The lower and middle school follow the French national curriculum with several exceptions: English is taught every day and, in middle school, experimental sciences, history and geography are taught in English. The curriculum is enriched at all levels, not only with a more advanced English language and literature curriculum, but also, for example,

with Chinese language instruction (compulsory in grades 3-4-5), an integrated science programme in lower school, and independent research projects in middle school.

In upper school, 10th graders follow the French national curriculum, albeit taught 50% in French and 50% in English. In 11th grade, pupils choose between the French track (international option of the French baccalaureate (OIB)) and the International Baccalaureate Diploma Programme (IBDP). Approximately 25% of our pupils opt for the IBDP. (Please note that, since the IBDP does not receive any government subsidies, its tuition is three times the French track tuition.)

Admission

Although admission is competitive, every effort is made to reserve space for international applicants, including children of families who expect to remain in France for a limited period of time and wish to combine a cultural immersion in French education with the ability to re-enter their own school systems and excel.

ÉCOLE Jeannine Manuel
International understanding through a bilingual education

(Founded 1992)

418 bis rue Albert Bailly, Marcq-en-Baroeul, 59700 France

Tel: +33 3 20 65 90 50

Fax: +33 3 20 98 06 41

Email: admissions-lille@ejm.net

Website: www.ecolejeanninemanuel.org

Head of School: Constance Devaux

School type: Coeducational Day & Boarding

Age range of pupils: 4–18 years

No. of pupils enrolled as at 01/09/2019: 870

Fees per annum as at 01/09/2019:

Day: €5,301

Full Boarding: €14,145–€21,465

IB Classes: €18,500

Average class size: 25 (15 in IBDP)

École Jeannine Manuel – Paris

École Jeannine Manuel is a non-profit pre-K-12 coeducational school founded in 1954 with the mission to promote international understanding through bilingual (French/English) education. An associated UNESCO school, École Jeannine Manuel welcomes pupils representing 80 nationalities and every major cultural tradition. The school's academic excellence matches its diversity: École Jeannine Manuel is regularly ranked among the top French high schools (state and independent) for its overall academic performance (ranked first for seven consecutive years). The school is accredited by the French Ministry of Education, the International Baccalaureate Organization (IBO), the Council of International Schools (CIS) and the New England Association of Schools and Colleges (NEASC).

Each year, the school welcomes more than 100 new non-French speaking pupils. These students, key to the cultural diversity of the school, are enrolled in an adaptation programme where they receive intensive and immersive French tuition tailored to their individual level.

The lower and middle school follow the French national curriculum with several exceptions: English is taught every day and, in middle school, experimental sciences, history and geography are taught in English. The curriculum is enriched at all levels, not only with a more advanced English language and literature curriculum, but also, for example, with Chinese language instruction (compulsory in grades 3-4-5), an integrated science programme in lower school, and independent research projects in middle school.

In upper school, 10th graders follow the French national curriculum, albeit taught 50% in French and 50% in English. In 11th grade, pupils choose between the French track (international option of the French baccalaureate (OIB)) and the International Baccalaureate Diploma Programme (IBDP). Approximately 25% of our pupils opt for the IBDP. (Please note that, since the IBDP does not receive any government subsidies, its tuition is three times the French track tuition.)

Over the past three years, approximately 20% of our graduating class have gone to US colleges or universities, 48% chose the UK or Canada, 37% entered the French higher education system, and the balance pursued their education all over the world.

Admission

Although admission is competitive and applications typically exceed available spaces by a ratio of 7:1, every effort is made to reserve space for international applicants, including children of families who expect to remain in France for a limited period of time and wish to combine a cultural immersion in French education with the ability to re-enter their own school systems and excel.

ÉCOLE Jeannine Manuel
International understanding through a bilingual education

(Founded 1954)

70 rue du Théâtre, Paris, 75015 France

Tel: +33 1 44 37 00 80

Fax: +33 1 45 79 06 66

Email: admissions@ejm.net

Website: www.ecolejeanninemanuel.org

Principal: Jérôme Giovendo

School type: Coeducational Day

Age range of pupils: 4–18 years

No. of pupils enrolled as at 01/09/2019: 2400

Fees per annum as at 01/09/2019:

Day: €6,417–€6,765

IB Classes: €21,390

Average class size: 25

EF Academy New York

EF Academy International Boarding Schools prepare students for a global future with an exceptional high school education in the US or UK. At EF Academy, we believe in every student's ability to succeed. We empower them to do so through our renowned curricula, as well as quality one-on-one relationships with teachers and mentors alike. Built into every course is an emphasis on multilingualism and intercultural exchange, which helps distinguish our students' academic credentials to both university admissions officers and future employers.

The Campus

Our private boarding school, which attracts students from 75 countries around the world, is located in upper New York State, approximately 45 minutes away from Manhattan. EF Academy's secure campus offers 100 acres of wooded grounds, running trails and playing fields in the quiet suburban town of Thornwood. Theater students step into the spotlight in our beautiful auditorium where full-length plays are staged twice a year. The science labs make use of cutting-edge technology like 3D printers and the art studio is stocked with all the supplies students need to create an outstanding portfolio showcasing their talent. Our students often complete their school day with physical activity in our fully equipped gym, dance studio, basketball court or off-road biking trails.

Students live in comfortable and secure on-campus residences. Resident Advisors and teachers provide support and mentorship around the clock, and ensure a safe "home away from home."

Academics

EF Academy New York is a four-year high school. In their first two years during grades 9 through 10, students can follow the IGCSE program or the US High School Diploma.

The IB Diploma Programme can be followed in the last two years of high school in grades 11 and 12. This exceptional program offers an extensive and balanced curriculum that prepares students for success in their furthering studies, career, and beyond.

Instruction and guidance at EF Academy New York is highly personal. Students engage in interactive lessons in small classes led by inspiring teachers, many of which are New York natives and know exactly how to highlight enriching and educational opportunities in the area.

University Placement

EF Academy New York graduates have been accepted to top-ranked universities such as Harvard University, Yale University, Johns Hopkins University, New York University, several schools in the University of California network, as well as international universities ranked highly for the fields of art, business and engineering. Dedicated university advisors work with students on a one-on-one basis to help them with everything from researching universities and writing university essays, to selecting a major that falls in line with their career goals.

Co-curricular Activities

Universities look for well-rounded students who extend their learning beyond the classroom. Students at EF Academy New York have access to a wide range of co-curricular activities. From subject-specific academic groups and competitions to club and varsity sports, there is an option for every student. Our school's activities coordinator also arranges teacher-led excursions for students on the weekends so they have several opportunities to explore Manhattan by visiting all the museums, musicals, and sights for which the city is known.

EF ACADEMY

**International
Boarding Schools**

582 Columbus Avenue, Thornwood, NY 10594 USA

Tel: +1 914 495 6028

Email: iaadmissionsny@ef.com

Website: www.ef.edu/academy

Head of School: Dr. Vladimir D. Kuskovski

School type: Coeducational Day & Boarding

Age range of pupils: 14–19

No. of pupils enrolled as at 01/09/2019: 650

Fees per annum as at 01/09/2019:

Grades 9 & 10 (IGCSE, US High School Diploma):
US$35,240

Grades 11 & 12: (IB Diploma, US High School Diploma):
US$41,000

EF Academy Pasadena

EF Academy International Boarding Schools prepare students for a global future with an exceptional high school education in the US or UK. At EF Academy, we believe in every student's ability to succeed. We empower them to do so through our renowned curricula, as well as quality one-on-one relationships with teachers and mentors alike.

Built into every course is an emphasis on multilingualism and intercultural exchange, which helps distinguish our students' academic credentials to both university admissions officers and future employers.

The Campus

Our private boarding school is located in beautiful Southern California and attracts students from around the world. Previously a private university campus, the brand-new EF Academy Pasadena campus will provide students with a perfect preview into a university-like lifestyle.

Our students will be able to take classes in the newly constructed, spacious classrooms. Theater students can step into the spotlight in our beautiful auditorium and the STEM center will be stocked with state-of-the-art equipment, while the welcoming art studios will not only enrich classes but feature gallery space for exhibitions.

Students will live in comfortable and secure on-campus dormitory accommodation. Resident Advisors and teachers will be there to provide support and mentorship around the clock, ensuring a safe "home away from home."

Academics

At EF Academy's international boarding schools, we offer our students the guidance and direction they need to pursue their passions. Students will engage in interactive lessons led by experienced teachers and benefit from the personalized support they will receive from dedicated pathway managers and university advisors who will help them achieve their goals.

At EF Academy Pasadena, students will be able to follow the US High School Diploma program. Students in Grades 8-10 can follow the IGCSE curriculum along with the US High School Diploma program to prepare for the IB curriculum, which can be studied in the final two years of high school.

With the IB curriculum, scientists gain experience in our labs, artists have multiple opportunities to hone their craft, and all of our business-minded students have the chance to gain real-world experience and earn an enriching education that will prepare them for their further studies.

University Placement

EF Academy graduates have been accepted to top-ranked universities such as Harvard University, Yale University, Johns Hopkins University, New York University, several schools in the University of California network, as well as international universities ranked highly for the fields of business, engineering, and art. Dedicated university advisors work with students on a one-on-one basis to help them with everything from researching universities and writing college essays, to selecting a major that falls in line with their career goals.

Co-curricular Activities

Universities look for well-rounded students who extend their learning beyond the classroom. Students at EF Academy Pasadena will have access to a wide range of co-curricular activities.

In addition to a wide variety of clubs on campus and teacher-led excursions, students can explore Southern California. They can learn to surf at the Santa Monica beach, hike Runyon Canyon, ski at Big Bear Lake and star gaze in Hollywood.

EF ACADEMY

**International
Boarding Schools**

(Founded 2020)

1539 E Howard St., Pasadena, CA 91104 USA

Tel: +1 914 495 6028

Email: iaadmissionsny@ef.com

Website: www.ef.edu/academy

Founding Head of School: Mr. George Stewart

School type: Coeducational Day & Boarding

Age range of pupils: 13–19

Geographical directory of schools

KEY TO SYMBOLS

- (♀) *Boys' school*
- (♀) *Girls' school*
- (🌐) *International school*
- (16) *Tutorial or sixth form college*
- (A) *A levels*
- (🛏) *Boarding accommodation*
- (£) *Bursaries*
- (IB) *International Baccalaureate*
- (✎) *Learning support*
- (16) *Entrance at 16+*
- (🎓) *Vocational qualifications*
- (IAPS) *Independent Association of Preparatory Schools*
- (HMC) *The Headmasters' & Headmistresses' Conference*
- (ISA) *Independent Schools Association*
- (GSA) *Girls' School Association*
- (BSA) *Boarding Schools' Association*
- (S) *Society of Heads*

Unless otherwise indicated, all schools are coeducational day schools.
Single-sex and boarding schools will be indicated by the relevant icon.

Channel Islands

KEY TO SYMBOLS
- (♂) *Boys' school*
- (♀) *Girls' school*
- (🌐) *International school*
- (16) *Tutorial or sixth form college*
- (A) *A levels*
- (🏫) *Boarding accommodation*
- (£) *Bursaries*
- (IB) *International Baccalaureate*
- (✎) *Learning support*
- (16) *Entrance at 16+*
- (⚙) *Vocational qualifications*
- (IAPS) *Independent Association of Preparatory Schools*
- (HMC) *The Headmasters' & Headmistresses' Conference*
- (ISA) *Independent Schools Association*
- (GSA) *Girls' School Association*
- (BSA) *Boarding Schools' Association*
- (S) *Society of Heads*

Unless otherwise indicated, all schools are coeducational day schools.
Single-sex and boarding schools will be indicated by the relevant icon.

Guernsey

Elizabeth College
The Grange, St Peter Port,
Guernsey GY1 2PY
Tel: 01481 726544
Principal: Jenny Palmer
Age range: B2½–18
No. of pupils: 520
Fees: Day £12,465
Ⓐ ⓔ 🖊 ⑯

Elizabeth College Junior School
Beechwood, Queen's Road, St
Peter Port, Guernsey GY1 1PU
Tel: 01481 722123
Headteacher: Richard Fyfe
Age range: 2½–11
No. of pupils: 270
Fees: Day £10,350–£11,370
🖊

The Ladies' College
Les Gravees, St Peter Port,
Guernsey GY1 1RW
Tel: 01481 721602
Principal: Ashley Clancy
Age range: G2½–18
No. of pupils: 600 VIth100
Fees: Day £10,560–£11,175
👤 Ⓐ ⑯

Jersey

Beaulieu Convent School
Wellington Road, St Helier,
Jersey JE2 4RJ
Tel: 01534 731280
Headmaster: Mr C Beirne
Age range: G4–18
No. of pupils: 762 VIth127
Fees: Day £5,835
👤 Ⓐ ⓔ 🖊 ⑯

De La Salle College
Wellington Road, St Saviour,
Jersey JE2 7TH
Tel: 01534 754100
Head of College: Mr Jason Turner
Age range: 3–18
No. of pupils: 762
Fees: Day £5,805
Ⓐ ⑯ 🏉

FCJ Primary School
Deloraine Road, St Saviour,
Jersey JE2 7XB
Tel: 01534 723063
Headmistress: Ms Donna Lenzi
Age range: 4–11
No. of pupils: 290
Fees: Day £4,440
🖊

Helvetia House School
14 Elizabeth Place, St
Helier, Jersey JE2 3PN
Tel: 01534 724928
Headmistress: Mrs Lindsey
Woodward BA, DipEd
Age range: G4–11
No. of pupils: 82
Fees: Day £4,725
👤

Jersey College For Girls
Le Mont Millais, St Saviour,
Jersey JE2 7YB
Tel: 01534 516200
Principal: Carl Howarth
Age range: G11–18
👤

**ST GEORGE'S PREPARATORY
SCHOOL**
For further details see p. 52
La Hague Manor, Rue de la
Hague, St Peter, Jersey JE3 7DB
Tel: 01534 481593
Email: admin@stgeorgesprep.co.uk
Website: www.stgeorgesprep.co.uk
Headmaster: Mr Cormac Timothy
Age range: 2–11
No. of pupils: 244
Fees: Day £5,796–£15,495
ⓔ 🖊

**ST MICHAEL'S PREPARATORY
SCHOOL**
For further details see p. 54
La Rue de la Houguette, St
Saviour, Jersey JE2 7UG
Tel: 01534 856904
Email: office@stmichaels.je
Website: www.stmichaels.je
Age range: 3–14
No. of pupils: 315
Fees: Day £10,230–£16,080
ⓔ 🖊

Victoria College
Le Mont Millais, St Helier, Jersey JE1 4HT
Tel: 01534 638200
Headmaster: Mr Alun Watkins
Age range: B11–18
No. of pupils: 720 VIth200
Fees: Day £5,310
👤 Ⓐ ⓔ 🖊 ⑯

**Victoria College
Preparatory School**
Pleasant Street, St Helier, Jersey JE2 4RR
Tel: 01534 723468
Headmaster: Dan Pateman BA (Hons)
Age range: B7–11
No. of pupils: 300
Fees: Day £5,268
👤 🖊

Central & West

KEY TO SYMBOLS
- ♂ *Boys' school*
- ♀ *Girls' school*
- *International school*
- 16- *Tutorial or sixth form college*
- Ⓐ *A levels*
- *Boarding accommodation*
- £ *Bursaries*
- IB *International Baccalaureate*
- *Learning support*
- 16- *Entrance at 16+*
- *Vocational qualifications*
- IAPS *Independent Association of Preparatory Schools*
- HMC *The Headmasters' & Headmistresses' Conference*
- ISA *Independent Schools Association*
- GSA *Girls' School Association*
- BSA *Boarding Schools' Association*
- S *Society of Heads*

Unless otherwise indicated, all schools are coeducational day schools.
Single-sex and boarding schools will be indicated by the relevant icon.

Bath & North-East Somerset

Bath Academy
27 Queen Square, Bath, Bath & North-East Somerset BA1 2HX
Tel: 01225 334577
Principal: Tim Naylor BA(Hons), MSc, PGCE
Age range: 14–19+
No. of pupils: 120
Fees: Day £23,700 FB £35,000
🌐 16· Ⓐ 🏛 16·

Downside School
Stratton-on-the-Fosse, Radstock, Bath, Bath & North-East Somerset BA3 4RJ
Tel: 01761 235103
Head Master: Andrew Hobbs
Age range: 11–18
No. of pupils: 350 VIth135
Fees: Day £16,242–£19,251 FB £25,236–£33,861
🌐 Ⓐ 🏛 £ 🖉 16·

King Edward's Junior School
North Road, Bath, Bath & North-East Somerset BA2 6JA
Tel: 01225 464218
Head: Mr Greg Taylor
Age range: 7–11
No. of pupils: 182
Fees: Day £11,250
🖉

King Edward's Pre-Prep & Nursery School
Weston Lane, Bath, Bath & North-East Somerset BA1 4AQ
Tel: 01225 421681
Head: Ms. Jayne Gilbert
Age range: 3–7
No. of pupils: 107
Fees: Day £8,370–£10,155

King Edward's Senior School
North Road, Bath, Bath & North-East Somerset BA2 6HU
Tel: 01225 464313
Head: Mr MJ Boden MA
Age range: 11–18
No. of pupils: 1085
Ⓐ £ 🖉 16·

Kingswood Preparatory School
College Road, Lansdown, Bath, Bath & North-East Somerset BA1 5SD
Tel: 01225 734460
Headmaster: Mr Mark Breary
Age range: 9 months–11
No. of pupils: 335
Fees: Day £10,002–£11,973 WB £19,809 FB £23,583–£24,720
🏛 £

Kingswood School
Lansdown Road, Bath, Bath & North-East Somerset BA1 5RG
Tel: 01225 734200
Age range: 9 months–18 years
No. of pupils: 772 VIth189
Fees: Day £10,293–£15,624 WB £20,385–£30,426 FB £24,267–£34,818
🌐 Ⓐ 🏛 £ 🖉 16·

Monkton Prep School
Church Road, Combe Down, Bath, Bath & North-East Somerset BA2 7ET
Tel: +44 (0)1225 837912
Headmaster: Mr M Davis
Age range: 7–13 (boarding from 8)
No. of pupils: 220
🏛 £ 🖉

Monkton Senior School
Monkton Combe, Bath, Bath & North-East Somerset BA2 7HG
Tel: 01225 721133
Principal: Mr Chris Wheeler
Age range: 13–18
No. of pupils: 377
🌐 Ⓐ 🏛 £ 🖉 16·

Prior Park College
Ralph Allen Drive, Bath, Bath & North-East Somerset BA2 5AH
Tel: 01225 831000
Head: Mr James Murphy-O'Connor
Age range: 11–18
No. of pupils: 580 VIth180
Fees: Day £15,000–£16,995 WB £20,745–£25,500 FB £23,505–£32,100
🌐 Ⓐ 🏛 £ 🖉 16·

The Paragon School
Lyncombe House, Lyncombe Vale, Bath, Bath & North-East Somerset BA2 4LT
Tel: 01225 310837
Headmaster: Mr Andrew Harvey
Age range: 3–11
No. of pupils: 252
Fees: Day £8,745–£10,245
£ 🖉

The Royal High School, Bath GDST
Lansdown Road, Bath, Bath & North-East Somerset BA1 5SZ
Tel: +44 (0)1225 313877
Head: Mrs Jo Duncan BA, MA
Age range: G3–18
No. of pupils: 640
Fees: Day £3,315–£4,700 WB £8,760–£9,257 FB £9,797–£10,298
🏃 🌐 Ⓐ 🏛 £ IB 🖉 16·

Bristol

Badminton Junior School
Westbury-on-Trym, Bristol BS9 3BA
Tel: 0117 905 5200
Head of the Junior School: Mrs E Davies
Age range: G3–11
No. of pupils: 130
Fees: Day £9,750–£11,235 FB £21,840–£24,945
🏃 Ⓐ 🏛 £ 🖉

Badminton School
Westbury-on-Trym, Bristol BS9 3BA
Tel: 0117 905 5271
Headmistress: Mrs Rebecca Tear BSc, MA, PGCE
Age range: G3–18
No. of pupils: 450
Fees: Day £9,750–£16,425 FB £21,840–£37,575
🏃 🌐 Ⓐ 🏛 £ 🖉 16·

Bristol Grammar School
University Road, Bristol BS8 1SR
Tel: 0117 973 6006
Headmaster: Mr Jaideep Barot
Age range: 4–18
🌐 Ⓐ £ IB 🖉 16·

Bristol Waldorf School
Redland Hill House, Redland, Bristol BS6 6UX
Tel: 0117 933 9990
Age range: 3–11
No. of pupils: 213
Fees: Day £7,977

Carmel Christian School
817A Bath Road, Brislington, Bristol BS4 5NL
Tel: 0117 977 5533
Headteacher: Jaap Van Wyk
Age range: 3–16
No. of pupils: 28
Fees: Day £1,440–£2,580

Cleve House School
254 Wells Road, Knowle, Bristol BS4 2PN
Tel: 0117 9777218
Headmaster: Mr Craig Wardle
Age range: 2–11
No. of pupils: 90
Fees: Day £6,525
🖉

Clifton College
32 College Road, Clifton, Bristol BS8 3JH
Tel: 0117 315 7000
Headmaster: Dr Tim Greene
Age range: 3–18
No. of pupils: 1330 VIth280
Fees: Day £10,020–£25,590 WB £16,305–£34,200 FB £24,180–£39,405
🌐 Ⓐ 🏛 £ 🖉 16·

Clifton College Preparatory School
The Avenue, Clifton, Bristol BS8 3HE
Tel: +44 (0)117 405 8396
Head of Preparatory School: Mr Jim Walton
Age range: 2–13
No. of pupils: 495
Fees: Day £10,020–£17,460 WB £16,305–£20,565 FB £24,180–£28,650
🏛 £ 🖉

Clifton High School
College Road, Clifton, Bristol BS8 3JD
Tel: 0117 973 0201
Head: Dr Alison M Neill BSc, PhD, PGCE
Age range: 3–18
No. of pupils: 527
Fees: Day £8,895–£14,985 FB £19,605
Ⓐ 🏛 £ 🖉 16·

Clifton Tutors Limited
31 Pembroke Road, Clifton, Bristol BS8 3BE
Tel: 0117 973 8376
Director of Studies: Sue Morgan
Age range: 7–19
16· Ⓐ

Colston's School
Stapleton, Bristol BS16 1BJ
Tel: 0117 965 5207
Headmaster: Jeremy McCullough
Age range: 3–18
No. of pupils: 581 VIth138
Fees: Day £7,680–£13,950
🌐 Ⓐ 🏛 £ ✏ 16

Ecole Française de Bristol
Fonthill Centre, Stanton Road,
Southmead, , Bristol BS10 5SJ
Tel: +44 (0) 117 9692410
Headmistress: Mathilde Monnet
Age range: 2–11
🌐

Fairfield School
Fairfield Way, Backwell, Bristol BS48 3PD
Tel: 01275 462743
Headmistress: Mrs Lesley Barton
Age range: 2–11
No. of pupils: 136
Fees: Day £7,650–£8,445
£ ✏

Gracefield Preparatory School
266 Overndale Road,
Fishponds, Bristol BS16 2RG
Tel: 0117 956 7977
Headmistress: Mrs E Morgan
Age range: 4–11
No. of pupils: 90
Fees: Day £5,382
✏

Queen Elizabeth's Hospital
Berkeley Place, Clifton, Bristol BS8 1JX
Tel: 0117 930 3040
Head: Mr Stephen Holliday
MA (Cantab)
Age range: B7–18 G16–18
No. of pupils: 688
Fees: Day £9,654–£14,406
♦ Ⓐ £ ✏ 16

Silverhill School
Swan Lane, Winterbourne,
Bristol BS36 1RL
Tel: 01454 772156
Principal: Mr Julian Capper
Age range: 2–11
No. of pupils: 185
Fees: Day £5,130–£9,150
✏

The Downs School
Wraxall, Bristol BS48 1PF
Tel: 01275 852008
Head: M A Gunn MA(Ed), BA, PGCE
Age range: 4–13
No. of pupils: 262
£ ✏

The Red Maids' Junior School
Grange Court Road, Westbury-
on-Trym, Bristol BS9 4DP
Tel: 0117 962 9451
Headteacher: Mrs Lisa
Brown BSc (Hons)
Age range: B3–7 G3–11
Fees: Day £3,135
♦ ✏

The Red Maids' Senior School
Westbury Road, Westbury-
on-Trym, Bristol BS9 3AW
Tel: +44 (0)117 962 2641
Headmistress: Mrs Isabel
Tobias BA (Hons)
Age range: G11–18
♦ 🌐 Ⓐ £ IB 16

Tockington Manor School
Washingpool Hill Road,
Tockington, Bristol BS32 4NY
Tel: 01454 613229
Headmaster: Mr Stephen Symonds
Age range: 2–14
No. of pupils: 250
Fees: Day £9,333–£14,553 FB £21,045
🏛 £ ✏

Torwood House School
8, 27-29 Durdham Park,
Redland, Bristol BS6 6XE
Tel: 0117 9735620
Headmistress: Mrs D Seagrove
Age range: 0–11
No. of pupils: 70
Fees: Day £7,500–£7,800
£ ✏

Buckinghamshire

Akeley Wood School
Akeley Wood, Buckingham,
Buckinghamshire MK18 5AE
Tel: 01280 814110
Headmaster: Dr Jerry Grundy BA, PhD
Age range: 12 months–18 years
No. of pupils: 833 VIth119
Fees: Day £7,185–£10,575
Ⓐ £ ✏ 16

Ashfold School
Dorton House, Dorton, Aylesbury,
Buckinghamshire HP18 9NG
Tel: 01844 238237
Headmaster: Mr Michael Chitty BSc
Age range: 3–13
No. of pupils: 280 VIth28
Fees: Day £9,525–£16,845 WB £20,190
🏛 £ ✏

**Broughton Manor
Preparatory School**
Newport Road, Broughton, Milton
Keynes, Buckinghamshire MK10 9AA
Tel: 01908 665234
Headmaster: Mr James Canwell
Age range: 2 months–11 years
No. of pupils: 250
Fees: Day £13,980
£

Caldicott
Crown Lane, Farnham Royal,
Buckinghamshire SL2 3SL
Tel: 01753 649301
Headmaster: Mr Jeremy
Banks BA (Hons) QTS, MEd
Age range: B7–13
No. of pupils: 250
Fees: Day £16,833–£18,780 WB
£24,918–£27,687 FB £24,918–£27,687
♦ 🏛 £ ✏

Chesham Preparatory School
Two Dells Lane, Chesham,
Buckinghamshire HP5 3QF
Tel: 01494 782619
Headmaster: Mr Jonathan Beale
Age range: 3–13
No. of pupils: 392
Fees: Day £9,270–£14,400
✏

Childfirst Day Nursery Aylesbury
Green End, off Rickford's Hill, Aylesbury,
Buckinghamshire HP20 2SA
Tel: 01296 392516
Registrar: Mrs Carole Angood
Age range: 2 months–7 years
No. of pupils: 80
Fees: Day £6,276

Childfirst Pre School Aylesbury
35 Rickfords Hill, Aylesbury,
Buckinghamshire HP20 2RT
Tel: 01296 433224

Crown House Preparatory School
Bassetsbury Manor, Bassetsbury
Lane, High Wycombe,
Buckinghamshire HP11 1QX
Tel: 01494 529927
Headmaster: Ben Kenyon
Age range: 3–11
No. of pupils: 120
Fees: Day £9,005–£10,185
✏

Dair House School
Bishops Blake, Beaconsfield
Road, Farnham Royal,
Buckinghamshire SL2 3BY
Tel: 01753 643964
Headmaster: Mr Terry Wintle BEd(Hons)
Age range: 3–11
No. of pupils: 125
Fees: Day £3,425–£4,345
£ ✏

Davenies School
Station Road, Beaconsfield,
Buckinghamshire HP9 1AA
Tel: 01494 685400
Headmaster: Mr Carl
Rycroft BEd (Hons)
Age range: B4–13
No. of pupils: 337
Fees: Day £11,985–£17,400

Filgrave School
Filgrave Village, Newport
Pagnell, Milton Keynes,
Buckinghamshire MK16 9ET
Tel: 01234 711534
Headteacher: Mrs H Schofield
BA(Hons), MA, PGCE
Age range: 2–7
No. of pupils: 27
Fees: Day £5,160

Focus School – Stoke Poges Campus
School Lane, Stoke Poges,
Buckinghamshire SL2 4QA
Tel: 01753 662167
Headteacher: Mr Connery Wiltshire
Age range: 11–16
No. of pupils: 120

Gateway School
1 High Street, Great Missenden,
Buckinghamshire HP16 9AA
Tel: 01494 862407
Headteacher: Mrs Sue
LaFarge BA(Hons), PGCE
Age range: 2–11
No. of pupils: 355
Fees: Day £2,235–£11,175

Godstowe Preparatory School
Shrubbery Road, High Wycombe,
Buckinghamshire HP13 6PR
Tel: 01494 529273
Headmistress: Sophie Green
Age range: B3–7 G3–13
No. of pupils: 409
Fees: Day £10,800–£16,620 FB £24,645

Griffin House Preparatory School
Little Kimble, Aylesbury,
Buckinghamshire HP17 0XP
Tel: 01844 346154
Headmaster: Mr Tim Walford
Age range: 3–11
No. of pupils: 100
Fees: Day £8,238–£8,580

Heatherton House School
Copperkins Lane, Chesham Bois,
Amersham, Buckinghamshire HP6 5QB
Tel: 01494 726433
Headteacher: Mrs Debbie Isaachsen
Age range: B3–4 G3–11
Fees: Day £1,140–£13,335

High March School
23 Ledborough Lane, Beaconsfield,
Buckinghamshire HP9 2PZ
Tel: 01494 675186
Headmistress: Mrs S J Clifford
BEd (Oxon), MA (London)
Age range: B3–4 G3–11
No. of pupils: 307
Fees: Day £5,730–£14,805

Milton Keynes Preparatory School
Tattenhoe Lane, Milton Keynes,
Buckinghamshire MK3 7EG
Tel: 01908 642111
Heads of School: Mr C
Bates & Mr S Driver
Age range: 2 months–11 years
No. of pupils: 500
Fees: Day £4,560–£15,120

Pipers Corner School
Pipers Lane, Great Kingshill, High
Wycombe, Buckinghamshire HP15 6LP
Tel: 01494 718 255
Headmistress: Mrs H J Ness-
Gifford BA(Hons), PGCE
Age range: G4–18
No. of pupils: VIth72
Fees: Day £8,880–£18,390

St Teresa's Catholic School & Nursery
Aylesbury Road, Princes Risborough,
Buckinghamshire HP27 0JW
Tel: 01844 345005
Joint Heads: Mrs Jane Draper
& Mrs Yasmin Roberts
Age range: 3–11
No. of pupils: 130
Fees: Day £8,985–£9,165

Stowe School
Buckingham, Buckinghamshire
MK18 5EH
Tel: 01280 818000
Headmaster: Dr Anthony Wallersteiner
Age range: 13–18
No. of pupils: 769 VIth318
Fees: Day £26,355 FB £36,660

Swanbourne House School
Swanbourne, Milton Keynes,
Buckinghamshire MK17 0HZ
Tel: 01296 720264
Head of School: Mrs Jane Thorpe
Age range: 3–13
No. of pupils: 323
Fees: Day £1,410–£18,360 FB £23,520

The Beacon School
Chesham Bois, Amersham,
Buckinghamshire HP6 5PF
Tel: 01494 433654
Headmaster: William Phelps
Age range: B3–13
No. of pupils: 470
Fees: Day £11,850–£17,250

The Chalfonts Independent Grammar School
19 London Road, High Wycombe,
Buckinghamshire HP11 1BJ
Tel: +44 (0)1494 875502
Principal: Mr David Shandley
Age range: 11–18

The Grove Independent School
Redland Drive, Loughton, Milton
Keynes, Buckinghamshire MK5 8HD
Tel: 01908 690590
Principal: Mrs Deborah Berkin
Age range: 3 months–13 years
No. of pupils: 210

The Webber Independent School
Soskin Drive, Stantonbury Fields, Milton
Keynes, Buckinghamshire MK14 6DP
Tel: 01908 574740
Principal: Mrs Hilary Marsden
Age range: 3–18
No. of pupils: 300 VIth15
Fees: Day £9,030–£12,705

WYCOMBE ABBEY
For further details see p. 80
High Wycombe,
Buckinghamshire HP11 1PE
Tel: +44 (0)1494 897008
Email: registrar@
wycombeabbey.com
Website: www.wycombeabbey.com
Headmistress: Mrs Jo Duncan MA
(St Andrews), PGCE (Cantab)
Age range: G11–18
No. of pupils: 636
Fees: Day £30,270 FB £40,350

THORNTON COLLEGE
For further details see p. 78
College Lane, Thornton,
Buckinghamshire MK17 0HJ
Tel: 01280 812610
Email: admissions@
thorntoncollege.com
Website: www.thorntoncollege.com
Headteacher: Mrs Val Holmes
Age range: B2–4 G2–18
No. of pupils: 437
Fees: Day £10,035–£16,005 WB
£17,310–£21,900 FB £21,525–£26,700

Walton Pre-Preparatory School & Nursery
The Old Rectory, Walton Drive, Milton
Keynes, Buckinghamshire MK7 6BB
Tel: 01908 678403
Headmistress: Mrs Chantelle
McLaughlan
Age range: 2 months–5 years
No. of pupils: 120
Fees: Day £7,200–£14,280

Gloucestershire

Airthrie School
29 Christchurch Road, Cheltenham,
Gloucestershire GL50 2NY
Tel: 01242 512837
Headteacher: Mrs Sara Jackson
Age range: 3–11
No. of pupils: 168
Fees: Day £6,770–£9,930

**Al-Ashraf Secondary
School for Girls**
Sinope Street, off Widden Street,
Gloucester, Gloucestershire GL1 4AW
Tel: 01452 300465
Head: Mufti Abdullah Patel
Age range: G11–16
No. of pupils: 67
Fees: Day £1,325–£2,000

Beaudesert Park School
Minchinhampton, Stroud,
Gloucestershire GL6 9AF
Tel: 01453 832072
Headmaster: Mr J P R
Womersley BA, PGCE
Age range: 3–13
No. of pupils: 450
Fees: Day £5,745–£17,661 FB £22,677

Berkhampstead School
Pittville Circus Road, Cheltenham,
Gloucestershire GL52 2QA
Tel: 01242 523263
Head: R P Cross BSc(Hons)
Age range: 3–11
No. of pupils: 215
Fees: Day £2,397–£10,380

Bredon School
Pull Court, Bushley, Tewkesbury,
Gloucestershire GL20 6AH
Tel: 01684 293156
Head Teacher: Mr Koen Claeys
Age range: 7–18
No. of pupils: 215
Fees: Day £11,040–£21,945 WB
£15,440–£26,345 FB £15,440–£26,345

Cheltenham College
Bath Road, Cheltenham,
Gloucestershire GL53 7LD
Tel: 01242 265600
Headmaster: Nicola Huggett
Age range: 13–18
No. of pupils: 650 VIth270
Fees: Day £27,585–£28,575
FB £36,780–£37,770

**Cheltenham College
Preparatory School**
Thirlestaine Road, Cheltenham,
Gloucestershire GL53 7AB
Tel: 01242 522697
Headmaster: Mr Tom O'Sullivan
Age range: 7–13
No. of pupils: 420
Fees: Day £11,985–£18,315
FB £18,255–£23,790

Cheltenham Ladies' College
Bayshill Road, Cheltenham,
Gloucestershire GL50 3EP
Tel: +44 (0)1242 520691
Principal: Eve Jardine-Young MA
Age range: G11–18
No. of pupils: 850 VIth305
Fees: Day £24,810–£28,230
FB £36,945–£41,610

**Dean Close Pre-Preparatory
& Preparatory School**
Lansdown Road, Cheltenham,
Gloucestershire GL51 6QS
Tel: 01242 512217
**Headmaster Preparatory
School:** Paddy Moss
Age range: 2+–13
No. of pupils: 292
Fees: Day £7,959–£18,750
FB £19,260–£25,365

Dean Close School
Shelburne Road, Cheltenham,
Gloucestershire GL51 6HE
Tel: 01242 258044
Headmaster: Mr Bradley
Salisbury MEd, PGCE
Age range: 13–18
No. of pupils: 490 VIth220
Fees: Day £23,316–£24,600
FB £34,455–£35,817

Dormer House School
High Street, Moreton-in-Marsh,
Gloucestershire GL56 0AD
Tel: 01608 650758
Headmistress: Mrs Alison Thomas
Age range: 2–11
Fees: Day £8,586

Eastbrook College
7a Eastbrook Education Trust,
Gloucester, Gloucestershire GL4 3DB
Tel: 01452 417722
Age range: 11–16
No. of pupils: 59

Focus School – Berkeley Campus
Wanswell, Berkeley,
Gloucestershire GL13 9RS
Tel: 01453 511282
Headteacher: Mrs Lucy Sherrin
Age range: 7–18
No. of pupils: 100

Hatherop Castle School
Hatherop, Cirencester,
Gloucestershire GL7 3NB
Tel: 01285 750206
Headmaster: Mr Nigel Reed
M.Ed, B.Sc (Hons), PGCE
Age range: 2–13
No. of pupils: 210
Fees: Day £6,285–£10,455
FB £15,270–£16,110

Hopelands Preparatory School
38 Regent Street, Stonehouse,
Gloucestershire GL10 2AD
Tel: 01453 822164
Headmistress: Mrs S Bradburn
Age range: 3–11
No. of pupils: 59
Fees: Day £6,288–£9,123

Kitebrook Preparatory School
Kitebrook House, Moreton-in-
Marsh, Gloucestershire GL56 0RP
Tel: 01608 674350
Headmistress: Mrs Susan McLean
Age range: 3–13
No. of pupils: 200

Rendcomb College
Rendcomb, Cirencester,
Gloucestershire GL7 7HA
Tel: 01285 831213
Headmaster: Mr R Jones BA(Hons), MEd
Age range: 3–18
No. of pupils: 350 VIth72
Fees: Day £2,070–£7,775 WB
£8,140–£9,785 FB £8,925–£11,995

St Edward's Preparatory School
London Road, Charlton
Kings, Cheltenham,
Gloucestershire GL52 6NR
Tel: 01242 538900
Headmaster: Mr Stephen
McKernan BA(Hons) MEd NPQH
Age range: 1–11
No. of pupils: 295
Fees: Day £7,770–£12,975

St Edward's School
Cirencester Road, Cheltenham,
Gloucestershire GL53 8EY
Tel: 01242 538600
Head: Mrs P Clayfield BSc
Age range: 11–18
No. of pupils: 344 VIth105
Fees: Day £14,550–£17,760

The Acorn School
Church Street, Nailsworth,
Gloucestershire GL6 0BP
Tel: 01453 836508
Headmaster: Mr Graeme E B Whiting
Age range: 7–18
No. of pupils: VIth30
Fees: Day £6,675–£12,045

The King's School
Gloucester, Gloucestershire GL1 2BG
Tel: 01452 337337
Headmaster: David Morton
Age range: 3–18
No. of pupils: VIth80
Fees: Day £7,350–£19,185

The Richard Pate School
Southern Road, Cheltenham,
Gloucestershire GL53 9RP
Tel: 01242 522086
Headmaster: Mr Robert MacDonald
Age range: 3–11 years
No. of pupils: 300
Fees: Day £3,330–£10,410

Westonbirt Prep School
Westonbirt, Tetbury,
Gloucestershire GL8 8QG
Tel: 01666 881400
Headmaster: Mr Sean Price
Age range: 3–11
Fees: Day £2,680–£3,865

Westonbirt School
Westonbirt, Tetbury,
Gloucestershire GL8 8QG
Tel: 01666 881333
Headmistress: Mrs Natasha
Dangerfield
Age range: 11–18 years
Fees: Day £4,995 FB £9,750

Wotton House International School
Wotton House, Horton Road,
Gloucester, Gloucestershire GL1 3PR
Tel: +44 (0)1452 764248
Principal: Dr Daniel Sturdy
Age range: 11–16
No. of pupils: 25

**Wycliffe Preparatory
& Senior School**
Bath Road, Stonehouse,
Gloucestershire GL10 2JQ
Tel: 01453 822432
Senior School Head: Mr
Nick Gregory BA, MEd
Age range: 2–18
No. of pupils: VIth178
Fees: Day £9,675–£20,985
FB £20,625–£38,115

Wynstones School
Whaddon Green, Gloucester,
Gloucestershire GL4 0UF
Tel: 01452 429220
**Chair of the College of
Teachers:** Marianna Law-Lindberg
Age range: 3–18
No. of pupils: VIth9
Fees: Day £2,820–£9,540 FB £8,160

Oxfordshire

Abingdon Preparatory School
Josca's House, Frilford, Abingdon,
Oxfordshire OX13 5NX
Tel: 01865 391570
Headmaster: Mr Craig Williams
Age range: B4–13
No. of pupils: B250
Fees: Day £12,090–£16,620

Abingdon School
Park Road, Abingdon,
Oxfordshire OX14 1DE
Tel: 01235 521563
Head: Michael Windsor
Age range: B11–18
No. of pupils: 1000
Fees: Day £19,950 WB £33,210 FB £39,750

Bloxham School
Bloxham, Banbury,
Oxfordshire OX15 4PE
Tel: 01295 720222 or 724301
Headmaster: Mr Paul Sanderson
Age range: 11–18
No. of pupils: 431
Fees: Day £17,985–£25,785 WB
£25,785 FB £33,675–£35,175

Burford School
Cheltenham Road, Burford,
Oxfordshire OX18 4PL
Tel: 01993 823303/823283
Headteacher: Mrs K Haig BA, MEd
Age range: 11–18
No. of pupils: 1156 VIth200
Fees: FB £9,900

Carfax College
25 Beaumont Street, Oxford,
Oxfordshire OX1 2NP
Tel: +44 1865 200 676
Principal: Dr Victoria Jefferson

Carrdus School
Overthorpe Hall, Banbury,
Oxfordshire OX17 2BS
Tel: 01295 263733
Head: Mr Edward Way
Age range: B3–8 G3–11
No. of pupils: 122
Fees: Day £735–£11,625

Chandlings
Bagley Wood, Kennington,
Oxford, Oxfordshire OX1 5ND
Tel: 01865 730771
Head: Christine Cook
Age range: 2–11
Fees: Day £10,110–£15,870

Cherwell College
Cantay House, Park End Street,
Oxford, Oxfordshire OX1 1JD
Tel: 01865 242670
Principal: Stephen Clarke
Age range: 15+
No. of pupils: 100
Fees: Day £26,520 FB £13,600

Childfirst Day Nursery Banbury
The Old Museum, 8 Horsefair,
Banbury, Oxfordshire OX16 0AA
Tel: 01295 273743

Childfirst Day Nursery Bicester
32 Launton Road, Bicester,
Oxfordshire OX26 6PY
Tel: 01869 323730
Headmistress: Miss J
Fowler BA(Hons), QTS
Age range: 2 months–7 years
Fees: Day £7,500

Christ Church Cathedral School
3 Brewer Street, Oxford,
Oxfordshire OX1 1QW
Tel: 01865 242561
Headmaster: Richard Murray
Age range: B3–13 G3–4
No. of pupils: 159
Fees: Day £5,667–£16,569 FB £7,560

Cokethorpe School
Witney, Oxfordshire OX29 7PU
Tel: 01993 703921
Headmaster: Mr D Ettinger
BA, MA, PGCE
Age range: 4–18
No. of pupils: 666 VIth133
Fees: Day £12,600–£19,200

Cothill House
Abingdon, Oxfordshire OX13 6JL
Tel: 01865 390800
Headmaster: Mr D M Bailey
Age range: B8–13
No. of pupils: 250
Fees: FB £27,660

Cranford House School
Moulsford, Wallingford,
Oxfordshire OX10 9HT
Tel: 01491 651218
Age range: B3–11 G3–16
No. of pupils: 380
Fees: Day £10,500–£16,530

d'Overbroeck's
333 Banbury Road, Oxford,
Oxfordshire OX2 7PL
Tel: 01865 310000
Acting Principal: Mr Jonathan Cuff
Age range: 11–18
No. of pupils: 595 VIth325
Fees: Day £18,150–£24,300
FB £34,800–£41,550

Dragon School
Bardwell Road, Oxford,
Oxfordshire OX2 6SS
Tel: 01865 315400
Head: Mr Crispin Hyde-Dunn
Age range: 4–13
No. of pupils: 844
Fees: Day £11,988–£21,135 FB £30,615

EF ACADEMY OXFORD
For further details see p. 60
Pullens Lane, Headington,
Oxfordshire OX3 0DT
Tel: +41 (0) 43 430 4095
Email: iaeurope@ef.com
Website: www.ef.com/academy
Head of School: Dr. Paul Ellis
Age range: 16–19
No. of pupils: 188

Emmanuel Christian School
Sandford Road, Littlemore,
Oxford, Oxfordshire OX4 4PU
Tel: 01865 395236
Principal: Mrs Elizabeth Nesbitt
Age range: 3–11
No. of pupils: 43
Fees: Day £5,550

GREENE'S TUTORIAL COLLEGE
For further details see p. 62
45 Pembroke Street, Oxford,
Oxfordshire OX1 1BP
Tel: 01865 664400
Email: enquiries@greenes.org.uk
Website: www.greenes.org.uk
Principal: Zoë Spilberg
No. of pupils: VIth49

Headington Preparatory School
26 London Road, Oxford,
Oxfordshire OX3 7PB
Tel: +44 (0)1865 759116
Head: Mrs Jane Crouch BA (Hons), MA
Age range: G3–11
No. of pupils: 280

HEADINGTON SCHOOL
For further details see p. 64
London Road, Oxford,
Oxfordshire OX3 7TD
Tel: +44 (0)1865 759100
Email: admissions@headington.org
Website: www.headington.org
Headmistress: Mrs Caroline
Jordan MA(Oxon)
Age range: G11–18
No. of pupils: VIth250

KINGHAM HILL SCHOOL
For further details see p. 66
Kingham, Chipping Norton,
Oxfordshire OX7 6TH
Tel: 01608 658999
Email: registrar@kinghamhill.org
Website: www.kinghamhill.org.uk
Age range: 11–18
No. of pupils: 352
Fees: Day £17,895–£20,385 WB
£25,350–£31,305 FB £26,160–£34,350

Magdalen College School
Cowley Place, Oxford,
Oxfordshire OX4 1DZ
Tel: 01865 242191
Master: Helen Pike
Age range: B7–18
No. of pupils: 669 VIth161
Fees: Day £17,799–£18,477

Moulsford Preparatory School
Moulsford-on-Thames,
Oxfordshire OX10 9HR
Tel: 01491 651438
Headmaster: Mr B Beardmore-Gray
Age range: B4–13
No. of pupils: 367
Fees: FB £7,120

New College School
2 Savile Road, Oxford,
Oxfordshire OX1 3UA
Tel: 01865 285 560
Headmaster: Mr N R Gullifer MA, FRSA
Age range: B4–13
No. of pupils: 160
Fees: Day £9,870–£15,951

Our Lady's Abingdon School
Radley Road, Abingdon,
Oxfordshire OX14 3PS
Tel: 01235 524658
Principal: Mr Stephen Oliver
Age range: 3–18
No. of pupils: 499 VIth81
Fees: Day £9,033–£15,300

Oxford High School GDST
Belbroughton Road, Oxford,
Oxfordshire OX2 6XA
Tel: 01865 559888
Head: Dr Phillip Hills
Age range: G4–18
No. of pupils: 900
Fees: Day £9,000–£15,546

Oxford Montessori School
Forest Farm, Elsfield, Oxford,
Oxfordshire OX3 9UW
Tel: 01865 358210
Principal: Judith Walker Mont Dip, NNEB
Age range: 5–10
No. of pupils: 169

OXFORD SIXTH FORM COLLEGE
For further details see p. 68
12-13 King Edward Street,
Oxford, Oxfordshire OX1 4HT
Tel: +44 (0)1865 793233
Email: admissions@
oxfordsixthformcollege.com
Website:
www.oxfordsixthformcollege.com
Principal: Mr Mark Love
Age range: 15–19
No. of pupils: 197

RADLEY COLLEGE
For further details see p. 70
Radley, Abingdon,
Oxfordshire OX14 2HR
Tel: 01235 543106
Email: admissions@radley.org.uk
Website: www.radley.org.uk
The Warden: Mr J S Moule
Age range: B13–18
No. of pupils: 690
Fees: FB £38,325

Rupert House School
90 Bell Street, Henley-on-Thames,
Oxfordshire RG9 2BN
Tel: 01491 574263
Headmistress: Mrs C Lynas
Age range: B4–7 G4–11
No. of pupils: 214
Fees: Day £5,640–£13,785

Rye St Antony
Pullens Lane, Oxford,
Oxfordshire OX3 0BY
Tel: 01865 762802
Headmistress: Miss A M Jones BA, PGCE
Age range: B3–11 G3–18
No. of pupils: 400 VIth70
Fees: Day £9,870–£15,330 WB
£21,000–£24,690 FB £22,230–£25,935

SHIPLAKE COLLEGE
For further details see p. 72
Henley-on-Thames,
Oxfordshire RG9 4BW
Tel: +44 (0)1189 402455
Email: registrar@shiplake.org.uk
Website: www.shiplake.org.uk
Headmaster: Mr T G
Howe MA, MSt, MBA
Age range: B11–18 G16–18
No. of pupils: 475 VIth195
Fees: Day £18,675–£23,460 WB
£26,175–£32,730 FB £34,890

Sibford School
Sibford Ferris, Banbury,
Oxfordshire OX15 5QL
Tel: 01295 781200
Head of School: Toby Spence
No. of pupils: VIth840
Fees: Day £9,180–£14,739 WB
£26,154–£26,670 FB £28,077–£28,644

St Clare's, Oxford
139 Banbury Road, Oxford,
Oxfordshire OX2 7AL
Tel: +44 (0)1865 552031
Principal: Mr Andrew Rattue
Age range: 15–18
No. of pupils: 257
Fees: Day £19,878 FB £41,375

St Edward's, Oxford
Woodstock Road, Oxford,
Oxfordshire OX2 7NN
Tel: +44 (0)1865 319200
Warden: Stephen Jones
Age range: 13–18
No. of pupils: 700
Fees: Day £10,095 FB £12,615

ST HELEN AND ST KATHARINE
For further details see p. 74
Faringdon Road, Abingdon,
Oxfordshire OX14 1BE
Tel: 01235 520173
Email: info@shsk.org.uk
Website: www.shsk.org.uk
Headmistress: Mrs Rebecca
Dougall BA MA
Age range: G9–18
No. of pupils: 730
Fees: Day £5,665

St Hugh's School
Carswell Manor, Faringdon,
Oxfordshire SN7 8PT
Tel: 01367 870700
Headmaster: Mr Andrew
Nott BA (Wales), PGCE
Age range: 3–13
Fees: Day £11,655–£20,085
WB £21,600–£23,100

St John's Priory School
St John's Road, Banbury,
Oxfordshire OX16 5HX
Tel: 01295 259607
Headmistress: Tracey Wilson
Age range: 3–11
Fees: Day £6,715–£9,450

St Mary's Preparatory School
13 St Andrew's Road, Henley-on-
Thames, Oxfordshire RG9 1HS
Tel: 01491 573118
Headmaster: Mr Rob Harmer (BA)Hons
Age range: 2–11
No. of pupils: 118
Fees: Day £4,010

Summer Fields
Mayfield Road, Oxford,
Oxfordshire OX2 7EN
Tel: 01865 454433
Headmaster: Mr David
Faber MA(Oxon)
Age range: B4–13
No. of pupils: 256
Fees: Day £12,000–£21,159 FB £30,360

The King's School, Witney
New Yatt Road, Witney,
Oxfordshire OX29 6TA
Tel: 01993 778463
Principal: Mr Steve Beegoo
Age range: 3–16
No. of pupils: 200
Fees: Day £5,244

The Manor Preparatory School
Faringdon Road, Abingdon,
Oxfordshire OX13 6LN
Tel: 01235 858458
Headmaster: Mr Alastair Thomas
Age range: 2–11 years
No. of pupils: 344
Fees: Day £4,510–£5,500

The Unicorn School
20 Marcham Road, Abingdon,
Oxfordshire OX14 1AA
Tel: 01235 530222
Headteacher: Mr. Andrew Day BEd
(Hons)University of Wales (Cardiff)
Age range: 6–16 years
No. of pupils: 74
Fees: Day £19,500

Tudor Hall School
Wykham Park, Banbury,
Oxfordshire OX16 9UR
Tel: 01295 263434
Headmistress: Miss Wendy Griffiths BSc
Age range: G11–18
No. of pupils: 325
Fees: Day £7,365 FB £11,870

Windrush Valley School
The Green, London Lane,
Ascott-under-Wychwood,
Oxfordshire OX7 6AN
Tel: 01993 831793
Headmaster: Mr Alan Wood MEd,
TCert, DipSpEd, ACP, FCollP
Age range: 3–11
No. of pupils: 125
Fees: Day £6,801

Wychwood School
74 Banbury Road, Oxford,
Oxfordshire OX2 6JR
Tel: 01865 557976
Headmistress: Mrs A K
Johnson BSc (Dunelm)
Age range: G11–18
No. of pupils: 120 VIth40
Fees: Day £15,900 WB
£24,300 FB £27,900

Somerset

Ashbrooke House School
9 Ellenborough Park North, Weston-
Super-Mare, Somerset BS23 1XH
Tel: 01934 629515
Headteacher: Karen Wallington
Age range: 3–11
Fees: Day £5,535–£6,411

Sidcot School
Oakridge Lane, Winscombe,
Somerset BS25 1PD
Tel: 01934 843102
Head: Iain Kilpatrick
Age range: 3–18
No. of pupils: 515 VIth170
Fees: Day £7,860–£17,640
FB £26,610–£31,830

West Berkshire

**Brockhurst & Marlston
House Schools**
Hermitage, Newbury, West
Berkshire RG18 9UL
Tel: 01635 200293
Head of School: Mr David Fleming
Age range: 2½–13
No. of pupils: 275
Fees: Day £10,650–£17,850
FB £23,925–£25,800

Cheam School
Headley, Newbury, West
Berkshire RG19 8LD
Tel: +44 (0)1635 268242
Headmaster: Mr Martin Harris
Age range: 3–13
No. of pupils: 407
Fees: Day £11,940–£21,285
FB £26,055–£27,630

Downe House School
Hermitage Road, Cold Ash,
Thatcham, West Berkshire RG18 9JJ
Tel: 01635 200286
Headmistress: Mrs E
McKendrick BA(Liverpool)
Age range: G11–18
No. of pupils: VIth174
Fees: Day £27,495 FB £37,530

Horris Hill
Newtown, Newbury, West
Berkshire RG20 9DJ
Tel: 01635 40594
Headmaster: Mr G F Tollit B.A.(Hons)
Age range: B4–13
No. of pupils: 120
Fees: Day £5,600 FB £8,900

**Marlston House
Preparatory School**
Hermitage, Newbury, West
Berkshire RG18 9UL
Tel: 01635 200293
Headmistress: Mrs Caroline
Riley MA, BEd
Age range: G3–13
No. of pupils: 110
Fees: Day £10,650–£17,850 FB £23,925

Newbury Hall
Enborne Road, (corner of
Rockingham Road), Newbury,
West Berkshire RG14 6AD
Tel: +44 (0)1635 36879

St Gabriel's
Sandleford Priory, Newbury,
West Berkshire RG20 9BD
Tel: 01635 555680
Principal: Mr Richard Smith
MA (Hons), MEd, PGCE
Age range: B6 months–11
G6 months–18
No. of pupils: 469 VIth40
Fees: Day £10,668–£17,418

St Michael's School
Harts Lane, Burghclere, Newbury,
West Berkshire RG20 9JW
Tel: 01635 278137
Headmaster: Rev. Fr. Patrick Summers
Age range: 5–18
No. of pupils: VIth5

The Cedars School
Church Road, Aldermaston,
West Berkshire RG7 4LR
Tel: 0118 971 4251
Headteacher: Mrs Jane O'Halloran
Age range: 4–11
No. of pupils: 50
Fees: Day £8,910

Thorngrove School
The Mount, Highclere, Newbury,
West Berkshire RG20 9PS
Tel: 01635 253172
Headmaster: Mr Adam King
Age range: 2–13
Fees: Day £14,070–£17,595

Wiltshire

Avondale School
High Street, Bulford, Salisbury,
Wiltshire SP4 9DR
Tel: 01980 632387
Head of School: Mr Ben Coombes
Age range: 2–11
Fees: Day £8,097

Bishopstrow College
Bishopstrow, Warminster,
Wiltshire BA12 9HU
Tel: +44 (0)1985 219210
Principal: Ms Lorraine Atkins
Age range: 7–17 years

Chafyn Grove School
33 Bourne Avenue, Salisbury,
Wiltshire SP1 1LR
Tel: 01722 333423
Headmaster: Mr Simon Head
Age range: 3–13
No. of pupils: 265

DAUNTSEY'S SCHOOL
For further details see p. 58
High Street, West Lavington,
Devizes, Wiltshire SN10 4HE
Tel: 01380 814500
Email: admissions@dauntseys.org
Website: www.dauntseys.org
Head Master: Mr Mark Lascelles
Age range: 11–18
No. of pupils: 820 VIth270
Fees: Day £19,650 FB £32,550

Emmaus School
School Lane, Staverton,
Trowbridge, Wiltshire BA14 6NZ
Tel: 01225 782684
Head: Mrs M Wiltshire
Age range: 5–16
No. of pupils: 75
Fees: Day £3,500–£4,400

Focus School – Wilton Campus
The Hollows, Wilton, Salisbury,
Wiltshire SP2 0JE
Tel: 01722 741910
Age range: 11–18
No. of pupils: 100

Godolphin Preparatory School
Laverstock Road, Salisbury,
Wiltshire SP1 2RB
Tel: 01722 430 652
Headmistress: Emma Hattersley
Age range: G3–11
No. of pupils: 100
Fees: Day £7,125–£13,935
WB £21,540 FB £25,230

Godolphin School
Milford Hill, Salisbury, Wiltshire SP1 2RA
Tel: 01722 430509
Headmistress: Mrs Emma Hattersley
BA (Dunelm) Postgrad RAM
Age range: G11–18
No. of pupils: 380 VIth100

Heywood Prep
The Priory, Corsham, Wiltshire SN13 0AP
Tel: 01249 713379
Headmistress: Rebecca Mitchell
Age range: 2–11
No. of pupils: 140
Fees: Day £5,760–£8,985

Leehurst Swan School
Campbell Road, Salisbury,
Wiltshire SP1 3BQ
Tel: 01722 333094
Headmaster (Interim): Mr
Terence Ayres
Age range: Reception–16 years
Fees: Day £8,985–£15,300

Maranatha Christian School
Queenlaines Farm, Sevenhampton,
Swindon, Wiltshire SN6 7SQ
Tel: 01793 762075
Headteacher: Mr Paul Medlock
Age range: 3–18
No. of pupils: 68

Marlborough College
Bath Road, Marlborough,
Wiltshire SN8 1PA
Tel: 01672 892300
Master: Louise Moelwyn-Hughes
Age range: 13–18
No. of pupils: 960
Fees: FB £37,815

**Meadowpark Nursery
& Pre-Preparatory**
Calcutt Street, Cricklade,
Wiltshire SN6 6BA
Tel: 01793 752600
Headteacher: Mrs R Kular
Age range: 0–11
Fees: Day £6,585–£8,550

Pinewood School
Bourton, Swindon, Wiltshire SN6 8HZ
Tel: 01793 782205
Headmaster: Mr P J Hoyland
Age range: 3–13
No. of pupils: 313
Fees: Day £8,790–£17,895 WB £22,260

Prior Park Preparatory School
Calcutt Street, Cricklade,
Wiltshire SN6 6BB
Tel: 01793 750275
Headteacher: Guy Barrett
Age range: 2–13
No. of pupils: 240
Fees: Day £6,900–£14,460

Salisbury Cathedral School
The Old Palace, 1 The Close,
Salisbury, Wiltshire SP1 2EQ
Tel: 01722 555300
Head Master: Mr Clive Marriott BEd MA
Age range: 3–13
No. of pupils: 220
Fees: Day £8,700–£15,690
FB £16,065–£23,053

Sandroyd School
Rushmore, Tollard Royal,
Salisbury, Wiltshire SP5 5QD
Tel: 01725 516264
Headmaster: Mr Alastair Speers
Age range: 5–13
No. of pupils: 225
Fees: Day £8,760–£25,410
FB £20,100–£25,410

St Francis School
Marlborough Road, Pewsey,
Wiltshire SN9 5NT
Tel: 01672 563228
Headmaster: Mr David Sibson
Age range: 0–13
Fees: Day £4,821–£12,571

St Margaret's Preparatory School
Curzon Street, Calne, Wiltshire SN11 0DF
Tel: 01249 857220
Headmistress: Mrs Karen Cordon
GLCM LLCM (TD) ALCM
Age range: 3–11
No. of pupils: 200
Fees: Day £9,900–£13,500

ST MARY'S CALNE
For further details see p. 76
Curzon Street, Calne,
Wiltshire SN11 0DF
Tel: 01249 857200
Email: office@stmaryscalne.org
Website: www.stmaryscalne.org
Headmistress: Dr Felicia Kirk
BA(University of MD), MA,
PhD(Brown University)
Age range: G11–18
No. of pupils: 365 VIth121
Fees: Day £29,745 FB £39,885

Stonar School
Cottles Park, Atworth, Melksham,
Wiltshire SN12 8NT
Tel: 01225 701740
Head of School: Dr Sally Divall
Age range: 2–18
No. of pupils: 330
Fees: Day £8,496–£16,500
FB £21,954–£33,195

Warminster School
Church Street, Warminster,
Wiltshire BA12 8PJ
Tel: +44 (0)1985 210100
Headmaster: Mr Mark
Mortimer MBA BA
Age range: 3–18
No. of pupils: 530
Fees: Day £5,110 FB £10,880

D320

East

KEY TO SYMBOLS
- 🜚 *Boys' school*
- 🜛 *Girls' school*
- 🌐 *International school*
- 16ᵗ *Tutorial or sixth form college*
- Ⓐ *A levels*
- 🏛 *Boarding accommodation*
- £ *Bursaries*
- ⒾⒷ *International Baccalaureate*
- ✎ *Learning support*
- 16⁺ *Entrance at 16+*
- 🎓 *Vocational qualifications*
- ⒾⒶⓅⓈ *Independent Association of Preparatory Schools*
- ⒽⓂⒸ *The Headmasters' & Headmistresses' Conference*
- ⒾⓈⒶ *Independent Schools Association*
- ⒼⓈⒶ *Girls' School Association*
- ⒷⓈⒶ *Boarding Schools' Association*
- Ⓢ *Society of Heads*

Unless otherwise indicated, all schools are coeducational day schools. Single-sex and boarding schools will be indicated by the relevant icon.

Bedfordshire

Bedford Girls' School
Cardington Road, Bedford,
Bedfordshire MK42 0BX
Tel: 01234 361900
Headmistress: Miss Jo
MacKenzie BSc, MSc
Age range: G7–18
No. of pupils: 903
♿ 🌐 Ⓐ £ ⒾⒷ 16+

Bedford Modern School
Manton Lane, Bedford,
Bedfordshire MK41 7NT
Tel: 01234 332500
Headmaster: Mr Alex Tate
Age range: 7–18
No. of pupils: 1236
Fees: Day £10,074–£13,821
Ⓐ £ 16+

Bedford Preparatory School
De Parys Avenue, Bedford,
Bedfordshire MK40 2TU
Tel: 01234 362271/362274
Headmaster: Ian Silk
Age range: B7–13
No. of pupils: 438
Fees: Day £12,333–£16,161 WB
£20,919–£25,038 FB £21,948–£26,067
♿ 🏫 ✎

Bedford School
De Parys Avenue, Bedford,
Bedfordshire MK40 2TU
Tel: +44 (0)1234 362216
Head Master: Mr James Hodgson BA
Age range: B7–18 years
No. of pupils: 1121
Fees: Day £12,333–£19,032 WB
£20,919–£31,125 FB £21,948–£32,190
♿ 🌐 Ⓐ 🏫 £ ⒾⒷ 16+

**Focus School –
Biggleswade Campus**
The Oaks, Potton Road, Biggleswade,
Bedfordshire SG18 0EP
Tel: 01767 602800
Age range: 7–18 years
No. of pupils: 75

Focus School – Dunstable Campus
Ridgeway Avenue, Dunstable,
Bedfordshire LU5 4QL
Tel: 01582 665676
Age range: 11–16
No. of pupils: 77

**Luton Pentecostal Church
Christian Academy**
15 Church Street, Luton,
Bedfordshire LU1 3JE
Tel: 01582 412276
Principal: Pastor Chris Oakey
Age range: 3–13
No. of pupils: 56
Fees: Day £2,280–£3,360
£

Orchard School & Nursery
High Gobion Road, Barton-le-Clay,
Bedford, Bedfordshire MK45 4LT
Tel: 01582 882054
Headteacher: Mrs A Burton
Age range: 0–6
No. of pupils: 127

Pilgrims Pre-Preparatory School
Brickhill Drive, Bedford,
Bedfordshire MK41 7QZ
Tel: 01234 369555
Head: Mrs J Webster BEd(Hons), EYPS
Age range: 3 months–7 years
No. of pupils: 385
Fees: Day £9,771–£13,980

Polam School
43-45 Lansdowne Road, Bedford,
Bedfordshire MK40 2BU
Tel: 01234 261864
Head: Mrs Jessica Harris
Age range: 1–9
No. of pupils: 100
Fees: Day £8,145

Rabia Girls' & Boys' School
12-16 Portland Road, Luton,
Bedfordshire LU4 8AX
Tel: 01582 493239
Headteacher: Hafsa Bilquees
Age range: 5–16
No. of pupils: 41

Rushmoor School
58-60 Shakespeare Road, Bedford,
Bedfordshire MK40 2DL
Tel: 01234 352031
Headteacher: Ian Daniel BA, NPQH
Age range: B3–16 G3–11
Fees: Day £6,429–£11,022
£ ✎

St Andrew's School
78 Kimbolton Road, Bedford,
Bedfordshire MK40 2PA
Tel: 01234 267272
Headmaster: Mr Ian Daniel
Age range: B3–9 G3–16
No. of pupils: 385
Fees: Day £5,598–£11,022
♿ ✎

St George's School
28 Priory Road, Dunstable,
Bedfordshire LU5 4HR
Tel: 01582 661471
Head Teacher: Ms Ellie Graham
Age range: 3–11
No. of pupils: 120
Fees: Day £6,852–£7,119
✎

Cambridgeshire

Abbey College Cambridge
Homerton Gardens, Purbeck Road,
Cambridge, Cambridgeshire CB2 8EB
Tel: 01223 578280
Principal: Dr Julian Davies
Age range: 13–21
No. of pupils: VIth370
Fees: Day £22,000 FB £39,000–£43,000
16+ Ⓐ 🏫 £ ✎ 16+

Bellerbys College Cambridge
Queens Campus, Bateman Street,
Cambridge, Cambridgeshire CB2 1LU
Tel: +44 (0)1223 652 800
Principal: Mr Nicholas Waite
Age range: 14–25
🌐 Ⓐ 🏫 £

Cambridge International School
The Temple, Bourn Bridge Road, Little
Abington, Cambridgeshire CB21 6AN
Tel: 01223 832719
Principal: Mr Joel Dixon
Age range: 11–16 years
🌐 £

**Cambridge Seminars
Tutorial College**
Logic House, 143-147 Newmarket Road,
Cambridge, Cambridgeshire CB5 8HA
Tel: 01223 313464
Principal: M R Minhas BSc, CEng
Age range: 16–20
Fees: Day £1,800–£24,000
16+ Ⓐ £

Cambridge Steiner School
Hinton Road, Fulbourn, Cambridge,
Cambridgeshire CB21 5DZ
Tel: 01223 882727
Age range: 2–14
No. of pupils: 125
Fees: Day £7,665
£

CATS College Cambridge
1 High Street, Chesterton, Cambridge,
Cambridgeshire CB4 1NQ
Tel: 01223 314431
Principal: Dr Craig Wilson
Age range: 14–19+
🌐 16+ Ⓐ 🏫 ✎

**CCSS (Cambridge Centre
for Sixth-form Studies)**
4-5 Bene't Place, Lensfield Road,
Cambridge, Cambridgeshire CB2 1EL
Tel: 01223 716890
Principal: Mr Stuart Nicholson
MA(Oxon), MBA, PGCE, NPQH, CPhys
Age range: 15–21
Fees: Day £18,750–£23,655
FB £25,050–£37,200
🌐 16+ Ⓐ 🏫 £ ✎ 16+

Kimbolton School
Kimbolton, Huntingdon,
Cambridgeshire PE28 0EA
Tel: 01480 860505
Headmaster: Jonathan Belbin BA
Age range: 4–18
No. of pupils: VIth170
Fees: Day £9,870–£15,795 FB £26,280
🌐 Ⓐ 🏫 £ ✎ 16+

**King's Acremont, King's
Ely Nursery & Pre-Prep**
30 Egremont Street, Ely,
Cambridgeshire CB6 1AE
Tel: 01353 660702
Head: Sue Freestone
Age range: 3–7
Fees: Day £10,077
✎

King's College School
West Road, Cambridge,
Cambridgeshire CB3 9DN
Tel: 01223 365814
Head: Mrs Yvette Day
BMus, MMus, GDL
Age range: 4–13
No. of pupils: 404
Fees: Day £12,240–£15,555 FB £24,210
🏫 £ ✎

KING'S ELY
For further details see p. 94
Ely, Cambridgeshire CB7 4EW
Tel: 01353 660707
Email: admissions@kingsely.org
Website: www.kingsely.org
Principal: Mr John
Attwater MA (Oxon)
Age range: 2–18
No. of pupils: 1120
Fees: Day £10,470–£22,305
FB £23,580–£32,280

King's Ely Junior
Ely, Cambridgeshire CB7 4DB
Tel: 01353 660707
Head: Mr Richard Whymark
Age range: 7–13
No. of pupils: 344
Fees: Day £14,232–£15,531
FB £22,692–£23,955

Magdalene House Preparatory School
North Brink, Wisbech,
Cambridgeshire PE13 1JX
Tel: 01945 586 780
Head: Mr Chris Staley
Age range: 3–11
No. of pupils: 180
Fees: Day £9,297–£9,597

MANDER PORTMAN WOODWARD – CAMBRIDGE
For further details see p. 96
3-4 Brookside, Cambridge,
Cambridgeshire CB2 1JE
Tel: 01223 350158
Email: cambridge@mpw.ac.uk
Website: www.mpw.ac.uk
Principal: Dr Markus Bernhardt
Age range: 15–19

Sancton Wood School
2 St Paul's Road, Cambridge,
Cambridgeshire CB1 2EZ
Tel: +44 (0)1223 471703
Head of School: Mr Richard Settle
Age range: 1–16
Fees: Day £10,740–£14,070

St Andrew's Cambridge
2A Free School Lane, Cambridge,
Cambridgeshire CB2 3QA
Tel: 01223 360040
Principal: Wayne Marshall
Age range: 14–20
No. of pupils: VIth130
Fees: FB £15,000–£17,000

ST FAITH'S
For further details see p. 104
Trumpington Road, Cambridge,
Cambridgeshire CB2 8AG
Tel: 01223 352073
Email: admissions@stfaiths.co.uk
Website: www.stfaiths.co.uk
Headmaster: Mr N L Helliwell
Age range: 4–13
No. of pupils: 540
Fees: Day £13,170–£16,590

St John's College School
73 Grange Road, Cambridge,
Cambridgeshire CB3 9AB
Tel: 01223 353532
Headmaster: Mr N. Chippington
MA(Cantab), FRCO
Age range: 4–13
No. of pupils: 453
Fees: Day £12,210–£15,330 FB £24,210

St Mary's School
Bateman Street, Cambridge,
Cambridgeshire CB2 1LY
Tel: 01223 353253
Headmistress: Ms Charlotte Avery
Age range: G4–18
No. of pupils: 619 VIth90
Fees: Day £9,909–£15,861 WB
£26,286–£28,032 FB £30,819–£32,562

Stephen Perse Foundation Junior School
St Eligius Street, Cambridge,
Cambridgeshire CB2 1HX
Tel: 01223 346 140
Head: Miss K Milne
Age range: 7–11
No. of pupils: 135
Fees: Day £15,150

Stephen Perse Foundation Senior School
Union Road, Cambridge,
Cambridgeshire CB2 1HF
Tel: 01223 454700
Principal: David Walker
Age range: 11–16 years
No. of pupils: VIth150
Fees: Day £17,550

Stephen Perse Pre-prep, Madingley
Cambridge Road,
Madingley, Cambridge,
Cambridgeshire CB23 8AH
Tel: 01954 210309
Head of Pre-prep: Mrs Sarah Holyoake
Age range: 3–7
No. of pupils: 60
Fees: Day £12,000

THE LEYS SCHOOL
For further details see p. 108
Trumpington Road, Cambridge,
Cambridgeshire CB2 7AD
Tel: 01223 508900
Email: admissions@theleys.net
Website: www.theleys.net
Headmaster: Mr Martin Priestley
Age range: 11–18
No. of pupils: 572
Fees: Day £16,545–£22,920
FB £24,960–£34,245

The Perse Pelican Nursery and Pre-Preparatory School
Northwold House, 92 Glebe Road,
Cambridge, Cambridgeshire CB1 7TD
Tel: 01223 403940
Headmistress: Mrs S C Waddington MA
Age range: 3–7
No. of pupils: 154
Fees: Day £13,530

The Perse Preparatory School
Trumpington Road, Cambridge,
Cambridgeshire CB2 8EX
Tel: 01223 403920
Head: Mr James Piper
Age range: 7–11
No. of pupils: 283
Fees: Day £15,705

The Perse School
Hills Road, Cambridge,
Cambridgeshire CB2 8QF
Tel: 01223 403800
Head: Mr Ed Elliott
Age range: 11–18
No. of pupils: 851 VIth250
Fees: Day £17,322

THE PETERBOROUGH SCHOOL
For further details see p. 110
Thorpe Road, Peterborough,
Cambridgeshire PE3 6AP
Tel: 01733 343357
Email: office@tpsch.co.uk
Website:
www.thepeterboroughschool.co.uk
Headmaster: Mr A D
Meadows BSc(Hons)
Age range: 6 weeks–18 years
No. of pupils: 440
Fees: Day £10,467–£15,642

Whitehall School
117 High Street, Somersham,
Cambridgeshire PE28 3EH
Tel: 01487 840966
Principal: Rebecca Hutley
Age range: 3–11
No. of pupils: 109
Fees: Day £6,975–£7,980

Wisbech Grammar School
North Brink, Wisbech,
Cambridgeshire PE13 1JX
Tel: 01945 583 631
Head: Mr Chris Staley BA, MBA
Age range: 11–18
No. of pupils: 410
Fees: Day £13,347

Essex

Alleyn Court Preparatory School
Wakering Road, Southend-on-Sea, Essex SS3 0PW
Tel: 01702 582553
Headmaster: Mr Rupert Snow
Age range: 2–11
Fees: Day £3,258–£12,729
£ 🏊

Brentwood Preparatory School
Middleton Hall, Brentwood, Essex CM15 8EQ
Tel: +44 (0)1277 243333
Headmaster: Mr Jason Whiskerd
Age range: 3–11
No. of pupils: 411
🏊

BRENTWOOD SCHOOL
For further details see p. 86
Middleton Hall Lane, Brentwood, Essex CM15 8EE
Tel: 01277 243243
Email: headmaster@brentwood.essex.sch.uk
Website: www.brentwoodschool.co.uk
Headmaster: Mr Michael Bond
Age range: 3–18
No. of pupils: 1620
Fees: Day £19,800 FB £38,799
🌐 Ⓐ 🏛 £ ⒤Ⓑ 🏊 ⒃

Colchester High School
Wellesley Road, Colchester, Essex CO3 3HD
Tel: 01206 573389
Principal: David Young BA(Hons), PGCE
Age range: 2–16
No. of pupils: 486
Fees: Day £3,300–£10,000
£ 🏊

Coopersale Hall School
Flux's Lane, off Stewards Green Road, Epping, Essex CM16 7PE
Tel: 01992 577133
Headmistress: Miss Kaye Lovejoy
Age range: 2–11
No. of pupils: 275
Fees: Day £10,350–£10,575

Dame Bradbury's School
Ashdon Road, Saffron Walden, Essex CB10 2AL
Tel: 01799 522348
Headmistress: Ms Tracy Handford
Age range: 3–11
No. of pupils: 254
Fees: Day £4,350–£13,800
£ 🏊

Elm Green Preparatory School
Parsonage Lane, Little Baddow, Chelmsford, Essex CM3 4SU
Tel: 01245 225230
Principal: Ms Ann Milner
Age range: 4–11
No. of pupils: 220
Fees: Day £8,844
🏊

Felsted Preparatory School
Felsted, Great Dunmow, Essex CM6 3JL
Tel: 01371 822610
Headmaster: Mr Simon James
Age range: 4–13
No. of pupils: 460
Fees: Day £9,285–£17,820 FB £23,250–£24,465
🏛 £ 🏊

FELSTED SCHOOL
For further details see p. 88
Felsted, Great Dunmow, Essex CM6 3LL
Tel: 01371 822605
Email: intadmissions@felsted.org
Website: www.felsted.org
Headmaster: Mr Chris Townsend
Age range: 13–18
No. of pupils: 556 VIth249
Fees: Day £24,495 WB £34,725 FB £37,485
🌐 Ⓐ 🏛 £ ⒤Ⓑ 🏊 ⒃

Gosfield School
Cut Hedge Park, Halstead Road, Gosfield, Halstead, Essex CO9 1PF
Tel: 01787 474040
Headteacher: Mr Guy Martyn
Age range: 4–18
No. of pupils: VIth21
Fees: Day £6,690–£15,525
🌐 Ⓐ 🏛 £ 🏊 ⒃

Heathcote School
Eves Corner, Danbury, Chelmsford, Essex CM3 4QB
Tel: 01245 223131
Headmistress: Caroline Forgeron
Age range: 2–11
Fees: Day £4,830–£7,245
£ 🏊

Herington House School
1 Mount Avenue, Hutton, Brentwood, Essex CM13 2NS
Tel: 01277 211595
Principal: Mr R. Dudley-Cooke
Age range: 3–11
No. of pupils: 130
Fees: Day £1,955–£3,865
£ 🏊

Holmwood House Preparatory School
Chitts Hill, Lexden, Colchester, Essex CO3 9ST
Tel: 01206 574305
Headmaster: Alexander Mitchell
Age range: 4–13
No. of pupils: 302
Fees: Day £10,140–£17,895 FB £35
🏛 🏊

Littlegarth School
Horkesley Park, Nayland, Colchester, Essex CO6 4JR
Tel: 01206 262332
Headmaster: Mr Peter H Jones
Age range: 2–11 years
No. of pupils: 318
Fees: Day £3,205–£3,723
£ 🏊

Maldon Court Preparatory School
Silver Street, Maldon, Essex CM9 4QE
Tel: 01621 853529
Headteacher: Elaine Mason
Age range: 3–11
Fees: Day £8,236
🏊

New Hall School
The Avenue, Boreham, Chelmsford, Essex CM3 3HS
Tel: 01245 467588
Principal: Mrs Katherine Jeffrey MA, BA, PGCE, MA(Ed Mg), NPQH
Age range: Coed 3-11, Single 11-16, Coed 16–18
No. of pupils: 1180 VIth217
Fees: Day £9,801–£19,878 WB £19,761–£28,569 FB £21,531–£30,681
🌐 Ⓐ 🏛 £ 🏊 ⒃

Oxford House School
2-4 Lexden Road, Colchester, Essex CO3 3NE
Tel: 01206 576686
Head Teacher: Mrs Sarah Leyshon
Age range: 2–11
No. of pupils: 158

Saint Nicholas School
Hillingdon House, Hobbs Cross Road, Harlow, Essex CM17 0NJ
Tel: 01279 429910
Headmaster: Mr D Bown
Age range: 4–16
No. of pupils: 400
Fees: Day £9,960–£12,660
£

Saint Pierre School
16 Leigh Road, Leigh-on-Sea, Southend-on-Sea, Essex SS9 1LE
Tel: 01702 474164
Headmaster: Mr Chris Perkins
Age range: 2–11+
Fees: Day £7,218–£8,181
£

ST CEDD'S SCHOOL
For further details see p. 100
178a New London Road, Chelmsford, Essex CM2 0AR
Tel: 01245 392810
Email: info@stcedds.org.uk
Website: www.stcedds.org.uk
Head: Mr Matthew Clarke
Age range: 3–11
No. of pupils: 400
Fees: Day £8,550–£10,935
🏊

St John's School
Stock Road, Billericay, Essex CM12 0AR
Tel: 01277 623070
Head Teacher: Mrs F Armour BEd(Hons)
Age range: 2–16 years
No. of pupils: 392
Fees: Day £5,328–£13,500
🏊

St Margaret's Preparatory School
Hall Drive, Gosfield, Halstead, Essex CO9 1SE
Tel: 01787 472134
Headmaster: Mr. Callum Douglas
Age range: 2–11
Fees: Day £3,240–£4,055
£ 🏊

St Mary's School
Lexden Road, Colchester, Essex CO3 3RB
Tel: 01206 572544   Admissions: 01206 216420
Principal: Mrs H K Vipond MEd, BSc(Hons), NPQH
Age range: B3–4 G3–16
No. of pupils: 430
Fees: Day £6,855–£14,985
🏛 £ 🏊

St Michael's Church Of England Preparatory School
198 Hadleigh Road, Leigh-on-Sea, Southend-on-Sea, Essex SS9 2LP
Tel: 01702 478719
Head: Steve Tompkins BSc(Hons), PGCE, MA, NPQH
Age range: 3–11
No. of pupils: 271
Fees: Day £4,104–£9,600

St Philomena's Catholic School
Hadleigh Road, Frinton-on-Sea, Essex CO13 9HQ
Tel: 01255 674492
Headmistress: Mrs B McKeown DipEd
Age range: 4–11
Fees: Day £6,240–£7,500

St. Anne's Preparatory School
New London Road, Chelmsford, Essex CM2 0AW
Tel: 01245 353488
Head Teacher: Ms Fiona Pirrie
Age range: 3–11
No. of pupils: 160
Fees: Day £3,450–£8,100

Thorpe Hall School
Wakering Road, Southend-on-Sea, Essex SS1 3RD
Tel: 01702 582340
Headmaster: Mr Andrew Hampton
Age range: 2–16 years
No. of pupils: 359
Fees: Day £9,000–£12,600

Ursuline Preparatory School
Old Great Ropers, Great Ropers Lane, Warley, Brentwood, Essex CM13 3HR
Tel: 01277 227152
Headmistress: Mrs Pauline Wilson MSc
Age range: 3–11
Fees: Day £6,450–£12,015

Widford Lodge School
Widford Road, Chelmsford, Essex CM2 9AN
Tel: 01245 352581
Headteacher: Miss Michelle Cole A.C.I.B. – P.G.C.E.
Age range: 2–11
No. of pupils: 230
Fees: Day £7,800–£9,657

Woodlands School, Great Warley
Warley Street, Great Warley, Brentwood, Essex CM13 3LA
Tel: 01277 233288
Head: Mr David Bell
Age range: 3 months–11 years

Woodlands School, Hutton Manor
428 Rayleigh Road, Hutton, Brentwood, Essex CM13 1SD
Tel: 01277 245585
Head: Paula Hobbs
Age range: 3 months–11 years

Hertfordshire

ABBOT'S HILL SCHOOL
For further details see p. 84
Bunkers Lane, Hemel Hempstead, Hertfordshire HP3 8RP
Tel: 01442 240333
Email: registrar@abbotshill.herts.sch.uk
Website: www.abbotshill.herts.sch.uk
Headmistress: Mrs Kathryn Gorman BA (Hons), PGCE, MEd
Age range: G4–16
No. of pupils: 530

Aldenham School
Elstree, Hertfordshire WD6 3AJ
Tel: 01923 858122
Headmaster: Mr James C Fowler MA
Age range: 3–18
No. of pupils: 700
Fees: Day £16,491–£22,614 FB £22,791–£33,234

Aldwickbury School
Wheathampstead Road, Harpenden, Hertfordshire AL5 1AD
Tel: 01582 713022
Headmaster: Mr V W Hales
Age range: B4–13
No. of pupils: 330
Fees: Day £13,110–£16,215

Beechwood Park School
Markyate, St Albans, Hertfordshire AL3 8AW
Tel: 01582 840333
Headmaster: Mr E Balfour BA (Hons), PGCE
Age range: 3–13
No. of pupils: 532
Fees: Day £11,025–£16,530 WB £20,460

Berkhamsted School
Overton House, 131 High Street, Berkhamsted, Hertfordshire HP4 2DJ
Tel: 01442 358001
Principal: Mr Richard Backhouse MA(Cantab)
Age range: 3–18
No. of pupils: 1792 VIth395
Fees: Day £10,620–£21,420 WB £7,350 FB £12,855

Bhaktivedanta Manor School
Hilfield Lane, Aldenham, Watford, Hertfordshire WD25 8EZ
Tel: 01923 851000 Ext:241
Headteacher: Guru Carana Padma dasi
Age range: 4–12
No. of pupils: 45
Fees: Day £1,860

Bishop's Stortford College
10 Maze Green Road, Bishop's Stortford, Hertfordshire CM23 2PJ
Tel: 01279 838575
Headmaster: Mr Jeremy Gladwin
Age range: 13–18
No. of pupils: VIth249
Fees: Day £20,349–£20,532 WB £31,569–£31,917 FB £33,402–£33,930

Bishop's Stortford College Prep School
Maze Green Road, Bishop's Stortford, Hertfordshire CM23 2PH
Tel: 01279 838607
Head of the Prep School: Mr Bill Toleman
Age range: 4–13
No. of pupils: 590
Fees: Day £9,408–£16,281 WB £22,359–£24,273 FB £23,610–£25,536

Charlotte House Preparatory School
88 The Drive, Rickmansworth, Hertfordshire WD3 4DU
Tel: 01923 772101
Head: Miss P Woodcock
Age range: G3–11
No. of pupils: 140
Fees: Day £3,432–£12,102

Duncombe School
4 Warren Park Road, Bengeo, Hertford, Hertfordshire SG14 3JA
Tel: 01992 414100
Headmaster: Mr Jeremy Phelan M.A. (Ed)
Age range: 2–11
No. of pupils: 301
Fees: Day £10,380–£14,565

Edge Grove School
Aldenham Village, Hertfordshire WD25 8NL
Tel: 01923 855724
Headmaster: Mr Ben Evans BA (Hons), PGCE
Age range: 3–13
No. of pupils: 494
Fees: Day £6,930–£16,935 WB £20,756–£23,150

Egerton Rothesay School
Durrants Lane, Berkhamsted, Hertfordshire HP4 3UJ
Tel: 01442 865275
Headteacher: Mr Colin Parker BSc(Hons), Dip.Ed (Oxon), PGCE, C.Math MIMA
Age range: 5–19
No. of pupils: 179
Fees: Day £16,020–£22,800

Haberdashers' Aske's School for Girls
Aldenham Road, Elstree,
Borehamwood, Hertfordshire WD6 3BT
Tel: 020 8266 2300
Head of School: Ms Rose Hardy
Age range: G4–18
No. of pupils: 1190
Fees: Day £17,826–£19,311
🚶 Ⓐ £ 16

HAILEYBURY
For further details see p. 90
Haileybury, Hertford,
Hertfordshire SG13 7NU
Tel: +44 (0)1992 706200
Email: admissions@haileybury.com
Website: www.haileybury.com
The Master: Mr Martin
Collier MA BA PGCE
Age range: 11–18
No. of pupils: 889 VIth348
Fees: Day £17,031–£25,620
FB £21,837–£34,422
🏠 Ⓐ 🏢 £ ⒾⒷ 🧭 16

Haresfoot School
Chesham Road, Berkhamsted,
Hertfordshire HP4 2SZ
Tel: 01442 872742
Principal: Karen O'Connor
BA PGCE NPQH
Age range: 3–7
Fees: Day £1,845–£7,770
🧭

HEATH MOUNT SCHOOL
For further details see p. 92
Woodhall Park, Watton-at-Stone,
Hertford, Hertfordshire SG14 3NG
Tel: 01920 830230
Email: registrar@heathmount.org
Website: www.heathmount.org
Headmaster: Mr Chris
Gillam BEd(Hons)
Age range: 3–13
No. of pupils: 478
Fees: Day £11,955–£18,435
🏢 £ 🧭

High Elms Manor School
High Elms Lane, Watford,
Hertfordshire WD25 0JX
Tel: 01923 681 103
Headmistress: Ms Liadain
O'Neill BA (Hons), AMI 0-3, AMI
3-6, Early Years FdA Dist.+
Age range: 2–12
No. of pupils: 100
Fees: Day £10,500–£12,675

Hockerill Anglo-European College
Dunmow Road, Bishops Stortford,
Hertfordshire CM23 5HX
Tel: 01279 658451
Head of School: Richard
Markham MA (Oxon)
Age range: 11–18
No. of pupils: 800
🏢 ⒾⒷ 16

Howe Green House School
Great Hallingbury, Bishop's
Stortford, Hertfordshire CM22 7UF
Tel: 01279 657706
Age range: 2–11
Fees: Day £8,235–£11,793
£

Immanuel College
87/91 Elstree Road, Bushey,
Hertfordshire WD23 4EB
Tel: 020 8950 0604
Headmaster: Mr Gary Griffin
Age range: 4–18
No. of pupils: 520 VIth127
Fees: Day £10,995
Ⓐ 🧭 16

Kingshott
Stevenage Road, St Ippolyts,
Hitchin, Hertfordshire SG4 7JX
Tel: 01462 432009
Headmaster: Mr Mark Seymour
Age range: 3–13 years
No. of pupils: 403
Fees: Day £11,280–£13,770
£ 🧭

Little Acorns Montessori School
Lincolnsfield Centre, Bushey Hall Drive,
Bushey, Hertfordshire WD23 2ER
Tel: 01923 230705
Age range: 12 months–6
No. of pupils: 28
Fees: Day £2,120
🧭

Lochinver House School
Heath Road, Little Heath, Potters
Bar, Hertfordshire EN6 1LW
Tel: 01707 653064
Headmaster: Ben Walker
BA(Hons), PGCE, CELTA
Age range: B4–13
No. of pupils: 349
Fees: Day £11,175–£14,685
🚶 £ 🧭

Lockers Park
Lockers Park Lane, Hemel
Hempstead, Hertfordshire HP1 1TL
Tel: 01442 251712
Headmaster: Mr C R Wilson
Age range: B4–13 G4–7
No. of pupils: 170
Fees: Day £10,050–£16,530 FB £23,160
🚶 🏢 £ 🧭

Longwood School
Bushey Hall Drive, Bushey,
Hertfordshire WD23 2QG
Tel: 01923 253715
Head Teacher: Claire May
Age range: 3 months–11
Fees: Day £3,705–£7,800
🧭

Manor Lodge School
Rectory Lane, Ridge Hill, Shenley,
Hertfordshire WD7 9BG
Tel: 01707 642424
Head of School: Mrs A Lobo BEd(Hons)
Age range: 3–11
No. of pupils: 427
Fees: Day £11,100–£12,300
£

Merchant Taylors' Prep
Moor Farm, Sandy Lodge Road,
Rickmansworth, Hertfordshire WD3 1LW
Tel: 01923 825648
Headmaster: Dr Karen McNerney
BSc (Hons), PGCE, MSc, EdD
Age range: B4–13
No. of pupils: 300
Fees: Day £5,148–£16,000
🚶 £

Princess Helena College
Preston, Hitchin, Hertfordshire SG4 7RT
Tel: 01462 443888
Headmistress: Mrs Sarah Davis
MA Hons (Edinburgh) PGCE
Age range: G11–18
No. of pupils: 194 VIth35
Fees: Day £16,125–£19,635
FB £22,965–£28,545
🚶 🏠 Ⓐ 🏢 £ 🧭 16

Queenswood
Shepherd's Way, Brookmans Park,
Hatfield, Hertfordshire AL9 6NS
Tel: 01707 602500
Principal: Mrs Jo Cameron
Age range: G11–18
No. of pupils: 400 VIth120
Fees: Day £20,925–£24,825 WB
£23,355–£31,035 FB £23,985–£33,750
🚶 Ⓐ 🏢 £ 🧭 16

Radlett Preparatory School
Kendal Hall, Watling Street,
Radlett, Hertfordshire WD7 7LY
Tel: 01923 856812
Principal: Mr G White BEd (Hons)
Age range: 4–11
Fees: Day £9,735

Sherrardswood School
Lockleys, Welwyn, Hertfordshire AL6 0BJ
Tel: 01438 714282
Headmistress: Mrs Anna Wright
Age range: 2–18
No. of pupils: 357
Fees: Day £10,383–£16,113
Ⓐ £ 🧭 16

St Albans High School for Girls
Townsend Avenue, St Albans,
Hertfordshire AL1 3SJ
Tel: 01727 853800
Headmistress: Mrs Jenny
Brown MA (Oxon)
Age range: G4–18
No. of pupils: 940 VIth170
🚶 Ⓐ £ 🧭 16

St Albans Independent College
69 London Road, St Albans,
Hertfordshire AL1 1LN
Tel: 01727 842348
Principals: Mr. A N Jemal
& Mr Elvis Cotena
Age range: 15+
Fees: Day £2,700–£5,900
16 Ⓐ 🧭

St Albans School
Abbey Gateway, St Albans,
Hertfordshire AL3 4HB
Tel: 01727 855521
Headmaster: Mr JWJ Gillespie
MA(Cantab), FRSA
Age range: B11–18 G16–18
No. of pupils: 870
Fees: Day £18,600
🚶 Ⓐ £ 🧭 16

St Christopher School
Barrington Road, Letchworth,
Hertfordshire SG6 3JZ
Tel: 01462 650 850
Head: Richard Palmer
Age range: 3–18
No. of pupils: 511 VIth78
Fees: Day £4,590–£18,075 WB
£19,950–£24,675 FB £31,650
🏠 Ⓐ 🏢 £ 🧭 16 🏃

ST COLUMBA'S COLLEGE
For further details see p. 102
King Harry Lane, St Albans,
Hertfordshire AL3 4AW
Tel: 01727 892040
Email: admissions@
stcolumbascollege.org
Website:
www.stcolumbascollege.org
Head: Mr David Buxton
Age range: B4–18
No. of pupils: 820

St Columba's College Prep School
King Harry Lane, St Albans,
Hertfordshire AL3 4AW
Tel: 01727 86261
Head of Prep: Mrs Ruth Loveman
Age range: B4–11
No. of pupils: 250
Fees: Day £10,482–£13,557

St Edmund's College
& Prep School
Old Hall Green, Nr Ware,
Hertfordshire SG11 1DS
Tel: 01920 824247
Head: Paulo Durán BA MA
Age range: 3–18
No. of pupils: 799 VIth135
Fees: Day £10,650–£17,205 WB
£22,665–£25,905 FB £26,040–£29,865

St Edmund's Prep
Old Hall Green, Ware,
Hertfordshire SG11 1DS
Tel: 01920 824239
Head: Mr Steven Cartwright
BSc (Surrey)
Age range: 3–11
No. of pupils: 185
Fees: Day £10,650–£13,365

St Francis' College
Broadway, Letchworth Garden
City, Hertfordshire SG6 3PJ
Tel: 01462 670511
Headmistress: Mrs B Goulding
Age range: G3–18
No. of pupils: 460 VIth75
Fees: Day £9,990–£16,980 WB
£22,350–£26,475 FB £27,990–£31,995

St Hilda's
High Street, Bushey,
Hertfordshire WD23 3DA
Tel: 020 8950 1751
Headmistress: Miss Sarah-
Jane Styles MA
Age range: B2–4 G2–11
Fees: Day £12,012–£12,843

St Hilda's School
28 Douglas Road, Harpenden,
Hertfordshire AL5 2ES
Tel: 01582 712307
Headmaster: Mr Dan Sayers
Age range: G3–11 years
No. of pupils: 144
Fees: Day £6,615–£11,535

St John's Preparatory School
The Ridgeway, Potters Bar,
Hertfordshire EN6 5QT
Tel: 01707 657294
Headmistress: Mrs C Tardios BA(Hons)
Age range: 4–11
No. of pupils: 184
Fees: Day £10,350–£10,980

St Joseph's In The Park
St Mary's Lane, Hertingfordbury,
Hertford, Hertfordshire SG14 2LX
Tel: 01992 513810
Age range: 3–11
No. of pupils: 150
Fees: Day £5,718–£16,899

ST MARGARET'S
SCHOOL, BUSHEY
For further details see p. 106
Merry Hill Road, Bushey,
Hertfordshire WD23 1DT
Tel: 020 8416 4400
Email: schooloffice@smbushey.com
Website:
www.stmargaretsbushey.co.uk
Acting Headmistress: Miss
Julie Chatkiewicz
Age range: G3–18 years
No. of pupils: 465

Stanborough School
Stanborough Park, Garston,
Watford, Hertfordshire WD25 9JT
Tel: 01923 673268
Acting Head Teacher: Ms Eileen Hussey
Age range: 3–17
No. of pupils: 300
Fees: Day £6,630–£10,224
WB £10,350–£13,995

Stormont
The Causeway, Potters Bar,
Hertfordshire EN6 5HA
Tel: 01707 654037
Age range: G4–11
Fees: Day £12,300–£13,050

The Christian School (Takeley)
Dunmow Road, Brewers End,
Takeley, Bishop's Stortford,
Hertfordshire CM22 6QH
Tel: 01279 871182
Headmaster: M E Humphries
Age range: 3–16
Fees: Day £6,012–£8,436

The Haberdashers'
Aske's Boys' School
Butterfly Lane, Elstree, Borehamwood,
Hertfordshire WD6 3AF
Tel: 020 8266 1700
Headmaster: Gus Lock MA (Oxon)
Age range: B5–18 years
No. of pupils: 1428
Fees: Day £15,339–£20,346

The King's School
Elmfield, Ambrose Lane, Harpenden,
Hertfordshire AL5 4DU
Tel: 01582 767566
Principal: Mr Clive John Case BA, HDE
Age range: 4–16
Fees: Day £7,680

The Purcell School, London
Aldenham Road, Bushey,
Hertfordshire WD23 2TS
Tel: 01923 331100
Headteacher: Dr Bernard Trafford
Age range: 10–18
No. of pupils: 180
Fees: Day £25,707 FB £32,826

TRING PARK SCHOOL FOR
THE PERFORMING ARTS
For further details see p. 112
Tring Park, Tring,
Hertfordshire HP23 5LX
Tel: 01442 824255
Email: info@tringpark.com
Website: www.tringpark.com
Principal: Mr Stefan Anderson
MA, ARCM, ARCT
Age range: 8–19
No. of pupils: 354 VIth150
Fees: Day £15,405–£24,510
FB £26,190–£37,050

Westbrook Hay Prep School
London Road, Hemel Hempstead,
Hertfordshire HP1 2RF
Tel: 01442 256143
Headmaster: Keith D Young BEd(Hons)
Age range: 3–13
No. of pupils: 300
Fees: Day £10,125–£14,580

York House School
Redheath, Sarratt Road,
Croxley Green, Rickmansworth,
Hertfordshire WD3 4LW
Tel: 01923 772395
Headmaster: Jon Gray BA(Ed)
Age range: 3–13
No. of pupils: 240
Fees: Day £10,440–£13,905

Norfolk

All Saints School
School Road, Lessingham,
Norwich, Norfolk NR12 0DJ
Tel: 01692 582083
Head teacher: P Wright
Age range: 7–16
Fees: Day £3,600–£5,400

Aurora Eccles School
Quidenham, Norwich,
Norfolk NR16 2NZ
Tel: 01953 887217
Headteacher: Chris Brown
Age range: 5–19

Beeston Hall School
Beeston Regis, West Runton,
Cromer, Norfolk NR27 9NQ
Tel: 01263 837324
Headmaster: Mr Fred de
Falbe BA(Hons) PGCE
Age range: 4–13
Fees: Day £8,550–£17,730
FB £18,360–£23,820

**Downham Preparatory School
& Montessori Nursery**
The Old Rectory, Stow Bardolph,
Kings Lynn, Norfolk PE34 3HT
Tel: 01366 388066
Headmistress: Mrs E Laffeaty-
Sharpe MontDip
Age range: 3 months–11
No. of pupils: 170
Fees: Day £6,426–£8,721

Focus School – Swaffham Campus
Turbine Way, Swaffham,
Norfolk PE37 7XD
Tel: 01760 336939
Headteacher: Mr John Shanahan
Age range: 7–18
No. of pupils: 161 VIth29

Glebe House School
2 Cromer Road, Hunstanton,
Norfolk PE36 6HW
Tel: 01485 532809
Headmaster: Mr Crofts
Age range: 0–13
No. of pupils: 110
Fees: Day £8,316–£13,290

**Gresham's Nursery and
Pre-Prep School**
Market Place, Holt, Norfolk NR25 6BB
Tel: 01263 714575
Headmistress: Mrs Sarah Hollingsworth
Age range: 2–7
No. of pupils: 90
Fees: Day £10,350–£11,100

Gresham's Prep School
Cromer Road, Holt, Norfolk NR25 6EY
Tel: 01263 714600
Head: Mrs Cathy Braithwaite
Age range: 7–13
No. of pupils: 240
Fees: Day £15,120–£18,630 FB £26,100

Gresham's Senior School
Cromer Road, Holt, Norfolk NR25 6EA
Tel: 01263 714 614
Headmaster: Mr Douglas
Robb MA, MEd
Age range: 13–18
No. of pupils: 495
Fees: Day £25,140 FB £36,030

**Langley Preparatory School
at Taverham Hall**
Taverham, Norwich, Norfolk NR8 6HU
Tel: 01603 868206
Headmaster: Mr Mike A
Crossley NPQH, BEd(Hons)
Age range: 2–13
Fees: Day £10,275–£14,175 WB £18,315

Langley School
Langley Park, Loddon,
Norwich, Norfolk NR14 6BJ
Tel: 01508 520210
Headmaster: Mr Dominic Findlay
Age range: 10–18
No. of pupils: 515
Fees: Day £15,720 WB £26,649 FB £31,941

Norwich High School for Girls GDST
95 Newmarket Road, Norwich,
Norfolk NR2 2HU
Tel: 01603 453265
Headmistress: Mrs Kirsty von Malaise
Age range: G3–18
No. of pupils: VIth120
Fees: Day £9,198–£14,562

Norwich School
70 The Close, Norwich, Norfolk NR1 4DD
Tel: 01603 728430
Head Master: Steffan D A Griffiths
Age range: 4–18
No. of pupils: 1065
Fees: Day £10,998–£16,212

Norwich Steiner School
Hospital Lane, Norwich,
Norfolk NR1 2HW
Tel: 01603 611175
Headteacher: Mr Andrew Vestrini
Age range: 3–18
No. of pupils: 91
Fees: Day £3,830–£7,010

Notre Dame Preparatory School
147 Dereham Road, Norwich,
Norfolk NR2 3TA
Tel: 01603 625593
Headmaster: Mr Rob Thornton
Age range: 2–11
No. of pupils: 213
Fees: Day £2,985–£6,465

**Riddlesworth Hall
Preparatory School**
Garboldisham, Diss, Norfolk IP22 2TA
Tel: 01953 681 246
Principal: Mrs Sally Judd
Age range: 2–13
No. of pupils: 137
Fees: Day £10,470 WB £16,500 FB £17,535

Thetford Grammar School
Bridge Street, Thetford, Norfolk IP24 3AF
Tel: 01842 752840
Headmaster: Mr Michael Brewer
Age range: 3–18
No. of pupils: 200
Fees: Day £8,250–£13,665

**Town Close House
Preparatory School**
14 Ipswich Road, Norwich,
Norfolk NR2 2LR
Tel: 01603 620180
Headmaster: Mr Nicholas Bevington
Age range: 3–13
No. of pupils: 455
Fees: Day £8,670–£13,152

Suffolk

**Barnardiston Hall
Preparatory School**
Barnardiston, Nr Haverhill,
Suffolk CB9 7TG
Tel: 01440 786316
Headmaster: Lt Col K A
Boulter MA(Cantab)
Age range: 6 months–13 years
No. of pupils: 220
Fees: Day £8,235–£13,725
WB £18,975 FB £20,580

Brookes Cambridge
Flempton Road, Risby, Bury St
Edmunds, Suffolk IP28 6QJ
Tel: 01284 760531
Director: Mr D Rose
Age range: 2–16
No. of pupils: 100
Fees: Day £9,150–£14,280
FB £19,590–£28,170

Culford Preparatory School
Culford, Bury St Edmunds,
Suffolk IP28 6TX
Tel: 01284 385383
Headmaster: Mr Mike Schofield
Age range: 7–13
No. of pupils: 214
Fees: Day £11,625–£15,225
FB £22,485–£23,985

Culford Pre-Preparatory School
Fieldgate House, Bury St
Edmunds, Suffolk IP28 6TX
Tel: 01284 385412
Headmistress: Mrs Sarah Preston BA
Age range: 1–7
Fees: Day £8,940–£9,645

Culford School
Culford, Bury St Edmunds,
Suffolk IP28 6TX
Tel: 01284 728615
Headmaster: Mr J F Johnson-
Munday MA, MBA
Age range: 1–18
No. of pupils: 650 VIth150
Fees: Day £8,940–£19,500
FB £22,485–£29,985

Fairstead House School
Fordham Road, Newmarket,
Suffolk CB8 7AA
Tel: 01638 662318
Head: Lynda Brereton
Age range: 9 months–11 years
No. of pupils: 118
Fees: Day £9,747–£10,611

Felixstowe International College
Maybush Lane, Felixstowe,
Suffolk IP11 7NA
Tel: 01394 282388
Principal: Rev Seungjin Peter Kim
Age range: 10–17
No. of pupils: 20
Fees: FB £24,000

Finborough School
The Hall, Great Finborough,
Stowmarket, Suffolk IP14 3EF
Tel: 01449 773600
Principal: Mr Steven Clark
Age range: 2–18
No. of pupils: 226 VIth20
Fees: Day £8,775–£13,590 WB
£16,455–£22,020 FB £20,475–£27,450

Framlingham College
College Road, Framlingham,
Suffolk IP13 9EY
Tel: 01728 723789
Headmaster: Mrs Louise North
Age range: 2–18
No. of pupils: 700
Fees: Day £8,409–£19,176 FB £29,823

Ipswich High School
Woolverstone, Ipswich, Suffolk IP9 1AZ
Tel: 01473 780201
Head of School: Ms Oona Carlin
Age range: 3–18
No. of pupils: 500 VIth40
Fees: Day £8,769–£14,322

Ipswich Preparatory School
3 Ivry Street, Ipswich, Suffolk IP1 3QW
Tel: 01473 282800
Headteacher: Mrs A H Childs
Age range: 2–11
No. of pupils: 311
Fees: Day £11,850–£12,984

Ipswich School
Henley Road, Ipswich, Suffolk IP1 3SG
Tel: 01473 408300
Headmaster: Mr Nicholas Weaver MA
Age range: 2–18
No. of pupils: 739 VIth218
Fees: Day £11,850–£15,579 WB
£24,402–£27,381 FB £26,376–£30,171

Moreton Hall Preparatory School
Mount Road, Bury St Edmunds,
Suffolk IP32 7BJ
Tel: 01284 753532
Headmaster: Mr Chris Moxon BA PGCE
Age range: 4–13
No. of pupils: 100
Fees: Day £8,700–£14,325
WB £19,425 FB £22,500

Old Buckenham Hall School
Old Buckenham Hall, Brettenham
Park, Ipswich, Suffolk IP7 7PH
Tel: 01449 740252
Headmaster: Mr David Griffiths
Age range: 3–13 years
No. of pupils: 202
Fees: Day £6,424 FB £8,370

ORWELL PARK SCHOOL
For further details see p. 98
Nacton, Ipswich, Suffolk IP10 0ER
Tel: 01473 659225
Email: admissions@orwellpark.org
Website: www.orwellpark.co.uk
Headmaster: Mr Adrian
Brown MA(Cantab)
Age range: 2–13
No. of pupils: 283

Queen's House School
Bredfield Street, Woodbridge,
Suffolk IP12 4NH
Tel: 01394 615070
Headteacher: Nicola Mitchell
Age range: 4–7

Saint Felix School
Halesworth Road, Southwold,
Suffolk IP18 6SD
Tel: 01502 722175
Headmaster: Mr. James Harrison
Age range: 2–18
No. of pupils: 312 VIth65
Fees: Day £7,485–£16,185 WB
£17,670–£22,470 FB £23,370–£28,170

South Lee Preparatory School
Nowton Road, Bury St
Edmunds, Suffolk IP33 2BT
Tel: 01284 754654
Headmaster: Mr Mervyn
Watch BEd (Hons)
Age range: 2–13
Fees: Day £9,645–£11,820

St Joseph's College
Birkfield, Belstead Road,
Ipswich, Suffolk IP2 9DR
Tel: 01473 690281
Principal: Mrs Danielle Clarke
Age range: 3–18
No. of pupils: 564
Fees: Day £6,045–£15,150 WB
£24,990–£27,315 FB £26,145–£33,795

Stoke College
Stoke-by-Clare, Sudbury,
Suffolk CO10 8JE
Tel: 01787 278141
Head: Mr Frank Thompson
Age range: 3–18
Fees: Day £6,132–£14,979 WB
£20,829–£24,231 FB £27,096–£31,518

Summerhill School
Leiston, Suffolk IP16 4HY
Tel: 01728 830540
Principal: Mrs Zoe Readhead
Age range: 5–17
No. of pupils: 69
Fees: Day £5,475–£11,205
FB £12,069–£19,041

The Abbey School
Church Street, Woodbridge,
Suffolk IP12 1DS
Tel: +44 (0)1394 382673
Head: Mrs N Mitchell
Age range: 7–11

The Meadows Montessori School
32 Larchcroft Road, Ipswich,
Suffolk IP1 6AR
Tel: 01473 233782
Headteacher: Ms Samantha Sims
Age range: 4–11
No. of pupils: 54

The Old School Henstead
Toad Row, Beccles, Suffolk NR34 7LG
Tel: 01502 741150
Head: Mr W J McKinney
Age range: 2–11
No. of pupils: 123
Fees: Day £6,990–£10,077

The Royal Hospital School
Holbrook, Ipswich, Suffolk IP9 2RX
Tel: +44 (0) 1473 326200
Headmaster: Mr Simon Lockyer
Age range: 11–18
No. of pupils: 700 VIth220
Fees: Day £15,690–£17,490 WB
£24,090–£29,910 FB £25,290–£32,595

Woodbridge School
Burkitt Road, Woodbridge,
Suffolk IP12 4JH
Tel: +44 (0)1394 615000
Acting Head: Miss Shona Norman
Age range: 4–18
No. of pupils: 901 VIth104
Fees: Day £9,741–£16,505 FB £30,885

D330

East Midlands

KEY TO SYMBOLS

- ⚹ *Boys' school*
- ⚹ *Girls' school*
- 🌐 *International school*
- 16 *Tutorial or sixth form college*
- Ⓐ *A levels*
- ⚐ *Boarding accommodation*
- £ *Bursaries*
- Ⓘ *International Baccalaureate*
- ✎ *Learning support*
- 16 *Entrance at 16+*
- *Vocational qualifications*
- (IAPS) *Independent Association of Preparatory Schools*
- (HMC) *The Headmasters' & Headmistresses' Conference*
- (ISA) *Independent Schools Association*
- (GSA) *Girls' School Association*
- (BSA) *Boarding Schools' Association*
- Ⓢ *Society of Heads*

Unless otherwise indicated, all schools are coeducational day schools.
Single-sex and boarding schools will be indicated by the relevant icon.

Derbyshire

Barlborough Hall School
Barlborough, Chesterfield,
Derbyshire S43 4TJ
Tel: 01246 810511
Headteacher: Mrs Karen Keeton
Age range: 3–11
No. of pupils: 210
Fees: Day £7,741–£10,318
£

Dame Catherine Harpur's School
Rose Lane, Ticknall, Derby,
Derbyshire DE73 7JW
Tel: 01332 862792
Head: Ms Whyte
Age range: 3–11
No. of pupils: 28
Fees: Day £4,794

Derby Grammar School
Rykneld Hall, Rykneld Road, Littleover,
Derby, Derbyshire DE23 4BX
Tel: 01332 523027
Head: Dr Ruth Norris
Age range: B7–18 G16–18
No. of pupils: 255
Fees: Day £8,823–£13,449
(*) (A) (£) (✏) (16)

Derby High School
Hillsway, Littleover, Derby,
Derbyshire DE23 3DT
Tel: 01332 514267
Headteacher: Mrs Denise Gould
Age range: B3–11 G3–18
No. of pupils: 576 VIth74
Fees: Day £8,820–£12,870
(A) (£) (✏) (16)

Emmanuel School
Juniper Lodge, 43 Kedleston Road,
Derby, Derbyshire DE22 1FP
Tel: 01332 340505
Headteacher: Mr Ian Birkin
Age range: 3–16
No. of pupils: 65
Fees: Day £3,519
✏

Foremarke Hall
Milton, Derby, Derbyshire DE65 6EJ
Tel: 01283 707100
Headmaster: Mr R Merriman
MA, BSc(Hons), FCollP
Age range: 3–13
(🏛) (£) (✏)

Michael House Steiner School
The Field, Shipley, Heanor,
Derbyshire DE75 7JH
Tel: 01773 718050
Age range: 3–16
No. of pupils: 150
Fees: Day £2,212–£6,088

Mount St Mary's College
College Road, Spinkhill,
Derbyshire S21 3YL
Tel: 01246 433388
Headmaster: Dr Nicholas Cuddihy
Age range: 11–18
No. of pupils: 360
Fees: Day £11,669–£13,406 WB
£18,202–£23,431 FB £22,128–£29,046
(🌐) (A) (🏛) (£) (✏) (16)

Normanton House Primary School
Normanton House, Village Street,
Derby, Derbyshire DE23 8DF
Tel: 01332 769333
Headteacher: Mr Nighat Sultana Khan
Age range: 5–10
No. of pupils: 97

Ockbrook School
The Settlement, Ockbrook,
Derby, Derbyshire DE72 3RJ
Tel: 01332 673532
Head: Mr Tom Brooksby
Age range: 2–18
No. of pupils: 409 VIth55
Fees: Day £8,955–£13,170
(🌐) (A) (🏛) (£) (✏) (16)

Old Vicarage School
11 Church Lane, Darley Abbey,
Derby, Derbyshire DE22 1EW
Tel: 01332 557130
Headmaster: Mr M J Adshead
Age range: 3–13
No. of pupils: 95
Fees: Day £7,650–£8,124
(£)

Repton School
The Hall, Repton, Derbyshire DE65 6FH
Tel: 01283 559222
Head: Mr W M A Land MA
Age range: 13–18
No. of pupils: 653 VIth299
Fees: Day £26,493 FB £35,712
(🌐) (A) (🏛) (£) (✏) (16)

S. Anselm's School
Stanedge Road, Bakewell,
Derbyshire DE45 1DP
Tel: 01629 812734
Headmaster: Peter Phillips BA
(Hons), MA, PGCE (SPLD), NPQH
Age range: 3–13
No. of pupils: 215
Fees: Day £10,950–£20,700 FB £26,100
(🏛) (£) (✏)

St Peter & St Paul School
Brambling House, Hady Hill,
Chesterfield, Derbyshire S41 0EF
Tel: 01246 278522
Headteacher: Mrs Jill Phinn
Age range: 3 months–11 years
No. of pupils: 120
Fees: Day £8,658–£9,159
(£) (✏)

St Wystan's School
High Street, Repton,
Derbyshire DE65 6GE
Tel: 01283 703258
Head Teacher: Karan Hopkinson
Age range: 3–11
Fees: Day £4,500–£8,655
(£) (✏)

Leicestershire

Al-Aqsa Schools Trust
The Wayne Way, Leicester,
Leicestershire LE5 4PP
Tel: 0116 2760953
Headteacher: Mrs Amina Patel
Age range: 5–16
No. of pupils: 231
✏

Ashby School
School House, Leicester Road, Ashby-
de-la-Zouch, Leicestershire LE65 1DH
Tel: +44 (0) 1530 413748
Headteacher: Mr Geoff Staniforth
Age range: B11–19
No. of pupils: 1643
(*) (A) (🏛) (£) (✏) (16) (🏉)

Brooke House College
Leicester Road, Market Harborough,
Leicestershire LE16 7AU
Tel: 01858 462452
Principal: Mr Mike Oliver
Age range: 14–20
No. of pupils: VIth73
Fees: Day £19,650–£21,525
FB £33,000–£36,000
(🌐) (16) (A) (🏛)

Brooke House Day School
Croft Road, Cosby, Leicester,
Leicestershire LE9 1SE
Tel: 0116 286 7372
Head: Mrs Joy Parker
Age range: 3–14

Darul Arqam Educational Institute
2 Overton Road, Leicester,
Leicestershire LE5 0JA
Tel: 0116 2741626
Headteacher: Mr Ahmed
Abdul Dadipatel
Age range: B5–16
No. of pupils: 75
(*)

Darul Uloom Leicester
119 Loughborough Road,
Leicester, Leicestershire LE4 5LN
Tel: 0116 2668922
Headteacher: Moulana Ishaq Boodi
Age range: B11–25
Fees: Day £1,800 FB £2,700
(*) (A) (🏛) (16)

Fairfield Preparatory School
Leicester Road, Loughborough,
Leicestershire LE11 2AE
Tel: 01509 215172
Headmaster: Mr A Earnshaw
BA Lancaster NPQH
Age range: 3–11
No. of pupils: 498
✏

Grace Dieu Manor School
Grace Dieu, Thringstone,
Leicestershire LE67 5UG
Tel: 01530 222276
Head of School: Mrs Margaret Kewell
Age range: 12 weeks–11
No. of pupils: 315
Fees: Day £10,280–£10,821
(£) (✏)

Jameah Girls Academy
49 Rolleston Street, Leicester,
Leicestershire LE5 3SD
Tel: 0116 262 7745
Headteacher: Ms Erfana Bora
Age range: G6–16
No. of pupils: 142
(*)

Leicester Grammar Junior School
London Road, Grea Glen,
Leicester, Leicestershire LE8 9FL
Tel: 0116 259 1950
Age range: 3–11
No. of pupils: 391
✏

Leicester Grammar School
London Road, Great Glen,
Leicester, Leicestershire LE8 9FL
Tel: 0116 259 1900
Head & Chief Executive: C P M King MA
Age range: 11–18
No. of pupils: 704 VIth188
Fees: Day £13,029
(A)(£)(✎)(16)

Leicester High School for Girls
454 London Road, Leicester,
Leicestershire LE2 2PP
Tel: 0116 2705338
Headmaster: Mr Alan Whelpdale
Age range: G3–18
No. of pupils: 435 VIth60
Fees: Day £2,995–£4,065
(♦)(A)(£)(16)

Leicester Islamic Academy
320 London Road, Leicester,
Leicestershire LE2 2PP
Tel: 0116 2705343
Headteacher: Mrs S Khan
Age range: 3–11
Fees: Day £1,980

Leicester Prep School
2 Albert Road, Leicester,
Leicestershire LE2 2AA
Tel: 0116 2707414
Headmaster: Paul Hitchcock
Age range: 3–11
No. of pupils: 130
Fees: Day £7,800
(✎)

Loughborough Amherst School
Gray Street, Loughborough,
Leicestershire LE11 2DZ
Tel: 01509 263901
Headmaster: Dr Julian Murphy
Age range: B4–11 G4–18
No. of pupils: 224
Fees: Day £9,816–£12,189
(♦)(A)(£)(✎)(16)

Loughborough Grammar School
6 Burton Walks, Loughborough,
Leicestershire LE11 2DU
Tel: 01509 233233
Headmaster: Mr Duncan Byrne
Age range: B10–18
No. of pupils: 1010
Fees: Day £12,549 WB £12,966
FB £16,203–£16,983
(♦)(🏠)(A)(£)(16)

Loughborough High School
Burton Walks, Loughborough,
Leicestershire LE11 2DU
Tel: 01509 212348
Headmistress: Mrs G Byrom
Age range: G11–18
No. of pupils: VIth170
Fees: Day £12,549
(♦)(A)(£)(✎)(16)

Ratcliffe College
Fosse Way, Ratcliffe on the Wreake,
Leicester, Leicestershire LE7 4SG
Tel: 01509 817000
Headmaster: Mr J Reddin
BSc, MSc, NPQH
Age range: 3–18
No. of pupils: 831 VIth142
Fees: Day £9,345–£16,287 WB
£20,676–£23,959 FB £25,959
(A)(🏠)(£)(✎)(16)

St Crispin's School
6 St Mary's Road, Stoneygate,
Leicester, Leicestershire LE2 1XA
Tel: 0116 2707648
Head Master: Andrew Atkin
Age range: 2–16
(£)(✎)(♣)

Stoneygate School
6 London Road, Great Glen,
Leicester, Leicestershire LE8 9DJ
Tel: 0116 259 2282
Headmaster: Mr J F Dobson
Age range: 4–16
No. of pupils: 180
Fees: Day £11,082–£14,028

The Dixie Grammar School
Station Road, Market Bosworth,
Leicestershire CV13 0LE
Tel: 01455 292244
Headmaster: Richard Lynn MA
Age range: 3–18
No. of pupils: 474 VIth71
Fees: Day £8,835–£12,015
(A)(£)(16)

Tiny Tots Pre-School & Primary
16-20 Beal Street, Leicester,
Leicestershire LE2 0AA
Tel: 0116 2515345
Principal: Mr N Hussein
Age range: 2–11
No. of pupils: 104
(✎)

Lincolnshire

Ayscoughfee Hall School
Welland Hall, London Road,
Spalding, Lincolnshire PE11 2TE
Tel: 01775 724733
Headmistress: Mrs Clare
Ogden BA(Hons), PGCE
Age range: 3–11
No. of pupils: 146
Fees: Day £4,560–£6,720
(✎)

Bicker Preparatory School & Early Years
School Lane, Bicker, Boston,
Lincolnshire PE20 3DW
Tel: 01775 821786
Head Teacher: Mrs J Miles BA.PGCE
Age range: 3–11
No. of pupils: 74
(✎)

Copthill Independent Day School
Barnack Road, Uffington,
Stamford, Lincolnshire PE9 3AD
Tel: 01780 757506
Headmaster: Mr J A Teesdale
BA(Hons), PGCE
Age range: 2–11
No. of pupils: 300
Fees: Day £9,255–£10,350
(£)(✎)

Dudley House School
1 Dudley Road, Grantham,
Lincolnshire NG31 9AA
Tel: 01476 400184
Headmistress: Mrs Jenny Johnson
Age range: 3–11
No. of pupils: 50
Fees: Day £5,220
(✎)

Grantham Preparatory International School
Gorse Lane, Grantham,
Lincolnshire NG31 7UF
Tel: +44 (0)1476 593293
Headmistress: Mrs K A Korcz
Age range: 3–11
No. of pupils: 142
Fees: Day £7,950–£9,690
(🏠)(£)(✎)

Greenwich House School
106 High Holme Road, Louth,
Lincolnshire LN11 0HE
Tel: 01507 609252
Headmistress: Mrs J Brindle
Age range: 9 months–11 years
No. of pupils: 50

Handel House Preparatory School
Northolme Road, Gainsborough,
Lincolnshire DN21 2JB
Tel: 01427 612426
Headmistress: Mrs Victoria Haigh
Age range: 2–11
Fees: Day £3,585–£4,320
(✎)

Kirkstone House School
Main Street, Baston, Peterborough,
Lincolnshire PE6 9PA
Tel: 01778 560350
Head: Mrs C Jones BSocSc
Age range: 3–18
No. of pupils: 234
Fees: Day £9,498–£11,640
(£)(✎)

Lincoln Minster School
Upper Lindum Street, Lincoln,
Lincolnshire LN2 5RW
Tel: 01522 551300
Headmaster: Mr J M Wallace
Age range: 2–18
No. of pupils: 840 VIth144
Fees: Day £9,276–£13,632 WB
£23,013–£26,715 FB £20,901–£24,186
(🏠)(A)(🏠)(£)(✎)(16)

St Hugh's School
Cromwell Avenue, Woodhall
Spa, Lincolnshire LN10 6TQ
Tel: 01526 352169
Head: C Ward BEd(Hons)
No. of pupils: 195
Fees: Day £8,880–£14,928 FB £18,750
💷 £ ✏️

Stamford Endowed Schools
Brazenose House, St Paul's Street,
Stamford, Lincolnshire PE9 2BE
Tel: 01780 750310
Principal: Mrs Vicky Buckman
Age range: 2–18
No. of pupils: 1634 VIth400
Fees: Day £9,414–£15,318 WB
£19,821–£24,801 FB £21,864–£28,446
♿ Ⓐ 💷 £ ✏️ 16

Stamford High School
St Martin's, Stamford,
Lincolnshire PE9 2LL
Tel: 01780 428200
Principal: Mrs Vicky Buckman
Age range: G11–18
No. of pupils: 633 VIth201
Fees: Day £15,318 WB £21,552–
£24,801 FB £28,446
♿ ♿ Ⓐ 💷 £ ✏️ 16

Stamford Junior School
Kettering Road, Stamford,
Lincolnshire PE9 2LR
Tel: 01780 484400
Headteacher: Mrs Emma Maria Smith
Age range: 2–11
No. of pupils: 344
Fees: Day £9,414–£12,102 WB
£17,415–£19,821 FB £21,864
💷 ✏️

Viking School
140 Church Road North, Skegness,
Lincolnshire PE25 2QJ
Tel: 01754 765749
Principal: Mrs S J Barker
Age range: 3–11
No. of pupils: 100
Fees: Day £4,050–£4,350
✏️

Witham Hall Preparatory School
Witham-on-the-Hill, Bourne,
Lincolnshire PE10 0JJ
Tel: +44(0)1778 590222
Headmaster: Mr Charles
Welch B.Ed (Hons)
Age range: 4–13
No. of pupils: 250
Fees: Day £9,555–£16,080 FB £21,690
💷 £ ✏️

Northamptonshire

Beachborough School
Westbury, Brackley,
Northamptonshire NN13 5LB
Tel: 01280 700071
Interim Head: Elizabeth Hill
Age range: 2–13
No. of pupils: 260
Fees: Day £10,728–£16,845
💷 £ ✏️

Bosworth Independent College
Nazareth House, Barrack
Road, Northampton,
Northamptonshire NN2 6AF
Tel: 01604 235090
Principal: Fiona Pocock MA PGCE
Age range: 13–University
No. of pupils: VIth250
Fees: Day £12,600 WB £20,030–
£21,230 FB £21,900–£23,100
16 Ⓐ 💷 £ ✏️

**Childfirst Day Nursery
Northampton**
Moulton Lodge, Moulton Way
North, Moulton, Northampton,
Northamptonshire NN3 7RW
Tel: 01604 790440
Headmistress: Mrs Mary
Heal BA(Hons)Ed
Age range: 2 months–7 years
Fees: Day £6,255

Laxton Junior School
East Road, Oundle, Peterborough,
Northamptonshire PE8 4BX
Tel: 01832 277275
Head of School: Mr Sam Robertson
Age range: 4–11
No. of pupils: 260
Fees: Day £10,185–£11,925
£ ✏️

Maidwell Hall
Maidwell, Northampton,
Northamptonshire NN6 9JG
Tel: 01604 686234
Headmaster: Mr R A
Lankester MA, PGCE
Age range: 7–13
No. of pupils: 124
Fees: Day £17,505 WB
£26,880 FB £26,880
💷 £ ✏️

Northampton High School GDST
Newport Pagnell Road,
Hardingstone, Northampton,
Northamptonshire NN4 6UU
Tel: 01604 765765
Headmistress: Dr Helen
Stringer DPhil, MA, PGCE
Age range: G2–18
No. of pupils: 649 VIth128
Fees: Day £9,750–£14,331
♿ Ⓐ 💷 £ ✏️ 16

Oundle School
Oundle, Peterborough,
Northamptonshire PE8 4GH
Tel: 01832 277 122
Head of School: Mrs Sarah Kerr-Dineen
Age range: 11–18
No. of pupils: 1107
Fees: Day £17,880–£23,505
FB £27,885–£36,690
♿ Ⓐ 💷 £ ✏️ 16

Overstone Park School
Overstone Park,
Overstone, Northampton,
Northamptonshire NN6 0DT
Tel: 01604 643787
Principal: Mrs M F Brown
BA(Hons), PGCE
Age range: 0–18
No. of pupils: 85
£ ✏️ ♿

Pitsford School
Pitsford Hall, Pitsford, Northampton,
Northamptonshire NN6 9AX
Tel: 01604 880306
Head of School: Dr C Walker
Age range: 4–18
No. of pupils: VIth49
Fees: Day £8,223–£14,277
Ⓐ £ ✏️ 16

Quinton House School
Upton Hall, Upton, Northampton,
Northamptonshire NN5 4UX
Tel: 01604 752050
Headteacher: Mr Tim Hoyle
Age range: 2–18
No. of pupils: 390
Fees: Day £8,040–£11,985
Ⓐ £ ✏️ 16

Spratton Hall
Smith Street, Spratton,
Northamptonshire NN6 8HP
Tel: 01604 847292
Head Master: Mr Simon Clarke
Age range: 4–13
No. of pupils: 376
Fees: Day £10,350–£15,660
£ ✏️

St Peter's Independent School
Lingswood Park,
Blackthorn, Northampton,
Northamptonshire NN3 8TA
Tel: 01604 411745
Acting Head: Julie Fenlon
Age range: 4–18
No. of pupils: 130
Fees: Day £6,825–£9,150
Ⓐ 16

St Peter's School
52 Headlands, Kettering,
Northamptonshire NN15 6DJ
Tel: 01536 512066
Headmistress: Mrs Maria Chapman
Age range: 2–11
No. of pupils: 161
£ ✏️

Wellingborough School
Wellingborough,
Northamptonshire NN8 2BX
Tel: 01933 222427
Headmaster: Mr A N Holman
Age range: 3–18
No. of pupils: VIth145
Fees: Day £9,420–£15,990
Ⓐ Ⓔ ✎ 16·

Winchester House School
High Street, Brackley,
Northamptonshire NN13 7AZ
Tel: 01280 702483
Head: Mrs Emma Goldsmith
Age range: 3–13
No. of pupils: 307
Fees: Day £10,905–£19,230 WB £24,330
🏫 Ⓔ ✎

Nottinghamshire

Colston Bassett Preparatory School
School Lane, Colston
bassett, Nottingham,
Nottinghamshire NG12 3FD
Tel: 01949 81118
Headteacher: Mrs Ruth O'Dell
Age range: 4–11
Fees: Day £7,098

Coteswood House School
19 Thackeray's Lane, Woodthorpe,
Nottingham, Nottinghamshire NG5 4HT
Tel: 0115 9676551
Head: Mrs S M Fernley
Age range: 3–11
No. of pupils: 40
Fees: Day £4,200

Highfields School
London Road, Newark,
Nottinghamshire NG24 3AL
Tel: 01636 704103
Headmaster: Mr R C R Thomson
BEd (Hons) NPQH
Age range: 2–11
No. of pupils: 140
Fees: Day £9,195
Ⓔ ✎

Hollygirt School
Elm Avenue, Nottingham,
Nottinghamshire NG3 4GF
Tel: 0115 958 0596
Headmistress: Mrs Pam Hutley
BA(Hons), PGCE, MSc
Age range: 3–16
No. of pupils: 200
Fees: Day £9,300–£12,234
Ⓔ ✎

Iona School
310 Sneinton Dale, Nottingham,
Nottinghamshire NG3 7DN
Tel: 01159 415295
Chair of College: Richard Moore
Age range: 3–11
Fees: Day £6,724

Jamia Al-Hudaa Residential College
Forest House, Berkeley Avenue,
Mapperley Park, Nottingham,
Nottinghamshire NG3 5TT
Tel: 0115 9690800
Principal: Raza ul-Haq Siakhvy
Age range: 11–19
No. of pupils: 224
🏃 🏫

Jubilee House Christian School
226 Nottingham Road, Eastwood,
Nottinghamshire NG16 3GR
Tel: 01773 688100
Headteacher: Mrs J Marks
Age range: 3–16
No. of pupils: 70
Ⓔ

Lammas School
Lammas Road, Sutton-in-Ashfield,
Nottinghamshire NG17 2AD
Tel: 0208 424 8475
Head: Mrs Sara Baldry
Age range: 4–19
No. of pupils: 57
Fees: Day £6,544–£8,489
Ⓐ ✎

Nottingham Girls' High School GDST
9 Arboretum Street, Nottingham,
Nottinghamshire NG1 4JB
Tel: 0115 9417663
Head: Miss Julie Keller
Age range: G4–18
No. of pupils: 786 VIth155
Fees: Day £9,873–£13,581
🏃 Ⓐ Ⓔ 16·

Nottingham High Infant and Junior School
Waverley Mount, Nottingham,
Nottinghamshire NG7 4ED
Tel: 0115 845 2214
Headteacher: Mrs Clare Bruce
Age range: 4–11
No. of pupils: 180
Fees: Day £3,393–£4,955
✎

Nottingham High School
Waverley Mount, Nottingham,
Nottinghamshire NG7 4ED
Tel: 0115 9786056
Headmaster: Mr Kevin Fear BA
Age range: 4–18
No. of pupils: 1053
Fees: Day £10,179–£14,865
Ⓐ Ⓔ ✎ 16·

Nottingham Islamia School
30 Bentinck Road, Hyson Green,
Nottingham, Nottinghamshire NG7 4AF
Tel: 0115 970 5858
Head: Dr Musharraf Hussain
Age range: 5–11

Plumtree School
Church Hill, Plumtree, Nottingham,
Nottinghamshire NG12 5ND
Tel: 0115 937 5859
Head Teacher: Phil Simpson
Age range: 3–11
Fees: Day £6,540
✎

Salterford House School
Salterford Lane, Calverton,
Nottingham, Nottinghamshire
NG14 6NZ
Tel: 0115 9652127
Head: Ms Kimberley Venables
Age range: 3–11
No. of pupils: 124
Fees: Day £7,800–£7,890
✎

Saville House School
11 Church Street, Mansfield
Woodhouse, Mansfield,
Nottinghamshire NG19 8AH
Tel: 01623 625068
Joint Head: Mrs See & Mrs Hill
Age range: 3–11
No. of pupils: 89
Fees: Day £5,475
✎

St Joseph's School
33 Derby Road, Nottingham,
Nottinghamshire NG1 5AW
Tel: 0115 9418356
Head Teacher: Mr Ashley Crawshaw
Age range: 1–11
Fees: Day £7,728
✎

The Orchard School
South Leverton, Retford,
Nottinghamshire DN22 0DJ
Tel: 01427 880395
Principal: Mrs S M Fox BA, PGCE
Age range: 5–16
No. of pupils: 150
Fees: Day £4,770–£7,575

Trent College
Derby Road, Long Eaton, Nottingham,
Nottinghamshire NG10 4AD
Tel: 0115 8494949
Head: Mr Bill Penty
Age range: 11–18
No. of pupils: 1117 VIth200
Fees: Day £13,890–£17,442 WB
£21,945–£23,568 FB £31,644–£32,517
🌐 Ⓐ 🏫 Ⓔ ✎ 16·

Wellow House School
Wellow, Newark,
Nottinghamshire NG22 0EA
Tel: 01623 861054
Principal: Kirsty Lamb
Age range: 3–13
No. of pupils: 152
Fees: Day £7,485–£11,985
🏫 Ⓔ ✎

Worksop College
Worksop, Nottinghamshire S80 3AP
Tel: 01909 537100
Headmaster: G W Horgan MA (Oxon)
Age range: 3–18
No. of pupils: 614 VIth141
Fees: Day £8,385–£17,985
FB £19,485–£29,085
🌐 Ⓐ 🏫 Ⓔ ✎ 16·

Worksop College Preparatory School, Ranby House
Retford, Nottinghamshire DN22 8HX
Tel: 01777 714387 (Admissions)
Headmaster: C S J Pritchard
MA, BA(Hons), QTS
Age range: 3–11 years
No. of pupils: 190
Fees: Day £8,385–£13,485
FB £19,485–£20,085
🏫 £ ✎

Rutland

Brooke Priory School
Station Approach, Oakham,
Rutland LE15 6QW
Tel: 01572 724778
Headmaster: Mr R Outwin-Flinders BEd (Hons)
Age range: 2–11
No. of pupils: 193
Fees: Day £7,395–£9,195
£ ✎

OAKHAM SCHOOL
For further details see p. 116
Chapel Close, Oakham,
Rutland LE15 6DT
Tel: 01572 758500
Email: admissions@oakham.rutland.sch.uk
Website: www.oakham.rutland.sch.uk
Headmaster: Mr Henry Price
Age range: 10–18
No. of pupils: VIth392
Fees: Day £17,250–£21,360
FB £26,115–£35,010
🌐 A 🏫 £ IB ✎ 16+

Uppingham School
Uppingham, Rutland LE15 9QE
Tel: 01572 822216 Admissions:
01572 820611
Headmaster: Dr Richard Maloney
Age range: 13–18
No. of pupils: 798 VIth344
Fees: Day £7,990 FB £12,906
🌐 A 🏫 £ ✎ 16+

Greater London

KEY TO SYMBOLS

- ⚲ *Boys' school*
- ⚲ *Girls' school*
- 🌐 *International school*
- 16· *Tutorial or sixth form college*
- Ⓐ *A levels*
- 🏫 *Boarding accommodation*
- £ *Bursaries*
- ⒾⒷ *International Baccalaureate*
- ✎ *Learning support*
- 16· *Entrance at 16+*
- ✿ *Vocational qualifications*
- (IAPS) *Independent Association of Preparatory Schools*
- (HMC) *The Headmasters' & Headmistresses' Conference*
- (ISA) *Independent Schools Association*
- (GSA) *Girls' School Association*
- (BSA) *Boarding Schools' Association*
- Ⓢ *Society of Heads*

Unless otherwise indicated, all schools are coeducational day schools.
Single-sex and boarding schools will be indicated by the relevant icon.

Essex

Al-Noor Primary School
Newton Industrial Estate, Eastern Avenue, Chadwell Heath, Romford, Essex RM6 5SD
Tel: 020 8597 7576
Head: Mrs Someera Butt
Age range: 4–10
No. of pupils: 175
Fees: Day £3,600

Avon House Preparatory School
490 High Road, Woodford Green, Essex IG8 0PN
Tel: 020 8504 1749
Headteacher: Mrs Amanda Campbell
Age range: 3–11
No. of pupils: 242
Fees: Day £9,750–£10,740

Bancroft's School
High Road, Woodford Green, Essex IG8 0RF
Tel: 020 8505 4821
Head: Mr Simon Marshall MA, PGCE (Cantab), MA, MPhil (Oxon)
Age range: 7–18
No. of pupils: 1130 VIth235

Beehive Preparatory School
233 Beehive Lane, Redbridge, Ilford, Essex IG4 5ED
Tel: 020 8550 3224
Headteacher: Miss Richards
Age range: 4–11
Fees: Day £5,685

Braeside School for Girls
130 High Road, Buckhurst Hill, Essex IG9 5SD
Tel: 020 8504 1133
Headmistress: Claire Osborn
Age range: G3–16
No. of pupils: 199
Fees: Day £8,700–£12,750

Chigwell School
High Road, Chigwell, Essex IG7 6QF
Tel: 020 8501 5700
Headmaster: Mr M E Punt MA, MSc
Age range: 4–18
No. of pupils: 915 VIth185
Fees: Day £11,985–£17,985 FB £30,885

Daiglen School
68 Palmerston Road, Buckhurst Hill, Essex IG9 5LG
Tel: 020 8504 7108
Headteacher: Mrs P Dear
Age range: 3–11
No. of pupils: 130
Fees: Day £10,125–£10,275

Eastcourt Independent School
1 Eastwood Road, Goodmayes, Ilford, Essex IG3 8UW
Tel: 020 8590 5472
Headmistress: Mrs Christine Redgrave BSc(Hons), DipEd, MEd
Age range: 3–11
Fees: Day £7,200

Gidea Park College
2 Balgores Lane, Gidea Park, Romford, Essex RM2 5JR
Tel: 01708 740381
Headmistress: Mrs Katherine Whiskerd
Age range: 3–11
No. of pupils: 177
Fees: Day £9,675

Guru Gobind Singh Khalsa College
Roding Lane, Chigwell, Essex IG7 6BQ
Tel: 020 8559 9160
Principal: Mr Amarjit Singh Toor BSc(Hons), BSc, BT
Age range: 3–19
Fees: Day £5,892–£6,720

Immanuel School
Havering Grange Centre, Havering Road North, Romford, Essex RM1 4HR
Tel: 01708 764449
Principal: Simon Reeves
Age range: 3–16

Loyola Preparatory School
103 Palmerston Road, Buckhurst Hill, Essex IG9 5NH
Tel: 020 8504 7372
Headteacher: Mrs Kirsty Anthony
Age range: B3–11
No. of pupils: 200
Fees: Day £10,485

Maytime Montessori Nursery – Cranbrook Road
341 Cranbrook Road, Ilford, Essex IG1 4UF
Tel: 020 8554 3079

Maytime Montessori Nursery – Eastwood Road
2 Eastwood Road, Goodmayes, Essex IG3 8XB
Tel: 020 8599 3744

Maytime Montessori Nursery – York Road
87 York Road, Ilford, Essex IG3 3AF
Tel: 020 8553 1524
Age range: 0–6

Oakfields Montessori School
Harwood Hall, Harwood Hall Lane, Upminster, Essex RM14 2YG
Tel: 01708 220117
Headmistress: Katrina Carroll
Age range: 2–11
No. of pupils: 201
Fees: Day £9,720–£10,500

Oaklands School
8 Albion Hill, Loughton, Essex IG10 4RA
Tel: 020 8508 3517
Group Managing Principal: Mr M Hagger
Age range: 2–16
No. of pupils: 243
Fees: Day £10,350–£10,575

Park School for Girls
20-22 Park Avenue, Ilford, Essex IG1 4RS
Tel: 020 8554 2466
Headmistress: Mrs Androulla Nicholas
Age range: G4–16
No. of pupils: 230 VIth19
Fees: Day £6,795–£10,260

Raphael Independent School
Park Lane, Hornchurch, Essex RM11 1XY
Tel: 01708 744735
Head of School: Mrs C Salmon
Age range: 4–16
No. of pupils: 135
Fees: Day £6,285–£9,045

St Aubyn's School
Bunces Lane, Woodford Green, Essex IG8 9DU
Tel: 020 8504 1577
Headmaster: Mr Leonard Blom BEd(Hons) BA NPQH
Age range: 3–13
No. of pupils: 525
Fees: Day £5,370–£12,195

St Mary's Hare Park School & Nursery
South Drive, Gidea Park, Romford, Essex RM2 6HH
Tel: 01708 761220
Head Teacher: Mrs K Karwacinski
Age range: 2–11
No. of pupils: 180
Fees: Day £8,775

The Ursuline Preparatory School Ilford
2-8 Coventry Road, Ilford, Essex IG1 4QR
Tel: 020 8518 4050
Headteacher: Mrs Victoria McNaughton
Age range: G3–11
No. of pupils: 159
Fees: Day £7,320–£9,828

Woodford Green Preparatory School
Glengall Road, Woodford Green, Essex IG8 0BZ
Tel: 020 8504 5045
Headmaster: Mr J P Wadge
Age range: 3–11
No. of pupils: 384
Fees: Day £3,390

Hertfordshire

Lyonsdown School
3 Richmond Road, New Barnet,
Barnet, Hertfordshire EN5 1SA
Tel: 020 8449 0225
Head: Mr C Hammond BA (Hons) PGCE
Age range: B3–7 G3–11
No. of pupils: 185
Fees: Day £4,080–£10,200
⊘

Mount House School
Camlet Way, Hadley Wood,
Barnet, Hertfordshire EN4 0NJ
Tel: 020 8449 6889
Principal: Mr Toby Mullins
Age range: 11–18
No. of pupils: 190
Fees: Day £16,560
♦Ⓐ⊘⑯

**Norfolk Lodge Montessori
Nursery & Pre-Prep School**
Dancers Hill Road, Barnet,
Hertfordshire EN5 4RP
Tel: 020 8447 1565
Nursery Manager: Suzanne Clarke
Age range: 6 months–7 years
No. of pupils: 140
⊘

Susi Earnshaw Theatre School
68 High Street, Barnet,
Hertfordshire EN5 5SJ
Tel: 020 8441 5010
Age range: 9–16
No. of pupils: 60
Fees: Day £9,000–£12,000
Ⓔ

The Royal Masonic School for Girls
Rickmansworth Park, Rickmansworth,
Hertfordshire WD3 4HF
Tel: 01923 773168
Headmaster: Mr Kevin Carson
M.Phil (Cambridge)
Age range: G4–18
No. of pupils: 930 VIth165
Fees: Day £11,475–£17,475 WB
£20,115–£27,495 FB £21,225–£29,835
♦ⒼⒶ⚑Ⓔ⊘⑯

Kent

Ashgrove School
116 Widmore Road,
Bromley, Kent BR1 3BE
Tel: 020 8460 4143
Principal: Patricia Ash CertEd,
BSc(Hons), PhD, CMath, FIMA
Age range: 4–11
No. of pupils: 106
Fees: Day £8,730
Ⓖ⊘

Babington House School
Grange Drive, Chislehurst, Kent BR7 5ES
Tel: 020 8467 5537
Headmaster: Mr Tim Lello
MA, FRSA, NPQH
Age range: 3–18
No. of pupils: 387
Ⓐ Ⓔ⊘

**Benedict House
Preparatory School**
1-5 Victoria Road, Sidcup,
Kent DA15 7HD
Tel: 020 8300 7206
Headteacher: Mr Malcolm Gough
Age range: 3–11
Fees: Day £3,807–£7,929
⊘

Bickley Park School
24 Page Heath Lane, Bickley,
Bromley, Kent BR1 2DS
Tel: 020 8467 2195
Headmaster: Mr Patrick Wenham
Age range: B3–13 G3–4
No. of pupils: 370
Fees: Day £6,990–£14,940
♦Ⓔ⊘

Bishop Challoner School
228 Bromley Road, Shortlands,
Bromley, Kent BR2 0BS
Tel: 020 8460 3546
Headteacher: Ms Paula Anderson
Age range: 3–18
No. of pupils: 363
Fees: Day £8,331–£11,547
Ⓐ Ⓔ⊘⑯

**BREASIDE PREPARATORY
SCHOOL**
For further details see p. 120
41-43 Orchard Road,
Bromley, Kent BR1 2PR
Tel: 020 8460 0916
Email: info@breaside.co.uk
Website: www.breaside.co.uk
Executive Principal: Mrs Karen A
Nicholson B.Ed, NPQH, Dip EYs
Age range: 2½–11
No. of pupils: 376
Fees: Day £11,580–£13,494

Bromley High School GDST
Blackbrook Lane, Bickley,
Bromley, Kent BR1 2TW
Tel: 020 8781 7000/1
Head: Mrs A M Drew
BA(Hons), MBA (Dunelm)
Age range: G4–18
No. of pupils: 892
Fees: Day £14,265–£17,691
♦Ⓐ Ⓔ⊘⑯

Darul Uloom London
Foxbury Avenue, Perry Street,
Chislehurst, Kent BR7 6SD
Tel: 020 8295 0637
Principal: Mufti Mustafa
Age range: B11–18
No. of pupils: 160
Fees: FB £2,400
♦Ⓐ⚑⑯

Farringtons School
Perry Street, Chislehurst, Kent BR7 6LR
Tel: 020 8467 0256
Head: Mrs Dorothy Nancekievill
Age range: 3–18
No. of pupils: 700 VIth100
Fees: Day £15,120 WB £29,850 FB £31,680
Ⓖ Ⓐ ⚑Ⓔ⊘⑯

Merton Court Preparatory School
38 Knoll Road, Sidcup, Kent DA14 4QU
Tel: 020 8300 2112
Headmaster: Mr Dominic
Price BEd, MBA
Age range: 3–11
Fees: Day £8,670–£12,765
Ⓔ

St Christopher's The Hall School
49 Bromley Road, Beckenham,
Kent BR3 5PA
Tel: 020 8650 2200
Headmaster: Mr A Velasco
MEd, BH(Hons), PGCE
Age range: 3–11
No. of pupils: 305
Fees: Day £3,750–£9,165

St. David's Prep
Justin Hall,, Beckenham Road,
West Wickham, Kent BR4 0QS
Tel: 020 8777 5852
Principal: Mrs J Foulger
Age range: 4–11
No. of pupils: 155
Fees: Day £5,850–£8,550
Ⓔ⊘

West Lodge School
36 Station Road, Sidcup, Kent DA15 7DU
Tel: 020 8300 2489
Head Teacher: Mr Robert Francis
Age range: 3–11
No. of pupils: 163
Fees: Day £5,475–£9,150
⊘

Wickham Court School
Schiller International, Layhams Road,
West Wickham, Kent BR4 9HW
Tel: 020 8777 2942
Head: Mrs Lisa Harries
Age range: 2–16
No. of pupils: 121
Fees: Day £6,983.40–£12,344.55

Middlesex

Acorn House College
39-47 High Street, Southall,
Middlesex UB1 3HF
Tel: 020 8571 9900
Principal: Dr Francis Choi
Age range: 13–19
No. of pupils: 121 VIth85
Fees: Day £4,100–£15,525
⑯ Ⓐ

**ACS Hillingdon
International School**
Hillingdon Court, 108 Vine
Lane, Hillingdon, Uxbridge,
Middlesex UB10 0BE
Tel: +44 (0) 1895 259 771
Head: Martin Hall
Age range: 4–18
No. of pupils: 520
Fees: Day £10,640–£24,400
Ⓖ Ⓔ ⒷⒷ⊘⑯

Alpha Preparatory School
21 Hindes Road, Harrow,
Middlesex HA1 1SH
Tel: 020 8427 1471
Head: C.J.W Trinidad BSc(Hons), PGCE
Age range: 3–11
No. of pupils: 154
Fees: Day £3,400–£3,750

Ashton House School
50-52 Eversley Crescent,
Isleworth, Middlesex TW7 4LW
Tel: 020 8560 3902
Headteacher: Mrs Angela Stewart
Age range: 3–11
Fees: Day £7,986–£11,586
⊘

Buckingham Preparatory School
458 Rayners Lane, Pinner,
Harrow, Middlesex HA5 5DT
Tel: 020 8866 2737
Head of School: Mrs Sarah Hollis
Age range: B3–11 G3–4
Fees: Day £9,600–£12,300
♦Ⓔ⊘

Buxlow Preparatory School
5/6 Castleton Gardens, Wembley,
Middlesex HA9 7QJ
Tel: 020 8904 3615
Headteacher: Mr Ralf Furse
Age range: 2–11
Fees: Day £8,970–£9,330

**Edgware Jewish Girls
– Beis Chinuch**
Yeshurun Synagogue, Fernhurst
Gardens, Edgware, Middlesex HA8 7PH
Tel: 020 8951 0239
Headteacher: Mr M Cohen
Age range: G3–7

Halliford School
Russell Road, Shepperton,
Middlesex TW17 9HX
Tel: 01932 223593
Head: Mr James Davies BMus (Hons)
LGSM FASC ACertCM PGCE
Age range: B11–18 G16–18
No. of pupils: 402
Fees: Day £15,960

**Hampton Prep and
Pre-Prep School**
Gloucester Road, Hampton,
Middlesex TW12 2UQ
Tel: 020 8979 1844
Headmaster: Mr Tim Smith
Age range: 3–11
Fees: Day £6,030–£13,935

Hampton School
Hanworth Road, Hampton,
Middlesex TW12 3HD
Tel: 020 8979 9273
Headmaster: Mr Kevin
Knibbs MA (Oxon)
Age range: B11–18
No. of pupils: 1200
Fees: Day £6,390

Harrow School
5 High Street, Harrow on the
Hill, Middlesex HA1 3HT
Tel: 020 8872 8000
Head Master: Mr Alastair Land
Age range: B13–18
No. of pupils: 830 VIth320
Fees: FB £40,050

Holland House School
1 Broadhurst Avenue, Edgware,
Middlesex HA8 8TP
Tel: 020 8958 6979
Headmistress: Mrs H Stanton-
Tonner BEd(Hons) PGCE
Age range: 4–11
No. of pupils: 150
Fees: Day £8,100

Jack and Jill School
30 Nightingale Road, Hampton,
Middlesex TW12 3HX
Tel: 020 8979 3195
Principal: Miss K Papirnik BEd(Hons)
Age range: B2–5 G2–7
No. of pupils: 155
Fees: Day £4,608–£13,143

Kew House School
Kew House, 6 Capital Interchange
Way, London, Middlesex TW8 0EX
Tel: 0208 742 2038
Headmaster: Mr Mark Hudson
Age range: 11–18
No. of pupils: 550
Fees: Day £7,129

Lady Eleanor Holles
Hanworth Road, Hampton,
Middlesex TW12 3HF
Tel: 020 8979 1601
Head of School: Mrs Heather Hanbury
Age range: G7–18
No. of pupils: 930
Fees: Day £20,802

**Lady Nafisa Independent
Secondary School for Girls**
83A Sunbury Road, Feltham,
Middlesex TW13 4PH
Tel: 020 8751 5610
Headteacher: Ms Fouzia Butt
Age range: G11–16

Menorah Grammar School
Abbots Road, Edgware,
Middlesex HA8 0QS
Tel: 020 8906 9756
Headteacher: Rabbi A M Goldblatt
Age range: B11–17
No. of pupils: 203

Merchant Taylors' School
Sandy Lodge, Northwood,
Middlesex HA6 2HT
Tel: 01923 820644
Head: Mr S J Everson MA (Cantab)
Age range: B11–18
No. of pupils: 865 VIth282
Fees: Day £19,998

Newland House School
Waldegrave Park, Twickenham,
Middlesex TW1 4TQ
Tel: 020 8865 1234
Headmaster: Mr D A Alexander
Age range: B3–13 G3–11
No. of pupils: 425
Fees: Day £3,848–£4,306

North London Collegiate School
Canons, Canons Drive, Edgware,
Middlesex HA8 7RJ
Tel: +44 (0)20 8952 0912
Headmistress: Mrs Sarah Clark
Age range: G4–18
No. of pupils: 1080
Fees: Day £5,641–£6,676

Northwood College for Girls GDST
Maxwell Road, Northwood,
Middlesex HA6 2YE
Tel: 01923 825446
Head Mistress: Miss Jacqualyn
Pain MA, MA, MBA
Age range: G3–18
No. of pupils: 840 VIth100

Oak Heights
3 Red Lion Court, Alexandra Road,
Hounslow, Middlesex TW3 1JS
Tel: 020 8577 1827
Head: Mr S Dhillon
Age range: 11–16
No. of pupils: 48
Fees: Day £6,000

Orley Farm School
South Hill Avenue, Harrow,
Middlesex HA1 3NU
Tel: 020 8869 7600
Headmaster: Mr Tim Calvey
Age range: 4–13
No. of pupils: 497
Fees: Day £14,160–£16,335

Quinton Hall School & Nursery
91 Hindes Road, Harrow,
Middlesex HA1 1RX
Tel: 020 8861 8861
Headmaster: S Ford BEd
(Hons), UWE Bristol
Age range: B2–13 G2–11
Fees: Day £11,025–£12,150

Radnor House
Pope's Villa, Cross Deep,
Twickenham, Middlesex TW1 4QG
Tel: 020 8891 6264
Age range: 9–18
No. of pupils: 417

Reddiford School
36-38 Cecil Park, Pinner,
Middlesex HA5 5HH
Tel: 020 8866 0660
Headteacher: Mrs J Batt CertEd, NPQH
Age range: 3–11
No. of pupils: 320
Fees: Day £4,860–£11,565

Regent College
Sai House, 167 Imperial Drive,
Harrow, Middlesex HA2 7HD
Tel: 020 8966 9900
Principal: Mrs Tharshiny Pankaj
Age range: 11–19
No. of pupils: 167
Fees: Day £4,100–£15,525

Roxeth Mead School
Buckholt House, 25 Middle Road,
Harrow, Middlesex HA2 0HW
Tel: 020 8422 2092
Headmistress: Mrs A Isaacs
Age range: 3–7
No. of pupils: 54
Fees: Day £4,800–£10,665

St Catherine's Prep
Cross Deep, Twickenham,
Middlesex TW1 4QJ
Tel: 020 8891 2898
Headmistress: Mrs Johneen
McPherson MA
Age range: G3–11
No. of pupils: 127
Fees: Day £10,794–£12,456

ST CATHERINE'S SCHOOL
For further details see p. 126
Cross Deep, Twickenham,
Middlesex TW1 4QJ
Tel: 020 8891 2898
Email: info@stcatherineschool.co.uk
Website:
www.stcatherineschool.co.uk
Headmistress: Mrs Johneen
McPherson MA
Age range: G3–18
No. of pupils: 440
Fees: Day £11,205–£15,585
🏃 👥 Ⓐ £ ✏ 16

St Christopher's School
71 Wembley Park Drive,
Wembley, Middlesex HA9 8HE
Tel: 020 8902 5069
Headteacher: Mr G. P. Musetti
Age range: 4–11
Fees: Day £9,006–£9,906

ST HELEN'S COLLEGE
For further details see p. 128
Parkway, Hillingdon, Uxbridge,
Middlesex UB10 9JX
Tel: 01895 234371
Email: info@sthelenscollege.com
Website: www.sthelenscollege.com
Head: Mrs. Shirley Drummond
BA, PGCert, MLDP, FCCT
Age range: 2–11
No. of pupils: 383
Fees: Day £9,900–£12,240

St Helen's School
Eastbury Road, Northwood,
Middlesex HA6 3AS
Tel: +44 (0)1923 843210
Headmistress: Dr Mary Short BA, PhD
Age range: G3–18
No. of pupils: VIth165
🏃 👥 Ⓐ £ 16

St John's School
Potter Street Hill, Northwood,
Middlesex HA6 3QY
Tel: 020 8866 0067
Headmaster: Mr M S Robinson BSc
Age range: B3–13 years
No. of pupils: 350
Fees: Day £10,420–£15,110
🏃 £

St John's Senior School
North Lodge, The Ridgeway,
Enfield, Middlesex EN2 8BE
Tel: 020 8366 0035
Headmaster: Mr Andrew Tardios
LLB(Hons), BA(Hons), CertEd
Age range: 11–18 years
No. of pupils: 309 VIth95
Fees: Day £13,170
Ⓐ 16

St Martin's School
40 Moor Park Road, Northwood,
Middlesex HA6 2DJ
Tel: 01923 825740
Headmaster: Mr D T
Tidmarsh BSc(Wales)
Age range: B3–13
No. of pupils: 400
Fees: Day £5,775–£15,135
🏃 £ ✏

Tashbar Primary School
Mowbray Road, Edgware,
Middlesex HA8 8JL
Tel: 020 8958 5162
Headteacher: Mr N Jaffe
Age range: B3–11
No. of pupils: 88
🏃

The Hall Pre-Preparatory
School & Nursery
The Grange Country House,
Rickmansworth Road, Northwood,
Middlesex HA6 2RB
Tel: 01923 822807
Headmistress: Mrs S M Goodwin
Age range: 1–7
Fees: Day £4,650–£9,900
£ ✏

THE JOHN LYON SCHOOL
For further details see p. 130
Middle Road, Harrow on the
Hill, Middlesex HA2 0HN
Tel: 020 8515 9400
Email: admissions@johnlyon.org
Website: www.johnlyon.org
Head: Miss Katherine
Haynes BA, MEd, NPQH
Age range: B11–18
No. of pupils: 600
🏃 Ⓐ £ ✏ 16

The Mall School
185 Hampton Road, Twickenham,
Middlesex TW2 5NQ
Tel: 0208 977 2523
Headmaster: Mr D C Price BSc, MA
Age range: B4–13
No. of pupils: 320
Fees: Day £12,240–£13,767
🏃 £ ✏

The St Michael Steiner School
Park Road, Hanworth Park,
London, Middlesex TW13 6PN
Tel: 0208 893 1299
Age range: 3–16 (17 from Jul 2014)
No. of pupils: 101
Fees: Day £3,850–£9,500
£ ✏

Twickenham Preparatory School
Beveree, 43 High Street, Hampton,
Middlesex TW12 2SA
Tel: 020 8979 6216
Head: Mr David Malam BA(Hons)
(Southampton), PGCE(Winchester)
Age range: B4–13 G4–11
No. of pupils: 273
Fees: Day £10,470–£11,340
£ ✏

Surrey

Al-Khair School
109-117 Cherry Orchard Road,
Croydon, Surrey CR0 6BE
Tel: 020 8662 8664
Headteacher: Mr Mohammad
R Chaudhry
Age range: 5–16
No. of pupils: 126

Broomfield House School
Broomfield Road, Kew Gardens,
Richmond, Surrey TW9 3HS
Tel: 020 8940 3884
Head Teacher: Mr N O York
BA(Hons), MA, MPhil, FRSA
Age range: 3–11
No. of pupils: 160
Fees: Day £4,389–£15,054
✏

Cambridge Tutors College
Water Tower Hill, Croydon,
Surrey CR0 5SX
Tel: 020 8688 5284/7363
Principal: Dr Chris Drew
Age range: 15–19
No. of pupils: 215 VIth200
Fees: Day £10,400–£22,995
16 Ⓐ 👥 £ 16

Canbury School
Kingston Hill, Kingston upon
Thames, Surrey KT2 7LN
Tel: 020 8549 8622
Headmistress: Ms Louise Clancy
Age range: 11–18
No. of pupils: 58
Fees: Day £16,401
£ ✏

Collingwood School
3 Springfield Road, Wallington,
Surrey SM6 0BD
Tel: 020 8647 4607
Headmaster: Mr Leigh Hardie
Age range: 3–11
No. of pupils: 120
Fees: Day £4,980–£8,925
✏

Croydon High School GDST
Old Farleigh Road, Selsdon, South
Croydon, Surrey CR2 8YB
Tel: 020 8260 7500
Headmistress: Mrs Emma Pattison
Age range: G3–18
No. of pupils: 580 VIth75
🏃 Ⓐ £ ✏ 16

Cumnor House Nursery
91 Pampisford Road, South
Croydon, Surrey CR2 6DH
Tel: +44 (0)20 8660 3445
Headmaster: Mr Daniel Cummings
Age range: 2–4
No. of pupils: 200
Fees: Day £4,980–£10,635

Cumnor House School for Boys
168 Pampisford Road, South
Croydon, Surrey CR2 6DA
Tel: 020 8645 2614
Headmaster: Mr Daniel Cummings
Age range: B2–13
No. of pupils: 423
Fees: Day £3,880–£4,655
🏃 ✏

Cumnor House School for Girls
1 Woodcote Lane, Purley,
Surrey CR8 3HB
Tel: 020 8645 2614
Headmistress: Mrs Amanda McShane
Age range: G2–11
No. of pupils: 138
Fees: Day £3,880–£4,655
🏃

Date Valley School
Mitcham Court, Cricket Green,
Mitcham, Surrey CR4 4LB
Tel: +44 (0)20 8648 4647
Headteacher: Naheed Mughal
Age range: 3–11
No. of pupils: 110
Fees: Day £4,152–£5,043
£ ✏

Educare Small School
12 Cowleaze Road, Kingston
upon Thames, Surrey KT2 6DZ
Tel: 020 8547 0144
Head Teacher: Mrs E Steinthal
Age range: 3–11
No. of pupils: 46
Fees: Day £6,240

Elmhurst School
44-48 South Park Hill Rd, South
Croydon, Surrey CR2 7DW
Tel: 020 8688 0661
Headmaster: Mr Tony Padfield
Age range: B3–11
No. of pupils: 207
Fees: Day £6,129–£11,403

Holy Cross Preparatory School
George Road, Kingston upon
Thames, Surrey KT2 7NU
Tel: 020 8942 0729
Headteacher: Mrs S Hair BEd(Hons)
Age range: G4–11
No. of pupils: 285
Fees: Day £12,996

Homefield Preparatory School
Western Road, Sutton, Surrey SM1 2TE
Tel: 0208 642 0965
Headmaster: Mr John Towers
Age range: B3–13
No. of pupils: 350
Fees: Day £6,210–£13,320

KEW COLLEGE
For further details see p. 122
24-26 Cumberland Road,
Kew, Surrey TW9 3HQ
Tel: 020 8940 2039
Email: enquiries@kewcollege.com
Website: www.kewcollege.com
Head: Mrs Marianne Austin
BSc(Hons), MA(Hons), ACA, PGCE
Age range: 3–11
No. of pupils: 296

Kew Green Preparatory School
Layton House, Ferry Lane, Kew
Green, Richmond, Surrey TW9 3AF
Tel: 020 8948 5999
Headmaster: Mr J Peck
Age range: 4–11
No. of pupils: 270
Fees: Day £6,120

King's House School
68 King's Road, Richmond,
Surrey TW10 6ES
Tel: 020 8940 1878
Head: Mr Mark Turner BA, PGCE, NPQH
Age range: B3–13 G3–4
No. of pupils: 460
Fees: Day £2,370–£5,560

Kingston Grammar School
70 London Rd, Kingston upon
Thames, Surrey KT2 6PY
Tel: 020 8456 5875
Head: Mr Stephen Lehec
Age range: 11–18
No. of pupils: 829
Fees: Day £6,225

LALEHAM LEA SCHOOL
For further details see p. 124
29 Peaks Hill, Purley, Surrey CR8 3JJ
Tel: 020 8660 3351
Email: secretary@lalehamlea.co.uk
Website: www.lalehamlea.co.uk
Headteacher: Ms K Barry
Age range: 3–11
No. of pupils: 112
Fees: Day £8,940

Marymount London
George Road, Kingston upon
Thames, Surrey KT2 7PE
Tel: +44 (0)20 8949 0571
Headmistress: Mrs Margaret Frazier
Age range: G11–18
No. of pupils: 250
Fees: Day £24,985 WB
£40,515 FB £42,305

Oakwood Independent School
Godstone Road, Purley,
Surrey CR8 2AN
Tel: 020 8668 8080
Headmaster: Mr Ciro Candia
BA(Hons), PGCE
Age range: 3–11
No. of pupils: 176
Fees: Day £9,030–£9,840

Old Palace of John Whitgift School
Old Palace Road, Croydon,
Surrey CR0 1AX
Tel: 020 8686 7347
Head: Mrs. C Jewell
Age range: B3 months–4 years
G3 months–19 years
No. of pupils: 740 VIth120
Fees: Day £11,316–£15,366

Old Vicarage School
48 Richmond Hill, Richmond,
Surrey TW10 6QX
Tel: 020 8940 0922
Headmistress: Mrs G D Linthwaite
Age range: G4–11
No. of pupils: 200
Fees: Day £4,740

Park Hill School
8 Queens Road, Kingston upon
Thames, Surrey KT2 7SH
Tel: 020 8546 5496
Headmaster: Mr Alistair Bond
Age range: 2–11
No. of pupils: 100
Fees: Day £10,440

Reedham Park School
71A Old Lodge Lane, Purley,
Surrey CR8 4DN
Tel: 020 8660 6357
Headteacher: Mrs Katie Shah
Age range: 4–11
No. of pupils: 122
Fees: Day £5,385

Rokeby School
George Road, Kingston upon
Thames, Surrey KT2 7PB
Tel: 020 8942 2247
Head: Mr J R Peck
Age range: B4–13
No. of pupils: 370
Fees: Day £13,377–£16,656

Royal Russell Junior School
Coombe Lane, Croydon,
Surrey CR9 5BX
Tel: 020 8651 5884
Junior School Headmaster: Mr
James C Thompson
Age range: 3–11
No. of pupils: 300
Fees: Day £11,160–£14,220

Royal Russell School
Coombe Lane, Croydon,
Surrey CR9 5BX
Tel: 020 8657 3669
Headmaster: Christopher Hutchinson
Age range: 11–18
No. of pupils: 590 VIth180
Fees: Day £18,480 FB £36,525

Seaton House School
67 Banstead Road South,
Sutton, Surrey SM2 5LH
Tel: 020 8642 2332
Headmistress: Mrs Debbie Morrison
Higher Diploma in Education (RSA)
Age range: B3–5 G3–11
No. of pupils: 164
Fees: Day £10,188

Shrewsbury House School
107 Ditton Road, Surbiton,
Surrey KT6 6RL
Tel: 020 8399 3066
Headmaster: Mr K Doble
BA, PDM, PGCE
Age range: B7–13
No. of pupils: 320
Fees: Day £18,060

St David's School
23/25 Woodcote Valley Road,
Purley, Surrey CR8 3AL
Tel: 020 8660 0723
Headmistress: Cressida Mardell
Age range: 3–11
No. of pupils: 167
Fees: Day £6,375–£10,650

St James Senior Boys School
Church Road, Ashford, Surrey TW15 3DZ
Tel: 01784 266930
Headmaster: Mr David Brazier
Age range: B11–18
No. of pupils: 403 VIth65
Fees: Day £18,930

Staines Preparatory School
3 Gresham Road, Staines upon
Thames, Surrey TW18 2BT
Tel: 01784 450909
Head of School: Ms Samantha
Sawyer B.Ed (Hons), M.Ed, NPQH
Age range: 3–11
No. of pupils: 364
Fees: Day £9,810–£11,460

Surbiton High School
13-15 Surbiton Crescent, Kingston
upon Thames, Surrey KT1 2JT
Tel: 020 8546 5245
Principal: Mrs Rebecca Glover
Age range: B4–11 G4–18
No. of pupils: 1210 VIth186
Fees: Day £10,857–£17,142

Sutton High School GDST
55 Cheam Road, Sutton,
Surrey SM1 2AX
Tel: 020 8642 0594
Headmistress: Mrs Katharine Crouch
Age range: G3–18
No. of pupils: 600 VIth60
Fees: Day £10,095–£17,043
(符)(A)(£)(符)(16)

The Cedars School
Coombe Road, Lloyd Park,
Croydon, Surrey CR0 5RD
Tel: 020 8185 7770
Headmaster: Robert Teague Bsc (Hons)
Age range: B11–18
(符)

The Falcons Preparatory School for Boys
41 Few Foot Road, Richmond,
Surrey TW9 2SS
Tel: 0844 225 2211
Headmistress: Franciska Bayliss
Age range: B7–13
No. of pupils: 100
Fees: Day £17,835
(符)(符)

The Royal Ballet School
White Lodge, Richmond,
Surrey TW10 5HR
Tel: 020 7836 8899
Artistic Director: Christopher Powney
Age range: 11–19
No. of pupils: VIth80
Fees: Day £18,939–£24,885
FB £29,328–£33,567
(A)(符)(£)(符)(16)

The Study School
57 Thetford Road, New
Malden, Surrey KT3 5DP
Tel: 020 8942 0754
Head of School: Mrs Donna
Brackstone-Drake
Age range: 3–11
No. of pupils: 134
Fees: Day £4,860–£11,388

Trinity School
Shirley Park, Croydon, Surrey CR9 7AT
Tel: 020 8656 9541
Head: Alasdair Kennedy MA (Cantab)
Age range: B10–18 G16–18
No. of pupils: 1007
Fees: Day £16,656
(符)(A)(£)(符)(16)

Unicorn School
238 Kew Road, Richmond,
Surrey TW9 3JX
Tel: 020 8948 3926
Headmaster: Mr Kit Thompson
Age range: 3–11
Fees: Day £6,930–£12,720
(£)(符)

Westbury House
80 Westbury Road, New
Malden, Surrey KT3 5AS
Tel: 020 8942 5885
Age range: 3–11
Fees: Day £4,860–£11,115

WHITGIFT SCHOOL
For further details see p. 132
Haling Park, South Croydon,
Surrey CR2 6YT
Tel: +44 20 8633 9935
Email: admissions@whitgift.co.uk
Website: www.whitgift.co.uk
Headmaster: Mr Christopher Ramsey
Age range: B10–18
No. of pupils: 1490
Fees: Day £20,640 WB
£33,081 FB £40,140
(符)(符)(A)(符)(£)(IB)(符)(16)

D344

London

KEY TO SYMBOLS

- 🛉 *Boys' school*
- 🛉 *Girls' school*
- 🌐 *International school*
- 16· *Tutorial or sixth form college*
- Ⓐ *A levels*
- 🏛 *Boarding accommodation*
- £ *Bursaries*
- ⒾⒷ *International Baccalaureate*
- ✎ *Learning support*
- 16· *Entrance at 16+*
- ✿ *Vocational qualifications*
- ⒾⒶⓅⓈ *Independent Association of Preparatory Schools*
- ⒽⓂⒸ *The Headmasters' & Headmistresses' Conference*
- ⒾⓈⒶ *Independent Schools Association*
- ⒼⓈⒶ *Girls' School Association*
- ⒷⓈⒶ *Boarding Schools' Association*
- Ⓢ *Society of Heads*

Unless otherwise indicated, all schools are coeducational day schools. Single-sex and boarding schools will be indicated by the relevant icon.

Central London

CATS London
43-45 Bloomsbury Square,
London WC1A 2RA
Tel: 02078 411580
Principal: Mario Di Clemente
Age range: 15–24

Charterhouse Square School
40 Charterhouse Square,
London EC1M 6EA
Tel: 020 7600 3805
Age range: 3–11
No. of pupils: 196
Fees: Day £5,680

CITY OF LONDON SCHOOL
For further details see p. 140
Queen Victoria Street,
London EC4V 3AL
Tel: 020 3680 6300
Email: admissions@
cityoflondonschool.org.uk
Website:
www.cityoflondonschool.org.uk
Head: Mr A R Bird MSc
Age range: B10–18
No. of pupils: 950 VIth250
Fees: Day £18,939

City of London School for Girls
St Giles' Terrace, Barbican,
London EC2Y 8BB
Tel: 020 7847 5500
Headmistress: Mrs E Harrop
Age range: G7–18
No. of pupils: 725

Dallington School
8 Dallington Street, Islington,
London EC1V 0BW
Tel: 020 7251 2284
Headteacher: Mogg Hercules
Age range: 3–11
No. of pupils: 138
Fees: Day £9,978–£12,630

École Jeannine Manuel – London
43-45 Bedford Square,
London WC1B 3DN
Tel: 020 3829 5970
Head of School: Pauline Prévot
Age range: 3–18 years
No. of pupils: 480
Fees: Day £18,324

Italia Conti Academy of Theatre Arts
Italia Conti House, 23 Goswell
Road, London EC1M 7AJ
Tel: 020 7608 0047
Director: Chris White
Age range: 10–21

ST PAUL'S CATHEDRAL SCHOOL
For further details see p. 162
2 New Change, London EC4M 9AD
Tel: 020 7248 5156
Email: admissions@spcs.
london.sch.uk
Website: www.spcslondon.com
Headmaster: Simon Larter-
Evans BA (Hons), PGCE, FRSA
Age range: 4–13
No. of pupils: 260
Fees: Day £4,911–£5,287 FB £2,970

The College of Central London
Tower Bridge Business Centre, 46-48
East Smithfield, London E1W 1AW
Tel: +44 (0) 20 3667 7607
Principal: Nicolas Kailides
Fees: Day £3,850

The Lyceum School
65 Worship Street, London EC2A 2DU
Tel: +44 (0)20 7247 1588
Head of School: Ms Hilary
Wyatt NPQH, MA, PGCE
Age range: 3–11
Fees: Day £16,185

Urdang Academy
The Old Finsbury Town Hall, Rosebery
Avenue, London EC1R 4RP
Tel: 020 7713 7710
Principal: Stephanie Pope
ARAD (dip PDTC)
Age range: 16+

East London

Al-Falah Primary School
48 Kenninghall Road,
Clapton, London E5 8BY
Tel: 020 8985 1059
Headteacher: Mr M A Hussain
Age range: 5–11
No. of pupils: 83
Fees: Day £7,200

Al-Mizan School
46 Whitechapel Road, London E1 1JX
Tel: 020 7650 3070
Head: Mr Askor Ali
Age range: B7–11
No. of pupils: 200 VIth13
Fees: Day £3,400

Azhar Academy
235A Romford Road, Forest
Gate, London E7 9HL
Tel: 020 8534 5959
Headteacher: Mrs R Rehman
Age range: G11–16
No. of pupils: 189

Beis Trana Girls' School
186 Upper Clapton Road,
London E5 9DH
Tel: 020 8815 8003
Age range: G3–16
No. of pupils: 270

Chingford House School
22 Marlborough Road, Waltham
Forest, London E4 9AL
Tel: 020 8527 2902; 07749 899 498
Head teacher: Helen McNulty
Age range: 0–5

Faraday School
Old Gate House, 7 Trinity Buoy
Wharf, London E14 0JW
Tel: 020 8965 7374
Head Teacher: Claire Murdoch
Age range: 4–11
No. of pupils: 105
Fees: Day £3,686

Forest School
College Place, Snaresbrook,
London E17 3PY
Tel: 020 8520 1744
Warden: Mr Cliff Hodges
Age range: 4–18
No. of pupils: 1355 VIth260
Fees: Day £13,095–£18,681

Gatehouse School
Sewardstone Road, Victoria
Park, London E2 9JG
Tel: 020 8980 2978
Acting Headmistress: Sevda Corby
Age range: 3–11
No. of pupils: 320
Fees: Day £11,610–£12,225

Grangewood Independent School
Chester Road, Forest
Gate, London E7 8QT
Tel: 020 8472 3552
Headteacher: Mrs B A Roberts
B.Ed (Hons); PG Cert (SEN)
Age range: 2–11
No. of pupils: 71
Fees: Day £5,157–£6,751

Hyland House School
Holcombe Road, Tottenham,
, London N17 9AD
Tel: 0208 520 4186
Head Teacher: Mrs Gina Abbequaye
Age range: 3–11
Fees: Day £2,520

London East Academy
46-80 Whitechapel Road,
London E1 1JX
Tel: 020 7650 3070
Headteacher: Musleh Faradhi
Age range: B11–18
No. of pupils: VIth18
Fees: Day £3,000

Lubavitch House School (Junior Boys)
135 Clapton Common, London E5 9AE
Tel: 020 8800 1044
Head: Mr R Leach
Age range: B5–11
No. of pupils: 101

Madani Girls School
Myrdle Street, London E1 1HL
Tel: 020 7377 1992
Headteacher: Muhammad S. Rahman
Age range: G11–18
No. of pupils: 248 VIth11
Fees: Day £2,400

Normanhurst School
68-74 Station Road, Chingford,
London E4 7BA
Tel: 020 8529 4307
Headmistress: Mrs Claire Osborn
Age range: 2–16
No. of pupils: 250
Fees: Day £10,350–£13,050

Paragon Christian Academy
233-241 Glyn Road, London E5 0JP
Tel: 020 8985 1119
Headteacher: Mrs Sharon Curry
Age range: 5–16
No. of pupils: 34

Pillar Box Montessori Nursery & Pre-Prep School
107 Bow Road, London E3 2AN
Tel: 020 8980 0700
Director: Lorraine Redknapp
Age range: 0–5
Fees: Day £12,000

PromisedLand Academy
St Cedds Hall, Webb Gardens,
Plaistow, London E13 8SR
Tel: 07572 614 770
Head: Mr A Coote
Age range: 4–16

Quwwat-ul Islam Girls School
16 Chaucer Road, Forest
Gate, London E7 9NB
Tel: 020 8548 4736
Head of School: Shazia Member
Age range: G4–11
No. of pupils: 150

River House Montessori School
3-4 Shadwell Pierhead, Glamis
Road, London E1W 3TD
Tel: 020 7538 9886
Headmistress: Miss S Greenwood
Age range: 3–16
Fees: Day £3,410–£3,625

Snaresbrook Preparatory School
75 Woodford Road, South
Woodford, London E18 2EA
Tel: 020 8989 2394
Head of School: Mr Ralph Dalton
Age range: 3–11
Fees: Day £8,922–£11,934

**ST JOSEPH'S CONVENT
SCHOOL FOR GIRLS**
For further details see p. 160
59 Cambridge Park,
Wanstead, London E11 2PR
Tel: +44 (0)20 8989 4700
Email: enquiries@
stjosephsconventschool.co.uk
Website:
www.stjosephsconventschool.co.uk
Interim Head Teacher: Ms
Sheila Birtles
Age range: G3–11

**Talmud Torah Machikei
Hadass School**
96-98 Clapton Common,
London E5 9AL
Tel: 020 8800 6599
Headteacher: Rabbi C Silbiger
Age range: B3–16
No. of pupils: 271

Winston House Preparatory School
140 High Road, London E18 2QS
Tel: 020 8505 6565
Head Teacher: Mrs Marian Kemp
Age range: 3–11

North London

Annemount School
18 Holne Chase, Hampstead
Garden Suburb, London N2 0QN
Tel: 020 8455 2132
Principal: Mrs G Maidment
BA(Hons), MontDip
Age range: 2–7
No. of pupils: 100
Fees: Day £3,275–£6,000

**Avenue Nursery & Pre-
Preparatory School**
2 Highgate Avenue, London N6 5RX
Tel: 020 8348 6815
Principal: Mrs. Mary Fysh
Age range: 2½–7½
No. of pupils: 79

Beis Chinuch Lebonos Girls School
Woodberry Down Centre,
Woodberry Down, London N4 2SH
Tel: 020 88097 737
Headmistress: Mrs Leah Klein
Age range: G2–16
No. of pupils: 421

Beis Malka Girls School
93 Alkham Road, London N16 6XD
Tel: 020 8806 2070
Headmaster: M Dresdner
Age range: G5–16
No. of pupils: 339

Beis Rochel D'Satmar Girls School
51-57 Amhurst Park, London N16 5DL
Tel: 020 8800 9060
Headmistress: Mrs E Katz
Age range: G2–18
No. of pupils: 788

Bnois Jerusalem School
79-81 Amhurst Park, London N16 5DL
Tel: 020 8802 7470
Head: Mrs Sonnenschein
Age range: G3–16

Channing School
The Bank, Highgate, London N6 5HF
Tel: 020 8340 2328
Head: Mrs B M Elliott
Age range: G4–18
No. of pupils: 746 VIth108
Fees: Day £17,610–£19,410

Dwight School London
6 Friern Barnet Lane, London N11 3LX
Tel: +44 (0)20 8920 0637
Head: Mrs Alison Cobbin
BA, Dip Ed, MBA
Age range: 3–18

Finchley & Acton Yochien School
6 Hendon Avenue, Finchley,
London N3 1UE
Tel: 020 8343 2191
Headteacher: J Tanabe
Age range: 2–6
No. of pupils: 145

Grange Park Preparatory School
13 The Chine, Grange Park,
Winchmore Hill, London N21 2EA
Tel: 020 8360 1469
Headteacher: Miss F Rizzo
Age range: G4–11
No. of pupils: 90
Fees: Day £10,300–£10,378

**Greek Secondary
School of London**
Avenue Lodge, Bounds Green
Road, London N22 7EU
Tel: 020 8881 9320
Headteacher: Georgia
Dimitrakopoulou
Age range: 13–18
No. of pupils: 200

Highgate
North Road, Highgate, London N6 4AY
Tel: 020 8340 1524
Head Master: Mr A S Pettitt MA
Age range: 3–18
No. of pupils: 1541 VIth312
Fees: Day £18,165–£20,970

Highgate Junior School
Cholmeley House, 3 Bishopswood
Road, London N6 4PL
Tel: 020 8340 9193
Principal: Mr S M James BA
Age range: 7–11
Fees: Day £19,230

Highgate Pre-Preparatory School
7 Bishopswood Road, London N6 4PH
Tel: 020 8340 9196
Principal: Mrs Diane Hecht
Age range: 3–7
No. of pupils: 150
Fees: Day £18,165

Keble Prep
Wades Hill, Winchmore
Hill, London N21 1BG
Tel: 020 8360 3359
Headmaster: Mr M J Mitchell
Age range: B4–13
No. of pupils: 228
Fees: Day £3,850–£4,930

Kerem School
Norrice Lea, London N2 0RE
Tel: 020 8455 0909
Head Teacher: Miss Alyson Burns
Age range: 3–11
Fees: Day £9,435

**Lubavitch House School
(Senior Girls)**
107-115 Stamford Hill, Hackney,
London N16 5RP
Tel: 020 8800 0022
Headmaster: Rabbi Shmuel Lew FRSA
Age range: G11–18
No. of pupils: 102
Fees: Day £3,900

Norfolk House School
10 Muswell Avenue, Muswell
Hill, London N10 2EG
Tel: 020 8883 4584
Head Teacher: Mr Paul Jowett
Age range: 4–11
No. of pupils: 130
Fees: Day £12,066

North London Grammar School
110 Colindeep Lane, Hendon,
London NW9 6HB
Tel: 0208 205 0052
Head Teacher: Mr Fatih Adak
Age range: 6–18
No. of pupils: 150
Fees: Day £10,800–£13,500
FB £18,900–£21,600

North London Rudolf Steiner School
1-3 The Campsbourne, London N8 7PN
Tel: 020 8341 3770
Age range: 0–7
No. of pupils: 40

Palmers Green High School
Hoppers Road, Winchmore Hill, London N21 3LJ
Tel: 020 8886 1135
Headmistress: Mrs Wendy Kempster
Age range: G3–16
No. of pupils: 300
Fees: Day £5,880–£15,930

Pardes House Grammar School
Hendon Lane, Finchley, London N3 1SA
Tel: 020 8349 4222
Headteacher: Rabbi Yitzchok Lev
Age range: B10–16
No. of pupils: 222

Phoenix Academy
85 Bounces Road, Edmonton, London N9 8LD
Tel: 020 8887 6888
Headteacher: Mr Paul Kelly
Age range: 5–18
No. of pupils: 19

Rosemary Works Independent School
1 Branch Place, London N1 5PH
Tel: 020 7739 3950
Head: Rob Dell
Age range: 3–11
No. of pupils: 104
Fees: Day £14,097

Salcombe Preparatory School
224-226 Chase Side, Southgate, London N14 4PL
Tel: 020 8441 5356
Headmistress: Mrs Sarah-Jane Davies BA(Hons) QTS MEd
Age range: 3–11
No. of pupils: 250
Fees: Day £11,673

St Paul's Steiner School
1 St Paul's Road, Islington, London N1 2QH
Tel: 020 7226 4454
College of Teachers: College of Teachers
Age range: 2–14
No. of pupils: 136

Sunrise Nursery, Stoke Newington
1 Cazenove Road, Stoke Newington, Hackney, London N16 6PA
Tel: 020 8806 6279
Principal: Didi Ananda Manika

Sunrise Primary School
55 Coniston Road, Tottenham, London N17 0EX
Tel: 020 8806 6279 (Office); 020 8885 3354 (School)
Head: Mrs Mary-Anne Lovage MontDipEd, BA
Age range: 2–11
No. of pupils: 30
Fees: Day £5,550

Talmud Torah Bobov Primary School
87 Egerton Road, London N16 6UE
Tel: 020 8809 1025
Headmaster: Mr Chaim Weissman
Age range: B3–13
No. of pupils: 320

Talmud Torah Chaim Meirim School
26 Lampard Grove, London N16 6XB
Tel: 020 8806 0017
Principal: Rabbi S Hoffman
Age range: B4–13

Talmud Torah Yetev Lev School
111-115 Cazenove Road, London N16 6AX
Tel: 020 8806 3834
Headteacher: Mr J Stauber
Age range: B2–11
No. of pupils: 567

Tawhid Boys School
21 Cazenove Road, London N16 6PA
Tel: 020 8806 2999
Headteacher: Mr Usman Mapara
Age range: B10–15
No. of pupils: 115

Tayyibah Girls School
88 Filey Avenue, Stamford Hill, London N16 6JJ
Tel: 020 8880 0085
Headmistress: Mrs N B Qureishi MSc
Age range: G5–18
No. of pupils: 270

The Children's House Upper School
King Henry's Walk, London N1 4PB
Tel: 020 7249 6273
Headteacher: Kate Orange
Age range: 4–7
No. of pupils: 60
Fees: Day £14,730

The Gower School Montessori Nursery
18 North Road, Islington, London N7 9EY
Tel: 020 7700 2445
Principal: Miss Emma Gowers
Age range: 3 months–5 years
No. of pupils: 237

The Gower School Montessori Primary
10 Cynthia Street, Barnsbury, London N1 9JF
Tel: 020 7278 2020
Principal: Miss Emma Gowers
Age range: 4–11
No. of pupils: 237
Fees: Day £15,576

TTTYY School
14 Heathland Road, London N16 5NH
Tel: 020 8802 1348
Headmaster: Rabbi A Friesel
Age range: B2–13
No. of pupils: 187

Vita et Pax School
Priory Close, Southgate, London N14 4AT
Tel: 020 8449 8336
Headteacher: Miss Gillian Chumbley
Age range: 3–11
Fees: Day £9,360

Yesodey Hatorah School
Egerton Road, London N16 6UB
Tel: 020 8826 5500
Headteacher: Rabbi Pinter
Age range: 3–16
No. of pupils: 920

North-West London

Abercorn School
38 Portland Place, London NW8 9XP
Tel: 020 7286 4785
High Mistress: Mrs Andrea Greystoke BA(Hons)
Age range: 2–13
No. of pupils: 360
Fees: Day £10,020–£20,055

Al-Sadiq & Al-Zahra Schools
134 Salusbury Road, London NW6 6PF
Tel: 020 7372 7706
Headteacher: Dr M Movahedi
Age range: 4–16
No. of pupils: 389

Arnold House School
1 Loudoun Road, St John's Wood, London NW8 0LH
Tel: 020 7266 4840
Headmaster: Mr Vivian Thomas
Age range: B5–13
No. of pupils: 270
Fees: Day £6,100

Barnet Hill Academy
10A Montagu Road, Hendon, London NW4 3ES
Tel: 02034112660
Headteacher: Mr Shakil Ahmed
Age range: 3–11 G11–16
Fees: Day £3,000

Beis Soroh Schneirer
Arbiter House, Wilberforce Road, London NW9 6AX
Tel: 020 8343 1190
Head: Mrs R Weiss
Age range: G2–11
No. of pupils: 150

Belmont, Mill Hill Preparatory School
The Ridgeway, London NW7 4ED
Tel: 020 8906 7270
Headmaster: Mr Leon Roberts MA
Age range: 7–13
No. of pupils: 540
Fees: Day £18,099

Beth Jacob Grammar School for Girls
Stratford Road, Hendon, London NW4 2AT
Tel: 020 8203 4322
Headteacher: Mrs M Gluck
Age range: G11–17
No. of pupils: 264

Brampton College
Lodge House, Lodge Road,
Hendon, London NW4 4DQ
Tel: 020 8203 5025
Principal: B Canetti BA(Hons), MSc
Age range: 15–20
Fees: Day £19,935
16ᵗ Ⓐ

Brondesbury College for Boys
8 Brondesbury Park, London NW6 7BT
Tel: 020 8830 4522
Headteacher: Mr Amzad Ali
Age range: B11–16
No. of pupils: 93
⚥ £

Collège Français Bilingue de Londres
87 Holmes Road, Kentish
Town, , London NW5 3AX
Tel: 020 7993 7400
Headteacher: François-Xavier Gabet
Age range: 5–15
No. of pupils: 700
Fees: Day £10,555–£11,575
🌀

DEVONSHIRE HOUSE PREPARATORY SCHOOL
For further details see p. 142
2 Arkwright Road, Hampstead,
London NW3 6AE
Tel: 020 7435 1916
Email: enquiries@
devonshirehouseprepschool.co.uk
Website:
www.devonshirehouseschool.co.uk
Headmistress: Mrs S. Piper BA(Hons)
Age range: B2½–13 G2½–11
No. of pupils: 650
Fees: Day £10,545–£19,470
£

Fine Arts College
Centre Studios, 41-43 England's
Lane, London NW3 4YD
Tel: +44 (0)207 586 0312
Principal: Ms Candida Cave
Age range: 13–18
Fees: Day £22,560
16ᵗ

Francis Holland School, Regent's Park, NW1
Clarence Gate, Ivor Place,
Regent's Park, London NW1 6XR
Tel: 020 7723 0176
Head: Mr C B Fillingham MA
(King's College London)
Age range: G11–18
No. of pupils: 495 VIth120
Fees: Day £19,260
⚥ Ⓐ £ 16ᵗ

Golders Hill School
666 Finchley Road, London NW11 7NT
Tel: 020 8455 2589
Headmistress: Mrs A T Eglash BA(Hons)
Age range: 2–7
No. of pupils: 180
Fees: Day £1,575–£13,827

Goodwyn School
Hammers Lane, Mill Hill,
London NW7 4DB
Tel: 020 8959 3756
Principal: Struan Robertson
Age range: 3–11
No. of pupils: 223
Fees: Day £5,120–£11,042

Grimsdell, Mill Hill Pre-Preparatory School
Winterstoke House, Wills Grove,
Mill Hill, London NW7 1QR
Tel: 020 8959 6884
Head: Mrs Kate Simon BA, PGCE
Age range: 3–7
No. of pupils: 191
Fees: Day £14,895
✎

Hampstead Hill Pre-Prep & Nursery School
St Stephen's Hall, Pond Street,
Hampstead, London NW3 2PP
Tel: 020 7435 6262
Principal: Mrs Andrea Taylor
Age range: B2–7+ G2–7+
Fees: Day £10,175–£16,830
✎

HEATHSIDE SCHOOL
For further details see p. 144
84-86 West Heath Road,
London NW3 7UN
Tel: +44 (0)20 3058 4011
Email: admissions@heathside.net
Website: www.heathsideprep.co.uk
Headteacher: Katherine Vintiner
Age range: 2–14
No. of pupils: 500
Fees: Day £15,000–£18,300
🎓 ✎

Hendon Prep School
20 Tenterden Grove, Hendon,
London NW4 1TD
Tel: 020 8203 7727
Age range: 2–13 years
No. of pupils: 165
Fees: Day £6,345–£14,175
£ ✎

Hereward House School
14 Strathray Gardens, London NW3 4NY
Tel: 020 7794 4820
Headmaster: Mr P Evans
Age range: B4–13
No. of pupils: 170
Fees: Day £15,615–£16,065
⚥

International Community School
7B Wyndham Place, London NW1 4PT
Tel: +44 (0) 20 7298 8817
Age range: 3–18
No. of pupils: 190
Fees: Day £19,400–£26,000
🌀 ⒾⒷ ✎ 16ᵗ

Iranian School
100 Carlton Vale, London NW6 5HE
Tel: 020 7372 8051
Headteacher: Mr Seyed Abbas Hosseini
Age range: 6–16
No. of pupils: 53

Islamia Girls' High School
129 Salusbury Road, London NW6 6PE
Tel: 020 7372 3472
Headteacher: Mrs Fawziah Islam
Age range: G11–16 years
Fees: Day £6,900
⚥

Lyndhurst House Prep School
24 Lyndhurst Gardens, Hampstead,
London NW3 5NW
Tel: 020 7435 4936
Head of School: Mr Andrew
Reid MA (Oxon)
Age range: B4–13
No. of pupils: 150
Fees: Day £6,190–£6,910
⚥ ✎

Maple Walk School
62A Crownhill Road, London NW10 4EB
Tel: 020 8963 3890
Head Teacher: Mrs S Gillam
Age range: 4–11
No. of pupils: 200
Fees: Day £3,580
£ ✎

Maria Montessori Institute
26 Lyndhurst Gardens, Hampstead,
London NW3 5NW
Tel: 020 7435 3646
Director of Training & School: Mrs Lynne
Lawrence BA, Mont Int Dip(AMI)
Age range: 2–12
No. of pupils: 50
Fees: Day £5,580–£13,560
16ᵗ

Maria Montessori School – Hampstead
26 Lyndhurst Gardens, Hampstead,
London NW3 5NW
Tel: +44 (0)20 7435 3646
Director of School: Miss L Kingston
Age range: 2 –12
No. of pupils: 100
Fees: Day £6,270–£13,560

Mill Hill School
The Ridgeway, Mill Hill Village,
London NW7 1QS
Tel: 020 8959 1176
Head: Mrs Jane Sanchez
BSc (Hons) PGCE
Age range: 13–18
No. of pupils: 689 VIth259
Fees: Day £21,141 WB £28,524 FB £33,717
🌀 Ⓐ 🛏 £ ✎ 16ᵗ

Naima Jewish Preparatory School
21 Andover Place, London NW6 5ED
Tel: 020 7328 2802
Headteacher: Mr Bill Pratt
Age range: 3–11
Fees: Day £7,605–£12,705
£ ✎

Nancy Reuben Primary School
Finchley Lane, Hendon,
London NW4 1DJ
Tel: 020 82025646
Head: Anthony Wolfson
Age range: 3–11
No. of pupils: 207

NORTH BRIDGE HOUSE NURSERY AND PRE-PREP SCHOOLS
For further details see p. 152
8 Netherhall Gardens,
London NW3 5RR
5960
Tel: 020 7428 1520
Head of School: Mrs C McLelland
Age range: 2 years 9 months–7 years
No. of pupils: 380
Fees: Day £15,975–£16,575
✎

NORTH BRIDGE HOUSE PREP SCHOOL REGENT'S PARK
For further details see p. 152
1 Gloucester Avenue,
London NW1 7AB
5959
Tel: 020 7428 1520
Head of School: Mr James Stenning
Age range: 7–13 years
No. of pupils: 460
Fees: Day £18,195

NORTH BRIDGE HOUSE SENIOR CANONBURY
For further details see p. 152
6-9 Canonbury Place,
Islington, London N1 2NQ
11880
Tel: 020 7428 1520
Head of School: Mr J. Taylor
Age range: 11–18 years
No. of pupils: 180
Fees: Day £17,295–£18,555

NORTH BRIDGE HOUSE SENIOR HAMPSTEAD
For further details see p. 152
65 Rosslyn Hill, London NW3 5UD
Tel: 020 7428 1520
Email: admissionsenquiries@
northbridgehouse.com
Website:
www.northbridgehouse.com
Head of Senior Hampstead: Mr.
Brendan Pavey
Age range: 11–16 years
No. of pupils: 1375
Fees: Day £7,635–£20,400

Rainbow Montessori School
13 Woodchurch Road,
Hampstead, London NW6 3PL
Tel: 020 7328 8986
Head Mistress: Maggy Miller MontDip
Age range: 5–12
Fees: Day £12,240–£12,417

Saint Christina's School
25 St Edmunds Terrace, Regent's
Park, London NW8 7PY
Tel: 020 7722 8784
Headteacher: Miss J Finlayson
Age range: 3–11
No. of pupils: 224
Fees: Day £13,500

Sarum Hall
15 Eton Avenue, London NW3 3EL
Tel: 020 7794 2261
Headmistress: Mrs Christine Smith
Age range: G3–11
No. of pupils: 170
Fees: Day £14,025–£15,180

South Hampstead High School GDST
3 Maresfield Gardens, London NW3 5SS
Tel: 020 7435 2899
Head of School: Mrs V Bingham
Age range: G4–18
No. of pupils: 900
Fees: Day £15,327–£18,654

Southbank International School – Hampstead
16 Netherhall Gardens,
London NW3 5TH
Tel: 020 7243 3803
Principal: Shirley Harwood
Age range: 3–11
No. of pupils: 210
Fees: Day £17,355–£27,015

St Anthony's School for Boys
90 Fitzjohn's Avenue, Hampstead,
London NW3 6NP
Tel: 020 7431 1066
Headmaster: Mr Paul Keyte
Age range: B4–13
No. of pupils: 310

St Christopher's School
32 Belsize Lane, Hampstead,
London NW3 5AE
Tel: 020 7435 1521
Head: Emma Crawford-Nash
Age range: G4–11
No. of pupils: 235
Fees: Day £14,700

St John's Wood Pre-Preparatory School
St Johns Hall, Lords Roundabout,
London NW8 7NE
Tel: 020 7722 7149
Principal: Adrian Ellis
Age range: 3–7

St Margaret's School
18 Kidderpore Gardens,
Hampstead, London NW3 7SR
Tel: 020 7435 2439
Principal: Mr M Webster BSc, PGCE
Age range: G4–16
No. of pupils: 156
Fees: Day £12,591–£14,589

St Martin's School
22 Goodwyn Avenue, Mill
Hill, London NW7 3RG
Tel: 020 8959 1965
Head: Dr Jason Walak
Age range: 3–11
No. of pupils: 90
Fees: Day £7,800

St Mary's School Hampstead
47 Fitzjohn's Avenue, Hampstead,
London NW3 6PG
Tel: 020 7435 1868
Head Teacher: Mrs Harriet Connor-Earl
Age range: B2 years 9 months–7
years G2 years 9 months–11 years
No. of pupils: 300
Fees: Day £7,305–£13,500

St Nicholas School
22 Salmon Street, London NW9 8PN
Tel: 020 8205 7153
Headmaster: Mr Matt Donaldson
BA (Hons), PGCE, PGDip (Surv)
Age range: 3 months–11
No. of pupils: 80
Fees: Day £8,550–£8,850

The Academy School
3 Pilgrims Place, Rosslyn Hill,
Hampstead, London NW3 1NG
Tel: 020 7435 6621
Headteacher: Mr Garth Evans
Age range: 6–14

The American School in London
One Waverley Place, London NW8 0NP
Tel: 020 7449 1221
Head: Robin Appleby
Age range: 4–18
No. of pupils: 1350
Fees: Day £27,050–£31,200

The Cavendish School
31 Inverness Street, Camden
Town, London NW1 7HB
Tel: 020 7485 1958
Headmistress: Miss Jane Rogers
Age range: G3–11
No. of pupils: 260
Fees: Day £15,300

The Hall School
23 Crossfield Road, Hampstead,
London NW3 4NU
Tel: 020 7722 1700
Headmaster: Mr Chris Godwin
Age range: B4–13
No. of pupils: 440
Fees: Day £17,940–£18,486

The King Alfred School
Manor Wood, North End
Road, London NW11 7HY
Tel: 020 8457 5200
Head: Robert Lobatto MA (Oxon)
Age range: 4–18
No. of pupils: 650 VIth100
Fees: Day £15,531–£18,723

The Mount, Mill Hill International
Milespit Hill, London NW7 2RX
Tel: +44 (0)20 3826 33
Head of School: Ms Sarah Bellotti
Age range: 13–17
No. of pupils: 68
Fees: Day £24,990 WB £34,461 FB £40,539

THE MULBERRY HOUSE SCHOOL
For further details see p. 166
7 Minster Road, West Hampstead,
London NW2 3SD
Tel: 020 8452 7340
Email: admissions@
mulberryhouseschool.com
Website:
www.mulberryhouseschool.com
Headteacher: Ms Victoria
Playford BA Hons, QTS
Age range: 2–7 years
No. of pupils: 190

The Village School
2 Parkhill Road, Belsize Park,
London NW3 2YN
Tel: 020 7485 4673
Headmistress: Miss C E F
Gay BSc(Hons), PGCE
Age range: G3–11
No. of pupils: 106
Fees: Day £15,525

Torah Vodaas
Brent Park Road, West Hendon
Broadway, London NW9 7AJ
Tel: 02036704670
Head of School: Rabbi Y Feldman
Age range: B2–11

Trevor-Roberts School
55-57 Eton Avenue, London NW3 3ET
Tel: 020 7586 1444
Headmaster: Simon Trevor-Roberts BA
Age range: 5–13
Fees: Day £14,700–£16,200

UCS Pre-Prep
36 College Crescent, London NW3 5LF
Tel: 020 7722 4433
Headmistress: Dr Zoe Dunn
Age range: B4–7
No. of pupils: 100

UNIVERSITY COLLEGE SCHOOL
For further details see p. 168
Frognal, Hampstead,
London NW3 6XH
Tel: 020 7435 2215
Email: seniorschool@ucs.org.uk
Website: www.ucs.org.uk
Headteacher: Mr Mark J Beard
Age range: B11–18 G16–18

University College School (Junior)
11 Holly Hill, London NW3 6QN
Tel: 020 7435 3068
Headmaster: Mr Lewis Hayward
MA (Oxon Lit. Hum), MA (OU,
ED. Management), PGCE
Age range: B7–11
No. of pupils: 250
Fees: Day £18,789

Wentworth College
6-10 Brentmead Place,
London NW11 9LH
Tel: 020 8458 8524/5
Principal: Manuel Guimaraes
Age range: 14–19
No. of pupils: 115

South-East London

Alleyn's School
Townley Road, Dulwich,
London SE22 8SU
Tel: 020 8557 1500
Headmaster: Dr G Savage
MA, PhD, FRSA
Age range: 4–18
No. of pupils: 1200
Fees: Day £18,363–£20,850

Bellerbys College London
Bounty House, Greenwich,
London SE8 3DE
Tel: +44 (0)208 694 7000
Principal: Ms Alison Baines
Age range: 15–19

Blackheath High School GDST
Vanbrugh Park, Blackheath,
London SE3 7AG
Tel: 020 8853 2929
Head: Mrs Carol Chandler-Thompson
BA (Hons) Exeter, PGCE Exeter
Age range: G3–18
No. of pupils: 780

Blackheath Preparatory School
4 St Germans Place, Blackheath,
London SE3 0NJ
Tel: 020 8858 0692
Acting Head: Mrs C Dawe
Age range: 3–11
No. of pupils: 377
Fees: Day £8,190–£13,680

Colfe's Junior School
Horn Park Lane, Lee, London SE12 8AW
Tel: 020 8463 8240
Head: Ms C Macleod
Age range: 3–11
No. of pupils: 355
Fees: Day £13,230–£13,995

Colfe's School
Horn Park Lane, Lee, London SE12 8AW
Tel: 020 8852 2283
Head: Mr R F Russell MA(Cantab)
Age range: 3–18
No. of pupils: 1120

DLD College London
199 Westminster Bridge
Road, London SE1 7FX
Tel: +44 (0)20 7935 8411
Principal: Irfan H Latif BSc
(Hons) PGCE FRSA FRSC
No. of pupils: 426
Fees: Day £23,500–£29,950
FB £18,000–£28,000

Dulwich College
London SE21 7LD
Tel: 020 8693 3601
Master: Dr J A F Spence
Age range: B0–18
No. of pupils: 1589 VIth470
Fees: Day £20,448 WB
£40,017 FB £42,681

Dulwich College Kindergarten & Infants School
Eller Bank, 87 College Road,
London SE21 7HH
Tel: 020 8693 1538
Head: Mrs Nicky Black
Age range: 3 months–7 years
No. of pupils: 251

Dulwich Prep London
42 Alleyn Park, Dulwich,
London SE21 7AA
Tel: 020 8766 5500
Headmaster: Mr M W
Roulston MBE, MEd
Age range: B3–13 G3–5
No. of pupils: 817
Fees: Day £13,074–£19,314

Eltham College
Grove Park Road, Mottingham,
London SE9 4QF
Tel: 0208 857 1455
Headmaster: Guy Sanderson
Age range: 7–18
No. of pupils: 907 VIth194

Greenwich Steiner School
Woodlands, 90 Mycenae Road,
Blackheath, London SE3 7SE
Tel: 020 8858 4404
Age range: 3–14
No. of pupils: 180
Fees: Day £7,310–£8,100

Heath House Preparatory School
37 Wemyss Road, Blackheath,
London SE3 0TG
Tel: 020 8297 1900
Head Teacher: Mrs Sophia
Laslett CertEd PGDE
Age range: 3–11
No. of pupils: 125
Fees: Day £13,485–£14,985

Herne Hill School
The Old Vicarage, 127 Herne
Hill, London SE24 9LY
Tel: 020 7274 6336
Headteacher: Mrs Ngaire Telford
Age range: 2–7
No. of pupils: 296
Fees: Day £6,225–£14,955

JAMES ALLEN'S GIRLS' SCHOOL
For further details see p. 146
144 East Dulwich Grove,
Dulwich, London SE22 8TE
Tel: 020 8693 1181
Email: enquiries@jags.org.uk
Website: www.jags.org.uk
Head of School: Mrs Sally-
Anne Huang MA, MSc
Age range: G4–18
No. of pupils: 1075

Kings Kids Christian School
New Testament Church of
God, Bawtree Road, New
Cross, London SE14 6ET
Tel: 020 8691 5813
Headteacher: Mrs M Okenwa
Age range: 5–11
No. of pupils: 36

London Christian School
40 Tabard Street, London SE1 4JU
Tel: 020 3130 6430
Headmistress: Miss N Collett-White
Age range: 3–11
No. of pupils: 105
Fees: Day £9,390

Marathon Science School
1-9 Evelyn Street, Surrey
Quays, London SE8 5RQ
Tel: +44 (0)20 7231 3232
Headteacher: Mr Uzeyir Onur
Age range: B11–16
No. of pupils: 67

Oakfield Preparatory School
125-128 Thurlow Park Road, West
Dulwich, London SE21 8HP
Tel: 020 8670 4206
Age range: 2–11 years
No. of pupils: 420
Fees: Day £10,785

Octavia House School, Kennington
214b Kennington Road,
London SE11 6AU
Tel: 020 3651 4396 (Option:3)
Executive Head: Mr James Waite

Octavia House School, Vauxhall
Vauxhall Primary School, Vauxhall
Street, London SE11 5LG
Tel: 02036 514396 (Option:1)
Executive Head: Mr James Waite
Age range: 5–14
No. of pupils: 65

Octavia House School, Walworth
Larcom House, Larcom
Street, , London SE17 1RT
Tel: 02036 514396 (Option:2)
Executive Head: Mr James Waite

Riverston School
63-69 Eltham Road, Lee
Green, London SE12 8UF
Tel: 020 8318 4327
Headmistress: Mrs S E Salathiel
Age range: 9 months–19 years
No. of pupils: 215
£ 🏊 16️⃣ 🐾

**Rosemead Preparatory
School & Nursery, Dulwich**
70 Thurlow Park Road, London SE21 8HZ
Tel: 020 8670 5865
Headmaster: Mr Phil Soutar
Age range: 2–11
No. of pupils: 366
Fees: Day £10,272–£11,286
£ 🏊

St Dunstan's College
Stanstead Road, London SE6 4TY
Tel: 020 8516 7200
Headmaster: Mr Nicholas Hewlett
Age range: 3–18
No. of pupils: 870
🌐 Ⓐ £ 16️⃣

St Olave's Preparatory School
106 Southwood Road, New
Eltham, London SE9 3QS
Tel: 020 8294 8930
Headteacher: Miss Claire
Holloway BEd, QTS
Age range: 3–11
No. of pupils: 220
Fees: Day £10,848–£12,300
🏊

Sydenham High School GDST
19 Westwood Hill, London SE26 6BL
Tel: 020 8557 7000
Headmistress: Mrs
Katharine Woodcock
Age range: G4–18
No. of pupils: 600 VIth70
Fees: Day £13,161–£16,737
🚹 Ⓐ £ 🏊 16️⃣

The Pointer School
19 Stratheden Road, Blackheath,
London SE3 7TH
Tel: 020 8293 1331
Headmaster: Mr R J S Higgins
MA, BEd, CertEd, FCollP
Age range: 3–11
No. of pupils: 370
Fees: Day £11,415–£13,449
£ 🏊

**The Villa Pre-Preparatory
School & Nursery**
54 Lyndhurst Grove, Peckham,
London SE15 5AH
Tel: 020 7703 6216
Head Teacher: Emma Champion
Age range: 2–7
No. of pupils: 210

South-West London

Al-Muntada Islamic School
7 Bridges Place, Parsons
Green, London SW6 4HW
Tel: 020 7471 8283
Headteacher: Amjad Malik
Age range: 4–11
No. of pupils: 165
Fees: Day £3,000–£7,000

Al-Risalah Secondary School
145 Upper Tooting Road,
London SW17 7TJ
Tel: 020 8767 6057
Headteacher: Suhayl Lee
Age range: 3–16
No. of pupils: 250

Beechwood School
55 Leigham Court Road,
Streatham, London SW16 2NJ
Tel: 020 8677 8778
Nursery Director: Ms Bamwo
Age range: 0–5
No. of pupils: 100

Bertrum House Nursery
290 Balham High Road,
London SW17 7AL
Tel: 020 8767 4051
Headteacher: Miss Vicky
Age range: 2–5
No. of pupils: 94
Fees: Day £1,775–£2,140
🏊

Broomwood Hall
68-74 Nightingale Lane,
London SW12 8NR
Tel: 020 8682 8810
Headmistress: Carole Jenkinson
Age range: B4–8 G4–13
No. of pupils: 620
Fees: Day £5,375–£6,595
🏊

CAMERON HOUSE
For further details see p. 138
4 The Vale, Chelsea,
London SW3 6AH
Tel: 020 7352 4040
Email: laura@
cameronhouseschool.org
Website:
www.cameronhouseschool.org
Headmistress: Mrs Dina Mallett
Age range: 4–11
Fees: Day £19,305
£ 🏊

Centre Academy London
92 St John's Hill, Battersea,
London SW11 1SH
Tel: 020 7738 2344
Headteacher: Rachel Maddison
Age range: 9–19
Fees: Day £27,600–£40,100
🌐 £ 🏊 16️⃣

Chelsea Independent College
517-523 Fulham Road, London SW6 1HD
Tel: +44 (0) 20 7610 1114
Principal: Dr Martin Meenagh
Age range: 14–19
No. of pupils: 164
16️⃣ 🏠

Collingham
23 Collingham Gardens,
London SW5 0HL
Tel: 020 7244 7414
Principal: Sally Powell
Age range: 14–19
No. of pupils: VIth200
Fees: Day £4,260–£22,560
16️⃣ Ⓐ £ 🏊

Dolphin School
106 Northcote Road,
London SW11 6QW
Tel: 020 7924 3472
Principal: Mrs. N. Baldwin
Age range: 2–11
No. of pupils: 292
Fees: Day £12,270–£13,485
£ 🏊

Donhead
33 Edge Hill, London SW19 4NP
Tel: 020 8946 7000
Headmaster: Mr P J J Barr
Age range: B4–11
No. of pupils: 280
Fees: Day £11,175–£11,622
🚹 £ 🏊

Eaton House Belgravia
3-5 Eaton Gate, London SW1W 9BA
Tel: 020 7924 6000
Head of School: Mr Huw May
Age range: B3–11
Fees: Day £17,850–£20,700
🚹 🏊

Eaton House The Manor
58 Clapham Common
Northside, London SW4 9RU
Tel: 020 7924 6000
Head: Mr Oliver Snowball
Age range: G4–11
Fees: Day £16,143
🚹 £ 🏊

**Eaton House The Manor
Pre Prep and Nursery**
58 Clapham Common
Northside, London SW4 9RU
Tel: 020 7924 6000
Nursery Head of School: Miss Roosha
Age range: B31/2–8
Fees: Day £16,143
🚹

**Eaton House The Manor
Prep School**
58 Clapham Common
Northside, London SW4 9RU
Tel: 020 7924 6000
Head: Mrs Sarah Segrave
Age range: B8–13
Fees: Day £19,743
🚹 £ 🏊

Eaton Square School Belgravia
79 Eccleston Square, London SW1V 1PP
Tel: +44 (0)20 7931 9469
Principal: Mr Sebastian Hepher
Age range: 4–11
🌐

Eaton Square School Kensington
24 Elvaston Place, London SW7 5NL
Tel: +44 (0)20 7225 3131
Headmistress: Mrs Trish Watt
Age range: 4–11

Ecole Charles De Gaulle – Wix
Clapham Common North
Side, London SW4 0AJ
Tel: +44 20 7738 0287
Headteacher: Mr Blanchard
Age range: 5–11
No. of pupils: 100
🌐

Ecole Marie D'Orliac
60 Clancarty Road, London SW6 3AA
Tel: +44 7736 020 58 63
Principal: Mr Olivier Rauch
Age range: 4–11
No. of pupils: 50
🌐

Emanuel School
Battersea Rise, London SW11 1HS
Tel: 020 8870 4171
Headmaster: Mr Robert Milne
Age range: 10–18
No. of pupils: 930
Fees: Day £18,372
Ⓐ Ⓔ 🖊 ⑯

Eveline Day & Nursery Schools
14 Trinity Crescent, Upper
Tooting, London SW17 7AE
Tel: 020 8672 4673
Headmistress: Ms Eveline Drut
Age range: 3 months–11 years
No. of pupils: 80
Fees: Day £13,859
🖊

Falkner House
19 Brechin Place, South
Kensington, London SW7 4QB
Tel: 020 7373 4501
Headteacher: Mrs Anita
Griggs BA(Hons), PGCE
Age range: B3–11 G3–11
🚹 🚺

Finton House School
171 Trinity Road, London SW17 7HL
Tel: 020 8682 0921
Head of School: Mr Ben Freeman
Age range: 4–11
No. of pupils: 300
Fees: Day £15,378–£15,588
Ⓔ 🖊

**Francis Holland School,
Sloane Square, SW1**
39 Graham Terrace, London SW1W 8JF
Tel: 020 7730 2971
Head: Mrs Lucy Elphinstone
MA(Cantab)
Age range: G4–18
No. of pupils: 520 VIth70
Fees: Day £17,760–£20,085
🚺 Ⓐ Ⓔ 🖊 ⑯

Garden House School
Boys' School & Girls' School,
Turk's Row, London SW3 4TW
Tel: 020 7730 1652
Boys' Head: Mr Christian
Warland BA(Hons), LLB.
Age range: 3–11
No. of pupils: 490
Fees: Day £17,700–£22,800
Ⓔ 🖊

Glendower School
86/87 Queen's Gate, London SW7 5JX
Tel: 020 7370 1927
Headmistress: Mrs Sarah
Knollys BA, PGCE
Age range: G4–11+
No. of pupils: 206
Fees: Day £19,200
🚺 Ⓔ 🖊

Hall School Wimbledon
Beavers Holt, Stroud Crescent,
Putney Vale, London SW15 3EQ
Tel: 020 8788 2370
Headmaster: Timothy J Hobbs MA
Age range: 4–16
No. of pupils: 520
Fees: Day £13,126–£17,336
🖊

**Hall School Wimbledon
Senior School**
17 The Downs, Wimbledon,
London SW20 8HF
Tel: 020 8879 9200
Headmaster: Timothy J Hobbs MA
Age range: 11–16
No. of pupils: 520
Fees: Day £17,336
🖊

Harrodian School
Lonsdale Road, London SW13 9QN
Tel: 020 8748 6117
Headmaster: James R Hooke
Age range: 4–18
No. of pupils: 890 VIth95
Fees: Day £15,000–£23,040
Ⓐ 🖊 ⑯

**Hill House International
Junior School**
17 Hans Place, Chelsea,
London SW1X 0EP
Tel: 020 7584 1331
Principals: Richard, Janet,
William & Edmund Townend
Age range: 4–13
No. of pupils: 740
Fees: Day £13,200–£17,400
🌐 Ⓔ 🖊

Hornsby House School
Hearnville Road, Balham,
London SW12 8RS
Tel: 020 8673 7573
Headmaster: Mr Edward Rees
Age range: 4–11
Fees: Day £14,280–£15,345
Ⓔ 🖊

Hurlingham Nursery and Pre-Prep
The Old Methodist Hall, Gwendolen
Avenue, London SW15 6EH
Tel: 020 8780 9446
Head: Jane Appleby
Age range: 2–7
No. of pupils: 115
🖊

Hurlingham School
122 Putney Bridge Road,
Putney, London SW15 2NQ
Tel: 020 8874 7186
Headteacher: Mr Jonathan Brough
Age range: 4–11
No. of pupils: 326
Fees: Day £15,540–£16,185
Ⓔ 🖊

Ibstock Place School
Clarence Lane, London SW15 5PY
Tel: 020 8876 9991
Head: Mrs Anna Sylvester-
Johnson BA(Hons), PGCE
Age range: 4–18
No. of pupils: 970
Fees: Day £16,290–£20,880
Ⓐ Ⓔ ⑯

Kensington Park School
59 Queen's Gate, South
Kensington, London SW7 5JP
Tel: +44 (0)20 7225 0577
Headmaster: Mr Paul Vanni MA
Age range: 11–18
Ⓐ 🏠

Kensington Prep School
596 Fulham Road, London SW6 5PA
Tel: 0207 731 9300
Head of School: Mrs Caroline
Hulme-McKibbin
Age range: G4–11
No. of pupils: 289
Fees: Day £17,193
🚹

King's College Junior School
Southside, Wimbledon
Common, London SW19 4TT
Tel: 020 8255 5335
Headmaster: Dr. G A Silverlock
Age range: B7–13
No. of pupils: 437
🚹 Ⓔ

King's College School
Southside, Wimbledon
Common, London SW19 4TT
Tel: 020 8255 5300
Head Master: A D Halls MA
Age range: B11–18 G16–18
No. of pupils: 971
Fees: Day £20,190–£22,335
🚹 🌐 Ⓐ Ⓔ ⒾⒷ ⑯

Knightsbridge School
67 Pont Street, Knightsbridge,
London SW1X 0BD
Tel: +44 (0)20 7590 9000
Head of School: Shona Colaço
Age range: 3–13
Fees: Day £18,756–£19,965

L'Ecole de Battersea
Trott Street, Battersea, London SW11 3DS
Tel: 020 7371 8350
Principal: Mrs F Brisset
Age range: 3–11
No. of pupils: 265
Fees: Day £12,600–£12,780

L'Ecole des Petits
2 Hazlebury Road, Fulham,
London SW6 2NB
Tel: 020 7371 8350
Principal: Mrs F Brisset
Age range: 3–6
No. of pupils: 130
Fees: Day £12,300–£12,450

London Steiner School
9 Weir Road, Balham, London SW12 0LT
Tel: 0208 772 3504
Age range: 3–14
Ⓔ

Lycée Français Charles de Gaulle
35 Cromwell Road, London SW7 2DG
Tel: 020 7584 6322
Head of School: Mr Olivier Rauch
Age range: 5–19
No. of pupils: 4000
🌐 Ⓐ Ⓔ 🖊 ⑯

**Mander Portman
Woodward – London**
90-92 Queen's Gate, London SW7 5AB
Tel: 020 7835 1355
Principal: Mr John Southworth BSc MSc
Age range: 14–19
No. of pupils: 620
Fees: Day £9,529
⑯ Ⓐ Ⓔ 🖊

More House School
22-24 Pont Street, Knightsbridge,
London SW1X 0AA
Tel: 020 7235 2855
Co-Heads: Mrs. Amanda Leach
& Mr. Michael Keeley
Age range: G11–18
No. of pupils: 206
Fees: Day £6,650
🚺 Ⓐ Ⓔ 🖊 ⑯

NEWTON PREP
For further details see p. 150
149 Battersea Park Road,
London SW8 4BX
Tel: 020 7720 4091
Email: enquiries@newtonprep.co.uk
Website:
www.newtonprepschool.co.uk
Headmistress: Mrs Alison
Fleming BA, MA Ed, PGCE
Age range: 3–13
No. of pupils: 631
Fees: Day £9,600–£20,340
(£)(✎)

Northcote Lodge School
26 Bolingbroke Grove, London SW11 6EL
Tel: 020 8682 8888
Headmaster: Clive Smith-Langridge
Age range: B8–13
No. of pupils: 260
Fees: Day £6,595
(✦)(✎)

Oliver House Preparatory School
7 Nightingale Lane, London SW4 9AH
Tel: 020 8772 1911
Headteacher: Mr Rob Farrell
Age range: 3–11
No. of pupils: 144
Fees: Day £6,600–£15,090

Parkgate House School
80 Clapham Common North
Side, London SW4 9SD
Tel: +44 (0)20 7350 2461
Principal: Miss Catherine Shanley
Age range: 21/2–11 years
No. of pupils: 220

Parsons Green Prep School
1 Fulham Park Road, Fulham,
London SW6 4LJ
Tel: 020 7371 9009
Headmaster: Tim Cannell
Age range: 4–11
No. of pupils: 200
Fees: Day £16,857–£18,201
(✎)

PROSPECT HOUSE SCHOOL
For further details see p. 156
75 Putney Hill, London SW15 3NT
Tel: 020 8246 4897
Email: info@prospecths.org.uk
Website: www.prospecths.org.uk
Headmaster: Mr Michael
Hodge BPED(Rhodes) QTS
Age range: 3–11
No. of pupils: 316
Fees: Day £9,210–£19,200
(£)(✎)

Putney High School GDST
35 Putney Hill, London SW15 6BH
Tel: 020 8788 4886
Headmistress: Mrs Suzie
Longstaff BA, MA, PGCE
Age range: G4–18
No. of pupils: 976 VIth150
(✦)(A)(£)(✎)(16)

QUEEN'S GATE SCHOOL
For further details see p. 158
133 Queen's Gate, London SW7 5LE
Tel: 020 7589 3587
Email: registrar@queensgate.org.uk
Website: www.queensgate.org.uk
Principal: Mrs R M Kamaryc
BA, MSc, PGCE
Age range: G4–18
No. of pupils: 538 VIth95
(✦)(A)(£)(✎)(16)

Redcliffe School Trust Ltd
47 Redcliffe Gardens, Chelsea,
London SW10 9JH
Tel: 020 7352 9247
Head: Sarah Lemmon
Age range: 3–11
Fees: Day £6,660–£17,730
(£)

Sinclair House Preparatory School
59 Fulham High Street,
Fulham, London SW6 3JJ
Tel: 0207 736 9182
Principal: Mrs Carlotta T M O'Sullivan
Age range: 2–11
No. of pupils: 120
Fees: Day £5,280–£17,025

**St Mary's Summerstown
Montessori**
46 Wimbledon Road, Tooting,
London SW17 0UQ
Tel: 020 8947 7359
Head: Liz Maitland NNEB, RSH, MontDip
Age range: 18 months–5 years
No. of pupils: 30
Fees: Day £1,300

St Nicholas Preparatory School
23 Princes Gate, Kensington,
London SW7 1PT
Tel: 020 7225 1277
Headmistress: Jill Walker
Age range: 3–11
No. of pupils: 200
(✎)

St Paul's Juniors
St Paul's School, Lonsdale
Road, London SW13 9JT
Tel: 020 8748 3461
Age range: B7–13
No. of pupils: 436
Fees: Day £20,010
(✦)(£)(✎)

St Paul's School
Lonsdale Road, Barnes,
London SW13 9JT
Tel: 020 8748 9162
High Master: Prof Mark Bailey
Age range: B13–18
No. of pupils: 897
Fees: Day £25,032 FB £37,611
(✦)(♿)(A)(🏠)(£)(✎)(16)

St Philip's School
6 Wetherby Place, London SW7 4NE
Tel: 020 7373 3944
Headmaster: Mr Wulffen-Thomas
Age range: B7–13
No. of pupils: 110
Fees: Day £16,200
(✦)(£)(✎)

**Streatham & Clapham
High School GDST**
42 Abbotswood Road,
London SW16 1AW
Tel: 020 8677 8400
Headmaster: Dr Millan Sachania
Age range: G3–18
No. of pupils: 603 VIth70
Fees: Day £10,431–£19,743
(✦)(A)(£)(✎)(16)

Sussex House School
68 Cadogan Square, London SW1X 0EA
Tel: 020 7584 1741
Headmaster: Mr N P Kaye
MA(Cantab), ACP, FRSA, FRGS
Age range: B8–13
No. of pupils: 182
Fees: Day £19,770
(✦)(£)

Swedish School
82 Lonsdale Road, London SW13 9JS
Tel: 020 8741 1751
Head of School: Ms. Annika
Simonsson Bergqvist
Age range: 3–18
No. of pupils: 300 VIth145
Fees: Day £8,600–£9,100
(16)

Thames Christian College
Wye Street, Battersea,
London SW11 2HB
Tel: 020 7228 3933
Executive Head: Stephen
Holsgrove PhD
Age range: 11–16
No. of pupils: 120
Fees: Day £15,780
(£)(✎)

The Falcons School for Girls
11 Woodborough Road,
Putney, London SW15 6PY
Tel: 020 8992 5189
Head of School: Mrs Sophia
Ashworth Jones
Age range: G3–11
No. of pupils: 102
Fees: Day £8,580–£15,705
(✦)(£)(✎)

The Hampshire School, Chelsea
15 Manresa Road, Chelsea,
London SW3 6NB
Tel: 020 7352 7077
Principal: Mr Donal Brennan
Age range: 3–13
No. of pupils: 300
Fees: Day £16,965–£17,955
(£)(✎)

The Laurels School
126 Atkins Road, Clapham,
London SW12 0AN
Tel: 020 8674 7229
Headmistress: Linda Sanders BA
Hons (Bristol), MA (Madrid)
Age range: G11–18
(✦)

THE MERLIN SCHOOL
For further details see p. 164
4 Carlton Drive, London SW15 2BZ
Tel: 020 8788 2769
Email: admissionenquiries@
merlinschool.net
Website: www.merlinschool.net
Principal: Mrs Kate Prest
Age range: 4–8
No. of pupils: 175
Fees: Day £5,041

The Moat School
Bishops Avenue, Fulham,
London SW6 6EG
Tel: 020 7610 9018
Head: Ms Clare King
Age range: 9–16
Fees: Day £30,000
(✎)

The Montessori Pavilion – The Kindergarten School
Vine Road, Barnes, London SW13 0NE
Tel: 020 8878 9695
Headmistress: Ms Georgina Dashwood
Age range: 3–8
No. of pupils: 50

The Norwegian School
28 Arterberry Road, Wimbledon, London SW20 8AH
Tel: 020 8947 6617
Head: Mr Ivar Chavannes
Age range: 3–16

The Roche School
11 Frogmore, London SW18 1HW
Tel: 020 8877 0823
Headmistress: Mrs Vania Adams BA(Hons), PGCE, MA
Age range: 2–11 years
No. of pupils: 316
Fees: Day £14,970–£15,690

The Rowans School
19 Drax Avenue, Wimbledon, London SW20 0EG
Tel: 020 8946 8220
Head Teacher: Mrs. Joanna Hubbard MA BA (Hons) PGCE QTS PGDipSEN
Age range: 3–8
Fees: Day £7,905–£13,170

The Study Preparatory School
Wilberforce House, Camp Road, Wimbledon Common, London SW19 4UN
Tel: 020 8947 6969
Headmistress: Mrs Susan Pepper MA Oxon, PGCE
Age range: G4–11
No. of pupils: 315

The White House Preparatory School & Woodentops Kindergarten
24 Thornton Road, London SW12 0LF
Tel: 020 8674 9514
Principal: Mrs. Mary McCahery
Age range: 2–11
Fees: Day £4,436–£4,740

Thomas's Preparatory School – Battersea
28-40 Battersea High Street, London SW11 3JB
Tel: 020 7978 0900
Head: Simon O'Malley
Age range: 4–13
No. of pupils: 547
Fees: Day £18,747–£20,868

Thomas's Preparatory School – Clapham
Broomwood Road, London SW11 6JZ
Tel: 020 7326 9300
Headmaster: Mr Philip Ward BEd(Hons)
Age range: 4–13
No. of pupils: 647
Fees: Day £17,262–£19,518

Thomas's Preparatory School – Fulham
Hugon Road, London SW6 3ES
Tel: 020 7751 8200
Head: Miss Annette Dobson BEd(Hons), PGCertDys
Age range: 4–11
Fees: Day £17,880–£20,016

Tower House School
188 Sheen Lane, London SW14 8LF
Tel: 020 8876 3323
Head: Mr Gregory Evans
Age range: B4–13
No. of pupils: 180
Fees: Day £13,089–£14,838

Ursuline Preparatory School
18 The Downs, London SW20 8HR
Tel: 020 8947 0859
Headmaster: Mr Chris McGrath
Age range: B3–4 G3–11
Fees: Day £6,615–£10,815

Wandsworth Preparatory School
The Old Library, 2 Allfarthing Lane, London SW18 2PQ
Tel: 0208 870 4133
Head of School: Miss Bridget Saul BA (Hons), PGCE, MA
Age range: 4–11
No. of pupils: 115
Fees: Day £4,570

Westminster Abbey Choir School
Dean's Yard, London SW1P 3NY
Tel: 0207 654 4918
Headmaster: Mr Peter Roberts
Age range: B8–13
No. of pupils: 35
Fees: FB £8,571

Westminster Cathedral Choir School
Ambrosden Avenue, London SW1P 1QH
Tel: 020 7798 9081
Headmaster: Mr Neil McLaughlan
Age range: B4–13
No. of pupils: 150
Fees: Day £16,350–£19,233 FB £10,086

Westminster School
Little Dean's Yard, Westminster, London SW1P 3PF
Tel: 020 7963 1003
Headmaster: Mr Patrick Derham
Age range: B13–18 G16–18
No. of pupils: 744
Fees: Day £26,130–£28,566 FB £37,740

Westminster Tutors
86 Old Brompton Road, South Kensington, London SW7 3LQ
Tel: 020 7584 1288
Principal: Virginia Maguire BA, MA, MLitt
Age range: 14–mature
No. of pupils: VIth40
Fees: Day £4,000–£25,000

Westminster Under School
Adrian House, 27 Vincent Square, London SW1P 2NN
Tel: 020 7821 5788
Headteacher: Mr Mark O'Donnell
Age range: B7–13
No. of pupils: 265
Fees: Day £19,344

Willington School
Worcester Road, Wimbledon, London SW19 7QQ
Tel: 020 8944 7020
Acting Headmaster: Mr Marcus Tattersal
Age range: B4–13
No. of pupils: 250
Fees: Day £12,150–£14,640

Wimbledon Common Preparatory
113 Ridgway, Wimbledon, London SW19 4TA
Tel: 020 8946 1001
Head Teacher: Mrs Tracey Buck
Age range: B4–8
No. of pupils: 160
Fees: Day £13,185

Wimbledon High School GDST
Mansel Road, Wimbledon, London SW19 4AB
Tel: 020 8971 0900
Headmistress: Mrs Jane Lunnon
Age range: G4–18
No. of pupils: 900 VIth155
Fees: Day £14,622–£18,810

West London

Albemarle Independent College
18 Dunraven Street, London W1K 7FE
Tel: 020 7409 7273
Co-Principals: Beverley Mellon & James Eytle
Age range: 16–19
No. of pupils: 160
Fees: Day £7,000–£24,000

Arts Educational Schools London Sixth Form
Cone Ripman House, 14 Bath Road, Chiswick, London W4 1LY
Tel: 020 8987 6666
Head Teacher: Mr Chris Hocking
Age range: 16–18
No. of pupils: 85
Fees: Day £16,830–£16,990

Arts Educational Schools London Years 7-11
Cone Ripman House, 14 Bath Road, Chiswick, London W4 1LY
Tel: 020 8987 6666
Head Teacher: Mr Chris Hocking
Age range: 11–16
No. of pupils: 141
Fees: Day £15,390–£15,540

Ashbourne Independent Sixth Form College
17 Old Court Place, Kensington, London W8 4PL
Tel: 020 7937 3858
Principal: M J Kirby MSc, BApSc
Age range: 16–19
No. of pupils: 170
Fees: Day £24,750–£26,250

Ashbourne Middle School
17 Old Court Place, Kensington, London W8 4PL
Tel: 020 7937 3858
Principal: M J Kirby MSc, BApSc
Age range: 13–16
No. of pupils: VIth150
Fees: Day £24,750–£26,250
Ⓐ Ⓔ ⑯

Avenue House School
70 The Avenue, Ealing, London W13 8LS
Tel: 020 8998 9981
Headteacher: Mr J Sheppard
Age range: 3–11
No. of pupils: 135
Fees: Day £11,250
🖉

Bales College
742 Harrow Road, Kensal Town, London W10 4AA
Tel: 020 8960 5899
Principal: William Moore
Age range: 11–19
No. of pupils: 90
Fees: Day £11,550–£12,750
🌐 ⑯ Ⓐ 🏫 Ⓔ

Barbara Speake Stage School
East Acton Lane, East Acton, London W3 7EG
Tel: 020 8743 1306
Headteacher: Mr David Speake BA (Hons)
Age range: 3–16
Fees: Day £7,500–£9,000
⑯ 🖉

BASSETT HOUSE SCHOOL
For further details see p. 136
60 Bassett Road, London W10 6JP
Tel: 020 8969 0313
Email: info@bassetths.org.uk
Website: www.bassetths.org.uk
Headmistress: Mrs Philippa Cawthorne MA (Soton) PGCE Mont Cert
Age range: 3–11
No. of pupils: 190
Fees: Day £5,499–£19,200
🖉

Bute House Preparatory School for Girls
Bute House, Luxemburg Gardens, London W6 7EA
Tel: 020 7603 7381
Head: Mrs Helen Lowe
Age range: G4–11
No. of pupils: 306
Fees: Day £16,458
🖉 Ⓔ

Chepstow House School
108a Lancaster Road, London W11 1QS
Tel: 0207 243 0243
Headteacher: Angela Barr
Age range: 2½–12 years

Chiswick & Bedford Park Prep School
Priory House, Priory Avenue, London W4 1TX
Tel: 020 8994 1804
Headmistress: Mrs S Daniell
Age range: B4–7+ G4–11
No. of pupils: 180
Fees: Day £13,275

Clifton Lodge
8 Mattock Lane, Ealing, London W5 5BG
Tel: 020 8579 3662
Executive Head: Mr. Floyd Steadman
Age range: 3–13
No. of pupils: 140
Fees: Day £12,240–£14,010
Ⓔ 🖉

Connaught House School
47 Connaught Square, London W2 2HL
Tel: 020 7262 8830
Principal: Mrs V Hampton
Age range: 4–11
No. of pupils: 75
Fees: Day £16,650–£18,300
Ⓔ

David Game College
31 Jewry Street, London EC3N 2ET
Tel: 020 7221 6665
Principal: D T P Game MA, MPhil
Age range: 14–19
No. of pupils: 200 VIth150
Fees: Day £3,680–£30,630
⑯ Ⓐ Ⓔ ⑯

Durston House
12-14 Castlebar Road, Ealing, London W5 2DR
Tel: 020 8991 6530
Headmaster: Mr Ian Kendrick MA, BEd(Hons)
Age range: B4–13
No. of pupils: 376
Fees: Day £4,160–£5,060
🖉 Ⓔ 🖉

Ealing Independent College
83 New Broadway, Ealing, London W5 5AL
Tel: 020 8579 6668
Principal: Dr Ian Moores
Age range: 13–19
No. of pupils: 100 VIth70
Fees: Day £2,910–£18,120
⑯ Ⓐ ⑯

Eaton Square School Mayfair
106 Piccadilly, Mayfair, London W1J 7NL
Tel: +44 (0)20 7491 7393
Co-Heads: Caroline Townshend (Lower) & John Wilson (Upper)
Age range: 11–18

Ecole Francaise Jacques Prevert
59 Brook Green, London W6 7BE
Tel: 020 7602 6871
Headteacher: Delphine Gentil
Age range: 4–11
🌐

Fulham Prep School
200 Greyhound Road, London W14 9SD
Tel: 020 7386 2444
Headmaster: Mr Will le Fleming
Age range: 4–18
No. of pupils: 647
Fees: Day £16,869–£19,749
🌐 Ⓐ 🖉

Great Beginnings Montessori School
The Welsh Church Hall, 82a Chiltern Street, Marylebone, London W1H 5JE
Tel: 020 7486 2276
Head: Mrs Wendy Innes
Age range: 2–6
Fees: Day £1,095–£1,650
🖉

Greek Primary School of London
3 Pierrepoint Road, Acton, London W3 9JR
Tel: 020 8992 6156
Age range: 1–11

Halcyon London International School
33 Seymour Place, , London W1H 5AU
Tel: +44 (0)20 7258 1169
Headteacher: Mr Barry Mansfield
Age range: 11–18
No. of pupils: 183
🌐 Ⓔ ⒾⒷ

Harvington School
20 Castlebar Road, Ealing, London W5 2DS
Tel: 020 8997 1583
Headmistress: Mrs Anna Evans
Age range: B3–4 G3–11
No. of pupils: 140
Fees: Day £6,525–£12,615
🖉 Ⓔ 🖉

Hawkesdown House School Kensington
27 Edge Street, Kensington, London W8 7PN
Tel: 020 7727 9090
Headmistress: Mrs. J. A. K. Mackay B.Ed (Hons)
Age range: 2–11
No. of pupils: 100
Fees: Day £16,350–£19,130
🖉

Heathfield House School
Heathfield Gardens, Chiswick, London W4 4JU
Tel: 020 8994 3385
Headteacher: Mrs Goodsman
Age range: 4–11
No. of pupils: 197
Fees: Day £2,471–£3,676

Holland Park Pre Prep School and Day Nursery
5, Holland Road, Kensington, London W14 8HJ
Tel: 020 7602 9066/020 7602 9266
Head Mistress: Mrs Kitty Mason
Age range: 3 months–8 years
No. of pupils: 39
Fees: Day £9,180–£18,120

Instituto Español Vicente Cañada Blanch
317 Portobello Road, London W10 5SZ
Tel: +44 (0) 20 8969 2664
Principal: Carmen Pinilla Padilla
Age range: 4–19
No. of pupils: 405
🌐

International School of London (ISL)
139 Gunnersbury Avenue, London W3 8LG
Tel: +44 (0)20 8992 5823
Principal: Mr Richard Parker
Age range: 3–18 years
No. of pupils: 470
Fees: Day £19,000–£26,300
🌐 ⒾⒷ 🖉 ⑯

King Fahad Academy
Bromyard Avenue, Acton, London W3 7HD
Tel: 020 8743 0131
Director General: Dr Abdulghani Alharbi
Age range: 3–19
No. of pupils: 500
Fees: Day £3,300–£4,300
🌐 Ⓐ Ⓔ ⒾⒷ ⑯

La Petite Ecole Francaise
73 Saint Charles Square,
London W10 6EJ
Tel: +44 208 960 1278
Principal: Mme Marjorie Lacassagne
Age range: 3–11

Latymer Prep School
36 Upper Mall, Hammersmith,
London W6 9TA
Tel: 020 7993 0061
Principal: Ms Andrea
Rutterford B.Ed (Hons)
Age range: 7–11
No. of pupils: 165
Fees: Day £18,330

Latymer Upper School
King Street, Hammersmith,
London W6 9LR
Tel: 020862 92024
Head: Mr D Goodhew MA(Oxon)
Age range: 11–18
No. of pupils: 1200
Fees: Day £20,130

Le Herisson
River Court Methodist
Church, Rover Court Road,
Hammersmith, London W6 9JT
Tel: 020 8563 7664
Director: Maria Frost
Age range: 2–6
Fees: Day £8,730–£8,970

L'Ecole Bilingue
St David's Welsh Church, St Mary's
Terrace, London W2 1SJ
Tel: 020 7224 8427
Headteacher: Ms Veronique Ferreira
Age range: 3–11
No. of pupils: 68
Fees: Day £9,960–£10,770

Leiths School of Food & Wine
16-20 Wendell Road, Shepherd's
Bush, London W12 9RT
Tel: 020 8749 6400
Managing Director: Camilla
Schneideman
Age range: 17–99
No. of pupils: 96

LLOYD WILLIAMSON SCHOOLS
For further details see p. 148
12 Telford Road, London W10 5SH
Tel: 020 8962 0345
Email: admin@lws.org.uk
Website: www.lloydwilliamson.co.uk
Co-Principals: Ms Lucy Meyer
& Mr Aaron Williams
Age range: 4 months–16 years
Fees: Day £14,400

**London Welsh School Ysgol
Cymraeg Llundain**
Hanwell Community Centre,
Westcott Crescent, London W7 1PD
Tel: 020 8575 0237
Lead Teacher: Mrs Rachel King
Age range: 3–11
No. of pupils: 30
Fees: Day £3,345

Maida Vale School
18 Saltram Crescent, London W9 3HW
Tel: 020 3196 1860
Headmaster: Steven Winter
Age range: 11–18

Norland Place School
162-166 Holland Park Avenue,
London W11 4UH
Tel: 020 7603 9103
Headmaster: Mr Patrick Mattar MA
Age range: B4–8 years G4–11 years
Fees: Day £16,107–£18,072

**Notting Hill & Ealing
High School GDST**
2 Cleveland Road, West
Ealing, London W13 8AX
Tel: (020) 8799 8400
Headmaster: Mr Matthew Shoults
Age range: G4–18
No. of pupils: 903 VIth150
Fees: Day £14,313–£18,561

Notting Hill Preparatory School
95 Lancaster Road, London W11 1QQ
Tel: 020 7221 0727
Headmistress: Mrs Jane Cameron
Age range: 4–13
No. of pupils: 325
Fees: Day £6,355

**One World Montessori
Nursery & Pre-Prep**
56 Minford Gardens, London W14 0AW
Tel: 020 7603 6065
Headteacher: Ms N Greer
Age range: 2–8
No. of pupils: 21
Fees: Day £4,200–£10,950

ORCHARD HOUSE SCHOOL
For further details see p. 154
16 Newton Grove, Bedford
Park, London W4 1LB
Tel: 020 8742 8544
Email: info@orchardhs.org.uk
Website: www.orchardhs.org.uk
Headmistress: Mrs Maria Edwards
BEd(Beds) PGCE(Man) Mont Cert
Age range: 3–11
No. of pupils: 290
Fees: Day £9,210–£19,200

Pembridge Hall
18 Pembridge Square, London W2 4EH
Tel: 020 7229 0121
Headteacher: Mr Henry Keighley-Elstub
Age range: G4–11
No. of pupils: 413

Portland Place School
56-58 Portland Place, London W1B 1NJ
Tel: 0207 307 8700
Head: Mr David Bradbury
Age range: 9–18
No. of pupils: 300 VIth50
Fees: Day £21,030

Queen's College
43-49 Harley Street, London W1G 8BT
Tel: 020 7291 7000
Principal: Mr Richard Tillet
Age range: G11–18
No. of pupils: 360 VIth90

**Queen's College
Preparatory School**
61 Portland Place, , London W1B 1QP
Tel: 020 7291 0660
Headmistress: Mrs Emma Webb
Age range: G4–11

**Ravenscourt Park
Preparatory School**
16 Ravenscourt Avenue, London W6 0SL
Tel: 020 8846 9153
Headmaster: Mr Carl Howes
MA (Cantab), PGCE (Exeter)
Age range: 4–11
No. of pupils: 419
Fees: Day £5,857

Ray Cochrane Beauty School
118 Baker Street, London W1U 6TT
Tel: 02033224738
Principal: Miss Baljeet Suri
Age range: 16–50
No. of pupils: 30
Fees: Day £650–£8,495

**Southbank International
School – Kensington**
36-38 Kensington Park
Road, London W11 3BU
Tel: +44 (0)20 7243 3803
Principal: Siobhan McGrath
Age range: 3–11
Fees: Day £17,355–£27,015

**Southbank International
School – Westminster**
63-65 Portland Place, London W1B 1QR
Tel: 020 7243 3803
Principal: Dr Paul Wood
Age range: 11–19
Fees: Day £29,100–£31,680

St Augustine's Priory
Hillcrest Road, Ealing, London W5 2JL
Tel: 020 8997 2022
Headteacher: Mrs Sarah
Raffray M.A., N.P.Q.H
Age range: B3–4 G3–18
No. of pupils: 485
Fees: Day £11,529–£16,398

St Benedict's School
54 Eaton Rise, Ealing, London W5 2ES
Tel: 020 8862 2000
Headmaster: Mr A Johnson BA
Age range: 3–18
No. of pupils: 1086 VIth213
Fees: Day £13,485–£17,655

St James Preparatory School
Earsby Street, London W14 8SH
Tel: 020 7348 1777
Headmistress: Mrs Catherine
Thomlinson BA(Hons)
Age range: 3–11
Fees: Day £16,425–£17,910

St James Senior Girls' School
Earsby Street, London W14 8SH
Tel: 020 7348 1777
Headmistress: Mrs Sarah Labram BA
Age range: G11–18
No. of pupils: 295 VIth67
Fees: Day £20,100
Ⓧ Ⓐ Ⓔ ⊘ ⑯

St Paul's Girls' School
Brook Green, London W6 7BS
Tel: 020 7603 2288
High Mistress: Mrs Sarah Fletcher
Age range: G11–18 years
No. of pupils: 750 VIth200
Fees: Day £24,891–£26,760
Ⓧ Ⓐ Ⓔ ⊘ ⑯

Sylvia Young Theatre School
1 Nutford Place, London W1H 5YZ
Tel: 020 7258 2330
Headteacher: Mrs Frances Chave
Age range: 10–16
⑯ Ⓔ ⊘

Tabernacle School
32 St Anns Villas, Holland
Park, London W11 4RS
Tel: 020 7602 6232
Headteacher: Mrs P Wilson
Age range: 3–16
Fees: Day £6,500–£9,500

The Falcons School for Boys
2 Burnaby Gardens, Chiswick,
London W4 3DT
Tel: 020 8747 8393
**Head of Pre-Preparatory
School:** Mr Andrew Forbes
Age range: B3–13
No. of pupils: 225
Fees: Day £8,475–£17,475
Ⓧ ⊘

**The Godolphin and
Latymer School**
Iffley Road, Hammersmith,
London W6 0PG
Tel: +44 (0)20 8741 1936
Head Mistress: Dr Frances Ramsey
Age range: G11–18
No. of pupils: 800
Fees: Day £21,615
Ⓧ Ⓐ Ⓐ Ⓔ ⒤Ⓑ ⊘ ⑯

The Japanese School
87 Creffield Road, Acton,
London W3 9PU
Tel: 020 8993 7145
Headteacher: Mrs Kiyoe Tsuruoka
Age range: 6–16
No. of pupils: 500

**Thomas's Preparatory
School – Kensington**
17-19 Cottesmore Gardens,
London W8 5PR
Tel: 020 7361 6500
Headmistress: Miss Joanna Ebner
MA, BEd(Hons)(Cantab), NPQH
Age range: 4–11
Fees: Day £20,526–£21,789
Ⓔ ⊘

Wetherby Preparatory School
48 Bryanston Square, London W1H 2EA
Tel: 020 7535 3520
Headteacher: Mr Nick Baker
Age range: B8–13
No. of pupils: 192
Fees: Day £21,660
Ⓧ ⊘

Wetherby Pre-Preparatory School
11 Pembridge Square, London W2 4ED
Tel: 020 7727 9581
Headmaster: Mr Mark Snell
Age range: B2½–8
No. of pupils: 350
Fees: Day £21,600
Ⓧ Ⓔ ⊘

Wetherby Senior School
100 Marylebone Lane,
London W1U 2QU
Tel: 020 7535 3530
Headmaster: Mr Seth Bolderow
Age range: B11–18
Fees: Day £22,995
Ⓧ Ⓐ

Young Dancers Academy
25 Bulwer Street, London W12 8AR
Tel: 020 8743 3856
Head: Mrs K Williams
Age range: 11–16
Fees: Day £12,237–£12,690

North-East

KEY TO SYMBOLS

- (†) *Boys' school*
- (♦) *Girls' school*
- (🌐) *International school*
- (16) *Tutorial or sixth form college*
- (A) *A levels*
- (🎓) *Boarding accommodation*
- (£) *Bursaries*
- (IB) *International Baccalaureate*
- (✎) *Learning support*
- (16) *Entrance at 16+*
- (⚙) *Vocational qualifications*
- (IAPS) *Independent Association of Preparatory Schools*
- (HMC) *The Headmasters' & Headmistresses' Conference*
- (ISA) *Independent Schools Association*
- (GSA) *Girls' School Association*
- (BSA) *Boarding Schools' Association*
- (S) *Society of Heads*

Unless otherwise indicated, all schools are coeducational day schools.
Single-sex and boarding schools will be indicated by the relevant icon.

Durham

Barnard Castle Preparatory School
Westwick Road, Barnard
Castle, Durham DL12 8UW
Tel: 01833 696032
Headmistress: Mrs Laura Turner
Age range: 4–11
No. of pupils: 180
Fees: Day £6,240–£9,450 FB £18,300
🏫 ✐

Barnard Castle Senior School
Barnard Castle, Durham DL12 8UN
Tel: 01833 690222
Headmaster: Mr Anthony
C Jackson BA (Hons)
Age range: 11–18
No. of pupils: 570 VIth160
Fees: Day £13,500 FB £24,300
🌐Ⓐ🏫£✐⑯

Bow, Durham School
South Road, Durham DH1 3LS
Tel: 0191 384 8233
Headmistress: Mrs Sally Harrod
Age range: 3–11
No. of pupils: 155
Fees: Day £5,676–£11,043
£✐

Durham High School for Girls
Farewell Hall, Durham DH1 3TB
Tel: 0191 384 3226
Headmistress: Mrs Lynne Renwick
Age range: G3–18
No. of pupils: 421
👤Ⓐ£✐⑯

Durham School
Durham City, Durham DH1 4SZ
Tel: +44 (0)191 386 4783
Headmaster: Mr K McLaughlin
Age range: 3–18
No. of pupils: 560 VIth156
Fees: Day £2,756–£5,331 WB
£7,347–£8,786 FB £8,460–£9,846
🌐Ⓐ🏫£✐⑯

The Chorister School
The College, Durham DH1 3EL
Tel: 0191 384 2935
Headmaster: Mr Ian Wicks
Age range: 3–13 years
No. of pupils: 214
Fees: Day £9,420–£12,825
FB £11,520–£21,960
🏫£✐

**The Independent Grammar
School: Durham**
Claypath, Durham DH1 1RH
Principal: Mr Chris Gray
Fees: Day £2,995

Northumberland

Longridge Towers School
Longridge Towers, Berwick-upon-
Tweed, Northumberland TD15 2XH
Tel: 01289 307584
Headmaster: Mr Jonathan Lee
Age range: 3–18
No. of pupils: VIth46
Fees: Day £9,300–£13,650 WB
£20,100–£21,600 FB £26,340–£29,400
🌐Ⓐ🏫£✐⑯

Mowden Hall School
Newton, Stocksfield,
Northumberland NE43 7TP
Tel: 01661 842147
Headmaster: Mr Neil Bailey
Age range: 3–13
Fees: Day £9,000–£17,160 FB £23,700
🏫£✐

Stockton-on-Tees

Red House School
36 The Green, Norton,
Stockton-on-Tees TS20 1DX
Tel: 01642 553370
Headmaster: Mr Ken James LLB
Age range: 3–16
No. of pupils: 363
Fees: Day £4,710–£10,620
£✐

Teesside High School
The Avenue, Eaglescliffe,
Stockton-on-Tees TS16 9AT
Tel: 01642 782095
Head of School: Mrs K Mackenzie
Age range: 3–18
No. of pupils: 350 VIth70
👤Ⓐ£✐⑯

Yarm Preparatory School
Grammar School Lane, Yarm,
Stockton-on-Tees TS15 9ES
Tel: 01642 781447
Headteacher: Mr William Sawyer
Age range: 3–11
No. of pupils: 360
Fees: Day £5,232–£10,755
✐

Yarm School
The Friarage, Yarm, Stockton-
on-Tees TS15 9EJ
Tel: 01642 786023
Headmaster: Mr D M Dunn BA
Age range: 3–18
No. of pupils: VIth200
Fees: Day £5,232–£12,888
Ⓐ£⑯

Tyne & Wear

ARGYLE HOUSE SCHOOL
For further details see p. 172
19-20 Thornhill Park, Sunderland,
Tyne & Wear SR2 7LA
Tel: 0191 5100726
Email: info@
argylehouseschool.co.uk
Website:
www.argylehouseschool.co.uk
Headteacher: Mr. Chris Johnson
Age range: 3–16
No. of pupils: 233
✐

Dame Allan Junior School
Hunters Road, Spital Tongues,
Newcastle upon Tyne, Tyne
& Wear NE2 4NG
Tel: 0191 275 0608
Head: Mr A J Edge
Age range: 3–11
No. of pupils: 140
Fees: Day £7,266–£10,419

Dame Allan's Boys' School
Fowberry Crescent, Fenham,
Newcastle upon Tyne,
Tyne & Wear NE4 9YJ
Tel: 0191 275 0608
Head: Mr P Wildsmith
Age range: B11–16
No. of pupils: 304
Fees: Day £12,936–£13,236
👤Ⓐ£✐⑯

Dame Allan's Girls' School
Fowberry Crescent, Fenham,
Newcastle upon Tyne,
Tyne & Wear NE4 9YJ
Tel: 0191 275 0708
Head: Mrs E Fiddaman
Age range: G11–16
No. of pupils: 225
Fees: Day £12,936–£13,236
👤Ⓐ£✐⑯

Dame Allan's Sixth Form
Fowberry Crescent, Fenham,
Newcastle upon Tyne,
Tyne & Wear NE4 9YJ
Tel: 0191 275 0608
Head: Mr D Henry
Age range: 16–18
No. of pupils: 200
Fees: Day £12,936–£13,236
16· (A) (£) 16·

**Gateshead Jewish
Boarding School**
10 Rydal Street, Gateshead,
Tyne & Wear NE8 1HG
Tel: 0191 477 1431
Principal: Rabbi Y Ziskind
Age range: B10–16
No. of pupils: 105
(♦)

**Gateshead Jewish High
School for Girls**
6 Gladstone Terrace, Gateshead,
Tyne & Wear NE8 4DY
Tel: 0191 4773471
Headteacher: Rabbi D Bowden
Age range: G11–16
No. of pupils: 132
(♦)

Gateshead Jewish Primary School
18-20 Gladstone Terrace,
Gateshead, Tyne & Wear NE8 4EA
Tel: 0191 477 2154 / 0191 478 5841
Headmasters: A Hammond & Y Spitzer
Age range: 5–11
No. of pupils: 446
Fees: Day £2,392–£3,016
(✎)

**Newcastle High School
for Girls GDST**
Tankerville Terrace, Jesmond,
Newcastle upon Tyne,
Tyne & Wear NE2 3BA
Tel: 0191 281 1768
Acting Head: Mr Michael Tippett
Age range: G3–18
No. of pupils: G850 VIth200
Fees: Day £8,409–£13,023
(♦) (A) (£) (✎) 16·

Newcastle Preparatory School
6 Eslington Road, Jesmond, Newcastle
upon Tyne, Tyne & Wear NE2 4RH
Tel: 0191 281 1769
Head of School: Ms Fiona Coleman
Age range: 3–11
No. of pupils: 270
Fees: Day £8,742–£11,307
(£) (✎)

Newcastle School for Boys
30 West Avenue, Gosforth, Newcastle
upon Tyne, Tyne & Wear NE3 4ES
Tel: 0191 255 9300
Headmaster: Mr David Tickner
Age range: B3–18
No. of pupils: 400
Fees: Day £7,194–£13,848
(♦) (A) (£) (✎) 16·

Royal Grammar School
Eskdale Terrace, Newcastle upon
Tyne, Tyne & Wear NE2 4DX
Tel: 0191 281 5711
Headmaster: Mr John Fern
Age range: 7–18
No. of pupils: 1325 VIth341
Fees: Day £10,662–£12,657
(A) (£) (✎) 16·

Westfield School
Oakfield Road, Gosforth, Newcastle
upon Tyne, Tyne & Wear NE3 4HS
Tel: 0191 255 3980
Headmaster: Mr Neil Walker
Age range: G3–18
No. of pupils: 315 VIth50
Fees: Day £7,755–£13,590
(♦) (🌐) (A) 16·

D362

North-West

KEY TO SYMBOLS

- 🏃 *Boys' school*
- 🏃 *Girls' school*
- 🌍 *International school*
- 16° *Tutorial or sixth form college*
- Ⓐ *A levels*
- 🏛 *Boarding accommodation*
- £ *Bursaries*
- ⒾⒷ *International Baccalaureate*
- ✎ *Learning support*
- 16° *Entrance at 16+*
- 🎓 *Vocational qualifications*
- ⒾⒶ⒫Ⓢ *Independent Association of Preparatory Schools*
- ⒽⓂⒸ *The Headmasters' & Headmistresses' Conference*
- ⒾⓈⒶ *Independent Schools Association*
- ⒼⓈⒶ *Girls' School Association*
- ⒷⓈⒶ *Boarding Schools' Association*
- Ⓢ *Society of Heads*

Unless otherwise indicated, all schools are coeducational day schools. Single-sex and boarding schools will be indicated by the relevant icon.

Cheshire

Abbey Gate College
Saighton Grange, Saighton,
Chester, Cheshire CH3 6EN
Tel: 01244 332077
Head: Mrs Tracy Pollard
Age range: 4–18
No. of pupils: 468 VIth71
Fees: Day £8,955–£12,840
Ⓐ Ⓔ ✎ 16+

Alderley Edge School for Girls
Wilmslow Road, Alderley
Edge, Cheshire SK9 7QE
Tel: 01625 583028
Head of School: Mrs Helen Jeys
Age range: G2–18
No. of pupils: 500 VIth60
Fees: Day £8,115–£12,450
⚘ Ⓐ ⒾⒷ ✎ 16+

Beech Hall School
Beech Hall Drive, Tytherington,
Macclesfield, Cheshire SK10 2EG
Tel: 01625 422192
Headmaster: Mr James Allen
Age range: 6 months–16 years
No. of pupils: 230
Fees: Day £9,720–£13,020
Ⓔ ✎

**Bowdon Preparatory
School for Girls**
Ashley Road, Altrincham,
Cheshire WA14 2LT
Tel: 0161 928 0678
Headmistress: Mrs Helen Gee
Age range: G3–11
No. of pupils: 200
⚘

Brabyns Preparatory School
34-36 Arkwright Road, Marple,
Stockport, Cheshire SK6 7DB
Tel: 0161 427 2395
Headteacher: Mr Lee Sanders
Age range: 2–11
No. of pupils: 134
Fees: Day £1,900–£2,640
Ⓔ ✎

Cransley School
Belmont Hall, Great Budworth,
Northwich, Cheshire CW9 6HN
Tel: 01606 891747
Head of School: Mr Richard Pollock
LL.B, PGCE, PG Dip (RNCM)
Age range: 4–16
No. of pupils: 150
Fees: Day £7,923–£11,172
Ⓔ ✎

**Greater Grace School of
Christian Education**
Church Lane, Backford,
Chester, Cheshire CH2 4BE
Tel: 01244 851 797
Head Teacher: Mrs A Mulligan
Age range: 5–18
Fees: Day £1,900

**Green Meadow Independent
Primary School**
Robson Way, Lowton, Warrington,
Cheshire WA3 2RD
Tel: 01942 671138
Head: Mrs S Green
Age range: 4–11

Hale Preparatory School
Broomfield Lane, Hale,
Cheshire WA15 9AS
Tel: 0161 928 2386
Headmaster: Mr J F Connor
Age range: 4–11
No. of pupils: 202
Fees: Day £7,650

Lady Barn House School
Schools Hill, Cheadle, Cheshire SK7 1JE
Tel: 0161 428 2912
Age range: 3–11
No. of pupils: 483
Fees: Day £8,640
Ⓔ ✎

Pownall Hall School
Carrwood Road, Pownall Park,
Wilmslow, Cheshire SK9 5DW
Tel: 01625 523141
Headmaster: Mr David Goulbourn
Age range: 2–11
Fees: Day £8,475–£9,975
✎

Terra Nova School
Jodrell Bank, Holmes Chapel,
Crewe, Cheshire CW4 8BT
Tel: 01477 571251
Headmaster: Mr Philip Stewart
Age range: 3–13
No. of pupils: 295
Fees: Day £5,940–£14,697
⚘ Ⓔ ✎

The Firs School
Newton Lane, Upton, Chester,
Cheshire CH2 2HJ
Tel: 01244 322443
Head Teacher: Mrs L Davies
BA (Hons) Durham, PGCE
(Exeter), PGCDL (York), NP+
Age range: 3–11
No. of pupils: 172
Fees: Day £9,147
Ⓔ ✎

The Grange School
Bradburns Lane, Hartford,
Northwich, Cheshire CW8 1LU
Tel: 01606 74007 or 77447
Headmistress: Mrs Deborah Leonard
Age range: 4–18
No. of pupils: 1185 VIth193
Fees: Day £8,340–£11,160
Ⓐ Ⓔ ✎ 16+

The Hammond School
Mannings Lane, Chester,
Cheshire CH2 4ES
Tel: 01244 305350
Principal: Ms Maggie Evans BA
(Hons) MA, PGCE, NPQH, FRSA
Age range: 6–19
No. of pupils: 280
Fees: Day £8,370–£18,750
FB £20,400–£27,600
⚘ Ⓐ ⚘ Ⓔ ✎ 16+

The King's School Chester
Wrexham Road, Chester,
Cheshire CH4 7QL
Tel: 01244 689500
Headmaster: G J Hartley MA, MSc
Age range: 4–18
No. of pupils: 1080 VIth218
Fees: Day £9,150–£13,515
Ⓐ Ⓔ ✎ 16+

The King's School in Macclesfield
Cumberland Street, Macclesfield,
Cheshire SK10 1DA
Tel: 01625 260000
Headmaster: Dr Simon Hyde
Age range: 3–18
No. of pupils: 1200 VIth250
Fees: Day £8,235–£12,990
Ⓐ Ⓔ ✎ 16+

The Queen's School
City Walls Road, Chester,
Cheshire CH1 2NN
Tel: 01244 312078
Headmistress: Mrs Sue
Wallace-Woodroffe
Age range: G4–18
No. of pupils: 610 VIth100
Fees: Day £9,351–£13,341
⚘ Ⓐ Ⓔ ✎ 16+

The Ryleys School
Ryleys Lane, Alderley Edge,
Cheshire SK9 7UY
Tel: 01625 583241
Headteacher: Mrs Julia Langford
Age range: 2–11
No. of pupils: 251
Fees: Day £10,260–£11,538
Ⓔ ✎

Wilmslow Preparatory School
Grove Avenue, Wilmslow,
Cheshire SK9 5EG
Tel: 01625 524246
Headteacher: Mrs Helen Rigby
Age range: 3–11
No. of pupils: 117
Fees: Day £4,635–£10,365
Ⓔ ✎

Yorston Lodge School
18 St John's Road, Knutsford,
Cheshire WA16 0DP
Tel: 01565 633177
Headmistress: Mrs J
Dallimore BEd(Hons)
Age range: 3–11
Fees: Day £8,250–£8,310

Cumbria

Austin Friars School
Etterby Scaur, Carlisle,
Cumbria CA3 9PB
Tel: 01228 528042
Headmaster: Mr Matt Harris
Age range: 3–18
No. of pupils: 507 VIth70
Fees: Day £7,653–£14,952
Ⓐ Ⓔ ✎ 16+

**Casterton, Sedbergh
Preparatory School**
Casterton, Carnforth, Cumbria LA6 2SG
Tel: 01524 279200
Headmaster: Mr Will Newman
BA(Ed) Hons MA
Age range: 3–13
No. of pupils: 210
⚘ Ⓔ ✎

Hunter Hall School
Frenchfield, Penrith, Cumbria CA11 8UA
Tel: 01768 891291
Head Teacher: Mrs Donna Vinsome
Age range: 3–11
No. of pupils: 101
Fees: Day £7,749–£8,979
Ⓔ ✎

Sedbergh School
Sedbergh, Cumbria LA10 5HG
Tel: 015396 20535
Headmaster: Mr A Fleck MA
Age range: 3–18
No. of pupils: 500 VIth200
Fees: Day £24,915 FB £33,840

Windermere School
Patterdale Road, Windermere,
Cumbria LA23 1NW
Tel: 015394 46164
Age range: 3–18
No. of pupils: 340
Fees: Day £17,775 WB £30,150 FB £31,335

Windermere School, Elleray Campus
Ambleside Road, Windermere,
Cumbria LA23 1AP
Tel: +44 (0) 15394 43308
Head: Mrs Julie King
Age range: 3–11
No. of pupils: 75

Greater Manchester

Abbey College Manchester
5-7 Cheapside, King Street,
Manchester, Greater
Manchester M2 4WG
Tel: 0161 817 2700
Principal: Ms Liz Elam
Age range: 15–19
No. of pupils: 220 VIth175
Fees: Day £12,750

Abbotsford Preparatory School
211 Flixton Road, Urmston, Manchester,
Greater Manchester M41 5PR
Tel: 0161 748 3261
Head Teacher: Catherine Howard
Age range: 3–11
No. of pupils: 106
Fees: Day £7,029–£7,704

Al Jamiah Al Islamiyyah (Bolton Darul Uloom)
Willows Lane, Bolton, Greater
Manchester BL3 4HF
Tel: 01204 62622
Headmaster: Maulana Suhail Manya
Age range: B12–18
No. of pupils: 140
Fees: Day £1,500 FB £2,800

Altrincham Preparatory School
Marlborough Road, Bowdon,
Altrincham, Greater
Manchester WA14 2RR
Tel: 0161 928 3366
Headmaster: Mr Andrew C Potts
Age range: B2–11
No. of pupils: 310
Fees: Day £6,300–£8,340

Beech House School
184 Manchester Road, Rochdale,
Greater Manchester OL11 4JQ
Tel: 01706 646309
Principal: Mr A Sartain BSc(Hons),
PGCE, DipSp, CBiol, FIBiol
Age range: 2–16
Fees: Day £5,376–£6,546

Beis Rochel School
1-7 Seymour Road, Crumpsall,
Manchester, Greater
Manchester M8 5BQ
Tel: 0161 795 1830
Headmistress: Mrs E Krausz
Age range: G3–16
No. of pupils: 200

Bnos Yisroel School
Foigel Esther Shine House,
Leicester Road, Manchester,
Greater Manchester M7 4DA
Tel: 0161 792 3896
Headmaster: Rabbi R Spitzer
Age range: G2–16
No. of pupils: 489

Bolton School (Boys' Division)
Chorley New Road, Bolton,
Greater Manchester BL1 4PA
Tel: 01204 840201
Headmaster: Philip J Britton MBE
Age range: B7–18
No. of pupils: VIth210
Fees: Day £9,771–£12,216

Bolton School (Girls' Division)
Chorley New Road, Bolton,
Greater Manchester BL1 4PB
Tel: 01204 840201
Headmistress: Miss Sue
Hincks MA(Oxon)
Age range: B0–7 G0–18
No. of pupils: VIth210
Fees: Day £9,771–£12,216

Branwood Preparatory School
Stafford Road, Monton,
Eccles, Manchester, Greater
Manchester M30 9HN
Tel: 0161 789 1054
Head of School: Mr Andrew Whittell
Age range: 3–11
No. of pupils: 156
Fees: Day £6,597

Bridgewater School
Drywood Hall, Worsley Road,
Worsley, Manchester, Greater
Manchester M28 2WQ
Tel: 0161 794 1463
Head Teacher: Mrs J A T Nairn
CertEd(Distinction)
Age range: 3–18
No. of pupils: 480

Bury Catholic Preparatory School
Arden House, Manchester Road,
Bury, Greater Manchester BL9 9BH
Tel: 0161 764 2346
Acting Headteacher: Mrs C Baumber
Age range: 3–11
Fees: Day £3,800–£6,486

Bury Grammar School Boys
Tenterden Street, Bury, Greater
Manchester BL9 0HN
Tel: 0161 797 2700
Headmaster: Mr D Cassidy
Age range: B7–18
No. of pupils: 602 VIth92
Fees: Day £7,992–£10,755

Bury Grammar School for Girls
Bridge Road, Bury, Greater
Manchester BL9 0HH
Tel: 0161 696 8600
Headmistress: Mrs J Anderson
Age range: B4–7 G4–18
No. of pupils: VIth120
Fees: Day £7,836–£10,755

Cheadle Hulme School
Claremont Road, Cheadle Hulme,
Cheadle, Greater Manchester SK8 6EF
Tel: 0161 488 3345
Head: Ms Lucy Pearson B.A. (Oxon)
Age range: 4–18
No. of pupils: 1396 VIth254
Fees: Day £8,950–£11,880

CHETHAM'S SCHOOL OF MUSIC
For further details see p. 176
Long Millgate, Manchester,
Greater Manchester M3 1SB
Tel: 0161 834 9644
Email: hello@chethams.com
Website: www.chethams.com
Head of School: Mr Alun Jones
Age range: 8–18
No. of pupils: 306
Fees: Day £25,821 FB £33,324

Clarendon Cottage School
Ivy Bank House, Half Edge Lane,
Eccles, Manchester, Greater
Manchester M30 9BJ
Tel: 0161 950 7868
Headteacher: Mrs A Hartley
Age range: 3–11
No. of pupils: 81
Fees: Day £4,590–£4,740

Clevelands Preparatory School
425 Chorley New Road, Bolton,
Greater Manchester BL1 5DH
Tel: 01204 843898
Headteacher: Mrs Lesley Parlane
Age range: 2–11
No. of pupils: 141
Fees: Day £7,485

Covenant Christian School
The Hawthorns, 48 Heaton
Moor Road, Stockport, Greater
Manchester SK4 4NX
Tel: 0161 432 3782
Head: Dr Roger Slack
Age range: 5–16
No. of pupils: 32

Darul Uloom Al Arabiya Al Islamiya
Holcombe Hall, Holcombe, Bury,
Greater Manchester BL8 4NG
Tel: 01706 826106
Head: Mr Mohammed Atcha
Age range: B12–16
No. of pupils: 326

Etz Chaim School at The Belmont
89 Middleton Road, Crumpsall,
Manchester, Greater
Manchester M8 4JY
Tel: 0161 740 6800
Headteacher: Rabbi Eli Cohen
Age range: B11–16
No. of pupils: 98

Farrowdale House Preparatory School
Farrow Street, Shaw, Oldham,
Greater Manchester OL2 7AD
Tel: 01706 844533
Headteacher: Miss Z. N.
Campbell BA (Hons) PGCE
Age range: 3–11
No. of pupils: 90
Fees: Day £5,790–£6,270

Forest Park School
Lauriston House, 27 Oakfield, Sale,
Greater Manchester M33 6NB
Tel: 0161 973 4835
Headteacher: Mr Tucker
Age range: 3–11
No. of pupils: 145
Fees: Day £6,690–£7,269

Forest Preparatory School
Moss Lane, Timperley, Altrincham,
Greater Manchester WA15 6LJ
Tel: 0161 980 4075
Headmaster: Rick Hyde
Age range: 2–11
No. of pupils: 197
Fees: Day £6,549–£7,395

Grafton House Preparatory School
1 Warrington Street, Ashton-under-
Lyne, Greater Manchester OL6 6XB
Tel: 0161 343 3015
Head: Mrs Pamela Oaks
Age range: 2–11
No. of pupils: 110

Greenbank Preparatory School
Heathbank Road, Cheadle Hulme,
Cheadle, Greater Manchester SK8 6HU
Tel: 0161 485 3724
Headmistress: Mrs J L Lowe
Age range: 3–11
Fees: Day £8,400

Hulme Hall Grammar School
Beech Avenue, Stockport,
Greater Manchester SK3 8HB
Tel: 0161 485 3524
Headteacher: Miss Rachael Allen
Age range: 2–16
No. of pupils: 272
Fees: Day £7,800–£9,057

Kassim Darwish Grammar School for Boys
Hartley Hall, Alexandra Road
South, Manchester, Greater
Manchester M16 8NH
Tel: 0161 8607676
Headteacher: Mr Akhmed Hussain
Age range: B11–16
No. of pupils: 170
Fees: Day £6,995

King of Kings School
142 Dantzic Street, Manchester,
Greater Manchester M4 4DN
Tel: 0161 834 4214
Head Teacher: Mrs B Lewis
Age range: 3–18
No. of pupils: 29

Lord's Independent School
53 Manchester Road, Bolton,
Greater Manchester BL2 1ES
Tel: 01204 523731
Headteacher: Mrs Anne Ainsworth
Age range: 11–16
No. of pupils: 83

Loreto Preparatory School
Dunham Road, Altrincham,
Greater Manchester WA14 4GZ
Tel: 0161 928 8310
Headteacher: Mrs Anne Roberts
Age range: G3–11
No. of pupils: 163
Fees: Day £6,390

Madrasatul Imam Muhammad Zakariya
Keswick Street, Bolton, Greater
Manchester BL1 8LX
Tel: 01204 384434
Headteacher: Mrs Amena Sader
Age range: G11–19
No. of pupils: 110

Manchester High School for Girls
Grangethorpe Road, Manchester,
Greater Manchester M14 6HS
Tel: 0161 224 0447
Head Mistress: Mrs A C Hewitt
Age range: G4–18
No. of pupils: 936 VIth182
Fees: Day £8,712–£11,874

Manchester Islamic High School for Girls
55 High Lane, Chorlton Cum
Hardy, Manchester, Greater
Manchester M21 9FA
Tel: 0161 881 2127
Headmistress: Mrs Mona Mohamed
Age range: G11–16
No. of pupils: 235
Fees: Day £5,800

Manchester Junior Girls School
64 Upper Park Road, Salford,
Greater Manchester M7 4JA
Tel: 0161 740 0566
Headmistress: Mrs Lieberman
Age range: G3–11
No. of pupils: 200

Manchester Muslim Preparatory School
551 Wilmslow Road, Withington,
Manchester, Greater
Manchester M20 4BA
Tel: 0161 445 5452
Head Teacher: Mrs Doris
Ghafori-Kanno
Age range: 3–11
No. of pupils: 186
Fees: Day £5,225–£5,500

Mechinoh L'Yeshivah
Shenstone House, 13 Upper Park Road,
Salford, Greater Manchester M7 4HY
Tel: 0161 795 9275
The Head: Headmaster
Age range: B11–15
No. of pupils: 49

Monton Village School
Francis Street, Monton,
Eccles, Manchester, Greater
Manchester M30 9PR
Tel: 0161 789 0472
Head: Mrs K S McWilliams
Age range: 1–7
No. of pupils: 109

Moor Allerton Preparatory School
131 Barlow Moor Road, West
Didsbury, Manchester, Greater
Manchester M20 2PW
Tel: 0161 445 4521
Headmistress: Mrs Adriana Ewart-Jones
Age range: 3–11
Fees: Day £8,310–£8,550

Oldham Hulme Grammar School
Chamber Road, Oldham,
Greater Manchester OL8 4BX
Tel: 0161 624 4497
Principal: Mr CJD Mairs
Age range: 2–18
No. of pupils: 766
Fees: Day £8,220–£11,235

OYY Lubavitch Girls School
Beis Menachem, Park Lane, Salford,
Greater Manchester M7 4JD
Tel: 0161 795 0002
Headmistress: Mrs J Hanson
Age range: 2–16
No. of pupils: 82

Prestwich Preparatory School
St Margaret's Building, 400 Bury
Old Road, Prestwich, Manchester,
Greater Manchester M25 1PZ
Tel: 0161 773 1223
Headmistress: Miss P Shiels
Age range: 2–11
No. of pupils: 122
Fees: Day £6,300

Ramillies Hall School
Cheadle Hulme, Cheadle,
Greater Manchester SK8 7AJ
Tel: 0161 485 3804
Headmistress: Mrs Denise Anthony
Age range: 0–16
No. of pupils: 166
Fees: Day £6,000–£8,550

Rochdale Islamic Academy
Greenbank Road, Rochdale,
Greater Manchester OL12 0HZ
Tel: 01706 710184
Headteacher: Mrs Aishah Akhtar
Age range: G11–16
No. of pupils: 165
Fees: Day £1,600

Saddleworth School
High Street, Uppermill, Oldham,
Greater Manchester OL3 6BU
Tel: 01457 872072
Headteacher: Mr M Milburn
Age range: 11–16

St Ambrose Preparatory School
Hale Barns, Altrincham, Greater
Manchester WA15 0HE
Tel: 0161 903 9193
Headmaster: F J Driscoll
Age range: B3–11 G3–4
No. of pupils: 150
Fees: Day £7,218

St Bede's College
Alexandra Park Road, Manchester,
Greater Manchester M16 8HX
Tel: 0161 226 3323
Headmaster: Dr Richard Robson
Age range: 3–18
Fees: Day £8,076–£11,325

Stella Maris Junior School
St Johns Road, Heaton Mersey,
Stockport, Greater Manchester SK4 3BR
Tel: 0161 432 0532
Headteacher: Mrs N Johnson
Age range: 3–11
No. of pupils: 68
Fees: Day £7,713

Stockport Grammar School
Buxton Road, Stockport, Greater
Manchester SK2 7AF
Tel: 0161 456 9000
Headmaster: Dr Paul Owen
Age range: 3–18
No. of pupils: 1439 VIth193
Fees: Day £8,766–£11,700

Tashbar School
20 Upper Park Road, Salford,
Greater Manchester M7 4HL
Tel: 0161 7208254
Headteacher: Mr Pinczewski
Age range: B5–11
No. of pupils: 325

The Chadderton Preparatory Grammar School
Broadway, Chadderton, Oldham,
Greater Manchester OL9 0AD
Tel: 0161 6206570
Headteacher: Mrs Caroline Greenwood
Age range: 2–11
Fees: Day £6,270

The Manchester Grammar School
Old Hall Lane, Fallowfield, Manchester,
Greater Manchester M13 0XT
Tel: 0161 224 7201
High Master: Dr Martin Boulton
Age range: B7–18
Fees: Day £12,570

Trinity Christian School
Birbeck Street, Stalybridge,
Greater Manchester SK15 1SH
Tel: 0161 303 0674
Head: Mr Michael Stewart
Age range: 3–16
Fees: Day £4,038–£5,874

Withington Girls' School
Wellington Road, Fallowfield,
Manchester, Greater
Manchester M14 6BL
Tel: 0161 224 1077
Headmistress: Mrs S J Haslam BA
Age range: G7–18
No. of pupils: 660 VIth150
Fees: Day £9,195–£12,252

Yeshivah Ohr Torah School
28 Broom Lane, Salford, Greater
Manchester M7 4FX
Tel: 0161 7921230
Headteacher: Rabbi Y Wind
Age range: B11–16
No. of pupils: 40

Isle of Man

King William's College
Castletown, Isle of Man IM9 1TP
Tel: +44 (0)1624 820110
Principal: Mr Joss Buchanan
Age range: 11–18
No. of pupils: 363
Fees: Day £18,250–£23,250
FB £29,250–£34,250

The Buchan School
West Hill, Castletown, Isle
of Man IM9 1RD
Tel: 01624 820481
Headteacher: Janet Billingsley-Evans
Age range: 4–11
No. of pupils: 195
Fees: Day £9,810–£12,420

Lancashire

Abrar Academy
34-36 Garstang Road, Preston,
Lancashire PR1 1NA
Tel: 01772 82 87 32
Head of School: Mr A Chowdhury
Age range: 11–21

AKS Lytham
Clifton Drive South, Lytham St
Annes, Lancashire FY8 1DT
Tel: 01253 784100
Headmaster: Mr. Mike Walton
BA, MA (Ed), PGCE, NPQH
Age range: 2–18
No. of pupils: 800 VIth165
Fees: Day £8,895–£11,787

Al-Islah Schools
108 Audley Range, Blackburn,
Lancashire BB1 1TF
Tel: 01254 261573
Headteacher: Nikhat Pardesi
Age range: G11–16
No. of pupils: 192

Ashbridge Independent School
Lindle Lane, Hutton, Preston,
Lancashire PR4 4AQ
Tel: 01772 619900
Headteacher: Karen Mehta
Age range: 0–11
No. of pupils: 315
Fees: Day £7,800

Ghausia Girls' High School
1-3 Cross Street, Nelson,
Lancashire BB9 7EN
Tel: 01282 699214
Headteacher: Aneela Masood
Age range: G11–16
No. of pupils: 35
Fees: Day £1,500

Heathland School
Broadoak, Sandy Lane, Accrington,
Lancashire BB5 2AN
Tel: 01254 234284
Principal: Mrs J Harrison
BA(Hons), CertEd, FRSA
Age range: 4–16
Fees: Day £6,390–£8,871

HIGHFIELD PRIORY SCHOOL
For further details see p. 178
Fulwood Row, Fulwood,
Preston, Lancashire PR2 5RW
Tel: 01772 709624
Email: schooloffice@
highfieldpriory.co.uk
Website: www.highfieldpriory.co.uk
Headmaster: Mr Jeremy
Duke BSc (Hons)
Age range: 18 months–11 years
No. of pupils: 273
Fees: Day £7,850
£

Islamiyah School
Willow Street, Blackburn,
Lancashire BB1 5RQ
Tel: 01254 661 259
Headteacher: Mr Yusuf Seedat
Age range: G11–16
No. of pupils: 178

Jamea Al Kauthar
Ashton Road, Lancaster,
Lancashire LA1 5AJ
Tel: 01524 389898
Headteacher: Fazle Haq Wadee
Age range: G11–16
No. of pupils: 392

Jamiatul-Ilm Wal-Huda UK School
15 Moss Street, Blackburn,
Lancashire BB1 5HW
Tel: 01254 673105
Headteacher: Mr A Ahmed
Age range: B11–16
No. of pupils: 348

KIRKHAM GRAMMAR SCHOOL
For further details see p. 180
Ribby Road, Kirkham, Preston,
Lancashire PR4 2BH
Tel: 01772 684264
Email: info@kirkhamgrammar.co.uk
Website:
www.kirkhamgrammar.co.uk
Headmaster: Mr Daniel Berry
Age range: 3–18 years
No. of pupils: 870 VIth180
Fees: Day £2,895–£3,875
WB £7,181 FB £7,355

Lancaster Steiner School
Lune Road, Lancaster,
Lancashire LA1 5QU
Tel: 01524 841351
Headteacher: Mrs Denise Randal
Age range: 0–14

Markazul Uloom
Park Lee Road, Blackburn,
Lancashire BB2 3NY
Tel: 01254 581569
Headteacher: Mr Nu'amaan Limbada
Age range: G11–19
Fees: Day £1,200 FB £2,700

Moorland School
Ribblesdale Avenue, Clitheroe,
Lancashire BB7 2JA
Tel: 01200 423833
Principal: Mr Jonathan Harrison
Age range: 3 months–16 years
Fees: Day £6,996–£9,996 WB
£18,000–£22,800 FB £19,800–£24,900

Oakhill School and Nursery
Wiswell Lane, Whalley, Clitheroe,
Lancashire BB7 9AF
Tel: 01254 823546
Principal: Mrs Carmel Crouch
Age range: 2–16
No. of pupils: 330
Fees: Day £7,440–£11,574

ROSSALL SCHOOL
For further details see p. 184
Broadway, Fleetwood,
Lancashire FY7 8JW
Tel: +44 (0)1253 774201
Email: admissions@rossall.org.uk
Website: www.rossall.org.uk
Head: Mr Jeremy Quartermain
Age range: 2–18
No. of pupils: 640 VIth190
Fees: Day £8,445–£13,740
FB £21,645–£39,210

Scarisbrick Hall School
Southport Road, Scarisbrisk,
Ormskirk, Lancashire L40 9RQ
Tel: 01704 841151
Headmaster: Mr J Shaw
Age range: 0–18
Fees: Day £7,185–£11,160

St Anne's College Grammar School
293 Clifton Drive South, Lytham
St Annes, Lancashire FY8 1HN
Tel: +44 (0)1253 725815
Principal: Mr S R Welsby
Age range: 2–18
No. of pupils: VIth16
Fees: Day £5,370–£7,320

St Joseph's School, Park Hill
Park Hill, Padiham Road,
Burnley, Lancashire BB12 6TG
Tel: 01282 455622
Headmistress: Mrs Annette Robinson
Age range: 3–11
Fees: Day £6,195

St Pius X Preparatory School
Oak House, 200 Garstang Road,
Fulwood, Preston, Lancashire PR2 8RD
Tel: 01772 719937
Acting Head Teacher: Mrs H Porter
Age range: 2–11
No. of pupils: 260
Fees: Day £7,800

Stonyhurst College
Stonyhurst, Clitheroe,
Lancashire BB7 9PZ
Tel: 01254 827073
Headmaster: Mr John
Browne BA LLB MBA
Age range: 13–18
No. of pupils: 727
Fees: Day £19,950 WB
£29,850 FB £36,300

Stonyhurst St Mary's Hall
Stonyhurst, Lancashire BB7 9PU
Tel: 01254 827073
Headmaster: Mr Ian Murphy
BA (Hons), PGCE Durham
Age range: 3–13
No. of pupils: 272
Fees: Day £8,370–£15,960
WB £21,330 FB £24,570

The Alternative School
The Old Library, Fern Lea Avenue,
Barnoldswick, Lancashire BB18 5DW
Tel: 01282 851800
**Founder and Executive
Head:** Ms Kirsty-Anne Pugh
Age range: 8–18

Westholme School
Meins Road, Blackburn,
Lancashire BB2 6QU
Tel: 01254 506070
Principal: Mrs Lynne Horner
Age range: 3 months–18 years
No. of pupils: 792 VIth72
Fees: Day £7,890–£10,875

Merseyside

Auckland College
65-67 Parkfield Road, Wavertree,
Liverpool, Merseyside L17 4LE
Tel: 0151 727 0083
Headteacher: Miss Stephanie Boyd
Age range: 0–18
No. of pupils: 172 VIth15
Fees: Day £5,000–£7,500

Avalon Preparatory School
Caldy Road, West Kirby, Wirral,
Merseyside CH48 2HE
Tel: 0151 625 6993
Age range: 2–11
No. of pupils: 178
Fees: Day £4,539–£8,469

Belvedere Preparatory School
23 Belvidere Road, Princes Park,
Aigburth, Liverpool, Merseyside L8 3TF
Tel: 0151 471 1137
Age range: 3–11
No. of pupils: 180

Birkenhead School
The Lodge, 58 Beresford Road,
Birkenhead, Merseyside CH43 2JD
Tel: 0151 652 4014
Headmaster: Mr Paul Vicars
Age range: 3 months–18 years
No. of pupils: VIth103
Fees: Day £8,010–£11,994

Carleton House Preparatory School
145 Menlove Avenue, Liverpool,
Merseyside L18 3EE
Tel: 0151 722 0756
Head of School: Mrs Sandy Coleman
Age range: 3–11
No. of pupils: 179
Fees: Day £7,771

Christian Fellowship School
Overbury Street, Edge Hill,
Liverpool, Merseyside L7 3HL
Tel: 0151 709 1642
Headteacher: Mr Richard Worsley
Age range: 4–16
No. of pupils: 136
Fees: Day £2,628–£5,220
£ ✐

Kingsmead School
Bertram Drive, Hoylake, Wirral,
Merseyside CH47 0LL
Tel: 0151 632 3156
Headmaster: Mr M G Gibbons
BComm, MSc, QTS
Age range: 2–18
Fees: Day £6,411–£10,800 WB
£14,100–£16,350 FB £19,500–£22,800
🌐 🏫 £ ✐

Merchant Taylors' Boys' School
186 Liverpool Road, Crosby,
Liverpool, Merseyside L23 0QP
Tel: 0151 928 3308
Headmaster: Mr Deiniol Williams
Age range: B7–18
No. of pupils: 727
Fees: Day £8,517–£11,394
✝ A £ ✐ 16

Merchant Taylors' Girls' School
Liverpool Road, Crosby,
Liverpool, Merseyside L23 5SP
Tel: 0151 924 3140
Headmistress: Mrs Claire Tao
Age range: B4–7 G4–18
No. of pupils: 801
Fees: Day £8,517–£11,394
♀ A £ ✐ 16

Prenton Preparatory School
Mount Pleasant, Oxton, Wirral,
Merseyside CH43 5SY
Tel: 0151 652 3182
Headteacher: Mr M Jones
BSC Hons, PGCE
Age range: 2 –11
Fees: Day £800–£8,586
£ ✐

Runnymede St Edward's School
North Drive, Sandfield Park,
Liverpool, Merseyside L12 1LE
Tel: 0151 281 2300
Headmaster: Mr Bradley Slater
Age range: 3–11
No. of pupils: 270
Fees: Day £7,191–£7,584
£ ✐

St Mary's College
Everest Road, Crosby, Liverpool,
Merseyside L23 5TW
Tel: 0151 924 3926
Principal: Mr Michael Kennedy Bsc, MA
No. of pupils: 880 VIth132
Fees: Day £7,573–£11,161
A £ ✐ 16

Tower College
Mill Lane, Rainhill, Prescot,
Merseyside L35 6NE
Tel: 0151 426 4333
Principal: Miss R J Oxley NNEB, RSH
Age range: 3–16
No. of pupils: 486
Fees: Day £6,972–£8,112
✐

South-East

KEY TO SYMBOLS

- ⚲ *Boys' school*
- ⚲ *Girls' school*
- 🌐 *International school*
- 16· *Tutorial or sixth form college*
- Ⓐ *A levels*
- ⚱ *Boarding accommodation*
- £ *Bursaries*
- ⒾⒷ *International Baccalaureate*
- ✐ *Learning support*
- 16· *Entrance at 16+*
- ❀ *Vocational qualifications*
- (IAPS) *Independent Association of Preparatory Schools*
- (HMC) *The Headmasters' & Headmistresses' Conference*
- (ISA) *Independent Schools Association*
- (GSA) *Girls' School Association*
- (BSA) *Boarding Schools' Association*
- Ⓢ *Society of Heads*

Unless otherwise indicated, all schools are coeducational day schools.
Single-sex and boarding schools will be indicated by the relevant icon.

Berkshire

Alder Bridge School
Bridge House, Mill Lane, Padworth,
Reading, Berkshire RG7 4JU
Tel: 0118 971 4471
Age range: 0–14 years
No. of pupils: 65
Fees: Day £6,015–£8,880

Bradfield College
Bradfield, Berkshire RG7 6AU
Tel: 0118 964 4516
Headmaster: Dr Christopher Stevens
Age range: 13–18
No. of pupils: 800
Fees: Day £29,925 FB £37,404

Caversham School
16 Peppard Road, Caversham,
Reading, Berkshire RG4 8JZ
Tel: 01189 478 684
Head: Mr Chris Neal
Age range: 4–11
No. of pupils: 60
Fees: Day £9,900

Claires Court Junior Boys
Maidenhead Thicket,
Maidenhead, Berkshire SL6 3QE
Tel: 01628 327700
Head: J M E Spanswick
Age range: B4–11
No. of pupils: 248
Fees: Day £9,270–£15,930

Claires Court Nursery, Girls and Sixth Form
1 College Avenue, Maidenhead,
Berkshire SL6 6AW
Tel: 01628 327700
Head of School: Mrs M Heywood
Age range: B16–18 G3–18
No. of pupils: 495 VIth111
Fees: Day £9,270–£16,740

Claires Court Senior Boys
Ray Mill Road East, Maidenhead,
Berkshire SL6 8TE
Tel: 01628 327700
Headmaster: Mr J M Rayer BSc, PGCE
Age range: B11–16
No. of pupils: 335 VIth112
Fees: Day £15,930–£16,740

Crosfields School
Shinfield, Reading, Berkshire RG2 9BL
Tel: 0118 987 1810
Headmaster: Mr Craig Watson
Age range: 3–13
No. of pupils: 510
Fees: Day £10,314–£15,159

Deenway Montessori School & Unicity College
3-5 Sidmouth Street, Reading,
Berkshire RG1 4QX
Tel: 0118 9574737
Headmaster: Mr Munawar Karim
LL.B (Hons), M.A, Mont. Dip.
Age range: 3–11

Dolphin School
Waltham Road, Hurst, Reading,
Berkshire RG10 0FR
Tel: 0118 934 1277
Head: Mr Adam Hurst
Age range: 3–13
Fees: Day £10,170–£14,070

EAGLE HOUSE SCHOOL
For further details see p. 198
Sandhurst, Berkshire GU47 8PH
Tel: 01344 772134
Email: info@eaglehouseschool.com
Website: www.eaglehouseschool.com
Headmaster: Mr A P N
Barnard BA(Hons), PGCE
Age range: 3–13
No. of pupils: 380
Fees: Day £12,030–£18,810 FB £25,275

Elstree School
Woolhampton, Reading,
Berkshire RG7 5TD
Tel: 0118 971 3302
Headmaster: Mr S Inglis
Age range: B3–13 G3–8
No. of pupils: 248
Fees: Day £11,550–£21,000 WB
£26,250–£26,850 FB £26,700–£27,300

Eton College
Windsor, Berkshire SL4 6DW
Tel: 01753 671249
Head Master: Simon Henderson MA
Age range: B13–18
No. of pupils: 1300 VIth520
Fees: FB £40,668

Eton End PNEU School
35 Eton Road, Datchet,
Slough, Berkshire SL3 9AX
Tel: 01753 541075
Headmistress: Sarah Stokes
BA(Hons), PGCE
Age range: B3–7 G3–11
No. of pupils: 245
Fees: Day £9,375–£11,985

Heathfield School
London Road, Ascot, Berkshire SL5 8BQ
Tel: 01344 898342
Head of School: Mrs Marina
Gardiner Legge
Age range: G11–18
No. of pupils: 200

Hemdean House School
Hemdean Road, Caversham,
Reading, Berkshire RG4 7SD
Tel: 0118 947 2590
Head Teacher: Mrs H Chalmers BSc
Age range: B4–11 G4–11
Fees: Day £8,490–£9,300

Herries Preparatory School
Dean Lane, Cookham
Dean, Berkshire SL6 9BD
Tel: 01628 483350
Headmistress: Fiona Long
Age range: 3–11
Fees: Day £9,210–£10,800

HIGHFIELD PREPARATORY SCHOOL
For further details see p. 206
2 West Road, Maidenhead,
Berkshire SL6 1PD
Tel: 01628 624918
Email: office@highfieldprep.org
Website: www.highfieldprep.org
Headteacher: Mrs Joanna Leach
Age range: B3–5 G3–11
Fees: Day £1,119–£12,675

Holme Grange School
Heathlands Road, Wokingham,
Berkshire RG40 3AL
Tel: 0118 978 1566
Headteacher: Mrs Claire Robinson
BA (Open) PGCE NPQH
Age range: 3–16 years
No. of pupils: 509
Fees: Day £11,160–£15,525

Lambrook School
Winkfield Row, Nr Ascot,
Berkshire RG42 6LU
Tel: 01344 882717
Headmaster: Mr Jonathan Perry
Age range: 3–13
No. of pupils: 540
Fees: Day £11,250–£19,737
WB £22,008–£23,664

Leighton Park School
Shinfield Road, Reading,
Berkshire RG2 7ED
Tel: 0118 987 9600
Head: Mr Matthew L S Judd BA, PGCE
Age range: 11–18
No. of pupils: 460

Long Close School
Upton Court Road, Upton,
Slough, Berkshire SL3 7LU
Tel: 01753 520095
Headteacher: Ms Kamaldeep
Nijjar BA (Hons), Med, MA
Age range: 2–16
No. of pupils: 329

Luckley House School
Luckley Road, Wokingham,
Berkshire RG40 3EU
Tel: 0118 978 4175
Head: Mrs Jane Tudor
Age range: G11–18
No. of pupils: 230
Fees: Day £16,620 WB
£26,955 FB £29,082

Ludgrove
Wokingham, Berkshire RG40 3AB
Tel: 0118 978 9881
Head of School: Mr Simon Barber
Age range: B8–13
No. of pupils: 190

LVS Ascot
London Road, Ascot, Berkshire SL5 8DR
Tel: 01344 882770
Headmistress: Mrs Christine
Cunniffe BA (Hons), MMus, MBA
Age range: 4–18
No. of pupils: 830
Fees: Day £10,380–£18,606
FB £26,562–£32,691

Meadowbrook Montessori School
Malt Hill Road, Warfield,
Bracknell, Berkshire RG42 6JQ
Tel: 01344 890869
Director of Education: Mrs S Gunn
Age range: 3–11
No. of pupils: 78
Fees: Day £10,044–£11,385

Newbold School
Popeswood Road, Binfield,
Bracknell, Berkshire RG42 4AH
Tel: 01344 421088
Headteacher: Mrs Jaki Crissey
MA, BA, PGCE Primary
Age range: 3–11
Fees: Day £4,500

Our Lady's Preparatory School
The Avenue, Crowthorne,
Wokingham, Berkshire RG45 6PB
Tel: 01344 773394
Headmistress: Mrs Helene Robinson
Age range: 3 months–11 years
No. of pupils: 100
Fees: Day £7,080

Padworth College
Padworth, Reading, Berkshire RG7 4NR
Tel: 0118 983 2644
Acting Principal: Mr Chris Randell
Age range: 13–19
No. of pupils: 116 VIth50
Fees: Day £14,400 FB £29,400

Pangbourne College
Pangbourne, Reading,
Berkshire RG8 8LA
Tel: 0118 984 2101
Headmaster: Thomas J C Garnier
Age range: 11–18
No. of pupils: 429 VIth62
Fees: Day £18,000–£25,380
FB £22,620–£36,660

Papplewick School
Windsor Road, Ascot, Berkshire SL5 7LH
Tel: 01344 621488
Head: Mr Tom Bunbury
Age range: B6–13
No. of pupils: 195

Queen Anne's School
6 Henley Road, Caversham,
Reading, Berkshire RG4 6DX
Tel: 0118 918 7300
Headmistress: Mrs Julia Harrington
BA(Hons), PGCE, NPQH
Age range: G11–18
No. of pupils: 336 VIth100
Fees: Day £24,135 WB
£32,070–£33,810 FB £35,580

Reading Blue Coat School
Holme Park, Sonning Lane, Sonning,
Reading, Berkshire RG4 6SU
Tel: 0118 944 1005
Headmaster: Mr Jesse Elzinga
Age range: B11–18 G16–18
No. of pupils: 710 VIth230
Fees: Day £16,695

Reddam House Berkshire
Bearwood Road, Sindlesham,
Wokingham, Berkshire RG41 5BG
Tel: 0118 974 8300
Principal: Mrs Tammy Howard
Age range: 3 months–18 years
No. of pupils: 570
Fees: Day £10,200–£17,280 WB
£27,075–£31,215 FB £28,665–£32,805

Redroofs School for the Performing Arts (Redroofs Theatre School)
26 Bath Road, Maidenhead,
Berkshire SL6 4JT
Tel: 01628 674092
Principal: June Rose
Age range: 8–18
No. of pupils: 100
Fees: Day £4,882–£5,527

St Andrew's School
Buckhold, Pangbourne,
Reading, Berkshire RG8 8QA
Tel: 0118 974 4276
Headmaster: Mr Jonathan
Bartlett BSc QTS
Age range: 3–13
Fees: Day £5,430–£18,150 WB £3,360

St Bernard's Preparatory School
Hawtrey Close, Slough, Berkshire SL1 1TB
Tel: 01753 521821
Head Teacher: Mr N Cheesman
Age range: 2–11
Fees: Day £8,850–£10,545

St Edward's Prep
64 Tilehurst Road, Reading,
Berkshire RG30 2JH
Tel: 0118 957 4342
Headmaster: Derek Suttie
Age range: B4–11
No. of pupils: 170
Fees: Day £6,585–£11,025

St George's Ascot
Wells Lane, Ascot, Berkshire SL5 7DZ
Tel: 01344 629920
Headmistress: Mrs Liz Hewer
MA (Hons) (Cantab) PGCE
Age range: G11–18
No. of pupils: 270 VIth70
Fees: Day £22,800 WB
£34,050–£34,680 FB £35,460

St George's School Windsor Castle
Windsor, Berkshire SL4 1QF
Tel: 01753 865553
Head Master: Mr J R Jones
Age range: 3–13
Fees: Day £10,044–£16,674
WB £20,700 FB £21,438

St John's Beaumont Preparatory School
Priest Hill, Old Windsor, Berkshire SL4 2JN
Tel: 01784 432428
Headmaster: Mr G E F Delaney
BA(Hons), PGCE, MSc
Age range: B3–13
No. of pupils: 290
Fees: Day £3,264–£6,244
FB £7,580–£9,573

St Joseph's College
Upper Redlands Road,
Reading, Berkshire RG1 5JT
Tel: 0118 966 1000
Headmaster: Mr Andrew Colpus
Age range: 3–18
No. of pupils: VIth65
Fees: Day £6,672–£11,406

St Mary's School Ascot
St Mary's Road, Ascot, Berkshire SL5 9JF
Tel: 01344 296614
Headmistress: Mrs Mary Breen BSc, MSc
Age range: G11–18
No. of pupils: 386 VIth120
Fees: Day £27,630 FB £38,790

St Piran's Preparatory School
Gringer Hill, Maidenhead,
Berkshire SL6 7LZ
Tel: 01628 594302
Headmaster: Mr J A Carroll
BA(Hons), BPhilEd, PGCE, NPQH
Age range: 3–11
Fees: Day £10,857–£16,566

Sunningdale School
Dry Arch Road, Sunningdale,
Berkshire SL5 9PY
Tel: 01344 620159
Headmaster: Tom Dawson MA, PGCE
Age range: B7–13
No. of pupils: 90

Teikyo School UK
Framewood Road, Wexham,
Slough, Berkshire SL2 4QS
Tel: 01753 663711
Headmaster: Tadashi Nakayama
Age range: 16–18

The Abbey School
Kendrick Road, Reading,
Berkshire RG1 5DZ
Tel: 0118 987 2256
Head: Mrs Rachel S E Dent
Age range: G3–18
No. of pupils: 1068
Fees: Day £10,680–£17,640

The Marist Preparatory School
King's Road, Sunninghill,
Ascot, Berkshire SL5 7PS
Tel: 01344 626137
Vice Principal: Jane Gow
Age range: G2–11
No. of pupils: 225
Fees: Day £9,780–£11,940

The Marist School
King's Road, Sunninghill,
Ascot, Berkshire SL5 7PS
Tel: 01344 624291
Principal: Mr Karl McCloskey
Age range: G3–18

The Oratory Preparatory School
Great Oaks, Goring Heath,
Reading, Berkshire RG8 7SF
Tel: 0118 984 4511
Headmaster: Mr Rob Stewart
Age range: 2–13
No. of pupils: 400
Fees: Day £10,266–£16,443
WB £21,153 FB £24,522

The Oratory School
Woodcote, Reading, Berkshire RG8 0PJ
Tel: 01491 683500
Head Master: Mr J J Smith
BA(Hons), MEd, PGCE
Age range: B11–18
No. of pupils: 380 Vlth120
Fees: Day £24,966 FB £34,299
(symbols)

The Vine Christian School
SORCF Christian Centre,
Basingstoke Road, Three Mile Cross,
Reading, Berkshire RG7 1AT
Tel: 0118 988 6464
Head of School: Mrs Eve Strike
Age range: 5–13
No. of pupils: 9

UPTON HOUSE SCHOOL
For further details see p. 238
115 St Leonard's Road,
Windsor, Berkshire SL4 3DF
Tel: 01753 862610
Email: registrar@uptonhouse.org.uk
Website: www.uptonhouse.org.uk
Head: Mrs Rhian Thornton BA
(Hons) NPQH LLE PGCE
Age range: 2–11 years
No. of pupils: 245
Fees: Day £3,143–£5,225
(symbols)

Waverley School
Waverley Way, Finchampstead,
Wokingham, Berkshire RG40 4YD
Tel: 0118 973 1121
Principal: Mr Guy Shore
Age range: 3–11
Fees: Day £8,589–£11,982
(symbols)

WELLINGTON COLLEGE
For further details see p. 242
Duke's Ride, Crowthorne,
Berkshire RG45 7PU
Tel: +44 (0)1344 444000
Email: admissions@
wellingtoncollege.org.uk
Website:
www.wellingtoncollege.org.uk
Master: Mr James Dahl
Age range: 13–18
No. of pupils: 1060 Vlth465
Fees: Day £30,375–
£34,890 FB £41,580
(symbols)

MALTMAN'S GREEN SCHOOL
For further details see p. 214
Maltman's Lane, Gerrards Cross,
Buckinghamshire SL9 8RR
Tel: 01753 883022
Email: registrar@
maltmansgreen.com
Website: www.maltmansgreen.com
Headmistress: Mrs Joanna
Pardon MA, BSc(Hons), PGCE
Age range: G2–11
No. of pupils: 365
Fees: Day £1,925–£5,275
(symbols)

St Mary's School
94 Packhorse Road, Gerrards
Cross, Buckinghamshire SL9 8JQ
Tel: 01753 883370
Head of School: Mrs P Adams
Age range: G3–18
No. of pupils: 350 Vlth50
Fees: Day £5,670–£16,980
(symbols)

Thorpe House School
Oval Way, Gerrards Cross,
Buckinghamshire SL9 8QA
Tel: 01753 882474
Headmaster: Mr Terence Ayres
Age range: B3–16
Fees: Day £10,950–£16,962
(symbols)

Buckinghamshire

Gayhurst School
Bull Lane, Gerrards Cross,
Buckinghamshire SL9 8RJ
Tel: 01753 882690
Headmaster: Gareth R A Davies
Age range: 3–11
Fees: Day £12,159–£15,438
(symbols)

East Sussex

Ashdown House School
Forest Row, East Sussex RH18 5JY
Tel: 01342 822574
Headmaster: Mike Davies
Age range: 4–13
No. of pupils: 141
Fees: Day £8,970–£20,100 FB £27,450
(symbols)

Bartholomews Tutorial College
22-23 Prince Albert Street,
Brighton, East Sussex BN1 1HF
Tel: 01273 205965/205141
Director of Studies: Mike Balmer BEd
Age range: 16+
No. of pupils: 40 Vlth25
Fees: Day £25,000 WB
£30,000 FB £30,000
(symbols)

Battle Abbey School
Battle, East Sussex TN33 0AD
Tel: 01424 772385
Headmaster: Mr D Clark BA(Hons)
Age range: 2–18
No. of pupils: 286 Vlth48
Fees: Day £6,939–£16,914
FB £26,649–£31,932
(symbols)

Bede's School
The Dicker, Upper Dicker,
Hailsham, East Sussex BN27 3QH
Tel: +44 (0)1323843252
Head: Mr Peter Goodyer
Age range: 3 months–18
No. of pupils: 800 Vlth295
Fees: Day £10,230–£17,400
FB £22,290–£25,650
(symbols)

Bellerbys College Brighton
1 Billinton Way, Brighton,
East Sussex BN1 4LF
Tel: +44 (0)1273 339333
Principal: Mr Simon Mower
Age range: 13–18
(symbols)

Bricklehurst Manor Preparatory
Bardown Road, Stonegate,
Wadhurst, East Sussex TN5 7EL
Tel: 01580 200448
Principal: Mrs C Flowers
Age range: 3–11
No. of pupils: 117
(symbols)

Brighton & Hove High School GDST
Montpelier Road, Brighton,
East Sussex BN1 3AT
Tel: 01273 280280
Head: Jennifer Smith
Age range: G3–18
No. of pupils: 680 Vlth70
Fees: Day £7,191–£14,421
(symbols)

Brighton & Hove Montessori School
67 Stanford Avenue, Brighton,
East Sussex BN1 6FB
Tel: 01273 702485
Headteacher: Mrs Daisy
Cockburn AMI, MontDip
Age range: 2–11
(symbols)

Brighton College
Eastern Road, Brighton,
East Sussex BN2 0AL
Tel: 01273 704200
Head Master: Richard Cairns MA
Age range: 3–18
No. of pupils: 950
Fees: Day £10,050–£24,540 WB
£33,390–£34,410 FB £37,470–£45,210
(symbols)

Brighton Steiner School
John Howard House, Roedean Road,
Brighton, East Sussex BN2 5RA
Tel: 01273 386300
**Chair of the College of
Teachers:** Carrie Rawle
Age range: 3–16
Fees: Day £7,800–£8,100
(symbols)

Buckswood School
Broomham Hall, Rye Road, Guestling,
Hastings, East Sussex TN35 4LT
Tel: 01424 813 813
School Director: Mr Giles Sutton
Age range: 10–19
No. of pupils: 420
🌐 Ⓐ 🏫 £ IB ⚲ 16

Buckswood St George's
Westwood House, 7-9 Holmesdale
Gardens, Hastings, East Sussex TN34 1LY
Tel: 01424 813696
College Director: Ian Godfrey
Age range: B16–19 G16–20
No. of pupils: VIth50
16 Ⓐ 🏫 £ IB 16

Charters Ancaster
Woodsgate Place, Gunters Lane,
Bexhill-on-Sea, East Sussex TN39 4EB
Tel: 01424 216670
Nursery Manager: Susannah Crump
Age range: 6 months–5
No. of pupils: 125
£ ⚲

Claremont Preparatory & Nursery School
Ebdens Hill, Baldslow, St Leonards-
on-Sea, East Sussex TN37 7PW
Tel: 01424 751555
Headmistress: Abra Stoakley
Age range: 1–13
Fees: Day £6,900–£12,600
Ⓐ £ ⚲

Claremont Senior & Sixth Form School
Bodiam, Nr Robertsbridge,
East Sussex TN32 5UJ
Tel: 01580 830396
Headmaster: Mr. Giles Perrin
Age range: 14–18
Fees: Day £17,400

Darvell School
Darvell Bruderhof, Robertsbridge,
East Sussex TN32 5DR
Tel: 01580 883300
Headteacher: Mr Arnold Meier
Age range: 4–16
No. of pupils: 121
⚲

Deepdene School
195 New Church Road, Hove,
East Sussex BN3 4ED
Tel: 01273 418984
Heads: Mrs Nicola Gane &
Miss Elizabeth Brown
Age range: 6 months–11 years
Fees: Day £8,349
£

Dharma School
The White House, Ladies Mile Road,
Patcham, Brighton, East Sussex BN1 8TB
Tel: 01273 502055
Headteacher: Clare Eddison
Age range: 3–11
Fees: Day £8,208
£ ⚲

Didac School
16 Trinity Trees, Eastbourne,
East Sussex BN21 3LE
Tel: +44 1323 417276
Age range: 16–18
🌐

Eastbourne College
Old Wish Road, Eastbourne,
East Sussex BN21 4JX
Tel: 01323 452323 (Admissions)
Headmaster: Mr Tom
Lawson MA (Oxon)
Age range: 13–18
No. of pupils: 650 VIth312
Fees: Day £23,895–£24,375
FB £36,420–£36,975
🌐 Ⓐ 🏫 £ ⚲ 16

Greenfields Independent Day & Boarding School
Priory Road, Forest Row,
East Sussex RH18 5JD
Tel: +44 (0)1342 822189
Executive Head: Mr. Jeff Smith
Age range: 2–19
🌐 Ⓐ 🏫 ⚲ 16

Lancing College Preparatory School at Hove
The Droveway, Hove,
East Sussex BN3 6LU
Tel: 01273 503452
Headmistress: Mrs Kirsty Keep BEd
Age range: 3–13
No. of pupils: 181
Fees: Day £3,960–£15,975
£ ⚲

Lewes Old Grammar School
High Street, Lewes, East Sussex BN7 1XS
Tel: 01273 472634
Headmaster: Mr Robert Blewitt
Age range: 3–18
No. of pupils: 463 VIth50
Fees: Day £8,760–£14,625
Ⓐ £ ⚲ 16

Mayfield School
The Old Palace, Mayfield,
East Sussex TN20 6PH
Tel: +44 (0)1435 874600
Head: Ms Antonia Beary MA,
Mphil (Cantab), PGCE
Age range: G11–18
No. of pupils: 365 VIth100
Fees: Day £21,000 FB £33,900
🌐 Ⓐ 🏫 £ ⚲ 16

Michael Hall School
Kidbrooke Park, Priory Road, Forest
Row, East Sussex RH18 5JA
Tel: 01342 822275
Age range: 0 years–18 years
No. of pupils: VIth102
Fees: Day £9,245–£12,670
🌐 Ⓐ 🏫 ⚲ 16

Roedean Moira House
Upper Carlisle Road, Eastbourne,
East Sussex BN20 7TE
Tel: 01323 644144
Headmaster: Mr Andrew Wood
Age range: G0–18
No. of pupils: 289
🧍 🌐 Ⓐ 🏫 £ ⚲ 16

Roedean School
Roedean Way, Brighton,
East Sussex BN2 5RQ
Tel: 01273 667500
Headmaster: Mr. Oliver Bond
BA(Essex), PGCE, NPQH
Age range: G11–18
No. of pupils: 607 VIth167
Fees: Day £5,480–£7,165 WB
£9,690–£10,805 FB £10,620–£12,855
🧍 🌐 Ⓐ 🏫 £ ⚲ 16

Sacred Heart School
Mayfield Lane, Durgates,
Wadhurst, East Sussex TN5 6DQ
Tel: 01892 783414
Headteacher: Mrs H Blake
BA(Hons), PGCE
Age range: 2–11
No. of pupils: 121
Fees: Day £8,355
£ ⚲

Skippers Hill Manor Prep School
Five Ashes, Mayfield, East
Sussex TN20 6HR
Tel: 01825 830234
Headmaster: Mr M Hammond
MA, BA, PGCE
Age range: 2–13
No. of pupils: 174
Fees: Day £8,400–£13,440
£ ⚲

St Andrew's Prep
Meads Street, Eastbourne,
East Sussex BN20 7RP
Tel: 01323 733203
Headmaster: Gareth Jones
MEd, BA(Hons), PGCE
Age range: 9 months–13 years
No. of pupils: 380
🏫 £ ⚲

St Bede's Preparatory School
Duke's Drive, Eastbourne,
East Sussex BN20 7XL
Tel: 01323 734222
Head: Mr Giles Entwisle
Age range: 3 months–13 years
No. of pupils: 395
Fees: Day £10,230–£17,400
FB £22,290–£25,650
🏫 £ ⚲

St Christopher's School
33 New Church Road, Hove,
East Sussex BN3 4AD
Tel: 01273 735404
Headmaster: Mr Julian Withers
Age range: 4–13
Fees: Day £8,370–£12,720
£ ⚲

The Drive Prep School
101 The Drive, Hove, East Sussex BN3 3JE
Tel: 01273 738444
Head Teacher: Mrs S Parkinson
CertEd, CertPerfArts
Age range: 7–16
⚲

Torah Montessori Nursery
29 New Church Road, Hove,
East Sussex BN3 4AD
Tel: 01273 328675
Principal: P Efune
Age range: 1–4
⚲

VINEHALL
For further details see p. 240
Robertsbridge, East Sussex TN32 5JL
Tel: 01580 880413
Email: admissions@
vinehallschool.com
Website: www.vinehallschool.com
Headmaster: Joff Powis
Age range: 2–13
No. of pupils: 235
Fees: Day £9,948–£18,543 WB
£21,765–£22,227 FB £23,559–£24,147
🏫 £ ⚲

Windlesham School
190 Dyke Road, Brighton,
East Sussex BN1 5AA
Tel: 01273 553645
Headmaster: Mr John Ingrassia
Age range: 3–11
No. of pupils: 195
Fees: Day £6,015–£8,955
£ ✎

Hampshire

Alton School
Anstey Lane, Alton,
Hampshire GU34 2NG
Tel: 01420 82070
Head: Graham Maher
Age range: 0–18
No. of pupils: 502 VIth53
Ⓐ £ 16

Ballard School
Fernhill Lane, New Milton,
Hampshire BH25 5SU
Tel: 01425 626900
Headmaster: Mr Andrew McCleave
Age range: 2–16 years
No. of pupils: 400
Fees: Day £8,340–£15,315
£ ✎

Bedales Prep School, Dunhurst
Petersfield, Hampshire GU32 2DP
Tel: 01730 300200
Head of School: Colin Baty
Age range: 8–13
No. of pupils: 200
Fees: Day £16,920–£18,765
FB £22,215–£24,930
Ⓐ 🏛 £ ✎

Bedales School
Church Road, Steep, Petersfield,
Hampshire GU32 2DG
Tel: 01730 711733
Head of School: Magnus Bashaarat
Age range: 13–18
No. of pupils: 463
Fees: Day £28,515 FB £36,285
🌐 Ⓐ 🏛 £ ✎ 16

Boundary Oak School
Roche Court, Fareham,
Hampshire PO17 5BL
Tel: 01329 280955/820373
Head: Mr James Polansky
Age range: 2–16
No. of pupils: 120
Fees: Day £8,949–£14,487 WB
£15,723–£20,514 FB £17,658–£22,449
🏛 £ ✎

Brockwood Park & Inwoods School
Brockwood Park, Bramdean,
Hampshire SO24 0LQ
Tel: +44 (0)1962 771744
Principal: Mr Antonio Autor
Age range: 14–19
No. of pupils: 112 VIth39
Fees: Day £5,630–£6,400 FB £21,400
🌐 Ⓐ 🏛 £ ✎ 16

CHURCHER'S COLLEGE
For further details see p. 192
Petersfield, Hampshire GU31 4AS
Tel: 01730 263033
Email: admissions@
churcherscollege.com
Website:
www.churcherscollege.com
Headmaster: Mr Simon
Williams MA, BSc
Age range: 3–18 years
Fees: Day £10,320–£16,035
Ⓐ £ ✎ 16

Daneshill School
Stratfield Turgis, Basingstoke,
Hampshire RG27 0AR
Tel: 01256 882707
Headmaster: Mr David Griffiths
Age range: 3–13
Fees: Day £10,650–£14,000
✎

Ditcham Park School
Ditcham Park, Petersfield,
Hampshire GU31 5RN
Tel: 01730 825659
Headmaster: Mr Graham
Spawforth MA, MEd
Age range: 2½–16
No. of pupils: 379
Fees: Day £2,835–£4,753
£ ✎

DURLSTON COURT
For further details see p. 196
Becton Lane, Barton-on-Sea, New
Milton, Hampshire BH25 7AQ
Tel: 01425 610010
Email: registrar@durlstoncourt.co.uk
Website: www.durlstoncourt.co.uk
Age range: 2–13
No. of pupils: 296
Fees: Day £3,540–£15,390
£ ✎

Farleigh School
Red Rice, Andover,
Hampshire SP11 7PW
Tel: 01264 710766
Headmaster: Father Simon Everson
Age range: 3–13
Fees: Day £5,385–£19,590
FB £21,675–£25,485
🏛 £ ✎

Farnborough Hill
Farnborough Road, Farnborough,
Hampshire GU14 8AT
Tel: 01252 545197
Head: Mrs A Neil BA, MEd, PGCE
Age range: G11–18
No. of pupils: 550 VIth90
Fees: Day £14,796
🏃 Ⓐ £ ✎ 16

Forres Sandle Manor
Fordingbridge, Hampshire SP6 1NS
Tel: 01425 653181
Headmaster: Mr M N Hartley BSc(Hons)
Age range: 3–13
No. of pupils: 264
Fees: Day £5–£
🏛 £ ✎

Glenhurst School
16 Beechworth Road, Havant,
Hampshire PO9 1AX
Tel: 023 9248 4054
Principal: Mrs E M Haines
Age range: 3 months–5 years
✎

Hampshire Collegiate School
Embley Park, Romsey,
Hampshire SO51 6ZE
Tel: 01794 512206
Headteacher: Mr Cliff Canning
Age range: 2–18
No. of pupils: 500
Fees: Day £8,754–£31,338
🌐 Ⓐ 🏛 £ ✎ 16

Highfield and Brookham Schools
Highfield Lane, Liphook,
Hampshire GU30 7LQ
Tel: 01428 728000
Headteachers: Mr Phillip Evitt and Mrs
Sophie Baber MA(Cantab), PGCE
Age range: 3–13
No. of pupils: 292
Fees: Day £3,775–£7,325
FB £24,825–£27,300
🏛 £ ✎

KING EDWARD VI SCHOOL
For further details see p. 210
Wilton Road, Southampton,
Hampshire SO15 5UQ
Tel: 023 8070 4561
Email: registrar@kes.hants.sch.uk
Website: www.kes.hants.sch.uk
Head Master: Mr N T Parker
Age range: 11–18
No. of pupils: 960
Fees: Day £16,605
Ⓐ £ ✎ 16

Kingscourt School
182 Five Heads Road, Catherington,
Hampshire PO8 9NJ
Tel: 023 9259 3251
Head of School: Mr Jamie Lewis
Age range: 3–11
No. of pupils: 158
Fees: Day £2,856

Lord Wandsworth College
Long Sutton, Hook, Hampshire RG29 1TB
Tel: 01256 862201
Head of School: Mr Adam Williams
Age range: 11–18 years
No. of pupils: 615
Fees: Day £21,240–£24,390 WB £29,400–£33,000 FB £30,345–£34,650

Mayville High School
35/37 St Simon's Road, Southsea, Portsmouth, Hampshire PO5 2PE
Tel: 023 9273 4847
Headteacher: Mrs Rebecca Parkyn
Age range: 6 months–16 years
No. of pupils: 479
Fees: Day £7,635–£11,235

Meoncross School
Burnt House Lane, Stubbington, Fareham, Hampshire PO14 2EF
Tel: 01329 662182
Headmaster: Mr Mark Cripps
Age range: 2–16
No. of pupils: 405
Fees: Day £8,736–£12,576

Moyles Court School
Moyles Court, Ringwood, Hampshire BH24 3NF
Tel: 01425 472856
Headmaster: Mr Richard Milner-Smith
Age range: 3–16
No. of pupils: 195
Fees: Day £6,885–£14,655 FB £21,246–£26,805

New Forest Small School
1 Southampton Road, Lyndhurst, Hampshire SO43 7BU
Tel: 02380 284 415
Headteacher: Mr Nicholas Alp
Age range: 3–16

Norman Court
West Tytherley, Stockbridge, Hampshire SP5 1NH
Tel: 01980 322 322

Portsmouth High School GDST
Kent Road, Southsea, Portsmouth, Hampshire PO5 3EQ
Tel: 023 9282 6714
Headmistress: Mrs Jane Prescott BSc NPQH
Age range: G3–18
No. of pupils: 500
Fees: Day £2,500–£4,663

Prince's Mead School
Worthy Park House, Kings Worthy, Winchester, Hampshire SO21 1AN
Tel: 01962 888000
Headmaster: Peter Thacker
Age range: 4–11

Ringwood Waldorf School
Folly Farm Lane, Ashley, Ringwood, Hampshire BH24 2NN
Tel: 01425 472664
Age range: 3–18
No. of pupils: 235
Fees: Day £6,240–£9,000

Rookwood School
Weyhill Road, Andover, Hampshire SP10 3AL
Tel: 01264 325900
Headmaster: Mr A Kirk-Burgess BSc, PGCE, MSc (Oxon)
Age range: 2–16
Fees: Day £9,360–£15,600 FB £23,250–£27,465

Salesian College
Reading Road, Farnborough, Hampshire GU14 6PA
Tel: 01252 893000
Headmaster: Mr Gerard Owens
Age range: B11–18 G16–18
No. of pupils: 650 VIth140
Fees: Day £11,961

Sherborne House School
Lakewood Road, Chandlers Ford, Eastleigh, Hampshire SO53 1EU
Tel: 023 8025 2440
Head Teacher: Mrs Heather Hopson-Hill
Age range: 3–11
No. of pupils: 293
Fees: Day £8,295–£9,675

SHERFIELD SCHOOL
For further details see p. 222
South Drive, Sherfield-on-Loddon, Hook, Hampshire RG27 0HU
Tel: 01256 884800
Email: admissions@sherfieldschool.co.uk
Website: www.sherfieldschool.co.uk
Headmaster: Mr Nick Brain BA(Hons), PGCE, MA, NPQH
Age range: 3 months–18 years
No. of pupils: 385
Fees: Day £10,320–£17,085 WB £18,960–£26,130 FB £22,125–£30,495

St John's College
Grove Road South, Southsea, Portsmouth, Hampshire PO5 3QW
Tel: 023 9281 5118
Headmaster: Mr Timothy Bayley BSc (Hons), MA, PGCE
Age range: 2–18
No. of pupils: 560 VIth86
Fees: Day £9,225–£12,090 FB £25,200–£28,740

ST NEOT'S SCHOOL
For further details see p. 228
St Neot's Road, Eversley, Hampshire RG27 0PN
Tel: 0118 9739650
Email: admissions@stneotsprep.co.uk
Website: www.stneotsprep.co.uk
Head of School: Deborah Henderson
Age range: 2–13 years
No. of pupils: 306
Fees: Day £4,828–£16,224

St Nicholas' School
Redfields House, Redfields Lane, Church Crookham, Fleet, Hampshire GU52 0RF
Tel: 01252 850121
Headmistress: Dr O Wright PhD, MA, BA Hons, PGCE
Age range: B3–7 G3–16
No. of pupils: 325

St Swithun's Prep
Alresford Road, Winchester, Hampshire SO21 1HA
Tel: 01962 835750
Headmistress: Mrs R Lyons-Smith BSc, PGCE, MBA
Age range: B3–7 G3–11
No. of pupils: 191
Fees: Day £5,424–£13,971

ST SWITHUN'S SCHOOL
For further details see p. 230
Alresford Road, Winchester SO21 1HA
Tel: 01962 835700
Email: office@stswithuns.com
Website: www.stswithuns.com
Head of School: Jane Gandee MA(Cantab)
Age range: G11–18
No. of pupils: 500 VIth140
Fees: Day £20,976 FB £34,776

St. Mary's Independent School
57 Midanbury Lane, Bitterne Park, Southampton, Hampshire SO18 4DJ
Tel: 023 8067 1267
Executive Head: Mrs C Charlemagne
Age range: 3–16
No. of pupils: 470
Fees: Day £7,620–£9,900

Stockton House School
Stockton Avenue, Fleet, Hampshire GU51 4NS
Tel: 01252 616323
Early Years Manager: Mrs Jenny Bounds BA EYPS
Age range: 2–5

STROUD SCHOOL
For further details see p. 234
Highwood House, Highwood Lane, Romsey, Hampshire SO51 9ZH
Tel: 01794 513231
Email: registrar@stroud-kes.org.uk
Website: www.stroud-kes.org.uk
Head: Mr Joel Worrall
Age range: 3–13

The Children's House and Grantham Farm Montessori School
Grantham Farm, Baughurst, Tadley, Hampshire RG26 5JS
Tel: 0118 981 5821
Head Teacher: Ms Emma Wetherley
Age range: 3–8

The Gregg Prep School
17-19 Winn Road, Southampton, Hampshire SO17 1EJ
Tel: 023 8055 7352
Head Teacher: Mrs J Caddy
Age range: 3–11
Fees: Day £8,295

The Gregg School
Townhill Park House, Cutbush Lane,
Southampton, Hampshire SO18 2GF
Tel: 023 8047 2133
Headteacher: Mrs S Sellers PGDip,
MSc, BSc(Hons), NPQH, PGCE
Age range: 11–16
No. of pupils: 300
Fees: Day £12,825
(£)

The King's School
Lakesmere House, Allington Lane,
Fair Oak, Eastleigh, Southampton,
Hampshire SO50 7DB
Tel: 023 8060 0986
Age range: 3–16
No. of pupils: 256
Fees: Day £4,560–£7,680

The Pilgrims' School
3 The Close, Winchester,
Hampshire SO23 9LT
Tel: 01962 854189
Headmaster: Mr Tom Burden
Age range: B4–13
No. of pupils: 250
Fees: Day £18,150–£19,245 FB £24,330
(†)(庄)(£)

The Portsmouth Grammar School
High Street, Portsmouth,
Hampshire PO1 2LN
Tel: +44 (0)23 9236 0036
Headmistress: Dr Anne Cotton
Age range: 2–18
No. of pupils: 1556 VIth336
Fees: Day £10,233–£15,951
(🌐)(A)(£)(IB)(🏃)(16)

The Westgate School
Cheriton Road, Winchester,
Hampshire SO22 5AZ
Tel: 01962 854757
Headteacher: Mrs Dean
Age range: 4–16
(庄)(🏃)

Twyford School
Twyford, Winchester,
Hampshire SO21 1NW
Tel: 01962 712269
Headmaster: Dr S J Bailey
BEd, PhD, FRSA
Age range: 3–13
Fees: Day £10,953–£19,509 WB £24,552
(庄)(£)(🏃)

Walhampton
Walhampton, Lymington,
Hampshire SO41 5ZG
Tel: 01590 613 300
Headmaster: Mr Titus Mills
Age range: 2–13
No. of pupils: 353
Fees: Day £9,000–£17,625
FB £20,250–£24,750
(庄)(£)(🏃)

West Hill Park Preparatory School
Titchfield, Fareham,
Hampshire PO14 4BS
Tel: 01329 842356
Headmaster: A P Ramsay
BEd(Hons), MSc
Age range: 2–13
No. of pupils: 288
Fees: Day £10,800–£18,300
FB £19,500–£22,650
(庄)(£)(🏃)

Winchester College
College Street, Winchester,
Hampshire SO23 9NA
Tel: 01962 621247
Headmaster: Dr. T R Hands
Age range: B13–18
No. of pupils: 690 VIth280
Fees: FB £39,912
(†)(🌐)(庄)(£)(🏃)(16)

Yateley Manor School
51 Reading Road, Yateley,
Hampshire GU46 7UQ
Tel: 01252 405500
Headmaster: Mr Robert Upton
Age range: 3–13
No. of pupils: 453
Fees: Day £11,160–£15,300
(£)(🏃)

Isle of Wight

Priory School
Beatrice Avenue, Whippingham,
Isle of Wight PO32 6LP
Tel: 01983 861222
Principal: Mr E J Matyjaszek
Age range: 4–18
Fees: Day £5,840–£9,900
(A)(£)(🏃)(16)

Ryde School with Upper Chine
Queen's Road, Ryde, Isle
of Wight PO33 3BE
Tel: 01983 617970
Headmaster: Mr M. A.
Waldron MA (Cantab)
Age range: 2½–18
No. of pupils: 768
Fees: Day £7,635–£13,230
WB £26,010 FB £29,160
(🌐)(A)(庄)(£)(IB)(🏃)(16)

Kent

Ashford School
East Hill, Ashford, Kent TN24 8PB
Tel: 01233 739030
Head: Mr Michael Hall
Age range: 3 months–18 years
No. of pupils: 835 VIth170
Fees: Day £10,500–£16,800
WB £24,000 FB £36,000
(🌐)(A)(庄)(£)(🏃)(16)

Beech Grove School
Beech Grove Bruderhof, Sandwich
Road, Nonington, Dover, Kent CT15 4HH
Tel: 01304 842980
Head: Mr Timothy Maas
Age range: 4–14
No. of pupils: 63

Beechwood Sacred Heart
12 Pembury Road, Tunbridge
Wells, Kent TN2 3QD
Tel: 01892 532747
Acting Head: Mrs Helen Rowe
Age range: 3–18
No. of pupils: 400 VIth70
Fees: Day £8,685–£17,385
WB £26,850 FB £29,850
(A)(庄)(£)(🏃)(16)

Benenden School
Cranbrook, Kent TN17 4AA
Tel: 01580 240592
Headmistress: Mrs S Price
Age range: G11–18
No. of pupils: 550
Fees: FB £12,650
(†)(🌐)(A)(庄)(£)(🏃)(16)

BETHANY SCHOOL
For further details see p. 188
Curtisden Green, Goudhurst,
Cranbrook, Kent TN17 1LB
Tel: 01580 211273
Email: admissions@
bethanyschool.org.uk
Website: www.bethanyschool.org.uk
Headmaster: Mr Francie
Healy BSc, HDipEd, NPQH
Age range: 11–18 years
No. of pupils: 333 VIth98
Fees: Day £17,310–£19,110 WB
£26,865–£29,670 FB £28,965–£32,610
(🌐)(A)(庄)(£)(🏃)(16)

Bronte School
Mayfield, 7 Pelham Road,
Gravesend, Kent DA11 0HN
Tel: 01474 533805
Headmistress: Ms Emma Wood
Age range: 3–11
No. of pupils: 120
Fees: Day £9,330
(🏃)

Bryony School
Marshall Road, Rainham,
Gillingham, Kent ME8 0AJ
Tel: 01634 231511
Joint Head: Mr D Edmunds
Age range: 2–11
No. of pupils: 168
Fees: Day £5,978–£6,511
(🏃)

CATS Canterbury
68 New Dover Road,
Canterbury, Kent CT1 3LQ
Tel: +44 (0)1227866540
Principal: Dr Sarah Lockyer
Age range: 14–18
No. of pupils: 400
(🌐)(16)(A)(庄)(IB)(16)

Chartfield School
45 Minster Road, Westgate
on Sea, Kent CT8 8DA
Tel: 01843 831716
Head & Proprietor: Miss L P Shipley
Age range: 4–11
No. of pupils: 50
Fees: Day £3,120–£3,450

Cobham Hall School
Cobham, Kent DA12 3BL
Tel: 01474 823371
Headmistress: Ms Maggie Roberts
Age range: G11–18
No. of pupils: 180

Cranbrook School
Waterloo Road, Cranbrook,
Kent TN17 3JD
Tel: 01580 711800
Head Teacher: Mr John Weeds
Age range: 13–18
No. of pupils: 757 VIth307
Fees: FB £13,362–£16,032

Derwent Lodge School for Girls
Somerhill, Tonbridge, Kent TN11 0NJ
Tel: 01732 352124
Head of School: Mrs Helen Hoffmann
Age range: G7–11
No. of pupils: 134
Fees: Day £15,465

Dover College
Effingham Crescent,
Dover, Kent CT17 9RH
Tel: 01304 205969
Headmaster: Mr Gareth
Doodes MA (Hons)
Age range: 3–18
No. of pupils: 301
Fees: Day £7,725–£16,050 WB
£21,000–£25,500 FB £24,750–£31,500

Dulwich Prep Cranbrook
Coursehorn, Cranbrook, Kent TN17 3NP
Tel: 01580 712179
Headmaster: Mr Paul David BEd(Hons)
Age range: 3–13
No. of pupils: 535
Fees: Day £5,970–£18,390

Elliott Park School
18-20 Marina Drive, Minster,
Sheerness, Kent ME12 2DP
Tel: 01795 873372
Head: Ms Colleen Hiller
Age range: 3–11
No. of pupils: 65
Fees: Day £5,431

Fosse Bank School
Mountains, Noble Tree
Road, Hildenborough,
Tonbridge, Kent TN11 8ND
Tel: 01732 834212
Headmistress: Miss Alison Cordingley
Age range: 3–11
No. of pupils: 124
Fees: Day £10,083–£12,543

Gad's Hill School
Higham, Rochester,
Medway, Kent ME3 7PA
Tel: 01474 822366
Headmaster: Mr Paul Savage
Age range: 3–16
No. of pupils: 370
Fees: Day £8,988–£12,504

Haddon Dene School
57 Gladstone Road,
Broadstairs, Kent CT10 2HY
Tel: 01843 861176
Head: Miss Alison Hatch
Age range: 3–11
No. of pupils: 200
Fees: Day £5,700–£7,230

Hilden Grange School
62 Dry Hill Park Road,
Tonbridge, Kent TN10 3BX
Tel: 01732 352706
Headmaster: Mr J Withers BA(Hons)
Age range: 3–13
No. of pupils: 311

Hilden Oaks School & Nursery
38 Dry Hill Park Road,
Tonbridge, Kent TN10 3BU
Tel: 01732 353941
Head of School: Mrs. K J M Joiner
Age range: 3 months–11
Fees: Day £8,985–£12,450

Holmewood House School
Barrow Lane, Langton Green,
Tunbridge Wells, Kent TN3 0EB
Tel: 01892 860000
Headmaster: Mr Scott Carnochan
Age range: 3–13
No. of pupils: 450

Kent College Junior School
Harbledown, Canterbury,
Kent CT2 9AQ
Tel: 01227 762436
Headmaster: Mr Andrew Carter
Age range: 0–11
No. of pupils: 202
Fees: Day £10,191–£16,332–£26,244

Kent College Pembury
Old Church Road, Pembury,
Tunbridge Wells, Kent TN2 4AX
Tel: +44 (0)1892 822006
Headmistress: Ms J Lodrick
Age range: G3–18
No. of pupils: 650 VIth102
Fees: Day £9,459–£20,571 WB
£25,710 FB £25,710–£32,778

KENT COLLEGE, CANTERBURY
For further details see p. 208
Whitstable Road, Canterbury,
Kent CT2 9DT
Tel: +44 (0)1227 763 231
Email: admissions@
kentcollege.co.uk
Website: www.kentcollege.com
Executive Head: Dr David Lamper
Age range: 0–18 years
(Boarding from 8)
No. of pupils: VIth200
Fees: Day £10,191–£18,864
FB £26,244–£35,628

**King's Preparatory
School, Rochester**
King Edward Road, Rochester,
Medway, Kent ME1 1UB
Tel: 01634 888577
Headmaster: Mr Tom Morgan
Age range: 8–13
No. of pupils: 220
Fees: Day £13,185–£14,955

**King's Pre-Preparatory
School, Rochester**
Chadlington House, Lockington
Grove, Rochester, Kent ME1 1RH
Tel: 01634 888566
Headmistress: Mrs C Openshaw
Age range: 3–8
No. of pupils: 149
Fees: Day £10,155–£11,010

KING'S ROCHESTER
For further details see p. 212
Satis House, Boley Hill,
Rochester, Kent ME1 1TE
Tel: 01634 888555
Email: admissions@kings-
rochester.co.uk
Website: www.kings-rochester.co.uk
Principal: Mr B Charles
Age range: 13–18
No. of pupils: 600 VIth95
Fees: Day £7,440–£20,190
FB £22,950–£33,015

Linton Park School
3 Eccleston Road, Tovil,
Maidstone, Kent ME17 4HT
Tel: 01622 740820
Headteacher: Kate Edwards
Age range: 7–18
No. of pupils: 134

Lorenden Preparatory School
Painter's Forstal, Faversham,
Kent ME13 0EN
Tel: 01795 590030
Headmistress: Mrs K Uttley
Age range: 3–11
No. of pupils: 120
Fees: Day £8,640–£12,540

Marlborough House School
High Street, Hawkhurst, Kent TN18 4PY
Tel: 01580 753555
Headmaster: Mr Martyn
Ward BEd (Hons)
Age range: 2–13
No. of pupils: 334
Fees: Day £8,730–£18,060

Meredale Independent Primary School
Solomon Road, Rainham,
Gillingham, Kent ME8 8EB
Tel: 01634 231405
Headteacher: Mrs Michelle Homer
Age range: 3–11
No. of pupils: 53
Fees: Day £6,945–£7,815
£ ✎

NORTHBOURNE PARK SCHOOL
For further details see p. 218
Betteshanger, Deal, Kent CT14 0NW
Tel: 01304 611215/218
Email: admissions@
northbournepark.com
Website:
www.northbournepark.com
Headmaster: Mr Sebastian
Rees BA(Hons), PGCE, NPQH
Age range: 3–13
No. of pupils: 181
Fees: Day £7,632–£17,007
WB £21,405 FB £24,786
🌐 ⚲ £ ✎

Radnor House, Sevenoaks
Combe Bank Drive,
Sevenoaks, Kent TN14 6AE
Tel: 01959 563720
Head: Mr David Paton
BComm (Hons) PGCE MA
Age range: 2½–18
No. of pupils: 250
Ⓐ £ ✎ 16+ 🐾

Rochester Independent College
254 St Margaret's Banks,
Rochester, Kent ME1 1HY
Tel: +44 (0)163 482 8115
Head of School: Mr Alistair Brownlow
Age range: 11–18
Fees: Day £13,000–£18,600
WB £12,400 FB £14,100
🌐 16+ ⚲

Rose Hill School
Coniston Avenue, Tunbridge
Wells, Kent TN4 9SY
Tel: 01892 525591
Head: Emma Neville
Age range: 3–13
Fees: Day £11,325–£15,225
£ ✎

Russell House School
Station Road, Otford,
Sevenoaks, Kent TN14 5QU
Tel: 01959 522352
Headmaster: Mr Craig McCarthy
Age range: 2–11
No. of pupils: 193

Sackville School
Tonbridge Rd, Hildenborough,
Tonbridge, Kent TN11 9HN
Tel: 01732 838888
Headmaster: Mr Justin Foster-Gandey BSc (hons)
Age range: 11–18
No. of pupils: 160 VIth29
Fees: Day £15,750
Ⓐ £ ✎ 16+ 🐾

Saint Ronan's School
Water Lane, Hawkhurst, Kent TN18 5DJ
Tel: 01580 752271
Headmaster: William Trelawny-Vernon BSc(Hons)
Age range: 3–13
No. of pupils: 300
Fees: Day £10,869–£18,624 FB £22,497
⚲ £ ✎

Sevenoaks Preparatory School
Godden Green, Sevenoaks,
Kent TN15 0JU
Tel: 01732 762336
Headmaster: Mr Luke Harrison
Age range: 2–13
No. of pupils: 388
Fees: Day £10,755–£14,865
£ ✎

Sevenoaks School
High Street, Sevenoaks, Kent TN13 1HU
Tel: +44 (0)1732 455133
Acting Head: Theresa
Homewood MA, DPhil
Age range: 11–18
No. of pupils: 1093
Fees: Day £24,291–£27,585
FB £38,790–£42,084
🌐 ⚲ £ ⒾⒷ ✎ 16+

Shernold School
Hill Place, Queens Avenue,
Maidstone, Kent ME16 0ER
Tel: 01622 752868
Head Teacher: Ms. Sandra
Dinsmore BA Hons. PGCE
Age range: 3–11
No. of pupils: 142
Fees: Day £7,245–£8,190
£

Solefield School
Solefield Road, Sevenoaks,
Kent TN13 1PH
Tel: 01732 452142
Headmaster: Mr D A Philps BSc(Hons)
Age range: B4–13
No. of pupils: 180
Fees: Day £12,600–£15,345
♂ ✎

Somerhill Pre-Prep
Somerhill, Five Oak Green Road,
Tonbridge, Kent TN11 0NJ
Tel: 01732 352124
**Principal of The Schools at
Somerhill:** Duncan Sinclair
Age range: 3–7
No. of pupils: 245
Fees: Day £10,050–£11,685

Spring Grove School
Harville Road, Wye, Ashford,
Kent TN25 5EZ
Tel: 01233 812337
Headmaster: Mr Bill Jones
Age range: 2–11
No. of pupils: 194
Fees: Day £9,000–£12,900
£ ✎

St Andrew's School
24-28 Watts Avenue, Rochester,
Medway, Kent ME1 1SA
Tel: 01634 843479
Principal: Mrs E Steinmann-Gilbert
Age range: 2–11
No. of pupils: 367
Fees: Day £7,725–£8,178
✎

St Edmund's Junior School
St Thomas Hill, Canterbury,
Kent CT2 8HU
Tel: 01227 475600
Head: Edward O'Connor
Age range: 3–13
No. of pupils: 230
Fees: Day £9,696–£16,101
WB £25,455 FB £27,933
⚲ ✎

St Edmund's School
St Thomas' Hill, Canterbury,
Kent CT2 8HU
Tel: 01227 475601
Head: Mr Edward O'Connor MA
(Cantab), MPhil (Ocon), MEd (Cantab)
Age range: 3–18
No. of pupils: 559
🌐 Ⓐ ⚲ £ ✎ 16+

St Faith's at Ash School
5 The Street, Ash, Canterbury,
Kent CT3 2HH
Tel: 01304 813409
Headmaster: Mr Lawrence Groves
Age range: 2–11
No. of pupils: 225
Fees: Day £5,415–£9,885
£ ✎

St Joseph's Convent Prep School
46 Old Road East, Gravesend,
Kent DA12 1NR
Tel: 01474 533012
Head Teacher: Miss D Buckley
Age range: 3–11
No. of pupils: 146
Fees: Day £8,580
✎

St Lawrence College
Ramsgate, Kent CT11 7AE
Tel: 01843 572931
Principal: Mr Antony Spencer
Age range: 3–18
No. of pupils: 640 VIth115
Fees: Day £7,470–£18,495
FB £26,055–£34,635
🌐 Ⓐ ⚲ £ ✎ 16+

St Michael's Preparatory School
Otford Court, Otford,
Sevenoaks, Kent TN14 5SA
Tel: 01959 522137
Headteacher: Mrs Jill Aisher
Age range: 2–13
No. of pupils: 472
Fees: Day £12,210–£14,835
£ ✎

Steephill School
Off Castle Hill, Fawkham,
Longfield, Kent DA3 7BG
Tel: 01474 702107
Head: Mrs Caroline Birtwell
BSc, MBA, PGCE
Age range: 3–11
No. of pupils: 131
Fees: Day £9,750
£ ✎

Sutton Valence Preparatory School
Chart Sutton, Maidstone, Kent ME17 3RF
Tel: 01622 842117
Head: Miss C Corkran
Age range: 3–11
No. of pupils: 320
Fees: Day £3,000–£4,610
✎

Sutton Valence School
North Street, Sutton Valence,
Kent ME17 3HL
Tel: 01622 845200
Headmaster: Bruce Grindlay MA
Cantab, MusB, FRCO, CHM
Age range: 11–18
No. of pupils: 570
🌐 Ⓐ ⚲ £ ✎ 16+

THE GRANVILLE SCHOOL
For further details see p. 236
2 Bradbourne Park Road,
Sevenoaks, Kent TN13 3LJ
Tel: 01732 453039
Email: secretary@
granvilleschool.org
Website: www.granvilleschool.org
Headmistress: Mrs Louise
Lawrance B. Prim. Ed. (Hons)
Age range: B3–4 G3–11

The Junior King's School, Canterbury
Milner Court, Sturry,
Canterbury, Kent CT2 0AY
Tel: 01227 714000
Head: Emma Károlyi
Age range: 3–13
Fees: Day £11,475–£19,290 FB £26,475

The King's School, Canterbury
The Precincts, Canterbury, Kent CT1 2ES
Tel: 01227 595501
Head: Mr Peter Roberts
Age range: 13–18
No. of pupils: 858 VIth385
Fees: Day £27,495 FB £38,955

The Mead School
16 Frant Road, Tunbridge
Wells, Kent TN2 5SN
Tel: 01892 525837
Headmaster: Mr Andrew Webster
Age range: 3–11
No. of pupils: 188
Fees: Day £4,536–£11,625

The New Beacon School
Brittains Lane, Sevenoaks,
Kent TN13 2PB
Tel: 01732 452131
Headmaster: Mr M Piercy BA(Hons)
Age range: B4–13
No. of pupils: 400
Fees: Day £11,400–£16,350

Tonbridge School
Tonbridge, Kent TN9 1JP
Tel: 01732 365555
Headmaster: Mr James Priory
Age range: B13–18
No. of pupils: 788

Walthamstow Hall Pre-Prep and Junior School
Sevenoaks, Kent TN13 3LD
Tel: 01732 451334
Headmistress: Miss S Ferro
Age range: G2 –11
No. of pupils: 218
Fees: Day £12,135–£15,300

Walthamstow Hall School
Sevenoaks, Kent TN13 3UL
Tel: 01732 451334
Headmistress: Miss S Ferro
Age range: G2 –18
No. of pupils: 500 VIth80

Wellesley House
114 Ramsgate Road,
Broadstairs, Kent CT10 2DG
Tel: 01843 862991
Headmaster: Mr G D Franklin
Age range: 7–13
No. of pupils: 133
Fees: Day £12,231–£19,917 FB £26,331

Yardley Court
Somerhill, Five Oak Green Road,
Tonbridge, Kent TN11 0NJ
Tel: 01732 352124
Headmaster: Duncan Sinclair
Age range: B7–13
No. of pupils: 260
Fees: Day £15,465

Surrey

Aberdour School
Brighton Road, Burgh Heath,
Tadworth, Surrey KT20 6AJ
Tel: 01737 354119
Headmaster: Mr S. D. Collins
Age range: 2–13 years
No. of pupils: 357
Fees: Day £1,500–£5,175

ACS Cobham International School
Heywood, Portsmouth Road,
Cobham, Surrey KT11 1BL
Tel: +44 (0) 1932 867251
Head of School: Mr Barnaby Sandow
Age range: 2–18
No. of pupils: 1460
Fees: Day £11,480–£27,650 WB
£39,590–£42,400 FB £45,060–£47,870

ACS Egham International School
Woodlee, London Road,
Egham, Surrey TW20 0HS
Tel: +44 (0) 1784 430 800
Head of School: Jeremy Lewis
Age range: 4–18
Fees: Day £11,090–£25,870

Aldro School
Shackleford, Godalming,
Surrey GU8 6AS
Tel: 01483 810266
Head: Mr and Mrs C P & L B Rose
Age range: B7–13
No. of pupils: 220
Fees: Day £17,544–£19,479
FB £23,346–£25,281

Amesbury
Hazel Grove, Hindhead,
Surrey GU26 6BL
Tel: 01428 604322
Head of School: Miss Sheina Wright
Age range: 2–13
No. of pupils: 360

Banstead Preparatory School
Sutton Lane, Banstead, Surrey SM7 3RA
Tel: 01737 363601
Headteacher: Miss Vicky Ellis
Age range: 2–11
No. of pupils: 225

Barfield School
Guildford Road, Runfold,
Farnham, Surrey GU10 1PB
Tel: 01252 782271
Head of School: James Reid BEd (Hons)
Age range: 2–13 years
No. of pupils: 170
Fees: Day £3,456–£14,895

Barrow Hills School
Roke Lane, Witley, Godalming,
Surrey GU8 5NY
Tel: +44 (0)1428 683639
Headmaster: Mr Philip Oldroyd
Age range: 2–13
No. of pupils: 223
Fees: Day £15,975

Belmont Preparatory School
Feldemore, Holmbury St Mary,
Dorking, Surrey RH5 6LQ
Tel: 01306 730852
Headmistress: Mrs Helen Skrine
BA, PGCE, NPQH, FRSA
Age range: 2–13
No. of pupils: 227
Fees: Day £9,390–£15,930
WB £22,215–£22,695

Bishopsgate School
Bishopsgate Road, Englefield
Green, Egham, Surrey TW20 0YJ
Tel: 01784 432109
Headmaster: Mr R Williams
Age range: 3–13
Fees: Day £5,580–£15,840

Box Hill School
Old London Road, Mickleham,
Dorking, Surrey RH5 6EA
Tel: 01372 373382
Headmaster: Mr Corydon Lowde
Age range: 11–18
No. of pupils: 425 VIth96
Fees: Day £17,985–£20,220 WB
£28,350–£29,595 FB £34,950–£36,450

Caterham School
Harestone Valley, Caterham,
Surrey CR3 6YA
Tel: 01883 343028
Head: Mr C. W. Jones MA(Cantab)
Age range: 11–18
No. of pupils: VIth321
Fees: Day £18,735–£19,620 WB
£30,936–£33,270 FB £36,795–£38,760

Charterhouse
Godalming, Surrey GU7 2DX
Tel: +44 (0)1483 291501
Headmaster: Dr Alex Peterken
Age range: B13–18 G16–18
No. of pupils: 810

Chinthurst School
Tadworth Street, Tadworth,
Surrey KT20 5QZ
Tel: 01737 812011
Head: Miss Catherine Trundle
Age range: B3–11
No. of pupils: 170
Fees: Day £11,010–£14,850

City of London Freemen's School
Ashtead Park, Ashtead, Surrey KT21 1ET
Tel: 01372 277933
Headmaster: Mr R Martin
Age range: 7–18
No. of pupils: 877 VIth213
Fees: Day £14,067–£19,194 WB
£29,784–£29,841 FB £30,780–£30,816

Claremont Fan Court School
Claremont Drive, Esher, Surrey KT10 9LY
Tel: 01372 467841
Head: Mr William Brierly
Age range: 2–18
No. of pupils: 840
Fees: Day £2,370–£18,375
(A) (£) (✎) (16+)

Coworth Flexlands School
Valley End, Chobham, Surrey GU24 8TE
Tel: 01276 855707
Head of School: Miss Nicola Cowell
Age range: B3–7 G3–11
No. of pupils: 135
(✎)

Cranleigh Preparatory School
Horseshoe Lane, Cranleigh,
Surrey GU6 8QH
Tel: 01483 274199
Headmaster: Mr Neil R Brooks BSc
Age range: 7–13
No. of pupils: 290
Fees: Day £16,062–£20,838 FB £25,164
(🏛)

CRANLEIGH SCHOOL
For further details see p. 194
Horseshoe Lane, Cranleigh,
Surrey GU6 8QQ
Tel: +44 (0) 1483 273666
Email: admissions@cranleigh.org
Website: www.cranleigh.org
Headmaster: Mr Martin
Reader MA, MPhil, MBA
Age range: 7–18 (including
Prep School)
No. of pupils: 654 VIth240
Fees: Day £32,370 FB £39,330
(🌐) (A) (🏛) (£) (✎) (16+)

Cranmore School
Epsom Road, West Horsley,
Surrey KT24 6AT
Tel: 01483 280340
Headmaster: Mr Michael
Connolly BSc, BA, MA, MEd
Age range: 2–13
No. of pupils: 420
Fees: Day £12,825–£15,300
(£) (✎)

Danes Hill School
Leatherhead Road, Oxshott,
Surrey KT22 0JG
Tel: 01372 842509
Headmaster: Mr W Murdock BA
Age range: 3–13
No. of pupils: 872
Fees: Day £14,421–£20,340
(£) (✎)

Danesfield Manor School
Rydens Avenue, Walton-on-
Thames, Surrey KT12 3JB
Tel: 01932 220930
Principal: Mrs Jo Smith
Age range: 2–11
No. of pupils: 170
Fees: Day £9,456–£10,098
(✎)

Downsend School
1 Leatherhead Road,
Leatherhead, Surrey KT22 8TJ
Tel: 01372 372197
Headmaster: Mr Ian Thorpe
Age range: 2–13
No. of pupils: 675
Fees: Day £13,230–£16,200
(✎)

**Downsend School
(Ashtead Pre-Prep)**
Ashtead Lodge, 22 Oakfield
Road, Ashtead, Surrey KT21 2RE
Tel: 01372 385439
Head Teacher: Tessa Roberts
Age range: 2–6
No. of pupils: 66
Fees: Day £11,535

**Downsend School
(Epsom Pre-Prep)**
Epsom Lodge, 6 Norman Avenue,
Epsom, Surrey KT17 3AB
Tel: 01372 385438
Head Teacher: Vanessa Conlan
Age range: 2–6
No. of pupils: 110
Fees: Day £11,535

**Downsend School
(Leatherhead Pre-Prep)**
Leatherhead Lodge, Epsom Road,
Leatherhead, Surrey KT22 8ST
Tel: 01372 385437
Headteacher: Mrs Gill Brooks
Age range: 2–6
No. of pupils: 106
Fees: Day £11,535

**Drayton House Pre-
School and Nursery**
35 Austen Road, Guildford,
Surrey GU1 3NP
Tel: 01483 504707
Headmistress: Mrs J Tyson-Jones
Froebel Cert.Ed. London University
Age range: 6 months–5 years
No. of pupils: 65
Fees: Day £4,420–£12,500
(✎)

Duke of Kent School
Peaslake Road, Ewhurst,
Surrey GU6 7NS
Tel: 01483 277313
Head: Mrs Sue Knox
Age range: 3–16
No. of pupils: 234
Fees: Day £7,245–£19,050
(🌐) (🏛) (£) (✎)

Dunottar School
High Trees Road, Reigate,
Surrey RH2 7EL
Tel: 01737 761945
Head of School: Mr Mark Tottman
Age range: 11–18
No. of pupils: 365
Fees: Day £17,055
(A) (£) (16+)

Edgeborough
Frensham, Farnham, Surrey GU10 3AH
Tel: 01252 792495
Headmaster: Mr Dan Thornburn
Age range: 2–13
No. of pupils: 285
Fees: Day £11,070–£17,970
(🏛) (£) (✎)

Emberhurst School
94 Ember Lane, Esher, Surrey KT10 8EN
Tel: 020 8398 2933
Headmistress: Mrs P Chadwick BEd
Age range: 2–7
No. of pupils: 70

Epsom College
Epsom, Surrey KT17 4JQ
Tel: 01372 821000
Headmaster: Mr Jay A Piggot MA
Age range: 11–18
No. of pupils: 884
Fees: Day £19,611–£26,151
WB £35,034 FB £38,568
(🌐) (A) (🏛) (£) (✎) (16+)

Essendene Lodge School
Essendene Road, Caterham,
Surrey CR3 5PB
Tel: 01883 348349
Head Teacher: Mrs K Ali
Age range: 2–11
No. of pupils: 153
Fees: Day £3,315–£7,305
(£) (✎)

Ewell Castle School
Church Street, Ewell, Epsom,
Surrey KT17 2AW
Tel: 020 8393 1413
Principal: Mr Silas Edmonds
Age range: 3–18
No. of pupils: 557
Fees: Day £5,175–£17,442
(A) (£) (✎) (16+)

FELTONFLEET SCHOOL
For further details see p. 200
Cobham, Surrey KT11 1DR
Tel: 01932 862264
Email: office@feltonfleet.co.uk
Website: www.feltonfleet.co.uk
Head of School: Mrs S Lance
Age range: 3–13
No. of pupils: 435
Fees: Day £12,315–£18,090
WB £18,090
(🏛) (£) (✎)

Focus School – Hindhead Campus
Tilford Road, Hindhead,
Surrey GU26 6SJ
Tel: 01428 601800
Consultant Head Teacher: Ms
Kim Popratnjak
Age range: 8–18
No. of pupils: 90

Frensham Heights
Rowledge, Farnham, Surrey GU10 4EA
Tel: 01252 792561
Head: Mr Rick Clarke
Age range: 3–18
No. of pupils: 497 VIth105
Fees: Day £7,110–£21,060
FB £27,450–£32,070
(🌐) (A) (🏛) (£) (✎) (16+)

Glenesk School
Ockham Road North, East
Horsley, Surrey KT24 6NS
Tel: 01483 282329
Headmistress: Mrs Sarah Bradley
Age range: 2–7
No. of pupils: 100
Fees: Day £11,658–£13,176
(£) (✎)

GORDON'S SCHOOL
For further details see p. 202
West End, Woking, Surrey GU24 9PT
Tel: 01276 858084
Email: registrar@gordons.school
Website: www.gordons.school
Head Teacher: Andrew Moss MEd
Age range: 11–18
No. of pupils: 836 VIth239
Fees: Day £5,994 WB
£16,698 FB £17,838
(A) (£) 16+

Greenfield School
Old Woking Road, Woking,
Surrey GU22 8HY
Tel: 01483 772525
Headmistress: Mrs Tania Botting BEd
Age range: 3–11
No. of pupils: 179
Fees: Day £5,976–£14,079
(£)

Guildford High School
London Road, Guildford,
Surrey GU1 1SJ
Tel: 01483 561440
Headmistress: Mrs F J Boulton BSc, MA
Age range: G4–18
No. of pupils: 980 VIth160
Fees: Day £11,052–£17,733
(A) (£) 16+

Hall Grove School
London Road, Bagshot,
Surrey GU19 5HZ
Tel: 01276 473059
Headmaster: Mr Alastair Graham
Age range: 3–13
No. of pupils: 430
Fees: Day £11,250–£15,450

Halstead Preparatory School
Woodham Rise, Woking,
Surrey GU21 4EE
Tel: 01483 772682
Headmistress: Mrs P Austin
Age range: G3–11
No. of pupils: 220
Fees: Day £10,800–£15,210
(£)

HAMPTON COURT HOUSE
For further details see p. 204
Hampton Court Road, East
Molesey, Surrey KT8 9BS
Tel: 020 8614 0857
Email: admissions@hchnet.co.uk
Website:
www.hamptoncourthouse.co.uk
Headmaster: Mr Guy Holloway
Age range: 3–18
(A)

HawleyHurst School
Fernhill Road, Blackwater,
Camberley, Surrey GU17 9HU
Tel: 01276 587190
Head Teacher: Miss V S Smit
Age range: 2–19
(£)

Hazelwood School
Wolf's Hill, Limpsfield, Oxted,
Surrey RH8 0QU
Tel: 01883 712194
Head: Mrs Lindie Louw
Age range: 2–13
No. of pupils: 399
Fees: Day £10,275–£16,380
(£)

Hoe Bridge School
Hoe Place, Old Woking Road,
Woking, Surrey GU22 8JE
Tel: 01483 760018 & 01483 772194
Headmaster: Mr C Webster
MA BSc (Hons) PGCE
Age range: 3–13
No. of pupils: 460
Fees: Day £5,940–£15,885
(£)

Hurtwood House
Holmbury St Mary, Dorking,
Surrey RH5 6NU
Tel: 01483 279000
Principal: Mr Cosmo Jackson
Age range: 16–18
No. of pupils: 300
Fees: Day £29,748 FB £44,622
16+ (A)

ISL Surrey Primary School
Old Woking Road, Woking,
Surrey GU22 8HY
Tel: +44 (0)1483 750409
Principal: Richard Parker
Age range: 2–11 years
No. of pupils: 100
Fees: Day £10,450–£15,500
(£)

King Edward's Witley
Godalming, Surrey GU8 5SG
Tel: +44 (0)1428 686700
Headmaster: Mr John Attwater MA
Age range: 11–18
No. of pupils: 400
Fees: Day £15,975–£21,285
FB £32,775–£34,050
(A) (£) (IB) 16+

Kingswood House School
56 West Hill, Epsom, Surrey KT19 8LG
Tel: 01372 723590
Headmaster: Mr Duncan
Murphy BA (Hons), MEd, FRSA
Age range: B4–16
No. of pupils: 210
(£)

Lanesborough
Maori Road, Guildford, Surrey GU1 2EL
Tel: 01483 880650
Head: Mrs Clare Turnbull BA(Hons) MEd
Age range: B3–13
No. of pupils: 350
Fees: Day £10,890–£15,270
(£)

Lingfield College
Racecourse Road, Lingfield,
Surrey RH7 6PH
Tel: 01342 833176
Headmaster: Mr R Bool B.A. Hons, MBA
Age range: 2–18
No. of pupils: 935
Fees: Day £11,250–£21,801
(A) (£) 16+

Longacre School
Hullbrook Lane, Shamley Green,
Guildford, Surrey GU5 0NQ
Tel: 01483 893225
Head of School: Mr Matthew Bryan
MA(Cantab.), MA(Oxon.), MSc, FRSA
Age range: 2–11
No. of pupils: 267
Fees: Day £10,290–£15,300
(£)

Lyndhurst School
36 The Avenue, Camberley,
Surrey GU15 3NE
Tel: 01276 22895
Head: Mr A Rudkin BEd(Hons)
Age range: 2–11
Fees: Day £9,300–£12,675
(£)

MANOR HOUSE SCHOOL, BOOKHAM
For further details see p. 216
Manor House Lane, Little Bookham,
Leatherhead, Surrey KT23 4EN
Tel: 01372 457077
Email: admin@
manorhouseschool.org
Website:
www.manorhouseschool.org
Headteacher: Ms Tracey
Fantham BA (Hons) MA NPQH
Age range: B2–4 G2–16
No. of pupils: 300
Fees: Day £9,555–£17,955
(£)

Micklefield School
10/12 Somers Road, Reigate,
Surrey RH2 9DU
Tel: 01737 224212
Head: Mr R Ardé
Age range: 3–11
No. of pupils: 272
Fees: Day £3,465–£13,125

Milbourne Lodge School
Arbrook Lane, Esher, Surrey KT10 9EG
Tel: 01372 462737
Head: Mrs Judy Waite
Age range: 4–13
No. of pupils: 283
Fees: Day £12,855–£16,155
(£)

Notre Dame School
Cobham, Surrey KT11 1HA
Tel: 01932 869990
Head of Seniors: Mrs Anna King
MEd, MA (Cantab), PGCE
Age range: 2–18
No. of pupils: 600
(A) (£) 16+

Oakhyrst Grange School
160 Stanstead Road,
Caterham, Surrey CR3 6AF
Tel: 01883 343344
Headmaster: Mr Alex Gear
Age range: 4–11 years
No. of pupils: 155

Parkside School
The Manor, Stoke d'Abernon,
Cobham, Surrey KT11 3PX
Tel: 01932 862749
Head: Nicole Janssen
Age range: B2–13 G2–4
No. of pupils: 382
Fees: Day £12,471–£17,109

Prior's Field
Priorsfield Road, Godalming,
Surrey GU7 2RH
Tel: 01483 810551
Age range: G11–18
No. of pupils: 450
Fees: Day £18,900 FB £30,825
(A) (£) 16+

Reed's School
Sandy Lane, Cobham, Surrey KT11 2ES
Tel: 01932 869001
Headmaster: Mr Mark
Hoskins BA MA MSc
Age range: B11–18 G16–18
No. of pupils: 650 VIth230
Fees: Day £20,430–£25,530
FB £27,225–£32,910

Reigate Grammar School
Reigate Road, Reigate, Surrey RH2 0QS
Tel: 01737 222231
Headmaster: Mr Shaun Fenton
MA (Oxon) MEd (Oxon)
Age range: 11–18
No. of pupils: 969 VIth262
Fees: Day £19,140–£19,350

**Reigate St Mary's Prep
& Choir School**
Chart Lane, Reigate, Surrey RH2 7RN
Tel: 01737 244880
Headmaster: Mr Marcus Culverwell MA
Age range: 3–11
No. of pupils: 350
Fees: Day £12,360–£15,300

Ripley Court School
Rose Lane, Ripley, Surrey GU23 6NE
Tel: 01483 225217
Acting Head: Mr Gavin Ryan
Age range: 3–13
No. of pupils: 281
Fees: Day £10,020–£15,300

Rowan Preparatory School
6 Fitzalan Road, Claygate,
Surrey KT10 0LX
Tel: 01372 462627
Headmistress: Mrs Susan
Clarke BEd, NPQH
Age range: G2–11
No. of pupils: 317
Fees: Day £11,526–£15,294

**Royal Alexandra and
Albert School**
Gatton Park, Reigate, Surrey RH2 0TD
Tel: 01737 649 000
Headmaster: Mr Mark Dixon
Age range: 7–18 years
No. of pupils: 1000 VIth200
Fees: FB £15,750

Royal Grammar School, Guildford
High Street, Guildford, Surrey GU1 3BB
Tel: 01483 880600
Headmaster: Dr J M Cox BSc, PhD
Age range: B11–18
No. of pupils: 940
Fees: Day £19,035

Rydes Hill Preparatory School
Rydes Hill House, Aldershot Road,
Guildford, Surrey GU2 8BP
Tel: 01483 563160
Headmistress: Mrs Sarah Norville
Age range: B3–7 G3–11
No. of pupils: 180

Shrewsbury Lodge School
22 Milbourne Lane, Esher,
Surrey KT10 9EA
Tel: 01372 462781
Head: Mr Jon Akhurst BA (Hons) PGCE
Age range: 3–7
Fees: Day £6,225–£13,740

SIR WILLIAM PERKINS'S SCHOOL
For further details see p. 224
Guildford Road, Chertsey,
Surrey KT16 9BN
Tel: 01932 574900
Email: office@swps.org.uk
Website: www.swps.org.uk
Head: Mr C C Muller
Age range: G11–18 years
No. of pupils: 600
Fees: Day £5,618

ST CATHERINE'S, BRAMLEY
For further details see p. 226
Station Road, Bramley,
Guildford, Surrey GU5 0DF
Tel: 01483 899609
Email: admissions@stcatherines.info
Website: www.stcatherines.info
Headmistress: Alice Phillips
Age range: G4–18
Fees: Day £9,240–£18,885 FB £30,285

St Christopher's School
6 Downs Road, Epsom, Surrey KT18 5HE
Tel: 01372 721807
Headteacher: Mrs A C
Thackray MA, BA(Hons)
Age range: 3–7
No. of pupils: 137
Fees: Day £10,485

St Edmund's School
Portsmouth Road, Hindhead,
Surrey GU26 6BH
Tel: 01428 604808
Headmaster: Mr A J Walliker
MA(Cantab), MBA, PGCE
Age range: 2–16
No. of pupils: 410
Fees: Day £9,585–£16,746

St George's College
Weybridge Road, Addlestone,
Weybridge, Surrey KT15 2QS
Tel: 01932 839300
Headmistress: Mrs Rachel Owens
Age range: 11–18
No. of pupils: 909 VIth250
Fees: Day £17,655–£20,100

St George's Junior School
Thames Street, Weybridge,
Surrey KT13 8NL
Tel: 01932 839400
Head Master: Mr Antony Hudson
MA (CANTAB), PGCE, NPQH
Age range: 3–11 years
No. of pupils: 644
Fees: Day £5,640–£14,640

St Hilary's School
Holloway Hill, Godalming,
Surrey GU7 1RZ
Tel: 01483 416551
Headmistress: Mrs Jane Whittingham
BEdCert, ProfPracSpLD
Age range: B2–11 G2–11
No. of pupils: 250
Fees: Day £10,092–£14,850

St Ives School
Three Gates Lane, Haslemere,
Surrey GU27 2ES
Tel: 01428 643734
Headteacher: Kay Goldsworthy
Age range: 2–11
No. of pupils: 149
Fees: Day £9,900–£13,950

St John's School
Epsom Road, Leatherhead,
Surrey KT22 8SP
Tel: 01372 373000
Head of School: Mrs Rowena Cole
Age range: 11–18
No. of pupils: 761
Fees: Day £19,590–£24,555
WB £24,780–£31,035

**St Teresa's Effingham
(Preparatory School)**
Effingham, Surrey RH5 6ST
Tel: 01372 453456
Headmaster: Mr. Mike Farmer
Age range: B2–4 G2–11
No. of pupils: 100
Fees: Day £1,185–£14,685
WB £25,515 FB £28,665

**St Teresa's Effingham
(Senior School)**
Beech Avenue, Effingham,
Surrey RH5 6ST
Tel: 01372 452037
Executive Director: Mr Mike Farmer
Age range: G11–18
No. of pupils: 640 VIth90
Fees: Day £17,865–£18,465 WB
£28,875–£29,175 FB £30,795–£31,455

ST. ANDREW'S SCHOOL
For further details see p. 232
Church Hill House, Horsell,
Woking, Surrey GU21 4QW
Tel: 01483 760943
Email: admin@st-andrews.
woking.sch.uk
Website:
www.st-andrews.woking.sch.uk
Headmaster: Mr A Perks
Age range: 3–13
No. of pupils: 315
Fees: Day £6,555–£15,495

Surbiton Preparatory School
3 Avenue Elmers, Surbiton,
Surrey KT6 4SP
Tel: 020 8390 6640
Principal: Mrs Rebecca Glover
Age range: B4–11 G4–11
No. of pupils: 135
Fees: Day £10,857–£13,974

**TASIS The American
School in England**
Coldharbour Lane, Thorpe,
Surrey TW20 8TE
Tel: +44 (0)1932 582316
Head of School: Mr Bryan Nixon
Age range: 3–18
No. of pupils: 620
Fees: Day £11,570–£24,620 FB £45,300

The Hawthorns School
Pendell Court, Bletchingley,
Redhill, Surrey RH1 4QJ
Tel: 01883 743048
Head of School: Mr Adrian Floyd
Age range: 2–13
No. of pupils: 520
Fees: Day £10,680–£15,780
£ 🖊

The Royal Junior School
Portsmouth Road, Hindhead,
Surrey GU26 6BW
Tel: 01428 607977
Principal: Mrs Anne J P Lynch
Age range: 6 weeks–11 years
Fees: Day £10,200–£11,955
🌐

The Royal School
Farnham Lane, Haslemere,
Surrey GU27 1HQ
Tel: 01428 605805
Principal: Mrs Anne Lynch
BA (Hons), PGCE, FRSA
Age range: 11–18 years
Fees: Day £17,925–£18,144 WB
£26,895–£27,114 FB £30,600–£30,819
🌐 Ⓐ 🏛 £ 🖊 16+

Tormead School
27 Cranley Road, Guildford,
Surrey GU1 2JD
Tel: 01483 575101
Headmistress: Mrs Christina Foord
Age range: G4–18
No. of pupils: 760 VIth120
Fees: Day £8,385–£15,915
🏃 Ⓐ 🏛 £ 🖊 16+

Warlingham Park School
Chelsham Common,
Warlingham, Surrey CR6 9PB
Tel: 01883 626844
Headmaster: Mrs S S Buist
Age range: 2–11
No. of pupils: 96
Fees: Day £4,230–£8,565
🖊

Weston Green School
Weston Green Road, Thames
Ditton, Surrey KT7 0JN
Tel: 020 8398 2778
Head: Mrs Sarah Evans
Age range: 4–11
Fees: Day £10,164–£11,427
🖊

Westward School
47 Hersham Road, Walton-on-
Thames, Surrey KT12 1LE
Tel: 01932 220911
Headmistress: Mrs Shelley Stevenson
Age range: 3–12
No. of pupils: 140
Fees: Day £7,380–£8,235
£ 🖊

Woldingham School
Marden Park, Woldingham,
Surrey CR3 7YA
Tel: 01883 349431
Headmistress: Mrs Alex Hutchinson
Age range: G11–18
No. of pupils: 530 VIth150
Fees: Day £21,300–£23,220
FB £34,740–£37,815
🏛 🌐 Ⓐ 🏛 £ 🖊 16+

Woodcote House School
Snows Ride, Windlesham,
Surrey GU20 6PF
Tel: 01276 472115
Headmaster: Mr D.M.K. Paterson
Age range: B7–13
No. of pupils: 100
Fees: Day £18,300 FB £24,600
🏛 🏛 £ 🖊

Yehudi Menuhin School
Stoke Road, Stoke d'Abernon,
Cobham, Surrey KT11 3QQ
Tel: 01932 864739
Interim Head: Richard Tanner
Age range: 7–19
No. of pupils: 80 VIth36
Fees: FB £34,299
🌐 Ⓐ 🏛 £ 🖊 16+

West Sussex

Ardingly College
College Road, Ardingly, Haywards
Heath, West Sussex RH17 6SQ
Tel: +44 (0)1444 893320
Headmaster: Mr Ben Figgis
Age range: 13–18
No. of pupils: 559
Fees:–£23,985 FB £35,865–£29,250
🌐 Ⓐ 🏛 £ IB 🖊 16+

Ardingly College Preparatory School
Haywards Heath, West Sussex RH17 6SQ
Tel: 01444 893200
Headmaster: Mr Harry Hastings
Age range: 2–13
Fees: Day £9,195–£15,750
🏛 £ 🖊

Ashton Park School
Brinsbury Campus East, Stane
Street, North Heath, Pulborough,
West Sussex RH20 1DJ
Tel: 01798 875836
Head: Mr G Holding
Age range: 11–16
No. of pupils: 66

Brambletye
Brambletye, East Grinstead,
West Sussex RH19 3PD
Tel: 01342 321004
Headmaster: Will Brooks
Age range: 2–13
No. of pupils: 280
Fees: Day £10,050–£21,660
FB £25,815–£26,415
🏛 £ 🖊

BURGESS HILL GIRLS
For further details see p. 190
Keymer Road, Burgess Hill,
West Sussex RH15 0EG
Tel: 01444 241050
Email: admissions@
burgesshillgirls.com
Website: burgesshillgirls.com
Head of School: Liz Laybourn
Age range: B2½–4 G2½–18
No. of pupils: 505 VIth70
Fees: Day £8,100–£20,100
FB £31,050–£35,850
🏛 🌐 Ⓐ 🏛 £ 🖊 16+

Christ's Hospital
Horsham, West Sussex RH13 0LJ
Tel: 01403 211293
Head Teacher: Mr Simon Reid
Age range: 11–18
No. of pupils: 900
Fees: Day £18,510–£23,310 FB £35,850
🌐 Ⓐ 🏛 £ IB 16+

Conifers School
Egmont Road, Midhurst,
West Sussex GU29 9BG
Tel: 01730 813243
Headmistress: Mrs Emma Smyth
Age range: 2–13
No. of pupils: 104
Fees: Day £7,350–£9,750
£ 🖊

Copthorne Prep School
Effingham Lane, Copthorne,
West Sussex RH10 3HR
Tel: 01342 712311
Headmaster: Mr Chris Jones
Age range: 2–13
No. of pupils: 340
Fees: Day £9,750–£16,740
WB £20,400 FB £25,500
🏛 £ 🖊

Cottesmore School
Buchan Hill, Pease Pottage,
West Sussex RH11 9AU
Tel: 01293 520648
Head: T F Rogerson
Age range: 4–13
No. of pupils: 170
Fees: Day £3,199–£4,267 FB £9,095
🏛 £ 🖊

Cumnor House Sussex
London Road, Danehill, Haywards
Heath, West Sussex RH17 7HT
Tel: 01825 792 006
Headmaster: Christian Heinrich
Age range: 2–13
No. of pupils: 385
Fees: Day £8,985–£19,530
WB £22,635 FB £23,250
🏛 £ 🖊

Dorset House School
The Manor, Church Lane, Bury,
Pulborough, West Sussex RH20 1PB
Tel: 01798 831456
Headmaster: Matt Thomas
Age range: 3–13
No. of pupils: 135
Fees: Day £8,550–£17,850
🏛 £ 🖊

Farlington School
Strood Park, Horsham,
West Sussex RH12 3PN
Tel: 01403 282573
Headmistress: Ms Louise
Higson BSc, PGCE
Age range: B4–6 G3–18
No. of pupils: 300
Fees: Day £5,400–£17,670 WB
£23,205–£28,515 FB £24,540–£29,850
🏃 🌐 Ⓐ 🏛 £ 🖊 16+

Great Ballard School
Eartham House, Eartham, Nr
Chichester, West Sussex PO18 0LR
Tel: 01243 814236
Head: Mr Richard Evans
Age range: 2–13
No. of pupils: 136
Fees: Day £8,580–£15,930 WB £17,010
🏛 £ 🖊

Great Walstead School
East Mascalls Lane, Lindfield,
Haywards Heath, West Sussex RH16 2QL
Tel: 01444 483528
Headmaster: Mr Chris Calvey
Age range: 2½–13
No. of pupils: 465
Fees: Day £11,055–£15,510

Handcross Park School
Handcross, Haywards Heath,
West Sussex RH17 6HF
Tel: 01444 400526
Headmaster: Mr Richard Brown
Age range: 2–13
No. of pupils: 339
Fees: Day £3,230–£6,360 WB
£5,370–£7,480 FB £6,030–£8,130

Hurstpierpoint College
College Lane, Hurstpierpoint,
West Sussex BN6 9JS
Tel: 01273 833636
Headmaster: Mr. T J Manly BA, MSc
Age range: 4–18
No. of pupils: 1156
Fees: Day £8,790–£22,860 WB £28,800

**Hurstpierpoint College
Prep School**
Hurstpierpoint, West Sussex BN6 9JS
Tel: 01273 834975
Head: Mr I D Pattison BSc
Age range: 4–13
No. of pupils: 360

Lancing College
Lancing, West Sussex BN15 0RW
Tel: 01273 465805
Head Master: Mr Dominic T Oliver MPhil
Age range: 13–18
No. of pupils: 550 VIth255
Fees: Day £8,190 FB £11,995

**Lancing College Preparatory
School at Worthing**
Broadwater Road, Worthing,
West Sussex BN14 8HU
Tel: 01903 201123
Head: Mrs Heather Beeby
Age range: 2–13
No. of pupils: 165
Fees: Day £8,115–£11,460

Oakwood Preparatory School
Chichester, West Sussex PO18 9AN
Tel: 01243 575209
Headteacher: Mrs Clare Bradbury
Age range: 2½–11
No. of pupils: 260
Fees: Day £1,715–£5,010

Our Lady of Sion School
Gratwicke Road, Worthing,
West Sussex BN11 4BL
Tel: 01903 204063
Headmaster: Dr Simon Orchard
Age range: 3–18
No. of pupils: 410
Fees: Day £8,640–£13,575

Pennthorpe School
Church Street, Horsham,
West Sussex RH12 3HJ
Tel: 01403 822391
Headmistress: Alexia Bolton
Age range: 2–13
No. of pupils: 362
Fees: Day £2,070–£16,605

Rikkyo School in England
Guildford Road, Rudgwick,
Horsham, West Sussex RH12 3BE
Tel: 01403 822107
Headmaster: Mr Roger Munechika
Age range: 10–18
No. of pupils: 116
Fees: FB £15,000–£21,600

SEAFORD COLLEGE
For further details see p. 220
Lavington Park, Petworth,
West Sussex GU28 0NB
Tel: 01798 867392
Email: headmasterpa@seaford.org
Website: www.seaford.org
Headmaster: J P Green MA BA
Age range: 6–18
No. of pupils: 842 VIth230
Fees: Day £10,725–£22,230 WB
£22,250–£30,120 FB £34,380

Shoreham College
St Julians Lane, Shoreham-by-
Sea, West Sussex BN43 6YW
Tel: 01273 592681
Headmaster: Mr R Taylor-West
Age range: 3–16 years
No. of pupils: 375
Fees: Day £9,750–£15,150

Slindon College
Slindon House, Slindon, Arundel,
West Sussex BN18 0RH
Tel: 01243 814320
Head Teacher: Mr Mark Birkbeck
Age range: B8–18 years
No. of pupils: 80 VIth17
Fees: Day £21,795 FB £32,280

**Sompting Abbotts Preparatory
School for Boys and Girls**
Church Lane, Sompting,
West Sussex BN15 0AZ
Tel: 01903 235960
Principal: Mrs P M Sinclair
Age range: 2–13
No. of pupils: 185
Fees: Day £9,195–£11,805

Steyning Grammar School
Shooting Field, Steyning,
West Sussex BN44 3RX
Tel: +44 (0)1903 814555
Headteacher: Mr Nick Wergan
Age range: 11–18
No. of pupils: 1975
Fees: WB £9,100 FB £11,100

The Prebendal School
52-55 West Street, Chichester,
West Sussex PO19 1RT
Tel: 01243 772220
Headteacher: Mrs L Salmond Smith
Age range: 3–13
No. of pupils: 181
Fees: Day £8,160–£15,495 WB
£18,975–£20,100 FB £22,290

The Towers Convent School
Convent of the Blessed Sacrement,
Henfield Road, Upper Beeding,
Steyning, West Sussex BN44 3TF
Tel: 01903 812185
Headmistress: Mrs Clare Trelfa
Age range: B4–11 G4–16
No. of pupils: 320
Fees: Day £8,190–£11,550

Westbourne House School
Shopwyke, Chichester,
West Sussex PO20 2BH
Tel: 01243 782739
Headmaster: Mr Martin Barker
Age range: 2½–13 years
No. of pupils: 420
Fees: Day £10,440–£17,985
FB £21,465–£24,105

**Willow Tree Montessori
Kindergarten**
Charlwood House, Charlwood
Road, Lowfield Heath, Crawley,
West Sussex RH11 0QA
Tel: 01293 820721
Headmistress: Mrs G Kerfante MontDip
Age range: 1–8
Fees: Day £2,310–£2,700

Windlesham House School
London Road, Washington,
Pulborough, West Sussex RH20 4AY
Tel: 01903 874701
Headmaster: Mr Richard
Foster BEd(Hons)
Age range: 4–13
No. of pupils: 340

Worth School
Paddockhurst Road, Turners Hill,
Crawley, West Sussex RH10 4SD
Tel: +44 (0)1342 710200
Head Master: Stuart McPherson
Age range: 11–18
No. of pupils: 580 VIth222
Fees: Day £15,960–£23,730
FB £21,210–£33,690

South-West

KEY TO SYMBOLS

- ⚊ Boys' school
- ⚊ Girls' school
- 🌐 International school
- 16 Tutorial or sixth form college
- Ⓐ A levels
- ⚓ Boarding accommodation
- £ Bursaries
- IB International Baccalaureate
- Learning support
- 16 Entrance at 16+
- Vocational qualifications
- IAPS Independent Association of Preparatory Schools
- HMC The Headmasters' & Headmistresses' Conference
- ISA Independent Schools Association
- GSA Girls' School Association
- BSA Boarding Schools' Association
- S Society of Heads

Unless otherwise indicated, all schools are coeducational day schools.
Single-sex and boarding schools will be indicated by the relevant icon.

Cornwall

Polwhele House School
Truro, Cornwall TR4 9AE
Tel: 01872 273011
Headmaster: Mr Alex McCullough
Age range: 3–13
No. of pupils: 100
Fees: Day £8,820–£13,620
⊞ £ ✎

St Joseph's School
15 St Stephen's Hill, Launceston,
Cornwall PL15 8HN
Tel: 01566 772580
Head Teacher: Mr Oliver Scott
Age range: 4–16
No. of pupils: 215
Fees: Day £5,490–£13,875
£ ✎

St Petroc's School
Ocean View Road, Bude,
Cornwall EX23 8NJ
Tel: 01288 352876
Headmaster: Mr Hilton
Age range: 0–11
Fees: Day £5,850–£8,850
£ ✎

St. Piran's School
14 Trelissick Road, Hayle,
Cornwall TR27 4HY
Tel: 01736 752612
Headteacher: Mrs Carol de
Labat BEd(Hons), CertEd
Age range: 4–16
Fees: Day £2,775–£7,080
£ ✎

The Valley Nursery
Trevowah Road, Crantock,
Newquay, Cornwall TR8 5RU
Tel: 01637 830680
Principal: Kerry Wilson
Age range: 3 months–5 years
£ ✎

Truro High School for Girls
Falmouth Road, Truro, Cornwall TR1 2HU
Tel: 01872 272830
Headmaster: Glenn Moodie
Age range: B3–5 G3–18
No. of pupils: 432 VIth60
Fees: Day £8,001–£13,896 WB
£25,185–£26,040 FB £27,261–£28,182
🏃 Ⓐ ⊞ £ ✎ ⑯

Truro School
Trennick Lane, Truro, Cornwall TR1 1TH
Tel: 01872 272763
Headmaster: Mr A S Gordon-
Brown BCom, MSc, CA (SA)
Age range: 3–18
No. of pupils: 780 VIth210
🌐 Ⓐ ⊞ £ ✎ ⑯

Devon

Abbey School
Hampton Court, St Marychurch,
Torquay, Devon TQ1 4PR
Tel: 01803 327868
Principal: Mrs Sylvia Greinig
Age range: 0–11 years
No. of pupils: 78
✎

Blundell's Preparatory School
Milestones House, Blundell's Road,
Tiverton, Devon EX16 4NA
Tel: 01884 252393
Head Master: Mr Andrew
Southgate BA Ed (Hons)
Age range: 2–11
No. of pupils: 220
Fees: Day £5,880–£12,195

Blundell's School
Tiverton, Devon EX16 4DN
Tel: 01884 252543
Head: Mr Bart Wielenga BComm,
Natal & Johannesburg, BEd
Age range: 11–18
No. of pupils: 604 VIth198
Fees: Day £14,130–£22,410 WB
£21,570–£30,660 FB £24,060–£35,205
🌐 Ⓐ ⊞ £ ✎ ⑯

Bramdean School
Richmond Lodge, Homefield Road,
Heavitree, Exeter, Devon EX1 2QR
Tel: 01392 273387
Head: Miss Diane Stoneman NAHT
Age range: 3–18
No. of pupils: 180 VIth12
Fees: Day £6,204–£11,490
🌐 Ⓐ £

EF Academy Torbay
Castle Road, Torquay, Devon TQ1 3BG
Tel: +41 (0) 43 430 4095
Head of School: Mr. Mark Howe
Age range: 14–19
No. of pupils: 300
🌐 ⑯ Ⓐ ⊞ IB

EXETER CATHEDRAL SCHOOL
For further details see p. 246
The Chantry, Palace Gate,
Exeter, Devon EX1 1HX
Tel: 01392 255298
Email: admissions@exetercs.org
Website:
www.exetercathedralschool.co.uk
Headmaster: James Featherstone
Age range: 21/2–13
No. of pupils: 255
Fees: Day £7,338–£12,234
FB £18,768–£19,866
⊞ £ ✎

Exeter School
Victoria Park Road, Exeter,
Devon EX2 4NS
Tel: 01392 273679
Headmaster: Mr Bob Griffin
Age range: 7–18
No. of pupils: 924
Fees: Day £12,525–£14,025
Ⓐ £ ✎ ⑯

Exeter Tutorial College
44/46 Magdalen Road,
Exeter, Devon EX2 4TE
Tel: 01392 278101
Principal: K D Jack BA, DipEd
Age range: 16+
No. of pupils: 75
⑯ Ⓐ

Fletewood School
88 North Road East, Plymouth,
Devon PL4 6AN
Tel: 01752 663782
Headteacher: Mrs R Gray
Age range: 3–11
No. of pupils: 70
Fees: Day £4,425

King's School
Hartley Road, Mannamead,
Plymouth, Devon PL3 5LW
Tel: 01752 771789
Headteacher: Mrs Jane Lee
Age range: 3–11
No. of pupils: 142
Fees: Day £5,895–£7,440
✎

KINGSLEY SCHOOL
For further details see p. 248
Northdown Road, Bideford,
Devon EX39 3LY
Tel: 01237 426200
Email: admissions@
kingsleyschoolbideford.co.uk
Website:
www.kingsleyschoolbideford.co.uk
Headmaster: Mr Pete Last
Age range: 0–18
No. of pupils: 395
Fees: Day £2,020 WB £5,695 FB £7,685
🌐 Ⓐ ⊞ £ ✎ ⑯ 🐾

Magdalen Court School
Mulberry House, Victoria Park
Road, Exeter, Devon EX2 4NU
Tel: 01392 494919
Head: Mrs Sarah Wrightson
Age range: 0–18+
No. of pupils: 150 VIth20
Fees: Day £5,670–£10,200
Ⓐ £ ✎ ⑯ 🐾

Mount Kelly
Parkwood Road, Tavistock,
Devon PL19 0HZ
Tel: +44 (0)1822 813100
Head of School: Mr. Guy Ayling
Age range: 3–18
No. of pupils: 600
Fees: Day £7,410–£18,000 WB
£17,641–£29,280 FB £19,500–£32,490
🌐 Ⓐ ⊞ £ ✎ ⑯

Park School
Park Road, Dartington,
Totnes, Devon TQ9 6EQ
Tel: 01803 864588
Teacher-in-charge: Amanda Bellamy
Age range: 3–12
Fees: Day £6,147–£9,654

Plymouth College
Ford Park, Plymouth, Devon PL4 6RN
Tel: +44 (0)1752 505100
Headmaster: Mr. Jonathan Standen
Age range: 3–18
No. of pupils: 501 VIth163
Fees: Day £7,680–£16,290
FB £27,435–£31,440

Plymouth College Preparatory School
St Dunstan's Abbey, The Millfields,
Plymouth, Devon PL1 3JL
Tel: 01752 201352
Headmaster: Chris Gatherer
Age range: 3–11
No. of pupils: 310
Fees: Day £7,680–£10,605

Sands School
Greylands, 48 East Street,
Ashburton, Devon TQ13 7AX
Tel: 01364 653666
Administrator: Sean Bellamy
MA(Cantab), PGCE
Age range: 11–16
Fees: Day £10,710

Shebbear College
Shebbear, Beaworthy, Devon EX21 5HJ
Tel: 01409 282000
Headmaster: Mr S. D. Weale MA (Oxon)
Age range: 3–18
No. of pupils: 350 VIth78
Fees: Day £5,235–£12,975 WB
£14,250–£14,985 FB £18,750–£26,325

South Devon Steiner School
Hood Manor, Buckfastleigh Road,
Dartington, Totnes, Devon TQ9 6AB
Tel: 01803 897 377
Education Manager: Jeff van Zyl
Age range: 3–19
No. of pupils: 307

St Christopher's Preparatory School
Mount Barton, Staverton,
Devon TQ9 6PF
Tel: 01803 762202
Headmistress: Alexandra Cottell
Age range: 3–11
No. of pupils: 100
Fees: Day £7,350–£9,900

St John's International School
Broadway, Sidmouth, Devon EX10 8RG
Tel: 01395 513984
Headmistress: Mrs Caroline Ward
Age range: 2–16
No. of pupils: 200
Fees: Day £6,906–£11,403
FB £19,422–£21,291

St Peter's School
Harefield, Lympstone,
Exmouth, Devon EX8 5AU
Tel: 01395 272148
Headmistress: Mrs Charlotte Johnston
Age range: 3–13
No. of pupils: 275
Fees: Day £7,650–£13,065 WB £19,935

St Wilfrid's School
25-29 St David's Hill, Exeter,
Devon EX4 4DA
Tel: 01392 276171
Headmistress: Mrs Alexandra E
M MacDonald-Dent DPhyEd
Age range: 5–16

Stover School
Newton Abbot, Devon TQ12 6QG
Tel: 01626 354505
Headmaster: Mr R W D Notman
Age range: 3–18
No. of pupils: 423 VIth67
Fees: Day £8,220–£12,780 WB
£18,450–£22,200 FB £21,210–£26,190

The Maynard School
Denmark Road, Exeter, Devon EX1 1SJ
Tel: 01392 273417
Headmistress: Miss Sarah Dunn
BSc (Hons) PGCE and NPQH
Age range: G4–18
No. of pupils: VIth80
Fees: Day £6,285–£13,248

The New School
The Avenue, Exminster,
Exeter, Devon EX6 8AT
Tel: 01392 496122
Headmistress: Miss M Taylor
BA(Hons), PGCE
Age range: 3–7
No. of pupils: 61
Fees: Day £7,497

Trinity School
Buckeridge Road, Teignmouth,
Devon TQ14 8LY
Tel: 01626 774138
Headmaster: Mr Lawrence Coen
Age range: 3–18
No. of pupils: 110
Fees: Day £7,755–£12,300 WB
£18,945–£25,590 FB £20,550–£27,750

West Buckland School
Barnstaple, Devon EX32 0SX
Tel: 01598 760281
Headmaster: Mr Phillip Stapleton
Age range: 3–18
No. of pupils: VIth135
Fees: Day £8,070–£15,060
FB £24,345–£30,720

Dorset

Bournemouth Collegiate School
St Osmunds Road, Parkstone,
Poole, Dorset BH14 9JY
Tel: 01202 436 550
Headmaster: Mr Russell Slatford
Age range: 2–18
No. of pupils: 301
Fees: Day £7,800–£14,430
WB £27,180 FB £29,670

Bryanston School
Blandford Forum, Dorset DT11 0PX
Tel: 01258 484633
Head: Ms S J Thomas
Age range: 13–18
No. of pupils: 694
Fees: Day £31,311 FB £38,184

Canford School
Canford Magna, Wimborne,
Dorset BH21 3AD
Tel: 01202 841254
Headmaster: B A M Vessey MA, MBA
Age range: 13–18
No. of pupils: 655
Fees: Day £9,241 FB £12,140

Castle Court School
Knoll Lane, Corfe Mullen,
Wimborne, Dorset BH21 3RF
Tel: 01202 694438
Headmaster: Mr Luke Gollings
Age range: 2–13
No. of pupils: 307
Fees: Day £8,790–£15,825

Claysmore Preparatory School
Iwerne Minster, Blandford
Forum, Dorset DT11 8PH
Tel: 01747 813155
Head of School: Mr William Dunlop
Age range: 3–13
No. of pupils: 230
Fees: Day £13,230–£18,750
FB £17,670–£25,110

Claysmore School
Iwerne Minster, Blandford
Forum, Dorset DT11 8LL
Tel: 01747 812122
Head of School: Mrs Jo Thomson
Age range: 13–18
No. of pupils: VIth161
Fees: Day £26,745 FB £36,444

Dumpton School
Deans Grove House, Deans Grove,
Wimborne, Dorset BH21 7AF
Tel: 01202 883818
Headmaster: Mr Christian Saenger
Age range: 2–13
No. of pupils: 328
Fees: Day £9,198–£16,482

Hanford School
Child Okeford, Blandford,
Dorset DT11 8HN
Tel: 01258 860219
Headmaster: Mr Rory Johnston
Age range: G7–13
No. of pupils: 100
Fees: Day £6,250 FB £7,500

Knighton House School and The Orchard Pre-prep
Durweston, Blandford
Forum, Dorset DT11 0PY
Tel: 01258 452065
Headmaster: Mr Robin Gainher
Age range: B3–7 G3–13
No. of pupils: 90
Fees: Day £2,325–£4,950
FB £5,800–£7,600

Leweston School – Prep School
Sherborne, Dorset DT9 6EN
Tel: 01963 210790
Head: Mrs Kate Reynolds
Age range: 0–11
Fees: Day £5,925–£11,520
WB £17,265 FB £20,700

Leweston School – Senior School
Sherborne, Dorset DT9 6EN
Tel: 01963 210691
Head: Mrs Kate Reynolds
Age range: G11–18
Fees: Day £15,420 WB £21,795 FB £27,780
Ⓐ Ⓐ 🏛 £ 🖉 16+

Milton Abbey School
Blandford Forum, Dorset DT11 0BZ
Tel: 01258 880484
Head: Judith Fremont-Barnes
Age range: 13–18
No. of pupils: 220
Fees: Day £21,630 FB £41,175
Ⓐ Ⓐ 🏛 £ 🖉 16+ ⚬

Park School
45-49 Queens Park, South Drive,
Bournemouth, Dorset BH8 9BJ
Tel: 01202 396640
Head of School: Mrs Melanie Dowler
Age range: 2–11
No. of pupils: 387
Fees: Day £7,275–£8,805
£ 🖉

Port Regis
Motcombe Park, Shaftesbury,
Dorset SP7 9QA
Tel: 01747 857800
Head of School: S L Ilett
Age range: 2–13
No. of pupils: 324
🏛 £ 🖉

Sherborne Girls
Bradford Road, Sherborne,
Dorset DT9 3QN
Tel: +44 (0)1935 818224
Headmistress: Dr Ruth Sullivan
BSc, PGCE, MSc, PhD
Age range: G11–18
No. of pupils: 485
Fees: Day £21,285 FB £28,920–£35,880
Ⓐ Ⓐ Ⓐ 🏛 £ Ⓘ🅑 16+

Sherborne International
Newell Grange, Newell,
Sherborne, Dorset DT9 4EZ
Tel: 01935 814743
Principal: Mr Tim Waters MA
(Oxon), MSc (Oxon)
Age range: 8–17
No. of pupils: 147
Ⓐ 🏛 🖉

Sherborne Preparatory School
Acreman Street, Sherborne,
Dorset DT9 3NY
Tel: 01935 812097
Headmaster: Mr Nick Folland
Bsc (Hons), MIAPS, MISI
Age range: 2–13
No. of pupils: 258
Fees: Day £9,060–£17,130 WB
£23,445–£24,540 FB £23,445–£24,540
🏛 £ 🖉

Sherborne School
Abbey Road, Sherborne,
Dorset DT9 3AP
Tel: +44 (0)1935 812249
Headmaster: Dr Dominic
Luckett BA, DPhil, FRSA,FHA
Age range: B13–18
No. of pupils: 596 VIth210
Fees: Day £30,375 FB £37,500
Ⓐ Ⓐ Ⓐ 🏛 £ 16+

St Martin's School
15 Stokewood Road,
Bournemouth, Dorset BH3 7NA
Tel: 01202 292011
Headteacher: Laura Richards
Age range: 4–11 years
No. of pupils: 100
Fees: Day £5,835–£7,533

St Mary's School
Shaftesbury, Dorset SP7 9LP
Tel: 01747 852416
Acting Headmistress: Mrs
Sarah Matthews
Age range: G9–18
No. of pupils: 220
Fees: Day £16,200–£20,850
FB £20,085–£31,470
Ⓐ Ⓐ Ⓐ 🏛 £ 🖉 16+

St Thomas Garnet's School
Parkwood Road, Boscombe,
Bournemouth, Dorset BH5 2BH
Tel: 01202 420172
Headteacher: Mr Craig Lickley
Age range: 3–11
Fees: Day £5,721–£7,995

Sunninghill Preparatory School
South Court, South Walks,
Dorchester, Dorset DT1 1EB
Tel: 01305 262306
Headmaster: Mr John Thorpe
BSc (Hons), PGCE
Age range: 3–13
No. of pupils: 184
Fees: Day £8,850–£15,450
£ 🖉

Talbot Heath
Rothesay Road, Bournemouth,
Dorset BH4 9NJ
Tel: 01202 761881
Head: Mrs A Holloway MA, PGCE
Age range: G3–18
No. of pupils: 582
Fees: Day £2,201–£4,801
WB £3,305 FB £3,704
Ⓐ Ⓐ Ⓐ 🏛 £ 🖉 16+

Talbot House Preparatory School
8 Firs Glen Road, Bournemouth,
Dorset BH9 2LR
Tel: 01202 510348
Headteacher: Mrs Emma Haworth
Age range: 3–11
Fees: Day £4,320–£8,097

Yarrells Preparatory School
Yarrells House, Upton, Poole,
Dorset BH16 5EU
Tel: 01202 622229
Headteacher: Mrs Sally Weber-Spokes
Age range: 2–13
No. of pupils: 253
Fees: Day £2,395–£4,250
£ 🖉

Somerset

All Hallows Preparatory School
Cranmore Hall, Shepton
Mallet, Somerset BA4 4SF
Tel: 01749 881600
Head of School: Dr Trevor Richards
Age range: 3–13
No. of pupils: 265
🏛 £

Bruton School for Girls
Sunny Hill, Bruton, Somerset BA10 0NT
Tel: 01749 814400
Headmistress: Mrs Nicola Botterill
Age range: G2–18
No. of pupils: 250
Fees: Day £8,505–£17,805 FB £30,330
Ⓐ Ⓐ Ⓐ 🏛 £ 🖉 16+

Chard School
Fore Street, Chard, Somerset TA20 1QA
Tel: 01460 63234
Head of School: Katie Hill
Age range: 0–11
No. of pupils: 100
Fees: Day £6,450–£7,650
£ 🖉

Hazlegrove Prep School
Hazlegrove House, Sparkford,
Somerset BA22 7JA
Tel: +44 (0)1963 442606
Headmaster: Mr Mark White MA (Hons)
Age range: 21/2–13
No. of pupils: 364
Fees: Day £2,928–£5,937
FB £6,886–£8,787
🏛 £ 🖉

King's Bruton
The Plox, Bruton, Somerset BA10 0ED
Tel: 01749 814200
Headmaster: Mr I S Wilmshurst MA
Age range: 13–18
No. of pupils: 350
Ⓐ Ⓐ 🏛 £ 🖉 16+

King's College
Taunton, Somerset TA1 3LA
Tel: 01823 328204
Headmaster: Richard Biggs
Age range: 13–18
No. of pupils: 440 VIth180
Fees: Day £22,380 FB £33,165
Ⓐ Ⓐ 🏛 £ 🖉 16+

King's Hall School
Kingston Road, Taunton,
Somerset TA2 8AA
Tel: 01823 285920
Headmaster: Mr Justin Chippendale
Age range: 2–13
Fees: Day £7,725–£16,500
FB £18,450–£23,985
🏛 £ 🖉

Millfield Preparatory School
Edgarley Hall, Glastonbury,
Somerset BA6 8LD
Tel: 01458 832446
Headmistress: Mrs S Shayler
Age range: 2–13
No. of pupils: 366
Fees: Day £10,815–£18,705
WB £28,380 FB £28,380
🏛 £ 🖉

Millfield School
Street, Somerset BA16 0YD
Tel: 01458 442291
Headmaster: Gavin Horgan
Age range: 13–18
No. of pupils: 1241
Fees: Day £25,605 FB £38,610
Ⓐ Ⓐ 🏛 £ 🖉 16+ ⚬

Perrott Hill
North Perrott, Crewkerne,
Somerset TA18 7SL
Tel: 01460 72051
Joint Acting Headteachers: Mr
Bryan Kane & Mr Will Silk
Age range: 3–13
No. of pupils: 183
Fees: Day £6,450–£15,750
WB £19,200 FB £22,740
🏛 £ 🖉

Queen's College

Trull Road, Taunton, Somerset TA1 4QS
Tel: 01823 272559
Headmistress: Dr Lorraine Earps
Age range: 3–18
No. of pupils: 784 VIth150
Fees: Day £6,450–£18,450
FB £14,655–£31,980
🌐 Ⓐ 🏫 £ ✏ 16·

Springmead Preparatory School & Nursery

Castle Corner, Beckington,
Frome, Somerset BA11 6TA
Tel: 01373 831555
Principal: Ms Madeleine Taylor
Age range: 2–11
No. of pupils: 105
Fees: Day £9,390
✏

Sunny Hill Prep School

Sunny Hill, Bruton, Somerset BA10 0NT
Tel: 01749 814 427
Head: Mrs Helen Snow BEd
Age range: B2–7 G2–11
No. of pupils: 68
Fees: Day £8,505–£13,116 WB
£21,300–£21,651 FB £23,529–£23,880
♀ 🏫 🏫 £ ✏

Taunton Preparatory School

Staplegrove Road, Taunton,
Somerset TA2 6AE
Tel: 01823 703305
Headmaster: Andrew Edwards
Age range: 0–13
No. of pupils: 418
Fees: Day £7,350–£15,375
FB £14,685–£25,500
🏫 £ ✏

Taunton School

Staplegrove Road, Taunton,
Somerset TA2 6AD
Tel: +44 (0)1823 703703
Headmaster: Mr. Lee Glaser
Age range: 0–18
No. of pupils: 520 VIth240
Fees: Day £7,350–£19,395
FB £14,685–£36,225
🌐 Ⓐ 🏫 £ IB ✏ 16·

The Park School

Chilton Cantelo, Yeovil,
Somerset BA22 8BG
Tel: 01935 850555
Head: Mrs J Huntington ARAM
GRSM LRAM CPSEd
Age range: 4–18+
No. of pupils: 168 VIth24
Fees: Day £6,360–£10,500 WB
£21,600–£23,100 FB £22,500–£26,250
🌐 Ⓐ 🏫 £ ✏ 16·

Wellington Prep School

South Street, Wellington,
Somerset TA21 8NT
Tel: 01823 668700
Headmaster: Adam Gibson
Age range: 3–11
Fees: Day £6,330–£11,520
✏

Wellington School

South Street, Wellington,
Somerset TA21 8NT
Tel: 01823 668800
Headmaster: Henry Price MA (Oxon)
Age range: 3–18
No. of pupils: VIth165
Fees: Day £6,330–£15,225 WB
£23,130–£24,105 FB £28,890–£30,810
🌐 Ⓐ 🏫 £ ✏ 16·

Wells Cathedral Junior School

8 New Street, Wells, Somerset BA5 2LQ
Tel: 01749 834400
Headteacher: Julie Barrow
Age range: 3–11
No. of pupils: 150
Fees: Day £7,641–£15,375 WB
£20,322–£22,900 FB £23,458–£26,036
🏫 £ ✏

Wells Cathedral School

The Liberty, Wells, Somerset BA5 2ST
Tel: 01749 834200
Head: Mr Alastair Tighe
Age range: 3–18
No. of pupils: 750 VIth194
Fees: Day £7,641–£18,801 WB
£20,322–£27,843 FB £23,458–£31,464
🌐 Ⓐ 🏫 £ ✏ 16·

D392

West Midlands

KEY TO SYMBOLS
- 🕴 *Boys' school*
- 🚶 *Girls' school*
- 🌐 *International school*
- 16⁻ *Tutorial or sixth form college*
- Ⓐ *A levels*
- 🏫 *Boarding accommodation*
- £ *Bursaries*
- ⒾⒷ *International Baccalaureate*
- ✎ *Learning support*
- 16⁺ *Entrance at 16+*
- 🎓 *Vocational qualifications*
- (IAPS) *Independent Association of Preparatory Schools*
- (HMC) *The Headmasters' & Headmistresses' Conference*
- (ISA) *Independent Schools Association*
- (GSA) *Girls' School Association*
- (BSA) *Boarding Schools' Association*
- Ⓢ *Society of Heads*

Unless otherwise indicated, all schools are coeducational day schools. Single-sex and boarding schools will be indicated by the relevant icon.

Herefordshire

Hereford Cathedral Junior School
28 Castle Street, Hereford,
Herefordshire HR1 2NW
Tel: 01432 363511
Headmaster: Mr Chris Wright
Age range: 3–11
Fees: Day £8,028–£10,320
£ ✎

Hereford Cathedral School
The Old Deanery, The Cathedral Close,
Hereford, Herefordshire HR1 2NG
Tel: 01432 363522
Headmaster: Mr Paul Smith
Age range: 3–18
No. of pupils: 535 VIth130
Ⓐ £ ✎ 16

LUCTON SCHOOL
For further details see p. 258
Lucton, Herefordshire HR6 9PN
Tel: 01568 782000
Email: admissions@luctonschool.org
Website: www.luctonschool.org
Headmistress: Mrs Gill Thorne MA
Age range: 1–18
No. of pupils: 350
Fees: Day £2,450–£4,750 WB
£7,800–£9,200 FB £9,295–£11,260
Ⓐ 🏛 £ ✎ 16

Shropshire

Adcote School for Girls
Little Ness, Shrewsbury,
Shropshire SY4 2JY
Tel: 01939 260202
Headmistress: Mrs Diane Browne
Age range: G7–18
No. of pupils: 220
Fees: Day £9,141–£14,838 WB
£17,263–£24,754 FB £19,618–£27,097
Ⓐ 🏛 £ ✎ 16

Bedstone College
Bedstone, Bucknell, Shropshire SY7 0BG
Tel: 01547 530303
Headmaster: Mr David Gajadharsingh
Age range: 4–18
No. of pupils: 230
Fees: Day £5,025–£14,655
FB £17,475–£26,520
Ⓐ 🏛 £ ✎ 16

Birchfield School
Albrighton, Wolverhampton,
Shropshire WV7 3AF
Tel: 01902 372534
Headmaster: Mr Paul Reynolds
Age range: B4–13 G4–12
No. of pupils: 145
Fees: Day £6,825–£14,250
🏛 £ ✎

Castle House School
Chetwynd End, Newport,
Shropshire TF10 7JE
Tel: 01952 567600
Headmaster: Mr Ian Sterling
Age range: 2–11
No. of pupils: 87
Fees: Day £7,500–£8,850
£ ✎

Concord College
Acton Burnell Hall, Shrewsbury,
Shropshire SY5 7PF
Tel: 01694 731631
Principal: N G Hawkins
MA(Cantab), PGCE
Age range: 13–19
No. of pupils: 521 VIth343
Fees: Day £14,280 FB £39,900
Ⓐ 🏛 £ ✎ 16

ELLESMERE COLLEGE
For further details see p. 254
Ellesmere, Shropshire SY12 9AB
Tel: 01691 622321
Email: registrar@ellesmere.com
Website: www.ellesmere.com
Head of School: Mr Brendan
Wignall MA, FRSA, MCMI
Age range: 7–18
No. of pupils: 550
Fees: Day £6,330 WB £8,217 FB £11,511
Ⓐ 🏛 £ IB ✎ 16

Moor Park
Richard's Castle, Ludlow,
Shropshire SY8 4DZ
Tel: 01584 777218
Headmaster: Mr Charles
G O'B Minogue
Age range: 3–13 years
No. of pupils: 176
Fees: Day £2,060–£5,745
FB £7,120–£8,530
🏛 £ ✎

Moreton First
Weston Rhyn, Oswestry,
Shropshire SY11 3EW
Tel: 01691 776028
Head: Mrs Catherine Ford M.A., B.Sc.
Age range: 6 months–11 years
No. of pupils: 187
Fees: Day £9,840–£13,890 FB £22,680
£ ✎ 16

Moreton Hall
Weston Rhyn, Oswestry,
Shropshire SY11 3EW
Tel: 01691 773671
Headteacher: George Budd
Age range: 11–18
Fees: Day £26,550–£28,725
FB £33,015–£34,875
🏛

Oswestry School
Upper Brook Street, Oswestry,
Shropshire SY11 2TL
Tel: 01691 655711
Headmaster: Mr Julian Noad BEng
Age range: 4–18
No. of pupils: VIth92
Fees: Day £8,700–£15,690 WB
£23,610 FB £26,850–£31,200
Ⓐ 🏛 £ ✎ 16

Packwood Haugh School
Ruyton XI Towns, Shrewsbury,
Shropshire SY4 1HX
Tel: 01939 260217
Headmaster: Clive Smith-
Langridge BA(Hons), PGCE
Age range: 4–13
No. of pupils: 212
Fees: Day £8,805–£18,330
FB £23,430–£26,430
🏛 £ ✎

Prestfelde Preparatory School
London Road, Shrewsbury,
Shropshire SY2 6NZ
Tel: 01743 245400
Head of School: Mrs F Orchard
Age range: 3–13
No. of pupils: 300
Fees: Day £9,570–£16,140
🏛 £ ✎

Shrewsbury High School GDST
32 Town Walls, Shrewsbury,
Shropshire SY1 1TN
Tel: 01743 494000
Head: Ms J Sharrock
Age range: B3–13 G3–18
No. of pupils: VIth120
Fees: Day £7,686–£14,481
Ⓐ 🏛 £ ✎ 16

SHREWSBURY SCHOOL
For further details see p. 264
The Schools, Shrewsbury,
Shropshire SY3 7BA
Tel: 01743 280552
Email: admissions@
shrewsbury.org.uk
Website: www.shrewsbury.org.uk
Headmaster: Mr. Leo Winkley
Age range: 13–18
No. of pupils: 830 VIth397
Fees: Day £25,770 FB £37,560
Ⓐ 🏛 £ ✎ 16

St Winefride's Convent School
Belmont, Shrewsbury, Shropshire SY1 1TE
Tel: 01743 369883
Headmistress: Sister M Felicity
CertEd, BA(Hons)
Age range: 3–11
No. of pupils: 179
Fees: Day £4,355–£4,380
✎

The Old Hall School
Stanley Road, Wellington,
Shropshire TF1 3LB
Tel: 01952 223117
Headmaster: Martin Stott
Age range: 4–11
No. of pupils: 239
Fees: Day £8,310–£13,065
£ ✎

White House School
Heath Road, Whitchurch,
Shropshire SY13 2AA
Tel: 01948 662730
Headmistress: Mrs H M Clarke
Age range: 3–11
Fees: Day £4,950
✎

Wrekin College
Wellington, Shropshire TF1 3BH
Tel: 01952 265600
Headmaster: Mr Tim Firth
Age range: 11–18
No. of pupils: 415 VIth140
Fees: Day £14,820–£17,925 WB
£21,360–£25,320 FB £27,360–£32,040
Ⓐ 🏛 £ ✎ 16

Staffordshire

Abbotsholme School
Rocester, Uttoxeter,
Staffordshire ST14 5BS
Tel: 01889 590217
Headmaster: Mr Bob Barnes
Age range: 2–18
No. of pupils: 310 VIth55
Fees: Day £8,985–£22,485 WB
£17,985–£26,775 FB £23,985–£32,985
🏇 Ⓐ ⬤ £ 16 🐎

Chase Grammar School
Lyncroft House, St John's Road,
Cannock, Staffordshire WS11 0UR
Tel: 01543 501800
Principal: Dr Paul Silverwood
MA(Cantab), MSc, PhD, QTS, CChem
Age range: 2–19
No. of pupils: 300 VIth100
Fees: Day £5,985–£11,685 FB £21,500
🏇 Ⓐ ⬤ £ 16

**Chase Grammar School
International Study Centre**
Lyncroft House, St John's Road,
Cannock, Staffordshire WS11 0UR
Tel: 01543 501800
Principal: Dr Paul Silverwood
Age range: 2–18
No. of pupils: 102
Fees: Day £5,985–£11,685
FB £21,500–£31,200
Ⓐ ⬤ £ 16

DENSTONE COLLEGE
For further details see p. 252
Uttoxeter, Staffordshire ST14 5HN
Tel: 01889 590484
Email: admissions@
denstonecollege.net
Website: www.denstonecollege.org
Headmaster: Mr Miles
Norris MA (Oxon)
Age range: 11–18
No. of pupils: 614 VIth198
Fees: Day £13,596–£16,434 WB
£19,698–£22,152 FB £19,698–£28,617
🏇 Ⓐ ⬤ £ 🌿 16

**Denstone College
Preparatory School**
Smallwood Manor, Uttoxeter,
Staffordshire ST14 8NS
Tel: 01889 562083
Headmaster: Mr Jerry Gear
Age range: 2–11
No. of pupils: 153
Fees: Day £10,185–£12,900
£ 🌿

Edenhurst Preparatory School
Westlands Avenue, Newcastle-
under-Lyme, Staffordshire ST5 2PU
Tel: 01782 619348
Headmaster: Mr Michael Hibbert
Age range: 3 months–11 years
Fees: Day £8,880–£10,749
£ 🌿

Lichfield Cathedral School
The Palace, The Close, Lichfield,
Staffordshire WS13 7LH
Tel: 01543 306170
Head: Mrs Susan E Hannam
BA (Hons) MA PGCE
Age range: 3–18 years
No. of pupils: 426
Fees: Day £8,805–£13,815
🏇 £ 🌿

Maple Hayes Dyslexia School
Abnalls Lane, Lichfield,
Staffordshire WS13 8BL
Tel: 01543 264387
Principal: Dr N E Brown MSc, BA, MINS,
MSCMe, AFBPsS, CPsychol, FRSA, CSci
Age range: 7–17
No. of pupils: 118
Fees: Day £15,165–£20,259
£

Newcastle-under-Lyme School
Mount Pleasant, Newcastle-under-
Lyme, Staffordshire ST5 1DB
Tel: 01782 631197
Headmaster: Mr Nick Vernon
Age range: 3–18
No. of pupils: 879 VIth152
Fees: Day £8,550–£11,745
Ⓐ £ 🌿 16

St Dominic's Priory School Stone
21 Station Road, Stone,
Staffordshire ST15 8EN
Tel: +44 (0)1785 814181
Head of School: Mrs Rebecca Harrison
Age range: 3–16
No. of pupils: 163
Fees: Day £7,560–£11,508
Ⓐ £ 🌿 16

St Joseph's Preparatory School
London Road, Trent Vale, Stoke-
on-Trent, Staffordshire ST4 5NT
Tel: 01782 417533
Head: Mrs S D Hutchinson
Age range: 3–11
Fees: Day £7,605–£8,040
£ 🌿

St. Dominic's Grammar School
32 Bargate Street, Brewood,
Staffordshire ST19 9BA
Tel: 01902 850248
Headteacher: Mr Peter
McNabb BSc Hons, PGCE
Age range: 2–18 years
No. of pupils: 198 VIth31
Fees: Day £6,834–£13,212
🏃 Ⓐ ⬤ £ 🌿 16

Stafford Grammar School
Burton Manor, Stafford,
Staffordshire ST18 9AT
Tel: 01785 249752
Headmaster: Mr M R Darley BA
Age range: 11–18
No. of pupils: 330 VIth96
Fees: Day £12,414
Ⓐ £ 🌿 16

Yarlet School
Yarlet, Stafford, Staffordshire ST18 9SU
Tel: 01785 286568
Headmaster: Mr I Raybould BEd(Hons)
Age range: 2–13
No. of pupils: 169
Fees: Day £7,380–£12,270
⬤ £ 🌿

Warwickshire

Arnold Lodge School
15-17 Kenilworth Road, Leamington
Spa, Warwickshire CV32 5TW
Tel: 01926 778050
Headmaster: David Preston
Age range: 4–18
No. of pupils: 250
Fees: Day £10,800–£13,116
£ 🌿

Bilton Grange
Dunchurch, Rugby,
Warwickshire CV22 6QU
Tel: 01788 810217
Headmaster: Mr Alex
Osiatynski MA Oxon PGCE
Age range: 3–13
No. of pupils: 300
⬤ £ 🌿

Crackley Hall School
St Joseph's Park, Kenilworth,
Warwickshire CV8 2FT
Tel: 01926 514444
Headmaster: Mr R Duigan
Age range: 2–11
No. of pupils: 233
Fees: Day £9,288–£9,888
£ 🌿

Hijaz College
Watling Street, Nuneaton,
Warwickshire CV11 6BE
Tel: 02476 325 859
Headteacher: Mr Tauqir Ishaq
Age range: B11–21
No. of pupils: 61
Fees: FB £4,550–£5,400
🏃 Ⓐ ⬤ 🌿

King's High School for Girls
Banbury Rd, Warwick,
Warwickshire CV34 6YE
Tel: 01926 494485
Head Master: Mr Richard
Nicholson MA (Oxon)
Age range: G11–18 years
🏃 Ⓐ £ 🌿 16

Milverton House School
Holman Way, Park Street,
Attleborough, Warwickshire CV11 4EL
Tel: 024 7664 1722
Head Teacher: Mr O Pipe
Age range: 0–11
No. of pupils: 275
Fees: Day £4,830–£7,050

Princethorpe College
Leamington Road, Princethorpe,
Rugby, Warwickshire CV23 9PX
Tel: 01926 634200
Headmaster: Mr Ed Hester
Age range: 11–18
No. of pupils: 817 VIth184
Fees: Day £12,693
Ⓐ Ⓔ ✎ 16

Rugby School
Rugby, Warwickshire CV22 5EH
Tel: +44 (0)1788 556274
Headmaster: Peter R.A. Green
Age range: 11–18
No. of pupils: 804 VIth366
Fees: Day £22,437 FB £35,760
🌐Ⓐ🏛Ⓔ✎16

Stratford Preparatory School
Church House, Old Town, Stratford-
upon-Avon, Warwickshire CV37 6BG
Tel: 01789 297993
Headmaster: Mr N Musk
MA(Jt Hons), PGCE
Age range: 2–11
Fees: Day £9,600–£11,280
✎

The Crescent School
Bawnmore Road, Bilton, Rugby,
Warwickshire CV22 7QH
Tel: 01788 521595
Headmaster: Mr J.P. Thackway
B.A.Hons, P.G.C.E.
Age range: 4–11
No. of pupils: 137
Fees: Day £8,094–£9,714
Ⓔ✎

The Croft Preparatory School
Alveston Hill, Loxley Road, Stratford-
upon-Avon, Warwickshire CV37 7RL
Tel: 01789 293795
Headmaster: Mr Marcus Cook
Age range: 2–11
No. of pupils: 425
Fees: Day £7,962–£12,213

The Kingsley School
Beauchamp Avenue, Leamington
Spa, Warwickshire CV32 5RD
Tel: 01926 425127
Headteacher: Ms Heather Owens
Age range: B3–11 G3–18
No. of pupils: 333 VIth61
Fees: Day £10,599–£13,254
👧Ⓐ Ⓔ ✎ 16

Twycross House Pre-Preparatory School
The Hollies, The Green, Atherstone,
Warwickshire CV9 3PQ
Tel: 01827 880725
Joint Heads: Mr S D Assinder
& Mrs R T Assinder
Age range: 4–8
Fees: Day £8,610

Twycross House School
Main Road, Twycross, Atherstone,
Warwickshire CV9 3QA
Tel: 01827 880651
Headmaster: Mr S D Assinder
Age range: 8–18
Fees: Day £9,270–£10,485
Ⓐ16

Warwick Preparatory School
Bridge Field, Banbury Road,
Warwick, Warwickshire CV34 6PL
Tel: 01926 491545
Headmistress: Hellen Dodsworth
Age range: B3–7 G3–11
No. of pupils: 438
Fees: Day £7,767–£12,666
✎

Warwick School
Myton Road, Warwick,
Warwickshire CV34 6PP
Tel: 01926 776400
Head Master: Dr D Smith
Age range: B7–18
No. of pupils: 1214 VIth249
Fees: Day £11,181–£13,194
WB £26,883 FB £28,758
👦🌐Ⓐ🏛Ⓔ✎16

West Midlands

Abu Bakr Girls School
154-160 Wednesbury Road, Palfrey,
Walsall, West Midlands WS1 4JJ
Tel: 01922 626829
Head: Moulana Ramzan
Age range: G11–16
👧

Al Huda Girls School
74-76 Washwood Heath Road, Saltley,
Birmingham, West Midlands B8 1RD
Tel: 0121 328 8999
Headmistress: Mrs Y Jawaid
Age range: G11–17
No. of pupils: 87
👧

Al-Ameen Primary School
Stanfield House, 447 Warwick Way,
Birmingham, West Midlands B11 2JR
Tel: 0121 706 3322
Head: Maulana Mohammed
Aminur Rahman
Age range: 3–11
No. of pupils: 22

Al-Burhan Grammar School
28A George Street, Balsall Heath,
Birmingham, West Midlands B12 9RG
Tel: 0121 4405454
Head: Dr Mohammad Nasrullah
Age range: G11–16
No. of pupils: 80
Fees: Day £11,700
👧

Al-Furqan Community College
Reddings Lane, Tyseley, Birmingham,
West Midlands B11 3EY
Tel: 0121 777 8666
Principal: Mr Amjad Ahmed BSc, PGCE
Age range: G11–16
Fees: Day £6,900
👧Ⓐ Ⓔ ✎16🧕

Al-Hijrah School
Cherrywood Centre, Burbidge
Road, Bordesley Green, Birmingham,
West Midlands B9 4US
Tel: 0121 7737979
Headteacher: Arshad Mohammed
Age range: 4–16
No. of pupils: 306

Archway Academy
86 Watery Lane Middleway, Bordesley,
Birmingham, West Midlands B9 4HN
Tel: 0121 772 7772
Executive Managing Director: Jim Ryan
Age range: 14–19

Bablake Junior School
Coundon Road, Coventry,
West Midlands CV1 4AU
Tel: 024 7627 1260
Headmaster: Mr N Price
Age range: 7–11
Fees: Day £9,411
Ⓔ✎

Bablake PrePrep
The Grange, Brownshill Green Road,
Coventry, West Midlands CV6 3EG
Tel: 024 7622 1677
Head of Pre Prep: Mrs T Horton
Age range: 3–7
Fees: Day £8,097

Bablake School
Coundon Road, Coventry,
West Midlands CV1 4AU
Tel: 024 7627 1200
Headmaster: Mr A M Wright
Age range: 11–18
Fees: Day £12,162
Ⓐ Ⓔ ✎16

Birchfield Independent Girls' School
Beacon House, 30 Beacon Hill, Aston,
Birmingham, West Midlands B6 6JU
Tel: 0121 327 7707
Head: Mrs R Mogra
Age range: G11–17
No. of pupils: 150 VIth100
Fees: Day £5,985
👧Ⓐ16🧕

Birmingham Muslim School
Bisley Works, Golden Hillock
Road, Sparkbrook, Birmingham,
West Midlands B11 2PY
Tel: 0121 7668129
Principal: Ms A Abdrabba
Age range: 4–10
No. of pupils: 90

Childfirst Day Nursery Solihull
Cooks Lane, Kingshurst, Solihull,
West Midlands B37 6NZ
Tel: 0121 788 8148

Copsewood School
168-170 Roland Avenue, Holbrooks,
Coventry, West Midlands CV6 4LX
Tel: 024 7668 0680
Headteacher: Mr A R G Shedden
Age range: 11–16
No. of pupils: 77

Darul Uloom Islamic High School
521 Coventry Road, Small Heath,
Birmingham, West Midlands B10 0LL
Tel: 0121 772 6408
Principal: Dr Asm Abdul Rahim
Age range: B11–16
No. of pupils: 70

Edgbaston High School for Girls
Westbourne Road, Edgbaston,
Birmingham, West Midlands B15 3TS
Tel: 0121 454 5831
Headmistress: Dr Ruth A
Weeks BSc, PhD
Age range: G2–18
No. of pupils: 920 VIth112
Fees: Day £8,592–£12,774

Elmfield Rudolf Steiner School
14 Love Lane, Stourbridge,
West Midlands DY8 2EA
Tel: 01384 394633
College of Teachers: Education Admin
Age range: 3–17
No. of pupils: VIth100
Fees: Day £5,220–£8,034

Elmhurst Ballet School
249 Bristol Road, Edgbaston,
Birmingham, West Midlands B5 7UH
Tel: 0121 472 6655
Principal: Jessica Wheeler
BA(Hons), NPQH
Age range: 11–19
No. of pupils: VIth69
Fees: Day £18,564–£19,239
FB £23,793–£25,650

Emmanuel School (Walsall)
36 Wolverhampton Road, Walsall,
West Midlands WS2 8PR
Tel: 01922 635810
Head Teacher: Mr Jonathan
Swain BA PGCE
Age range: 3–16
No. of pupils: 82
Fees: Day £4,044

Eversfield Preparatory School
Warwick Road, Solihull,
West Midlands B91 1AT
Tel: 0121 705 0354
Headmaster: Mr R A Yates
BA, PGCE, LPSH
Age range: 2–11
Fees: Day £9,583–£10,971

Green Heath School
43-51 Whitmore Road, Small Heath,
Birmingham, West Midlands B10 0NR
Tel: 0121 213 1171
Age range: 11–19

Greenfields Primary School
472 Coventry Road, Birmingham,
West Midlands B10 0UG
Tel: 0121 7724567
Headteacher: P. Sa'eed Alam
Age range: 5–11

HALLFIELD SCHOOL
For further details see p. 256
Church Road, Edgbaston,
Birmingham, West Midlands B15 3SJ
Tel: 0121 454 1496
Email: office@hallfieldschool.co.uk
Website: www.hallfieldschool.co.uk
Headmaster: Mr Keith Morrow
Age range: 3 months–13

Hamd House Preparatory School
730 Bordesley Green, Birmingham,
West Midlands B9 5PQ
Tel: +44 (0) 121 771 3030
Headteacher: Mr S Ali
Age range: 3–11
No. of pupils: 206

Highclare School
10 Sutton Road, Erdington,
Birmingham, West Midlands B23 6QL
Tel: 0121 373 7400
Head: Dr Richard Luker
Age range: B1–12 G1–18
No. of pupils: 638 VIth28
Fees: Day £5,420–£12,645

Hydesville Tower School
25 Broadway North, Walsall,
West Midlands WS1 2QG
Tel: 01922 624374
Headmaster: Mr Warren Honey
BSc (Hons), PGCE Durham
University, MEd Open Univ+
Age range: 3–16
No. of pupils: 289
Fees: Day £9,273–£13,179

**Jamia Islamia Birmingham
Islamic College**
Fallows Road, Sparkbrook,
Birmingham, West Midlands B11 1PL
Tel: 0121 7726400
Headteacher: Mohammed Govalia
Age range: 11–16
No. of pupils: 111

**King Edward VI High
School for Girls**
Edgbaston Park Road, Birmingham,
West Midlands B15 2UB
Tel: 0121 472 1834
Principal: Ms Ann Clark
Age range: G11–18
No. of pupils: 591
Fees: Day £12,888

King Edward's School
Edgbaston Park Road, Birmingham,
West Midlands B15 2UA
Tel: 0121 472 1672
Chief Master: Dr Katy Ricks M.A, DPhil
Age range: B11–18
No. of pupils: 885 VIth221
Fees: Day £13,692

King Henry VIII Preparatory School
Kenilworth Road, Coventry,
West Midlands CV3 6PT
Tel: 024 7627 1307
Headteacher: Mrs Gillian
Bowser BA (QTS Hons), NPQH
Age range: 3–11
Fees: Day £8,652–£8,991

King Henry VIII School
Warwick Road, Coventry,
West Midlands CV3 6AQ
Tel: 024 7627 1111
Headmaster: Mr J Slack MA Ed
Age range: 11–18
No. of pupils: 724 VIth210
Fees: Day £11,694

Kingswood School
St James Place, Shirley, Solihull,
West Midlands B90 2BA
Tel: 0121 744 7883
Headmaster: Mr Rob Luckham
BSc(Hons), PGCE
Age range: 3–11
No. of pupils: 89

Lambs Christian School
113 Soho Hill, Hockley, Birmingham,
West Midlands B19 1AY
Tel: 0121 5543790
Headteacher: Mrs Patricia Ekhuenelo
Age range: 3–11
No. of pupils: 43

Lote Tree Primary
643 Foleshill Road, Coventry,
West Midlands CV6 5JQ
Tel: 024 7626 1803
Head: Mrs Ashique
Age range: 2–11
No. of pupils: 97

**MANDER PORTMAN
WOODWARD – BIRMINGHAM**
For further details see p. 262
17-18 Greenfield Crescent,
Edgbaston, Birmingham,
West Midlands B15 3AU
Tel: 0121 454 9637
Email: birmingham@mpw.ac.uk
Website: www.mpw.ac.uk
Principal: Mr Mark Shingleton
Age range: 14–19

Mayfield Preparatory School
Sutton Road, Walsall, West
Midlands WS1 2PD
Tel: 01922 624107
Headmaster: Mr Matthew Draper
Age range: 2–11
No. of pupils: 212
Fees: Day £5,220–£8,700

Newbridge Preparatory School
51 Newbridge Crescent,
Tettenhall, Wolverhampton,
West Midlands WV6 0LH
Tel: 01902 751088
Headmistress: Mrs Sarah Fisher
Age range: B3–4 G3–11
No. of pupils: 148

Norfolk House School
4 Norfolk Road, Edgbaston,
Birmingham, West Midlands B15 3PS
Tel: 0121 454 7021
Headmistress: Mrs Sarah
Morris BA (Hons), PGCE
Age range: 3–11
No. of pupils: 146
Fees: Day £7,176–£10,380

Pattison College
86-90 Binley Road, Coventry,
West Midlands CV3 1FQ
Tel: 024 7645 5031
Principal: Mrs E.A.P.
McConnell B.Ed. (Hons)
Age range: 3–16
No. of pupils: 110 VIth16
Fees: Day £6,585–£8,895

Priory School
39 Sir Harry's Road, Edgbaston,
Birmingham, West Midlands B15 2UR
Tel: 0121 440 4103
Headmaster: Mr J Cramb
Age range: 6 months–18 years
No. of pupils: 438 VIth23
Fees: Day £3,275–£4,950
(A) (£) 🖉 (16)

Rosslyn School
1597 Stratford Road, Hall Green,
Birmingham, West Midlands B28 9JB
Tel: 0121 744 2743
Principal: Mr Khan
Age range: 2–11
Fees: Day £3,588–£6,252
🖉

Ruckleigh School
17 Lode Lane, Solihull, West
Midlands B91 2AB
Tel: 0121 705 2773
Headmistress: Mrs Barbara Forster
Age range: 3–11
Fees: Day £8,640–£9,120
🖉

Saint Martin's School
Malvern Hall, Brueton Avenue,
Solihull, West Midlands B91 3EN
Tel: 0121 705 1265
Headmistress: Mrs Nicola Smillie
BA (Hons), PGCE, NPQH
Age range: G3–18
No. of pupils: 430 VIth40
Fees: Day £9,900–£12,750
(👤) (A) (£) 🖉 (16)

Solihull School
Warwick Road, Solihull,
West Midlands B91 3DJ
Tel: 0121 705 0958
Headmaster: Mr David E J J Lloyd
Age range: 7–18
No. of pupils: 1013 VIth279
Fees: Day £10,491–£12,897
(A) (£) 🖉 (16)

St George's School, Edgbaston
31 Calthorpe Road, Birmingham,
West Midlands B15 1RX
Tel: 0121 625 0398
Head of School: Mr Gary
Neal BEd (Hons)
Age range: 3–18
No. of pupils: 368 VIth48
Fees: Day £6,060–£9,765
(A) (£) 🖉 (16)

TETTENHALL COLLEGE
For further details see p. 266
Wood Road, Tettenhall,
Wolverhampton, West
Midlands WV6 8QX
Tel: 01902 751119
Email: admissions@tettcoll.co.uk
Website:
www.tettenhallcollege.co.uk
Headteacher: Mr David Williams
Age range: 2–18
No. of pupils: 420
Fees: FB £10,279–£11,166
(🌐) (A) (🏫) (£) 🖉 (16)

The Birmingham Theatre School
The Old Rep Theatre, Station Street,
Birmingham, West Midlands B5 4DY
Tel: 0121 440 1665
Principal: C Rozanski BA(Hons)
Age range: 5–65
Fees: Day £5,400
(£) 🖉 (16) 🐾

The Blue Coat School
Somerset Road, Edgbaston,
Birmingham, West Midlands B17 0HR
Tel: 0121 410 6800
Headmaster: Mr N G Neeson
Age range: 2–11
Fees: Day £4,059–£12,714
(£) 🖉

**THE ROYAL SCHOOL
WOLVERHAMPTON**
For further details see p. 268
Penn Road, Wolverhampton,
West Midlands WV3 0EG
Tel: +44 (0)1902 341230
Email: info@theroyal.school
Website: www.theroyalschool.co.uk
Age range: 4–19
No. of pupils: 1328
Fees: FB £12,300
(A) (🏫)

The Shrubbery School
Walmley Ash Road, Walmley, Sutton
Coldfield, West Midlands B76 1HY
Tel: 0121 351 1582
Head Teacher: Hilary Atkins
Age range: 3–11
Fees: Day £3,765–£8,808
🖉

WEST HOUSE SCHOOL
For further details see p. 270
24 St James's Road, Edgbaston,
Birmingham, West Midlands B15 2NX
Tel: 0121 440 4097
Email: secretary@
westhouseprep.com
Website: www.westhouseprep.com
Headmaster: Mr Alistair M J
Lyttle BA(Hons), PGCE, NPQH
Age range: B1–11 G1–4
No. of pupils: 350
Fees: Day £1,466–£4,083
(👤) (A) (£) 🖉

Wolverhampton Grammar School
Compton Road, Wolverhampton,
West Midlands WV3 9RB
Tel: 01902 421326
Head: Kathy Crewe-Read BSc
Age range: 7–18
No. of pupils: 738 VIth156
Fees: Day £3,457–£4,554
(A) (£) 🖉 (16)

Woodstock Girls' School
11-15 Woodstock Road, Moseley,
Birmingham, West Midlands B13 9BB
Tel: 0121 4496690
Headteacher: Mrs
Na'zihah Ahmed-Atif
Age range: G11–16
No. of pupils: 123
(👤)

Worcestershire

Abberley Hall
Abberley Hall, Worcester,
Worcestershire WR6 6DD
Tel: 01299 896275
Headmaster: Mr Will Lockett
Age range: 2–13
Fees: Day £9,120–£19,410 FB £24,375
(🏫) (£) 🖉

Bowbrook House School
Peopleton, Pershore,
Worcestershire WR10 2EE
Tel: 01905 841242
Headteacher: Mr C D Allen BSc(Hons)
Age range: 3–16
Fees: Day £5,775–£11,388
(£) 🖉

Bromsgrove Preparatory School
Old Station Road, Bromsgrove,
Worcestershire B60 2BU
Tel: 01527 579600
Headmistress: Jacqui Deval-Reed
Age range: 7–13
Fees: Day £11,640–£15,105 WB
£17,685–£21,390 FB £24,240–£29,895
(🏫) (£) 🖉

**Bromsgrove Pre-preparatory
& Nursery School**
Avoncroft House, Hanbury Road,
Bromsgrove, Worcestershire B60 4JS
Tel: 01527 873007
Headmistress: Jacqui Deval-Reed
Age range: 2–7
Fees: Day £5,625–£8,790

Bromsgrove School
Worcester Road, Bromsgrove,
Worcestershire B61 7DU
Tel: +44 (0)1527 579679
Headmaster: Peter Clague
Age range: 13–18
No. of pupils: 1300 VIth374
Fees: Day £16,655 WB
£24,720 FB £37,290
(🌐) (A) (🏫) (£) (IB) 🖉 (16) 🐾

Cambian New Elizabethan School
Quarry Bank, Hartlebury,
Kidderminster, Worcestershire DY11 7TE
Tel: 01299 250258
Headteacher: Mr Craig Moreton
Age range: 7–19
No. of pupils: 45
£ ✐

Dodderhill Independent Girls
Crutch Lane, Droitwich,
Worcestershire WR9 0BE
Tel: 01905 778290
Headmistress: Mrs C Mawston
Age range: G4–16
No. of pupils: 190
Fees: Day £6,870–£11,700
👤 £ ✐

Heathfield Knoll School
Wolverley Road, Wolverley, Nr.
Kidderminster, Worcestershire DY10 3QE
Tel: 01562 850204
Head of School: Mr. L. G. Collins
B.Sc.(Hons), M.A.,P.G.C.E.
Age range: 3 months–16 years
No. of pupils: 251
Fees: Day £7,800–£12,465
£ ✐

King's College Saint Michaels
Oldwood Road, Tenbury Wells,
Worcestershire WR15 8PH
Tel: +44 (0)1584 811300
Head of School: Nicola Walker
BSc, MEd, MBA,NPQH
Age range: 13–18 (academic
programmes)
No. of pupils: 109
Fees: FB £27,600
🌐 Ⓐ 🏫 16+

King's Hawford
Hawford Lock Lane, Claines,
Worcester, Worcestershire WR3 7SE
Tel: 01905 451292
Headmaster: Mr J Turner
Age range: 2–11
No. of pupils: 330
Fees: Day £7,344–£13,221
£ ✐

King's St Alban's School
Mill Street, Worcester,
Worcestershire WR1 2NJ
Tel: 01905 354906
Headmaster: Mr R Chapman
Age range: 4–11
No. of pupils: 216
Fees: Day £7,008–£12,678
£

King's Worcester
5 College Green, Worcester,
Worcestershire WR1 2LL
Tel: 01905 721700
Age range: 11–18
No. of pupils: 935 VIth270
Fees: Day £13,989
Ⓐ £ 16+

Madinatul Uloom Islamic College
Butts Lane, Stone, Kidderminster,
Worcestershire DY10 4BH
Tel: 01562 66894
The Head: Head
Age range: B11–24
No. of pupils: 200
👤 Ⓐ 🏫 16+

Madresfield Early Years Centre
Hayswood Farm, Madresfield,
Malvern, Worcestershire WR13 5AA
Tel: 01684 574378
Head: Mrs A Bennett M.B.E.
Age range: 1–5
No. of pupils: 216
Fees: Day £5,800–£6,500
£ ✐

Malvern College
College Road, Malvern,
Worcestershire WR14 3DF
Tel: 01684 581500
Headmaster: Antony
Clark MA (Cantab)
Age range: 13–18
No. of pupils: 650
Fees: Day £8,485 FB £12,709–£13,153
🌐 Ⓐ 🏫 £ IB ✐ 16+

**MALVERN ST JAMES
GIRLS' SCHOOL**
For further details see p. 260
15 Avenue Road, Great Malvern,
Worcestershire WR14 3BA
Tel: 01684 892288
Email: admissions@
malvernstjames.co.uk
Website: www.malvernstjames.co.uk
Headteacher: Mrs Olivera
Raraty BA PGCE
Age range: G4–18
No. of pupils: 410
Fees: Day £7,170–£19,875 WB
£20,520–£34,620 FB £22,905–£38,190
👤 🌐 Ⓐ 🏫 £ ✐ 16+

RGS Springfield
Springfield, Britannia Square,
Worcester, Worcestershire WR1 3DL
Tel: 01905 24999
Headmistress: Mrs Laura Brown
Age range: 2–11
No. of pupils: 140
Fees: Day £8,160–£12,546
£

RGS The Grange
Grange Lane, Claines, Worcester,
Worcestershire WR3 7RR
Tel: 01905 451205
Headmaster: Mr Gareth Hughes
Age range: 2–11
No. of pupils: 350
Fees: Day £8,160–£12,546
✐

River School
Oakfield House, Droitwich Road,
Worcester, Worcestershire WR3 7ST
Tel: 01905 457047
Principal: Mr Adrian Parsonage
Age range: 2–16
Fees: Day £6,600

The Downs Malvern
Colwall, Malvern,
Worcestershire WR13 6EY
Tel: 01684 544100
Headmaster: Mr Alastair Cook
Age range: 3–13
Fees: Day £7,107–£17,076 WB
£12,882–£19,890 FB £14,640–£22,602
🏫 £ ✐

The Elms
Colwall, Malvern,
Worcestershire WR13 6EF
Tel: 01684 540344
Headmaster: Mr Chris Hattam
Age range: 3–13
No. of pupils: 200
Fees: Day £8,085–£19,500
FB £24,000–£24,480
🏫 £ ✐

**The Royal Grammar
School Worcester**
Upper Tything, Worcester,
Worcestershire WR1 1HP
Tel: 01905 613391
Headmaster: Mr John Pitt
Age range: 11–18
No. of pupils: 764
Fees: Day £13,080
Ⓐ £ ✐ 16+

Winterfold House
Chaddesley Corbett, Kidderminster,
Worcestershire DY10 4PW
Tel: 01562 777234
Headmistress: Mrs Denise Toms
Age range: 6 weeks–13 years
£ ✐

D400

Yorkshire & Humberside

KEY TO SYMBOLS

- ⚤ Boys' school
- ⚤ Girls' school
- 🌐 International school
- 16 Tutorial or sixth form college
- Ⓐ A levels
- ♨ Boarding accommodation
- £ Bursaries
- IB International Baccalaureate
- ✎ Learning support
- 16 Entrance at 16+
- ☯ Vocational qualifications
- IAPS Independent Association of Preparatory Schools
- HMC The Headmasters' & Headmistresses' Conference
- ISA Independent Schools Association
- GSA Girls' School Association
- BSA Boarding Schools' Association
- S Society of Heads

Unless otherwise indicated, all schools are coeducational day schools.
Single-sex and boarding schools will be indicated by the relevant icon.

East Riding of Yorkshire

**Focus School –
Cottingham Campus**
Old Victorian School, Hallgate,
Cottingham, East Riding of
Yorkshire HU16 4DD
Tel: 01482 840722
Headteacher: Mrs Kimberley Hutton
Age range: 11–16
No. of pupils: 40

Froebel House School
5 Marlborough Avenue, Kingston upon
Hull, East Riding of Yorkshire HU5 3JP
Tel: 01482 342272
Headmaster: Mr A Roberts
M.Ed BA Hons PGCE
Age range: 4–11
No. of pupils: 131
Fees: Day £4,398–£4,623
Ⓐ

Hessle Mount School
Jenny Brough Lane, Hessle, East
Riding of Yorkshire HU13 0JZ
Tel: 01482 643371
Headmistress: Miss Sarah Cutting
Age range: 3–8
No. of pupils: 155
Fees: Day £6,000–£6,300

Hull Collegiate School
Tranby Croft, Anlaby, Kingston upon
Hull, East Riding of Yorkshire HU10 7EH
Tel: 01482 657016
Headteacher: Mrs Alex Wilson
Age range: 3–18
No. of pupils: 650
Fees: Day £5,013–£11,796
Ⓐ Ⓔ Ⓐ ⑯

Hymers College
Hymers Avenue, Kingston upon Hull,
East Riding of Yorkshire HU3 1LW
Tel: 01482 343555
Headmaster: Mr D Elstone
Age range: 8–18
No. of pupils: 977 VIth215
Fees: Day £9,459–£11,358
Ⓐ Ⓔ ⑯

North Yorkshire

Ampleforth College
York, North Yorkshire YO62 4ER
Tel: 01439 766000
Acting Head: Miss Deirdre Rowe
Age range: 11–18
No. of pupils: VIth255
Fees: Day £24,636 FB £35,424
Ⓐ Ⓐ Ⓐ Ⓔ Ⓐ ⑯

Ashville College
Green Lane, Harrogate,
North Yorkshire HG2 9JP
Tel: 01423 566358
Headmaster: Mr Richard Marshall
Age range: 3–18
No. of pupils: 870
Fees: Day £8,430–£14,640
FB £18,390–£27,780
Ⓐ Ⓐ Ⓐ Ⓔ ⑯

Aysgarth School
Newton le Willows, Bedale,
North Yorkshire DL8 1TF
Tel: 01677 450240
No. of pupils: 200
Fees: Day £2,700–£6,630 WB
£995–£1,325 FB £8,630
Ⓐ Ⓐ Ⓔ Ⓐ

Belmont Grosvenor School
Swarcliffe Hall, Birstwith, Harrogate,
North Yorkshire HG3 2JG
Tel: 01423 771029
Headmistress: Mrs Sophia
Ashworth Jones
Age range: 3 months–11 years
No. of pupils: 153
Fees: Day £9,600–£11,370

Bootham Junior School
Rawcliffe Lane, York, North
Yorkshire YO30 6NP
Tel: 01904 655021
Head: Mrs Helen Todd
Age range: 3–11
Fees: Day £6,930–£10,365
Ⓐ

Bootham School
York, North Yorkshire YO30 7BU
Tel: 01904 623261
Headmaster: Chris Jeffery BA, FRSA
Age range: 11–18
No. of pupils: 480 VIth172
Fees: Day £16,200–£17,865 WB
£18,885–£27,765 FB £18,885–£30,465
Ⓐ Ⓐ Ⓐ Ⓔ Ⓐ ⑯

Brackenfield School
128 Duchy Road, Harrogate,
North Yorkshire HG1 2HE
Tel: 01423 508558
Headteacher: Ms Patricia Sowa
Age range: 2–11
No. of pupils: 179
Fees: Day £8,235–£8,850
Ⓐ

**Chapter House
Preparatory School**
Thorpe Underwood Hall, Ouseburn,
York, North Yorkshire YO26 9SZ
Tel: 01423 333330
Head Teacher: Mrs Karen Kilkenny BSc
Age range: 3–10
No. of pupils: 122
Fees: Day £4,020–£11,100
FB £30,960–£33,270
Ⓐ Ⓔ Ⓐ

Clifton School and Nursery
York, North Yorkshire YO30 6AB
Tel: 01904 527361
Head: Philip Hardy BA (Hons) PGCE
Age range: 3–8
No. of pupils: 199
Fees: Day £7,980–£9,240

Cundall Manor School
Helperby, York, North
Yorkshire YO61 2RW
Tel: 01423 360200
Joint Heads: Mrs Amanda Kirby
BA (Hons) PGCE, NPQH & Mr John
Sample BSc (Hons) PGCE
Age range: 2–16
No. of pupils: 350
Fees: Day £9,738–£15,612
WB £20,313–£20,529
Ⓐ Ⓔ Ⓐ

Fyling Hall School
Robin Hood's Bay, Whitby,
North Yorkshire YO22 4QD
Tel: 01947 880353
Headmaster: Mr. Steven Allen
Age range: 4–18
No. of pupils: VIth54
Fees: Day £6,684–£9,177 WB
£9,207–£11,778 FB £16,230–£19,995
Ⓐ Ⓐ Ⓐ Ⓔ Ⓐ ⑯

Giggleswick Junior School
Mill Lane, Giggleswick, Settle,
North Yorkshire BD24 0DG
Tel: 01729 893100
Headmaster: Mr. James Mundell
Age range: 3–11 (boarding from 9)
No. of pupils: 75
Fees: Day £7,965–£12,765 FB £21,240
Ⓐ Ⓔ Ⓐ

Giggleswick School
Giggleswick, Settle, North
Yorkshire BD24 0DE
Tel: 01729 893000
Head: Mr Mark Turnbull
Age range: 11–18
No. of pupils: 320 VIth145
Fees: Day £15,585–£20,985
FB £23,550–£33,750
Ⓐ Ⓐ Ⓐ Ⓔ Ⓐ ⑯

Harrogate Ladies' College
Clarence Drive, Harrogate,
North Yorkshire HG1 2QG
Tel: 01423 504543
Principal: Mrs Sylvia Brett
Age range: G11–18
No. of pupils: 300
Fees: Day £16,035 FB £29,115–£36,510
Ⓐ Ⓐ Ⓐ Ⓐ Ⓔ ⑯

Highfield Prep School
Clarence Drive, Harrogate,
North Yorkshire HG1 2QG
Tel: 01423 504 543
Head: James Savile
Age range: 4–11
No. of pupils: 216
Fees: Day £9,420–£10,740 FB £23,820

Pocklington Prep School
West Green, Pocklington, York,
North Yorkshire YO42 2NH
Tel: 01759 321228
Headmaster: Mr I D Wright
BSc(Hons), PGCE, NPQH
Age range: 3–11
No. of pupils: 225
Fees: Day £7,812–£12,255 WB
£18,366–£21,393 FB £20,202–£23,046
🏫 £ ✎

POCKLINGTON SCHOOL
For further details see p. 274
West Green, Pocklington, York,
North Yorkshire YO42 2NJ
Tel: 01759 321200
Email: enquiry@
pocklingtonschool.com
Website:
www.pocklingtonschool.com
Headmaster: Mr Toby
Seth MA (Cantab)
Age range: 3–18
No. of pupils: 759 VIth155
Fees: Day £15,057 WB
£26,991 FB £29,346
🏫 Ⓐ 🏫 £ ✎ 16·

**QUEEN ETHELBURGA'S
COLLEGIATE FOUNDATION**
For further details see p. 276
Thorpe Underwood Hall, Ouseburn,
York, North Yorkshire YO26 9SS
Tel: 01423 33 33 30
Email: info@qe.org
Website: www.qe.org
Principal: Steven Jandrell BA
Age range: 3–19
No. of pupils: 1545 VIth605
🏫 Ⓐ 🏫 £ ✎ 16· 🏐

Queen Margaret's School
Escrick Park, York, North
Yorkshire YO19 6EU
Tel: 01904 727600
Head of School: Mrs Jessica Miles
Age range: G11–18
No. of pupils: 302 VIth120
Fees: Day £21,270 FB £30,400
🏃 🏫 Ⓐ 🏫 ✎ 16·

Queen Mary's School
Baldersby Park, Topcliffe, Thirsk,
North Yorkshire YO7 3BZ
Tel: 01845 575000
Head: Carole Cameron
Age range: B3–8 G3–16
No. of pupils: 235
Fees: Day £8,265–£18,420
FB £20,475–£24,165
🏃 🏫 🏫 £ ✎

Scarborough College
Filey Road, Scarborough,
North Yorkshire YO11 3BA
Tel: +44 (0)1723 360620
Headmaster: Mr Charles Ellison
Age range: 3–18
No. of pupils: 418 VIth84
Fees: Day £7,488–£14,694 WB
£17,217–£19,440 FB £22,041–£28,458
🏫 🏫 £ IB ✎ 16·

St Martins Ampleforth
Gilling Castle, Gilling East, York,
North Yorkshire YO62 4HP
Tel: 01439 766600
Headmaster: Dr D Moses
Age range: 11–13 years
No. of pupils: 155
Fees: Day £16,401 FB £25,251
🏫 £ ✎

St Olave's School
Clifton, York, North Yorkshire YO30 6AB
Tel: 01904 527416
The Master: Mr A Falconer
Age range: 8–13
No. of pupils: 355
Fees: Day £12,345–£14,955
FB £23,160–£25,560
🏫 £ ✎

St Peter's School
Clifton, York, North Yorkshire YO30 6AB
Tel: 01904 527300
Head Master: Mr L Winkley
MA(Oxon), MEd(OU)
Age range: 13–18
No. of pupils: 375 VIth231
Fees: Day £18,075 FB £30,030
🏫 Ⓐ 🏫 £ ✎ 16·

Terrington Hall
Terrington, York, North
Yorkshire YO60 6PR
Tel: 01653 648227
Headmaster: Mr. Stephen
Mulryne B.Ed (Hons) Liverpool
Age range: 3–13
No. of pupils: 150
🏫 £ ✎

The Minster School
Deangate, York, North
Yorkshire YO1 7JA
Tel: 0844 939 0000
Headmaster: Mr A Donaldson
Age range: 3–13
Fees: Day £3,855–£10,398
✎

The Mount Junior School
Dalton Terrace, York, North
Yorkshire YO24 4DD
Tel: 01904 667513
Head: Mr Martyn Andrews
BSc(Hons), PGCE
Age range: 3–11
Fees: Day £1,710–£2,280
✎

The Mount School York
Dalton Terrace, York, North
Yorkshire YO24 4DD
Tel: 01904 667500
Principal: Miss Adrienne Richmond
BSc (Hons), PGCE, MA, NPQH
Age range: B2–11 G2–18
No. of pupils: 260 VIth47
Fees: Day £5,850–£16,950 WB
£18,060–£26,253 FB £20,391–£29,691
🏃 🏫 Ⓐ 🏫 £ ✎ 16·

The Read School
Drax, Selby, North Yorkshire YO8 8NL
Tel: 01757 618248
Acting Head: M A Voisey
Age range: 3–18
No. of pupils: VIth36
Fees: Day £8,457–£11,970 WB
£21,279–£24,429 FB £22,743–£26,019
🏫 Ⓐ 🏫 £ ✎ 16·

Wharfedale Montessori School
Bolton Abbey, Skipton, North
Yorkshire BD23 6AN
Tel: 01756 710452
Headmistress/Principal: Mrs Jane Lord
Age range: 2–12
Fees: Day £7,350
✎

York Steiner School
Danesmead, Fulford Cross, York,
North Yorkshire YO10 4PB
Tel: 01904 654983
Administrator: Maurice Dobie
Age range: 3–14
No. of pupils: 197
Fees: Day £6,750
✎

North-East Lincolnshire

Montessori School
Station Road, Stallingborough,
North-East Lincolnshire DN41 8AJ
Tel: 01472 886000
Headteacher: Ms Theresa Ellerby
Age range: 4–11
No. of pupils: 21

St James' School
22 Bargate, Grimsby, North-
East Lincolnshire DN34 4SY
Tel: 01472 503260
Headmaster: Dr J Price
Age range: 2–18
No. of pupils: 238 VIth25
🏫 Ⓐ 🏫 £ ✎ 16·

St Martin's Preparatory School
63 Bargate, Grimsby, North-
East Lincolnshire DN34 5AA
Tel: 01472 878907
Headmaster: Mr S Thompson BEd
Age range: 2–11
Fees: Day £5,580–£6,780
✎

South Yorkshire

Al-Mahad-Al-Islam School
1 Industry Road, Sheffield,
South Yorkshire S9 5FP
Tel: 0114 242 3138
Headteacher: Mrs Juwairiah Khan
Age range: G11–17
No. of pupils: 70
🚹

Bethany School
Finlay Street, Sheffield,
South Yorkshire S3 7PS
Tel: 0114 272 6994
Headteacher: Mrs Judith Baxter
Age range: 4–16
No. of pupils: 76
🖉

Birkdale School
Oakholme Road, Sheffield,
South Yorkshire S10 3DH
Tel: 0114 2668409
Acting Head: Mr Nicholas Pietrek
Age range: B4–18 G16–18
No. of pupils: VIth200
Fees: Day £8,445–£12,630
🚹 Ⓐ £ 🖉 16

Hill House School
6th Avenue, Auckley, Doncaster,
South Yorkshire DN9 3GG
Tel: +44 (0)1302 776300
Principal: David Holland
Age range: 3–18
Fees: Day £8,700–£13,200

Mylnhurst Preparatory School & Nursery
Button Hill, Woodholm Road, Ecclesall,
Sheffield, South Yorkshire S11 9HJ
Tel: 0114 2361411
Headmaster: Christopher Emmott BSc(Hons), PGCE
Age range: 3–11
No. of pupils: 185
Fees: Day £9,333
🖉

Sheffield High School GDST
10 Rutland Park, Sheffield,
South Yorkshire S10 2PE
Tel: 0114 266 0324
Headmistress: Nina Gunson
Age range: G4–18
No. of pupils: 1020
Fees: Day £9,216–£12,975
🚹 Ⓐ £ 🖉 16

Sycamore Hall Preparatory School
1 Hall Flat Lane, Balby, Doncaster,
South Yorkshire DN4 8PT
Tel: 01302 856800
Headmistress: Miss J Spencer
Age range: 3–11
Fees: Day £4,890

Westbourne School
Westbourne Road, Sheffield,
South Yorkshire S10 2QT
Tel: 0114 2660374
Headmaster: Mr John B Hicks MEd
Age range: 3–16
No. of pupils: 338
Fees: Day £8,925–£12,750
£ 🖉

West Yorkshire

Ackworth School
Pontefract Road, Ackworth, nr.
Pontefract, West Yorkshire WF7 7LT
Tel: 01977 611401
Head: Mr. Anton Maree
BA Rhodes (HDE)
Age range: 3–18
No. of pupils: 490
Fees: Day £8,145–£13,518 FB £29,151
🌐 Ⓐ 🏛 £ 🖉 16

Al Mu'min Primary School
Clifton St, Bradford, West
Yorkshire BD8 7DA
Tel: 01274 488593
Headteacher: Mr M M Azam
Age range: 4–11
No. of pupils: 102

Al-Furqan Preparatory School
Drill Hall House, Bath Street,
Dewsbury, West Yorkshire WF13 2JR
Tel: 01924 453 661
Headteacher: Mr Bilal Aswat
Age range: 3–11
No. of pupils: 139

Bradford Christian School
Livingstone Road, Bolton Woods,
Bradford, West Yorkshire BD2 1BT
Tel: 01274 532649
Headmaster: P J Moon BEd(Hons)
Age range: 4–16
Fees: Day £2,460–£4,440
🖉

Bradford Grammar School
Keighley Road, Bradford,
West Yorkshire BD9 4JP
Tel: 01274 542492
Headmaster: Dr Simon Hinchliffe
Age range: 6–18
No. of pupils: VIth266
Ⓐ £ 🖉 16

Bronte House School
Apperley Bridge, Bradford,
West Yorkshire BD10 0NR
Tel: 0113 2502811
Headmaster: Simon W Dunn
Age range: 2–11
No. of pupils: 340
Fees: Day £9,000–£13,575 WB
£26,160–£26,625 FB £27,900–£28,020
🏛 £ 🖉

Crystal Gardens
38-40 Greaves Street, Bradford,
West Yorkshire BD5 7PE
Tel: 01274 575400
Headteacher: Rashta Bibi
Age range: 4–11
No. of pupils: 20

Dale House Independent School
Ruby Street, Carlinghow, Batley,
West Yorkshire WF17 8HL
Tel: 01924 422215
Headmistress: Mrs S M G
Fletcher BA, CertEd
Age range: 2–11
No. of pupils: 100
£ 🖉

Darul Uloom Dawatul Imaan
Harry Street, Off Wakefield Road,
Bradford, West Yorkshire BD4 9PH
Tel: 01274 402233
Principal: Mr Mohamed Bilal Lorgat
Age range: B11–13
No. of pupils: 112
🚹

Eternal Light Secondary School
Christopher Street, Off Little Horton
Lane, Bradford, West Yorkshire BD5 9DH
Tel: 01274 501597
Headteacher: Mr Yusuf Collector
Age range: B11–15
No. of pupils: 91
🚹

Focus School – York Campus
Bishopthorpe Road, York,
West Yorkshire YO23 2QA
Tel: 01904 663 300
Headteacher: Mr Paul Easton
Age range: 7–18
No. of pupils: 44

Fulneck School
Fulneck, Pudsey, Leeds,
West Yorkshire LS28 8DS
Tel: 0113 257 0235
Principal: Mr Paul Taylor
Age range: 3–18
No. of pupils: 350
Fees: Day £7,545–£13,650
WB £24,405 FB £26,985
🌐 Ⓐ 🏛 £ 🖉 16

Gateways School
Harewood, Leeds, West
Yorkshire LS17 9LE
Tel: 0113 2886345
Headmistress: Dr Tracy Johnson
Age range: B2–11 G2–18
No. of pupils: 394 VIth48
Fees: Day £8,445–£13,614
🚹 Ⓐ £ 🖉 16

Ghyll Royd School and Pre-School
Greystone Manor, Ilkley Road, Burley in
Wharfedale, West Yorkshire LS29 7HW
Tel: 01943 865575
Headteacher: Mr David
Martin BA MA PGCE
Age range: 2–11
No. of pupils: 110
Fees: Day £2,900–£2,990
£ 🖉

Hipperholme Grammar School
Bramley Lane, Hipperholme,
Halifax, West Yorkshire HX3 8JE
Tel: 01422 202256
Head: Mrs Jackie Griffiths
Age range: 3–18
No. of pupils: VIth30
Fees: Day £8,799–£10,995
Ⓐ £ 🖉 16

Huddersfield Grammar School
Royds Mount, Luck Lane, Marsh,
Huddersfield, West Yorkshire HD1 4QX
Tel: 01484 424549
Headmaster: Mr Mike Seaton
Age range: 3–16
No. of pupils: 510
Fees: Day £8,598–£10,602
£ ✎

Institute of Islamic Education
South Street, Savile Town, Dewsbury,
West Yorkshire WF12 9NG
Tel: 01924 485712/01924 455762
Principal: Mr Mohamed Aswat
Age range: B11–25
No. of pupils: 184
♦ ☱

Islamia Girls High School
2 Thornton Lodge Road,
Thornton Lodge, Huddersfield,
West Yorkshire HD1 3JQ
Tel: 01484 518 817
Head: Mrs Samira El-Turabi
Age range: G11–16
Fees: Day £1,300
♦ ✎

**Islamic Tarbiyah
Preparatory School**
Ambler Street, Bradford,
West Yorkshire BD8 8AW
Tel: 01274 490462
Headteacher: Mr S A Nawaz
Age range: 5–10
No. of pupils: 123

**Jaamiatul Imaam Muhammad
Zakaria School**
Thornton View Road, Clayton,
Bradford, West Yorkshire BD14 6JX
Tel: 01274 882007
Headteacher: Mrs Z Hajee
Age range: G11–16
No. of pupils: 416
♦

Lady Lane Park School & Nursery
Lady Lane, Bingley, West
Yorkshire BD16 4AP
Tel: 01274 551168
Headmaster: Mr Nigel Saunders
Age range: 2–11
No. of pupils: 150
Fees: Day £8,016
✎

Leeds Menorah School
393 Street Lane, Leeds, West
Yorkshire LS17 6HQ
Tel: 0113 268 3390
Headteacher: Rabbi J Refson
Age range: 5–16
No. of pupils: 55

M A Institute
Lumb Lane, Bradford, West
Yorkshire BD8 7RZ
Tel: 01274 395454
Age range: B11–16
No. of pupils: 68
♦

Madni Muslim Girls High School
Thornie Bank, Off Scarborough
St, Savile Town, Dewsbury,
West Yorkshire WF12 9AX
Tel: 01924 520720
Headmistress: Mrs S A Mirza
Age range: G3–18
No. of pupils: 250
♦ Ⓐ ☙

Mill Cottage Montessori School
Wakefield Road, Brighouse,
West Yorkshire HD6 4HA
Tel: 01484 400500
Principal: Ailsa Nevile
Age range: 0–11

Moorfield School
Wharfedale Lodge, 11 Ben Rhydding
Road, Ilkley, West Yorkshire LS29 8RL
Tel: 01943 607285
Headmistress: Mrs Jessica Crossley
Age range: 2–11
Fees: Day £9,600
£ ✎

Moorlands School
Foxhill, Weetwood Lane, Leeds,
West Yorkshire LS16 5PF
Tel: 0113 2785286
Headteacher: Miss J Atkinson
Age range: 2–11
No. of pupils: 149
Fees: Day £8,985–£10,566
£ ✎

Mount School
3 Binham Road, Edgerton,
Huddersfield, West Yorkshire HD2 2AP
Tel: 01484 426432
Headteacher: Janet Brook
Age range: 3–11
Fees: Day £7,095
✎

Netherleigh & Rossefield School
Parsons Road, Heaton, Bradford,
West Yorkshire BD9 4AY
Tel: 01274 543162
Headteacher: Miss A Leary
Age range: 2–11
No. of pupils: 141
Fees: Day £6,735
£ ✎

New Horizon Community School
Newton Hill House, Newton Hill Road,
Leeds, West Yorkshire LS7 4JE
Tel: 0113 262 4001
Acting Head: Qudisia Butt
Age range: G11–16
No. of pupils: 87
Fees: Day £1,800
♦ ✎

Olive Secondary School
Byron Street, Bradford, West
Yorkshire BD3 0AD
Tel: +44+ (0)1274 725005 /
+44 (0)1274 725013
Headteacher: Mr Amjad Mohammed
Age range: 11–18
No. of pupils: 115
Fees: Day £2,075

Paradise Primary School
1 Bretton Street, Dewsbury,
West Yorkshire WF12 9BB
Tel: 01924 439803
Headteacher: Mrs Hafsa Patel
Age range: 2–11
No. of pupils: 217

**Queen Elizabeth Grammar
School (Junior School)**
158 Northgate, Wakefield,
West Yorkshire WF1 3QY
Tel: 01924 373821
Head: Mrs L A Gray
Age range: B4–11
No. of pupils: 261
Fees: Day £9,153–£9,987
♦ £

**Queen Elizabeth Grammar
School (Senior School)**
154 Northgate, Wakefield,
West Yorkshire WF1 3QY
Tel: 01924 373943
Headmaster: David Craig
Age range: B11–18
No. of pupils: 677
Fees: Day £12,636
♦ Ⓐ £ ⑯

Queenswood School
Queen Street, Morley, Leeds,
West Yorkshire LS27 9EB
Tel: 0113 2534033
Headteacher: Mrs J A Tanner
MMus, BA, FTCL, ARCO
Age range: 4–11
Fees: Day £6,000–£6,447

Rastrick Independent School
Ogden Lane, Rastrick, Brighouse,
West Yorkshire HD6 3HF
Tel: 01484 400344
Headmistress: Mrs S A Vaughey
Age range: 0–16
No. of pupils: 200
Fees: Day £7,680–£9,470
Ⓐ £ ✎ ⑯ ☙

Richmond House School
170 Otley Road, Leeds, West
Yorkshire LS16 5LG
Tel: 0113 2752670
Headteacher: Mrs Helen Stiles
Age range: 3–11
No. of pupils: 219
Fees: Day £5,850–£9,150
£ ✎

Rishworth School
Rishworth, Halifax, West
Yorkshire HX6 4QA
Tel: 01422 822217
Head: Dr Paul Silverwood
Age range: 3–18
No. of pupils: 600 VIth90
Fees: Day £6,465–£12,660 WB
£24,975–£27,300 FB £27,510–£29,985
⚕ Ⓐ ☱ £ ✎ ⑯

Silcoates School
Wrenthorpe, Wakefield,
West Yorkshire WF2 0PD
Tel: 01924 291614
Headmaster: Philip Rowe
Age range: 4–18
No. of pupils: 768
Fees: Day £7,530–£13,785
Ⓐ £ ⑯

The Branch Christian School
Dewsbury Revival Centre,
West Park Street, Dewsbury,
West Yorkshire WF13 4LA
Tel: +44 (0)1924 452511
Head of School: Jo Holt
Age range: 3–16
No. of pupils: 26
✎

THE FROEBELIAN SCHOOL
For further details see p. 278
Clarence Road, Horsforth,
Leeds, West Yorkshire LS18 4LB
Tel: 0113 2583047
Email: office@froebelian.co.uk
Website: www.froebelian.com
Head Teacher: Mrs Catherine
Dodds BEd (Hons), PGCE
Age range: 3–11
No. of pupils: 188
Fees: Day £5,220–£7,785
(£)(✎)

The Gleddings School
Birdcage Lane, Savile Park,
Halifax, West Yorkshire HX3 0JB
Tel: 01422 354605
School Director: Mrs Jill Wilson CBE
Age range: 3–11
No. of pupils: 191
Fees: Day £3,555–£5,910
(✎)

The Grammar School at Leeds
Alwoodley Gates, Harrogate Road,
Leeds, West Yorkshire LS17 8GS
Tel: 0113 2291552
Principal: Mrs Sue Woodroofe
Age range: 3–18
No. of pupils: 2120 VIth418
Fees: Day £9,441–£13,788
(A)(£)(✎)(16·)

**Wakefield Girls' High
School (Junior School)**
2 St John's Square, Wakefield,
West Yorkshire WF1 2QX
Tel: 01924 374577
Headmistress: Mrs Rachel Edwards BEd
Age range: G4–11
No. of pupils: 493
Fees: Day £9,153–£9,987
(⚥)(£)(✎)

**Wakefield Girls' High
School (Senior School)**
Wentworth Street, Wakefield,
West Yorkshire WF1 2QS
Tel: 01924 372490
Headmistress: Ms Heidi-
Jayne Boyes BSc
Age range: G11–18
No. of pupils: 715
Fees: Day £12,636
(⚥)(A)(£)(✎)(16·)

Wakefield Independent School
The Nostell Centre, Doncaster
Road, Nostell, Wakefield,
West Yorkshire WF4 1QG
Tel: 01924 865757
Headmistress: Mrs K E Caryl
Age range: 2¹/2–16
No. of pupils: 190
Fees: Day £5,100–£7,050
(£)(✎)

**West Cliffe Montessori
School & Nursery**
33, Barlow Road, access
Belgrave Road, Keighley,
West Yorkshire BD21 2TA
Tel: 01535 609797
Principal: Mrs T Bisby
Age range: 0–8
No. of pupils: 42
(✎)

**Westville House
Preparatory School**
Carter's Lane, Middleton, Ilkley,
West Yorkshire LS29 0DQ
Tel: 01943 608053
Headteacher: Mrs Nikki
Hammond BA(Hons) PGCE
Age range: 3–11
Fees: Day £5,619–£9,735
(✎)

Woodhouse Grove School
Apperley Bridge, Bradford,
West Yorkshire BD10 0NR
Tel: 0113 250 2477
Headmaster: Mr James Lockwood MA
Age range: 2–18
No. of pupils: 1090
Fees: Day £9,000–£13,575
FB £27,900–£28,020
(🌐)(A)(🏫)(£)(✎)(16·)(👥)

Northern Ireland

KEY TO SYMBOLS

- 🚹 *Boys' school*
- 🚺 *Girls' school*
- 🌐 *International school*
- 16 *Tutorial or sixth form college*
- Ⓐ *A levels*
- 🏛 *Boarding accommodation*
- £ *Bursaries*
- IB *International Baccalaureate*
- ✎ *Learning support*
- 16 *Entrance at 16+*
- 🌐 *Vocational qualifications*
- IAPS *Independent Association of Preparatory Schools*
- HMC *The Headmasters' & Headmistresses' Conference*
- ISA *Independent Schools Association*
- GSA *Girls' School Association*
- BSA *Boarding Schools' Association*
- S *Society of Heads*

Unless otherwise indicated, all schools are coeducational day schools.
Single-sex and boarding schools will be indicated by the relevant icon.

County Antrim

Belfast Royal Academy
7 Cliftonville Road, Belfast,
County Antrim BT14 6JL
Tel: 028 9074 0423
Principal: Mrs Hilary Woods
Age range: 11–18
No. of pupils: VIth382
Fees: Day £140
Ⓐ 16·

Campbell College
Belfast, County Antrim BT4 2ND
Tel: 028 9076 3076
Headmaster: Mr Robert Robinson
Age range: B11–18
No. of pupils: 896 VIth200
Fees: Day £2,708–£8,363
FB £14,095–£19,750
🚹🌍Ⓐ♨£🖋16·🐾

Campbell College Junior School
Belmont Road, Belfast,
County Antrim BT4 2ND
Tel: 028 9076 3076
Head: Miss Andrea Brown
Age range: B3–11 G3–4
Fees: Day £4,145–£4,449
🚹🖋

Hunterhouse College
Finaghy, Belfast, County
Antrim BT10 0LE
Tel: 028 9061 2293
Principal: Mr A Gibson MA, DipEd, PQH
Age range: G11–18
No. of pupils: 710 VIth180
Fees: Day £320
🚹Ⓐ🖋16·

Inchmarlo
Cranmore Park, Belfast,
County Antrim BT9 6JR
Tel: 028 9038 1454
🚹

Methodist College
1 Malone Road, Belfast,
County Antrim BT9 6BY
Tel: 028 9020 5205
Principal: Mr J Scott W Naismith
Age range: 4–19
No. of pupils: 2307 VIth548
🌍Ⓐ🖋16·

Royal Belfast Academical Institution
College Square East, Belfast,
County Antrim BT1 6DL
Tel: 028 9024 0461
Principal: Miss J A Williamson
MA(Oxon), NPQH
Age range: B4–18
No. of pupils: 1290 VIth275
Fees: Day £940–£4,140
🚹Ⓐ♨£🖋16·

St Mary's Christian Brothers Grammar School
Glen Road, Belfast, County
Antrim BT11 8NR
Tel: 028 9029 4000
Head of School: Mrs Siobhan Kelly
Age range: B12–18
No. of pupils: 112
🚹Ⓐ16·

Victoria College Belfast
Cranmore Park, Belfast,
County Antrim BT9 6JA
Tel: 028 9066 1506
Principal: Ms Patricia Slevin
Age range: G2–18
No. of pupils: 1070 VIth224
Fees: Day £4,825–£7,550
FB £11,100–£18,650
🚹Ⓐ♨🖋16·

County Armagh

The Royal School
College Hill, Armagh, County
Armagh BT61 9DH
Tel: 02837 522807
Headmaster: Mr Graham Montgomery
Age range: 11–18
No. of pupils: 654 VIth157
Fees: Day £3,700–£4,415
WB £7,275 FB £10,925
Ⓐ♨16·🐾

County Down

Bangor Grammar School
Gransha Road, Bangor,
County Down BT19 7QU
Tel: 028 91 473734
Principal: Mrs E P Huddleson
B.Ed., M.SSc., PQH(NI)
Age range: B3–18
No. of pupils: 900 VIth220
Fees: Day £140–£395
🚹Ⓐ🖋16·

Holywood Steiner School
34 Croft Road, Holywood,
County Down BT18 0PR
Tel: 028 9042 8029
Chairperson of the School Management Team: Julie Higgins
Age range: 3–17 years
No. of pupils: 110
Fees: Day £4,008–£4,512
£

Rockport School
Craigavad, Holywood,
County Down BT18 0DD
Tel: 028 9042 8372
Headmaster: Mr George Vance
Age range: 3–18
No. of pupils: 200
Fees: Day £6,540–£15,810 WB
£17,970–£22,770 FB £21,450–£26,160
🌍Ⓐ♨£🖋

County Tyrone

The Royal School Dungannon
2 Ranfurly Road, Dungannon,
County Tyrone BT71 6EG
Tel: 028 8772 2710
Headmaster: Dr David Burnett
Age range: 11–18
No. of pupils: 652 VIth156
Fees: Day £70–£150 WB £7,950
FB £10,650–£19,050
🌍Ⓐ♨🖋16·

Scotland

KEY TO SYMBOLS
- (♂) *Boys' school*
- (♀) *Girls' school*
- (🌐) *International school*
- (16) *Tutorial or sixth form college*
- (A) *A levels*
- (⌂) *Boarding accommodation*
- (£) *Bursaries*
- (IB) *International Baccalaureate*
- (✐) *Learning support*
- (16+) *Entrance at 16+*
- (🌐) *Vocational qualifications*
- (IAPS) *Independent Association of Preparatory Schools*
- (HMC) *The Headmasters' & Headmistresses' Conference*
- (ISA) *Independent Schools Association*
- (GSA) *Girls' School Association*
- (BSA) *Boarding Schools' Association*
- (S) *Society of Heads*

Unless otherwise indicated, all schools are coeducational day schools. Single-sex and boarding schools will be indicated by the relevant icon.

Aberdeen

Albyn School
17-23 Queen's Road,
Aberdeen AB15 4PB
Tel: 01224 322408
Headmaster: Ian E Long
AKC, PhD, FRGS, FRSA
Age range: 2–18
No. of pupils: 675 VIth57
Fees: Day £8,637–£13,636
WB £27,811 FB £29,948
£ 16+

Robert Gordon's College
Schoolhill, Aberdeen AB10 1FE
Tel: 01224 646346
Head of College: Mr Simon Mills
Age range: 4–18
No. of pupils: 1573 VIth350
Fees: Day £8,435–£13,130
£ 16+

St Margaret's School for Girls
17 Albyn Place, Aberdeen AB10 1RU
Tel: 01224 584466
Headmistress: Miss A Tomlinson
MTheol (Hons), PGCE
Age range: B3–5 years G3–18 years
No. of pupils: 380 VIth34
Fees: Day £7,954–£12,600
£ 16+

**The International School
of Aberdeen**
Pitfodels House, North Deeside Road,
Pitfodels, Cults, Aberdeen AB15 9PN
Tel: 01224 730300
Head of School: Ms Sarah Bruce
Age range: 3–18
No. of pupils: 409 VIth39
Fees: Day £12,830–£14,100
£ IB 16+

Angus

Lathallan School
Brotherton Castle, Johnshaven,
Montrose, Angus DD10 0HN
Tel: 01561 362220
Headmaster: Mr R Toley
No. of pupils: 220
Fees: Day £5,031–£6,067
FB £7,281–£8,317
£ 16+

Argyll & Bute

Lomond School
10 Stafford Street, Helensburgh,
Argyll & Bute G84 9JX
Tel: +44 (0)1436 672476
Principal: Mrs Johanna Urquhart
Age range: 3–18
No. of pupils: 360
Fees: Day £8,640–£11,970 FB £27,750
£ 16+

Borders

St Mary's Prep School
Abbey Park, Melrose, Borders TD6 9LN
Tel: 01896 822517
Headmaster: Mr Liam Harvey
Age range: 2–13
Fees: Day £13,200–£16,050 WB £17,982
£

Clackmannanshire

Dollar Academy
Dollar, Clackmannanshire FK14 7DU
Tel: 01259 742511
Rector: Mr David Knapman Mphil
Age range: 5–18
No. of pupils: 1200 VIth142
Fees: Day £9,792–£13,095 WB
£25,335–£28,638 FB £27,000–£30,303
£ 16+

Dundee

High School of Dundee
Euclid Crescent, Dundee DD1 1HU
Tel: 01382 202921
Rector: Dr John Halliday
Age range: 3–18
No. of pupils: 1067 VIth102
Fees: Day £9,159–£12,999
£ 16+

East Lothian

Belhaven Hill
Dunbar, East Lothian EH42 1NN
Tel: 01368 862785
Headmaster: Mr. Henry Knight
Age range: 8–13
No. of pupils: 122
Fees: Day £11,520–£16,875 FB £23,760
£

Loretto Junior School
North Esk Lodge, 1 North High Street,
Musselburgh, East Lothian EH21 6JA
Tel: 0131 653 4570
Headmaster: Mr Andrew Dickenson
Age range: 3–12
No. of pupils: 200
Fees: Day £9,180–£15,900 FB £22,335
£

Loretto School
Pinkie House, Linkfield Road,
Musselburgh, East Lothian EH21 7AF
Tel: +44 (0)131 653 4455
Head of School: Dr.
Graham R. W. Hawley
Age range: 0 years–18 years
No. of pupils: 618
Fees: Day £2,833–£8,100
FB £7,750–£11,900
£ 16+

The Compass School
West Road, Haddington,
East Lothian EH41 3RD
Tel: 01620 822642
Headmaster: Mr Mark Becher
MA(Hons), PGCE
Age range: 4–12
No. of pupils: 125
Fees: Day £6,450–£9,735
£

Edinburgh

Basil Paterson Tutorial College
66 Queen Street, Edinburgh EH2 4NA
Tel: 0131 225 3802
Head of School: Claire Samuel
Age range: 14+
No. of pupils: 40
Fees: Day £3,990–£12,000
16+ A

Cargilfield School
45 Gamekeeper's Road,
Edinburgh EH4 6HU
Tel: 0131 336 2207
Headmaster: Mr. Robert Taylor
Age range: 3–13
No. of pupils: 325
Fees: Day £6,051–£15,843 WB £19,443
£

Clifton Hall
Newbridge, Edinburgh EH28 8LQ
Tel: 0131 333 1359
Headmaster: Mr R Grant
Age range: 3–18
No. of pupils: 385
Fees: Day £5,100–£12,270
£ 16+

EDINBURGH STEINER SCHOOL
For further details see p. 282
60-64 Spylaw Road,
Edinburgh EH10 5BR
Tel: 0131 337 3410
Email: info@
edinburghsteinerschool.org.uk
Website:
www.edinburghsteinerschool.org.uk
Age range: 3½–18
No. of pupils: 300
£ 16+

Fettes College
Carrington Road, Edinburgh EH4 1QX
Tel: +44 (0)131 332 2281
Head of School: Mrs Helen Harrison
Age range: 7–18
No. of pupils: 764 VIth249
Fees: Day £16,500–£28,200
FB £24,210–£34,800
🚹 Ⓐ ⚽ £ ⒤ ✐ 16+

Fettes College Preparatory School
East Fettes Avenue, Edinburgh EH4 1QZ
Tel: 0131 332 2976
Headmaster: Mr A A Edwards
Age range: 7–13
No. of pupils: 169
Fees: Day £16,500 FB £24,210
Ⓐ ⚽ £ ⒤

George Heriot's School
Lauriston Place, Edinburgh EH3 9EQ
Tel: 0131 229 7263
Principal: Mrs Lesley Franklin
Age range: 3–18
No. of pupils: 1641 VIth352
Fees: Day £8,349–£12,522
£ ✐ 16+ 🐾

George Watson's College
69-71 Colinton Road,
Edinburgh EH10 5EG
Tel: 0131 446 6000
Principal: Mr Melvyn Roffe
Age range: 3–18
No. of pupils: 2400
🚹 Ⓐ £ ⒤ ✐ 16+ 🐾

Merchiston Castle School
294 Colinton Road, Edinburgh EH13 0PU
Tel: 0131 312 2201
Headmaster: Mr Jonathan Anderson
Age range: B7–18
No. of pupils: 440
Fees: Day £15,030–£25,530
FB £21,660–£35,190
🚹 🚹 Ⓐ ⚽ £ ✐ 16+

St George's School for Girls
Garscube Terrace, Edinburgh EH12 6BG
Tel: 0131 311 8000
Head: Mrs Alex Hems BA(Hons) Oxon
Age range: B2–5 years G2–18 years
No. of pupils: 815 VIth170
Fees: Day £8,550–£13,875
FB £26,175–£29,010
🚹 🚹 Ⓐ ⚽ £ ✐ 16+ 🐾

St Mary's Music School
Coates Hall, 25 Grosvenor
Crescent, Edinburgh EH12 5EL
Tel: 0131 538 7766
Headteacher: Dr Kenneth Taylor
BSc Hons, PhD, PGCE, PG Dip
Age range: 9–19
No. of pupils: VIth13
🚹 Ⓐ ⚽ 16+

Stewart's Melville College
Queensferry Road, Edinburgh EH4 3EZ
Tel: 0131 311 1000
Principal: Mrs Linda Moule
Age range: B12–18 G16–18
No. of pupils: 864
Fees: Day £11,637 FB £23,349
🚹 🚹 ⚽ £ ✐ 16+

The Edinburgh Academy
42 Henderson Row, Edinburgh EH3 5BL
Tel: 0131 556 4603
Rector: Barry Welsh
Age range: 2–18
No. of pupils: 992 VIth93
Fees: Day £8,433–£14,121
Ⓐ £ ✐ 16+

The Mary Erskine & Stewart's Melville Junior School
Queensferry Road, Edinburgh EH4 3EZ
Tel: 0131 311 1111
Headmaster: Mr Bryan Lewis
Age range: 3–11
No. of pupils: 1218
Fees: Day £8,142–£9,123 WB
£20,250 FB £20,835
£ ✐

The Mary Erskine School
Ravelston, Edinburgh EH4 3NT
Tel: 0131 347 5700
Headmaster: Mrs Linda Moule
Age range: B16–18 G12–18
Fees: Day £11,637 FB £23,349
🚹 🚹 ⚽ £ 16+

Wallace College
12 George IV Bridge, Edinburgh EH1 1EE
Tel: 0131 220 3634
Age range: 8–18
Fees: Day £1,410–£6,900
FB £4,070–£9,590
16+ Ⓐ ⚽

Fife

Osborne House School
Orchard Croft, West Port,
Dysart, Fife KY1 2TD
Tel: 01592 651461
Headteacher: Miss Eunice Cameron
Age range: 10–17
Fees: Day £7,800

St Leonards School
St Andrews, Fife KY16 9QJ
Tel: 01334 472126
Head of School: Dr Michael Carslaw
Age range: 5–18
No. of pupils: 535
Fees: Day £8,700–£14,208
FB £22,746–£34,653
🚹 🚹 £ ⒤ ✐ 16+

Glasgow

Belmont House School
Sandringham Avenue, Newton
Mearns, Glasgow G77 5DU
Tel: 0141 639 2922
Principal: Mr Melvyn D Shanks
BSc, DipEd, MInstP, CPhys, SQH
Age range: 3–18
No. of pupils: 300
Fees: Day £5,841–£13,263
£ ✐ 16+

Craigholme School
72 St Andrews Drive, Pollokshields,
Glasgow G41 4HS
Tel: 0141 427 0375
Principal: June Gilliland
Age range: B3–5 G3–18
No. of pupils: 442 VIth30
Fees: Day £8,265–£10,047
🚹 £ ✐ 16+

Fernhill School
Fernbrae Avenue, Burnside,
Rutherglen, Glasgow G73 4SG
Tel: 0141 634 2674
Headteacher: Dr Laura Murphy
Age range: B4–11 G4–18
No. of pupils: 300 VIth16
Fees: Day £7,580–£11,090
🚹 £ ✐ 16+

Hutchesons' Grammar School
21 Beaton Road, Glasgow G41 4NW
Tel: 0141 423 2933
Rector: Mr Colin Gambles
BSc (Hons) PGCE
Age range: 5–18
No. of pupils: 1242 VIth139
Fees: Day £7,320–£12,168
Ⓐ £ ✐ 16+

Kelvinside Academy
33 Kirklee Road, Glasgow G12 0SW
Tel: 0141 357 3376
Rector: Mr Ian Munro BSc,
PGCE, MEd(Cantab), FRSB
Age range: 3–18
No. of pupils: 640 VIth73
Fees: Day £7,995–£12,660
Ⓐ £ ✐ 16+

St Aloysius' College
45 Hill Street, Glasgow G3 6RJ
Tel: 0141 332 3190
Head Master: Mr Matthew Bartlett
MA (Cantab), PGCE, NLE, NPQH
Age range: 3–18
No. of pupils: 925 VIth110
Fees: Day £7,263–£12,825
£ ✐ 16+

The Glasgow Academy
Colebrooke Street, Kelvinbridge,
Glasgow G12 8HE
Tel: 0141 334 8558
Rector: Mr Peter Brodie MA, MA(Ed)
Age range: 3–18
No. of pupils: 1148 VIth221
Fees: Day £5,220–£11,623
£ ✐ 16+ 🐾

The Glasgow Academy Dairsie
54 Newlands Road, Newlands,
Glasgow G43 2JG
Tel: 0141 632 0736
Rector: Mr Peter Brodie
Age range: 3–8
No. of pupils: 74
Fees: Day £4,770–£12,029

The Glasgow Academy, Milngavie
Mugdock Road, Milngavie,
Glasgow G62 8NP
Tel: +44 (0)1419 563758
Rector: Mr Peter Brodie
Age range: 3–8
No. of pupils: 121
Fees: Day £4,680–£9,861

The High School of Glasgow
637 Crow Road, Glasgow G13 1PL
Tel: 0141 954 9628
Rector: John O'Neill
Age range: 3–18
No. of pupils: 1022 VIth97
Fees: Day £4,419–£12,768
£ ✐ 16+

Moray

Drumduan School
Clovenside Road, Forres,
Moray IV36 2RD
Tel: + 44 (0)1309 676300
Principal Teacher: Krzysztof
Zajaczkowski
Age range: 3–18

GORDONSTOUN
For further details see p. 284
Elgin, Moray IV30 5RF
Tel: 01343 837829
Email: admissions@
gordonstoun.org.uk
Website: www.gordonstoun.org.uk
Principal: Ms Lisa Kerr BA
Age range: 4½–18
No. of pupils: 542 VIth189
Fees: Day £5,350–£9,950 WB
£8,650 FB £8,650–£13,750
(icons)

Perth & Kinross

Ardvreck School
Crieff, Perth & Kinross PH7 4EX
Tel: 01764 653112
Headmistress: Mrs Ali Kinge
Age range: 3–13
No. of pupils: 110
(icons)

Craigclowan Preparatory School
Edinburgh Road, Perth,
Perth & Kinross PH2 8PS
Tel: 01738 626310
Head of School: John Gilmour
Age range: 3–13
No. of pupils: 222
Fees: Day £4,220
(icons)

Glenalmond College, Perth
Glenalmond, Perth, Perth
& Kinross PH1 3RY
Tel: 01738 842000
Warden: Elaine Logan
Age range: 12–18
No. of pupils: 400 VIth175
Fees: Day £16,881–£22,503
FB £25,851–£36,510
(icons)

Kilgraston School
Bridge of Earn, Perth, Perth
& Kinross PH2 9BQ
Tel: 01738 812257
Head: Mrs Dorothy MacGinty
Age range: G5–18
No. of pupils: 260
Fees: Day £10,890–£17,640
FB £23,025–£30,135
(icons)

Morrison's Academy
Crieff, Perth & Kinross PH7 3AN
Tel: 01764 653885
Principal: Mr Gareth Warren BSc (Hons)
Age range: 3–18
No. of pupils: VIth50
Fees: Day £8,625–£12,996
(icons)

STRATHALLAN SCHOOL
For further details see p. 286
Forgandenny, Perth, Perth
& Kinross PH2 9EG
Tel: 01738 812546
Email: admissions@strathallan.co.uk
Website: www.strathallan.co.uk
Headmaster: Mr Mark
Lauder MA Hons
Age range: 9–18
No. of pupils: 520
Fees: Day £15,435–£23,532
FB £24,729–£34,650
(icons)

Perthshire

Queen Victoria School
Dunblane, Perthshire FK15 0JY
Tel: 01786 822 288
Head: Donald Shaw BSc(Hons) PGCE
Age range: 11–18
No. of pupils: 267 VIth30
Fees: FB £1,403
(icons)

Renfrewshire

Cedars School of Excellence
31 Ardgowan Square, Greenock,
Renfrewshire PA16 8NJ
Tel: 01475 723905
Headteacher: Mrs Alison Speirs
Age range: 5–18
No. of pupils: 95
Fees: Day £5,200–£7,180
(icons)

St Columba's School
Duchal Road, Kilmacolm,
Renfrewshire PA13 4AU
Tel: 01505 872238
Head of School: Mrs
Andrea Y Angus BSc
Age range: 3–18
No. of pupils: 701 VIth125
Fees: Day £3,080–£12,095
(icons)

South Ayrshire

Wellington School
Carleton Turrets, Ayr, South
Ayrshire KA7 2XH
Tel: 01292 269321
Head: Mr S Johnson MA
(Cantab) PGCE
Age range: 3–18
No. of pupils: VIth45
Fees: Day £6,900–£12,900
(icons)

South Lanarkshire

Hamilton College
Bothwell Road, Hamilton,
South Lanarkshire ML3 0AY
Tel: 01698 282700
Principal: Mr Tom McPhail
Age range: 3–18
No. of pupils: VIth49
Fees: Day £7,635–£10,800
(icons)

Wales

KEY TO SYMBOLS

- ⚥ *Boys' school*
- ⚥ *Girls' school*
- 🌐 *International school*
- 16 *Tutorial or sixth form college*
- Ⓐ *A levels*
- 🏛 *Boarding accommodation*
- £ *Bursaries*
- IB *International Baccalaureate*
- ✐ *Learning support*
- 16 *Entrance at 16+*
- ⚙ *Vocational qualifications*
- IAPS *Independent Association of Preparatory Schools*
- HMC *The Headmasters' & Headmistresses' Conference*
- ISA *Independent Schools Association*
- GSA *Girls' School Association*
- BSA *Boarding Schools' Association*
- S *Society of Heads*

Unless otherwise indicated, all schools are coeducational day schools. Single-sex and boarding schools will be indicated by the relevant icon.

Cardiff

Cardiff Sixth Form College
1-3 Trinity Court, 21-27 Newport Road, , Cardiff CF24 0AA
Tel: +44 (0)29 2049 3121
Principal: Mr Gareth Collier
Age range: 15–18
Fees: Day £17,700 FB £42,700–£46,450

Carmarthenshire

LLANDOVERY COLLEGE
For further details see p. 290
Queensway, Llandovery, Carmarthenshire SA20 0EE
Tel: +44 (0)1550 723005
Email: admissions@ llandoverycollege.com
Website: www.llandoverycollege.com
Warden: Dominic Findlay
Age range: 4–18 years
No. of pupils: 250
Fees: Day £6,165–£18,225
FB £18,450–£27,525

St Michael's School
Bryn, Llanelli, Carmarthenshire SA14 9TU
Tel: 01554 820325
Age range: 3–18
No. of pupils: 420 VIth80
Fees: Day £5,064–£12,369
FB £19,722–£22,269

Clwyd

Rydal Penrhos Preparatory School
Pwllycrochan Avenue, Colwyn Bay, Clwyd LL29 7BP
Tel: 01492 530381
Age range: 2–11
No. of pupils: 180
Fees: Day £7,452–£9,930

ST DAVID'S COLLEGE
For further details see p. 292
Gloddaeth Hall, Llandudno, Clwyd LL30 1RD
Tel: 01492 875974
Email: admissions@ stdavidscollege.co.uk
Website: www.stdavidscollege.co.uk
Headmaster: Mr Andrew Russell
Age range: 9–19
No. of pupils: 254
Fees: Day £3,930–£6,230
FB £8,120–£11,630

Conwy

Rydal Penrhos School
Pwllycrochan Avenue, Colwyn Bay, Conwy LL29 7BT
Tel: +44 (0)1492 530155
Head of School: Mrs Alison Hind
Age range: 2–18
No. of pupils: 530
Fees: Day £7,452–£16,785 WB £20,901–£23,385 FB £27,159–£33,450

Denbighshire

Fairholme School
The Mount, Mount Road, St Asaph, Denbighshire LL17 0DH
Tel: 01745 583505
Principal: Mrs E Perkins MA(Oxon)
Age range: 3–11
No. of pupils: 110
Fees: Day £6,300–£8,400

Ruthin School
Ruthin, Denbighshire LL15 1EE
Tel: 01824 702543
Headmaster: Mr T J Belfield
Age range: 3–18
No. of pupils: 240 VIth41
Fees: Day £11,000–£14,000 FB £34,500

Glamorgan

Cardiff Academy
40-41 The Parade, Cardiff, Glamorgan CF24 3AB
Tel: 029 2040 9630
Principal: Dr S R Wilson
Age range: 14–18
No. of pupils: 51 VIth44
Fees: Day £12,000–£15,000

Ffynone House School
36 St James's Crescent, Swansea, Glamorgan SA1 6DR
Tel: 01792 464967
Headteacher: Mr Michael Boulding
Age range: 11–18
No. of pupils: VIth25
Fees: Day £10,845–£11,010

Howell's School, Llandaff GDST
Cardiff Road, Llandaff, Cardiff, Glamorgan CF5 2YD
Tel: 029 2056 2019
Principal: Mrs Sally Davis BSc
Age range: 16–18 G3–18
No. of pupils: 780
Fees: Day £7,755–£14,070

Kings Monkton School
6 West Grove, Cardiff, Glamorgan CF24 3XL
Tel: 02920 482854
Principal: Mr Paul Norton
Age range: 3–18
No. of pupils: 250
Fees: Day £2,700–£4,068

Oakleigh House School
38 Penlan Crescent, Uplands, Swansea, Glamorgan SA2 0RL
Tel: 01792 298537
Headmistress: Mrs Rhian Ferriman BA(Hons)Ed, MEd
Age range: 2½–11
No. of pupils: 210
Fees: Day £6,255–£8,250

St Clare's School
Newton, Porthcawl, Glamorgan CF36 5NR
Tel: 01656 782509
Head of School: Helen Hier
Age range: 3–18
No. of pupils: 298 VIth45
Fees: Day £6,753–£11,799

St John's College, Cardiff
College Green, Old St Mellons, Cardiff, Glamorgan CF3 5YX
Tel: 029 2077 8936
Headteacher: Mr Shaun Moody BA (Hons) PGCE
Age range: 3–18
No. of pupils: 548
Fees: Day £7,443–£14,400

The Cathedral School, Llandaff
Llandaff, Cardiff, Glamorgan CF5 2YH
Tel: 029 2056 3179
Head: Clare Sherwood
Age range: 3–18
Fees: Day £7,785–£12,714

WESTBOURNE SCHOOL
For further details see p. 294
Hickman Road, Penarth, Glamorgan CF64 2AJ
Tel: 029 2070 5705
Email: enquiries@ westbourneschool.com
Website: www.westbourneschool.com
Headteacher: Dr GW Griffiths BSc, PhD, ARCS, PGCE
Age range: 2–18
No. of pupils: 220
Fees: Day £8,100–£14,010
FB £32,750–£35,850

Gwynedd

St Gerard's School
Ffriddoedd Road, Bangor,
Gwynedd LL57 2EL
Tel: 01248 351656
Head Teacher: Mr Campbell Harrison
Age range: 4–18
No. of pupils: 175
Fees: Day £7,050–£10,695
Ⓐ £ 16·

Monmouthshire

Monmouth School for Boys
Almshouse Street, Monmouth,
Monmouthshire NP25 3XP
Tel: 01600 713143
Head: Dr Andrew Daniel BSc, MEd, PhD
Age range: B7–18 years
No. of pupils: 645
Fees: Day £11,415–£16,275
FB £20,868–£33,498
⚹ 🌐 Ⓐ 🏛 £ ✎ 16·

Monmouth School for Girls
Hereford Road, Monmouth,
Monmouthshire NP25 5XT
Tel: 01600 711100
Head: Mrs Jessica Miles
MA (Oxon), PGCE
Age range: G7–18 years
No. of pupils: 600
Fees: Day £11,415–£16,275
FB £20,868–£33,498
⚹ 🌐 Ⓐ 🏛 £ ✎ 16·

Monmouth Schools Pre-Prep & Nursery
Dixton Lane, Monmouth,
Monmouthshire NP25 3SY
Tel: 01600 713970
Head of School: Mrs Jennie Phillips
Age range: 3–7 years
No. of pupils: 80
Fees: Day £4,518–£7,572

Rougemont School
Llantarnam Hall, Malpas Road,
Newport, Monmouthshire NP20 6QB
Tel: 01633 820800
Headmaster: Mr Robert Carnevale
Age range: 3–18
No. of pupils: 700 VIth111
Fees: Day £7,245–£13,536
Ⓐ £ ✎ 16·

St John's-on-the-Hill
Tutshill, Chepstow,
Monmouthshire NP16 7LE
Tel: 01291 622045
Head: Mrs Ruth Frett
Age range: 3 months–13 years
No. of pupils: 362
Fees: Day £8,280–£13,632 FB £19,362
🏛 £ ✎

Pembrokeshire

Nant-y-Cwm Steiner School
Llanycefn, Clunderwen,
Pembrokeshire SA66 7QJ
Tel: 01437 563 640
Age range: 0–14

Redhill Preparatory School
The Garth, St David's
Road, Haverfordwest,
Pembrokeshire SA61 2UR
Tel: 01437 762472
Principal: Mrs Lovegrove
Age range: 0–11
Fees: Day £7,650–£7,800
£ ✎

Powys

Christ College
Brecon, Powys LD3 8AF
Tel: 01874 615440
Head: Mr Gareth Pearson
Age range: 7–18
No. of pupils: 370
Fees: Day £9,165–£18,536
FB £17,544–£29,043
🌐 Ⓐ 🏛 £ ✎ 16·

Vale of Glamorgan

UWC Atlantic College
St Donat's Castle, St Donat's, Llantwit
Major, Vale of Glamorgan CF61 1WF
Tel: +44 (0)1446 799000
Head of College: Mr Peter T. Howe
Age range: 16–19
No. of pupils: 350
🌐 🏛 £ IB 16·

Examinations and qualifications

Common Entrance

What is Common Entrance?

The Common Entrance examinations are used in UK independent schools (and some independent schools overseas) for transfer from junior to senior schools at the ages of 11+ and 13+. They were first introduced in 1904 and are internationally recognised as being a rigorous form of assessment following a thorough course of study. The examinations are produced by the Independent Schools Examinations Board and backed by HMC (Headmasters' and Headmistresses' Conference), GSA (Girls' Schools Association), and IAPS (Independent Association of Prep Schools) which together represent the leading independent schools in the UK, and many overseas.

Common Entrance is not a public examination as, for example, GCSE, and candidates may normally be entered only in one of the following circumstances:

a) they have been offered a place at a senior school subject to their passing the examination, or

b) they are entered as a 'trial run', in which case the papers are marked by the junior school concerned

Candidates normally take the examination in their own junior or preparatory schools, either in the UK or overseas.

How does Common Entrance fit into the progression to GCSEs?

Rapid changes in education nationally and internationally have resulted in regular reviews of the syllabuses for all the Common Entrance examinations. Reviews of the National Curriculum, in particular, have brought about a number of changes, with the Board wishing to ensure that it continues to set high standards. It is also a guiding principle that Common Entrance should be part of the natural progression from 11-16, and not a diversion from it.

Common Entrance at 11+

At 11+, the examination consists of papers in English, mathematics and science. It is designed so that it can be taken by candidates either from independent preparatory schools or by candidates from schools in the maintained sector or overseas who have had no special preparation. The examination is normally taken in January for entrance to senior schools in the following September.

Common Entrance at 13+

At 13+, most candidates come from independent preparatory schools. The compulsory subjects are English, mathematics and science. Papers in French, geography, German, Classical Greek, history, Latin, religious studies and Spanish are also available and candidates usually offer as many subjects as they can. In most subjects, papers are available at more than one level to cater for candidates of different abilities. There are three examination sessions each year, with the majority of candidates sitting in the summer prior to entry to their senior schools in September.

Marking and grading

The papers are set centrally but the answers are marked by the senior school for which a candidate is entered. Mark schemes are provided by the Board but senior schools are free to set their own grade boundaries. Results are available within two weeks of the examinations taking place.

Pre-Testing and the ISEB Common Pre-Tests

A number of senior independent schools 'pre-test' pupils for entry, prior to them taking their main entrance examinations at a later date. Usually, these pre-tests take place when a pupil is in Year 6 or Year 7 of his or her junior school and will then be going on to sit Common Entrance in Year 8. The tests are designed to assess a pupil's academic potential and suitability for a particular senior school so that the child, the parents and the school know well in advance whether he/she is going to be offered a place at the school, subject to a satisfactory performance in the entrance examinations. The tests enable senior schools which are heavily oversubscribed to manage their lists and help to ensure that pupils are not entered for examinations in which they are unlikely to be successful. In short, it reduces uncertainty for all concerned.

Pre-tests may be written specifically for the senior school for which the candidate is entered but a growing number of schools are choosing to use the Common Pre-Tests provided by the Independent Schools Examinations Board. These online tests are usually taken in the candidate's own junior school and one of their main advantages is that a pupil need sit the tests only once, with the results then made available to any senior school which wishes to use them. The multiple-choice tests cover verbal reasoning, non-verbal reasoning, English and mathematics, with the results standardised according to the pupil's age when they are taken. Further information is available on the ISEB website at www.iseb.co.uk.

Parents are advised to check the entrance requirements for senior schools to see if their child will be required to sit a pre-test.

Further information

Details of the Common Entrance examinations and how to register candidates are available on the ISEB website www.iseb.co.uk. Copies of past papers and a wide range of textbooks and other resources can be purchased from Galore Park Publishing Ltd at www.galorepark.co.uk. Support materials are also available from Hodder Education and other publishers; see the Resources section of the ISEB website for details.

Independent Schools Examinations Board
Endeavour House, Crow Arch Lane,
Ringwood, Hampshire BH24 1HP

Telephone: 01425 470555
Email: enquiries@iseb.co.uk
Web: www.iseb.co.uk

7+ Entrance Exams

What is the 7+?

The 7+ is the descriptive name given to the entrance exams set by an increasing number of independent schools for pupils wishing to gain admission into their Year 3.

7+ entrance exams may be simply for admission into a selective preparatory school, which will then prepare the child for Common Entrance exams to gain a place at senior school. Alternatively, the 7+ can be a route into a school with both prep and senior departments, therefore often effectively bypassing the 11+ or 13+ Common Entrance exams.

The Independent Schools Examinations Board provides Common Entrance examinations and assessments for pupils seeking entry to independent senior schools at 11+ and 13+, but there is as yet no equivalent for the 7+. The testing is largely undertaken by the individual schools, although some schools might commission the test from external agencies. Many schools in the incredibly competitive London area offer entrance exams at 7+ and some, such as Haberdasher's Aske's Boys' School, share specimen papers on their website to clarify what 7+ children will face.

Who sits the 7+?

The 7+ is sat by Year 2 children, who may be moving from a state primary school or a stand-alone pre-prep school to an independent prep school (although many prep schools now have their own pre-prep department, with a cohort of children poised to pass into Year 3 there).

Registration for 7+ entrance exams usually closes in the November of Year 2, with the exams then sat in January or February, for entry that September.

How is the 7+ assessed?

Written exam content will be primarily English and maths based, whilst spelling, dictation, mental arithmetic and more creative skills may be assessed verbally on a one-to-one basis. Group exercises are also sometimes used to look at a child's initiative and their ability to work with others.

Schools will not only be looking for academic potential, but also good citizens and a mixture of personalities to produce a well-rounded year group. For this reason, children are often asked to attend an interview. Some schools interview all candidates, whilst others may call back a limited number with good test results. They will be looking for a child's ability to look an adult in the eye and think on their feet, but also simply to show some spark and personality.

After the assessments, children will be told if they have been successful in gaining a firm place, or a place on a waiting list.

Further Information

As the 7+ is not centrally regulated, it is best for parents to seek accurate admissions and testing information direct from the schools in which they are interested. In addition to a school's facilities and ethos, choosing a school for admission at 7+ will probably also involve whether the school has a senior department and if not, the prep school's record in gaining its students places at target senior schools.

Experienced educational consultants may be able to help parents decide which independent prep school is best suited for their child, based on their personality, senior school ambitions and academic potential. Many parents enlist the help of tutors to prepare children for the 7+, if only to reduce the fear of the unknown in these very young children. This is achieved by teaching them the required curriculum, what to expect on their test and interview days, and giving them the opportunity to practice tackling the type of assessments they will face.

Prep School Baccalaureate

The Prep School Baccalaureate (PSB) is a framework of study for children in junior and preparatory schools that was introduced in 2012, and focuses on the active development and assessment of 6 core skills: Communication, Collaboration, Leadership, Independence, Reviewing and Improving and Thinking and Learning. Member schools promote the core skills across all areas of school life, and provide guidance for pupils in progressing these skills, which are seen as essential for developing capable and balanced adults able to make the most of the opportunities of a fast-changing world. A strong but appropriate knowledge base compliments this, with the use of focused tutoring, pastoral care and Well Being programmes.

Schools do not work to a prescribed curriculum and the emphasis is upon promoting an independent approach which works for each individual school. There are subject INSET days for PSB school staff annually and these are supported by senior school colleagues, to ensure that work done in PSB schools compliments the demands of education at higher levels.

The PSB is a whole school initiative from Early Years to either Year 6 or Year 8, at which point the certificate is awarded at the time of matriculation to senior schools. An additional PSB Year 9 framework is being developed together with international membership.

The development of skills is now recognised as essential by the Independent Schools Inspectorate (ISI), and recent ISI reports on PSB schools highlight the excellent contribution the PSB has in schools achieving excellence.

Assessment

The PSB has a 10 point scale for all subjects studied with a compulsory spine covering: English, Maths, Science, Modern Languages, The Humanities, Art, Design Technology, Music, Sport and PE with each pupil additionally completing a cross curricular project. Optional subjects are agreed with schools but these must be supported by a scheme of work clearly identifying appropriate core skills which are assessed on a 5 point scale. There are distinction levels on both scales and the 10 point scale cross references both ISEB and National Curriculum assessment levels.

Pupils moving on to senior school do so via individual senior school pre-testing arrangements, the award of the PSB certificate, core ISEB papers or a combination of the above.

Membership categories

Partner membership is available to schools developing the PSB with support given from existing schools and the Communications director.

Full membership entitles schools to use the PSB matriculation certificate and join the PSB committee as voting members.

Affiliated membership is for schools that have developed their own skills based approach, in line with PSB principles; staff can participate in all training opportunities and the Heads of Affiliated Schools join committee meetings as non-voting guests.

Membership of the above categories is dependent upon strong ISI reports, the development of a skills based curriculum, with skills clearly identified in schemes of work and excellent teaching.

Associate membership is for senior schools that actively support the PSB in providing staff for subject meetings, hosting meetings, conferences and committee meetings and offer a valuable perspective on the demands of GCSE, A Level and the International Baccalaureate.

Further details

The PSB is an entirely independent charity overseen by a Board of Trustees who have expertise in both primary and secondary education. Details of the PSB can be found on the website – psbacc.org – together with contact details for the General Secretary who can provide further details on request.

General Certificate of Secondary Education (GCSE)

What are the GCSE qualifications?

GCSE qualifications were first introduced in 1986 and are the principal means of assessment at Key Stage 4 across a range of academic subject areas. They command respect and have status not only in the UK but worldwide.

Main features of the GCSE

There are four unitary awarding organisations for GCSEs in England (see 'Awarding organisations and examination dates' section, p435). WJEC and CCEA also offer GCSE qualifications in Wales and Northern Ireland. Each examining group designs its own specifications but they are required to conform to set criteria. For some aspects of the qualification system, the exam boards adopt common ways of working. When the exam boards work together in this way they generally do so through the Joint Council of Qualifications (JCQ). The award of a grade is intended to indicate that a candidate has met the required level of skills, knowledge and understanding.

In 2015 GCSEs began a series of reform starting with English Language, English literature, and mathematics. New GCSEs in ancient languages (classical Greek, Latin), art and design, biology, chemistry, citizenship studies, combined science (double award), computer science, dance, drama, food preparation and nutrition, geography, history, modern foreign languages (French, German, Spanish), music, physics, physical education and religious studies were first taught in September 2016, with first results in summer 2018. Assessment in these reformed GCSEs consists primarily of formal examinations taken at the end of the student's two-year course. Other types of assessment, non-exam assessment (NEA), is used where there are skills and knowledge which cannot be assessed through exams. Ofqual have set the percentage of the total marks that will come from NEA.

The reformed GCSEs feature new and more demanding content, as required by the government and developed by the exam boards. Courses are designed for two years of study (linear assessment) and no longer divided into different modules.

Exams can only be split into 'foundation tier' and 'higher tier' if one exam paper does not give all students the opportunity to show their knowledge and their abilities. Such tiering is only available in maths, science and modern foreign languages; other subjects do not have tiers. Resit opportunities will only be available each November in English language and maths, and then only for students who have turned 16 by the 31st of August in the year of the November assessment.

New GCSEs taught from September 2017: ancient history, astronomy, business, classical civilisation, design and technology, economics, electronics, engineering, film studies, geology, media studies, psychology, sociology, statistics, other (minority) foreign languages e.g. Italian, Polish.

New GCSEs taught from September 2018: ancient languages (biblical Hebrew) and modern foreign languages (Gujarati, Persian, Portuguese, Turkish).

Grading

The basic principle that exam boards follow when setting grade boundaries is that if the group of students (the cohort) taking a qualification in one year is of similar ability to the cohort in the previous year then the overall results (outcomes) should be comparable.

The reformed exams taken in summer 2017 were the first to show a new grading system, with the A* to G grades being phased out.

The new grading system is 9 to 1, with 9 being the top grade. Ofqual says this allows greater differentiation between students. It expects that broadly the same proportion of students will achieve a grade 4 and above as currently achieve a grade C and above, that broadly the same proportion of students will achieve a grade 7 and above as currently achieve a grade A and above. There are three anchor points between the new grading system and the old one: the bottom of the new 1 grade is the same as the bottom of the old G grade, the bottom of the new 4 grade is the bottom of the old C grade, and the bottom of the 7 grade is the same as the bottom of the old A grade. Grade 9 will be set using the tailored approach formula in the first award.

Grades 2, 3, 5 and 6 will be awarded arithmetically so that the grade boundaries are equally spaced in terms of marks from neighbouring grades.

The government's definition of a 'strong pass' will be set at grade 5 for reformed GCSEs. A grade 4 – or 'standard pass' – will continue to be a level 2 achievement. The DfE does not expect employers, colleges or universities to raise the bar to a grade 5 if a grade 4 would meet their requirements.

Can anyone take GCSE qualifications?

GCSEs are intended mainly for 16-year-old pupils, but are open to anyone of any age, whether studying full-time or part-time at a school, college or privately. There are no formal entry requirements.

Students normally study up to ten subjects over a two-year period. Short course GCSEs are available in some subjects (including PE and religious studies) – these include half the content of a full GCSE, so two short course GCSEs are equivalent to one full GCSE.

The English Baccalaureate

The English Baccalaureate (EBacc) is a school performance measure. It allows people to see how many pupils get a grade C or above (current grading) in the core academic subjects at Key Stage 4 in any government-funded school.

The DfE introduced the EBacc measure in 2010. In June 2015, it announced its intention that all pupils who start year 7 in September 2015 take the EBacc subjects when they reach their GCSEs in 2020.

Progress 8 and Attainment 8

Progress 8 aims to capture the progress a pupil makes from the end of primary school to the end of secondary school. It is a type of value added measure, which means that pupils' results are compared to the actual achievements of other pupils with the same prior attainment.

The new performance measures are designed to encourage schools to offer a broad and balanced curriculum with a focus on an academic core at Key Stage 4, and reward schools for the teaching of all their pupils, measuring performance across 8 qualifications. Every increase in every grade a pupil achieves will attract additional points in the performance tables.

Progress 8 will be calculated for individual pupils solely in order to calculate a school's Progress 8 score, and there will be no need for schools to share individual Progress 8 scores with their pupils. Schools should continue to focus on which qualifications are most suitable for individual pupils, as the grades pupils achieve will help them reach their goals for the next stage of their education or training.

Attainment 8 will measure the achievement of a pupil across 8 qualifications including mathematics (double weighted) and English (double weighted), 3 further qualifications that count in the English Baccalaureate (EBacc) measure and 3 further qualifications that can be GCSE qualifications (including EBacc subjects) or any other non-GCSE qualification on the DfE approved list.

General Certificate of Education (GCE) Advanced level (A level)

Typically, A level qualifications are studied over a two-year period. There are no lower or upper age limits. Schools and colleges usually expect students aged 16-18 to have obtained grades A*-C (grade 5 in the new criteria) in five subjects at GCSE level before taking an advanced level course. This requirement may vary between centres and according to which specific subjects are to be studied. Mature students may be assessed on different criteria as to their suitability to embark on the course.

GCE Qualifications

Over the past few years, AS level and A level qualifications have been in a process of reform. New subjects have been introduced gradually, with the first wave taught from September 2015. Subjects that have not been reformed are no longer be available for teaching.

GCE qualifications are available at two levels: the Advanced Subsidiary (AS), which is generally delivered over one year and is seen as half an A level; and the A level (GCE). Nearly 70 titles are available, covering a wide range of subject areas, including humanities, sciences, language, business, arts, mathematics and technology.

One of the major reforms is that AS level results no longer count towards an A level (they previously counted for 50%). The two qualifications are linear, with AS assessments typically taking place after one year and A levels after two.

New-style AS and A levels were first taught from September 2015 for: art and design, biology, business studies, chemistry, computer studies, economics, English language, English language and literature, English literature, history, physics, psychology, and sociology.

Subjects first taught from September 2016 include: ancient languages such as Latin or Greek, dance, drama (theatre studies), geography, modern languages such as Spanish or French, music, physical education, religious studies.

Those introduced for first teaching from September 2017: accounting, design and technology, music technology, history of art, environmental science, philosophy, maths, further maths, archaeology, accounting, electronics, ancient history, law, classical civilisation, film studies, media studies, politics, geology, statistics, Chinese, Italian, Russian. In 2018 Biblical Hebrew, Modern Hebrew & languages such as Bengali, Polish and Urdu were available for first teaching.

Some GCE AS and A levels, particularly the practical ones, contain a proportion of coursework. All GCE A levels that contain one or more types of assessment will have an element of synoptic assessment that tests students' understanding of the whole specification. GCE AS are graded A-E and A levels are graded A*-E.

Overall the amount of coursework at A level has been reduced in the reforms. In some subjects, such as the sciences, practical work will not contribute to the final A level but will be reported separately in a certificate of endorsement. In the sciences, students will do at least 12 practical activities, covering apparatus and techniques. Exam questions about practical work will make up at least 15% of the total marks for the qualification and students will be assessed on their knowledge, skills and understanding of practical work.

Cambridge International AS & A Level

Cambridge International AS & A Level is an internationally benchmarked qualification, taught in over 130 countries worldwide. It is typically for learners aged 16 to 19 years who need advanced study to prepare for university. It was created specifically for an international audience and the content has been devised to suit the wide variety of schools worldwide and avoid any cultural bias.

Cambridge International A Level is typically a two-year course, and Cambridge International AS Level is typically one year. Some subjects can be started as a Cambridge International AS Level and extended to a Cambridge International A Level. Students can either follow a broad course of study, or specialise in one particular subject area.

Learners use Cambridge International AS and A Levels to gain places at leading universities worldwide, including the UK, Ireland, USA, Canada, Australia, New Zealand, India, Singapore, Egypt, Jordan, South Africa, the Netherlands, Germany and Spain. In places such as the US and Canada, good grades in

carefully chosen Cambridge International A Level subjects can result in up to one year of university course credit.

Assessment options:

Cambridge International AS & A Levels have a linear structure with exams at the end of the course. Students can choose from a range of assessment options:

Option 1: take Cambridge International AS Levels only. The Cambridge International syllabus content is half a Cambridge International A Level.

Option 2: staged assessment, which means taking the Cambridge International AS Level in one exam session and the Cambridge International A Level at a later session. However, this route is not possible in all subjects.

Option 3: take all Cambridge International A Level papers in the same examination session, usually at the end of the course.

Grades and subjects

Cambridge International A Levels are graded from A*-E. Cambridge International AS Levels are graded from A-E.

Subjects available: Afrikaans, Afrikaans – Language (AS only), Arabic, Arabic – Language (AS only), Art & Design, Biology, Business, Chemistry, Chinese – Language (AS only), Chinese (A Level only), Classical Studies, Computer Science, Design & Technology, Design & Textiles, Digital Media & Design, Divinity, Divinity (AS only), Drama, Economics, English – Language, English – Language and Literature (AS only), English – Literature, English General Paper (AS only), Environmental Management (AS only), Food Studies, French – Language (AS only), French – Literature (AS only), French (A Level only), General Paper (AS only), General Paper (AS only), Geography, German – Language (AS only), German (A Level only), Global Perspectives and Research, Hindi – Language (AS only), Hindi – Literature (AS only), Hindi (A Level only), Hinduism, Hinduism (AS only), History, Information Technology, Islamic Studies, Islamic Studies (AS only), Japanese Language (AS only), Law, Marathi – Language (AS only), Marathi (A Level only), Marine Science, Mathematics, Mathematics – Further,

Media Studies, Music, Music (AS only), Nepal Studies (AS only), Physical Education, Physics, Portuguese – Language (AS only), Portuguese – Literature (AS only), Portuguese (A Level only), Psychology, Sociology, Spanish – First Language (AS only), Spanish – Language (AS only), Spanish – Literature (AS only), Spanish (A Level only), Tamil, Tamil – Language (AS only), Thinking Skills, Travel & Tourism, Urdu – Language (AS only), Urdu – Pakistan only (A Level only), Urdu (A Level only).
Website: www.cambridgeinternational.org/alevel

Cambridge International GCSE (IGCSE)

Cambridge IGCSE is the world's most popular international qualification for 14 to 16 year olds. It develops skills in creative thinking, enquiry and problem solving, in preparation for the next stage in a student's education. Cambridge IGCSE is taken in over 150 countries, and is widely recognised by employers and higher education institutions worldwide.

Cambridge IGCSE is graded from A*-G. In the UK, Cambridge IGCSE is accepted as equivalent to the GCSE. It can be used as preparation for Cambridge International A & AS Levels, UK A and AS levels, IB or AP and in some instances entry into university. Cambridge IGCSE First Language English and Cambridge IGCSE English Language qualifications are recognised by a significant number of UK universities as evidence of competence in the language for university entrance.

Subjects available: Accounting, Accounting (9-1), Afrikaans – First Language, Afrikaans – Second Language, Agriculture, Arabic – First Language, Arabic – First Language (9-1), Arabic – Foreign Language, Art & Design, Art & Design (9-1), Bahasa Indonesia, Bangladesh Studies, Biology, Biology (9-1), Business Studies, Business Studies (9-1), Chemistry, Chemistry (9-1), Child Development, Chinese - First Language, Chinese – Second Language, Computer Science, Computer Science (9-1), Czech – First Language, Design & Technology, Design & Technology

(9-1), Development Studies, Drama, Drama (9-1), Dutch – First Language, Dutch – Foreign Language, Economics, Economics (9-1), English – First Language, English – First Language (9-1), English – First Language (9–1) (UK only), English – First Language (US), English – Literature (9-1) (UK only), English – Literature (English), English – Literature (US), English – Literature in English, English – Literature in English (9-1), English as a Second Language (Count-in speaking), English as a Second Language (Count-in Speaking) (9-1), English as a Second Language (Speaking endorsement), English Second Language (Speaking Endorsement) (9-1), Enterprise, Environmental Management, Food & Nutrition, French – First Language, French – Foreign Language, French (9-1), Geography, Geography (9-1), German – First Language, German – Foreign Language, German (9-1), Global Perspectives, Greek – Foreign Language, Hindi as a Second Language, History, History – American (US), History (9-1), India Studies, Indonesian – Foreign Language, Information & Communication Technology, Information & Communication Technology (9-1), IsiZulu as a Second Language, Islamiyat, Italian – Foreign Language, Italian (9-1), Japanese – Foreign Language, Kazakh as a Second Language, Korean (First Language), Latin, Malay – First Language, Malay – Foreign Language, Mandarin Chinese – Foreign Language, Marine Science (Maldives only), Mathematics, Mathematics – Additional, Mathematics – Additional (US), Mathematics – International, Mathematics (9-1), Mathematics (9-1) (UK only), Mathematics (US), Music – 0410, Music (9-1), Pakistan Studies, Physical Education, Physical Education (9-1, Physical Science, Physics, Physics (9-1), Portuguese – First Language, Portuguese – Foreign Language, Religious Studies, Russian – First Language, Sanskrit, Science – Combined, Sciences – Co-ordinated (9-1), Sciences – Co-ordinated (Double), Sociology, Spanish – First Language, Spanish – Foreign Language, Spanish – Literature, Spanish (9-1), Swahili, Thai – First Language, Travel & Tourism, Turkish – First Language, Urdu as a Second Language, World Literature.
Website: www.cambridgeinternational.org/igcse

Cambridge Pre-U

Cambridge Pre-U is a post-16 qualification that equips students with the skills they need to succeed at university, developed with universities.

Cambridge Pre-U is a linear course, with exams taken at the end of two years. It encourages the development of well-informed, open and independent-minded individuals; promotes deep understanding through subject specialisation, with a depth and rigour appropriate to progression to higher education; and develops skills in independent research valued by universities.

Assessment
Cambridge Pre-U Principal Subjects are examined at the end of two years. Cambridge Pre-U Short Courses are available in some subjects and are typically examined at the end of one year. Students can study a combination of A Levels and Principal Subjects.

In order to gain the Cambridge Pre-U Diploma, students must study at least three Cambridge Pre-U Principal Subjects (up to two A Levels can be substituted for Principal Subjects) and Cambridge Pre-U Global Perspectives & Research (GPR). Cambridge Pre-U GPR includes an extended project in the second year, developing skills in research and critical thinking.

Grades and subjects
Cambridge Pre-U reports achievement on a scale of nine grades, with Distinction 1 being the highest grade and Pass 3 the lowest grade.

Subjects available: Art & Design, Art History, Biology, Business & Management, Chemistry, Classical Greek, Economics, English, French, Further Mathematics, Geography, German, Global Perspectives & Independent Research (UK only), Global Perspectives (Short Course) (UK only), History, Italian, Latin, Mandarin Chinese, Mathematics, Music, Philosophy & Theology, Physics, Psychology, Russian, Spanish
Website: www.cambridgeinternational.org/cambridgepreu

Edexcel International GCSEs

Pearson's Edexcel International GCSEs are academic qualifications aimed at learners aged 14 to 16. They're equivalent to a UK General Certificate of Secondary Education (GCSE), and are the main requirement for Level 3 studies, including progression to GCE AS or A levels, BTECs or employment. International GCSEs are linear qualifications, meaning that students take all of the exams at the end of the course. They are available at Level 1 (grades 3-1) and Level 2 (grades 9-4). There are currently more than 100,000 learners studying Edexcel International GCSEs, in countries throughout Asia, Africa, Europe, the Middle East and Latin America. Developed by subject specialists and reviewed regularly, many of Pearson's Edexcel International GCSEs include specific international content to make them relevant to students worldwide.

Pearson's Edexcel International GCSEs were initially developed for international schools. They have since become popular among independent schools in the UK, but are not approved for use in UK state schools.

Free Standing Maths Qualifications (FSMQ)

Aimed at those students wishing to acquire further qualifications in maths, specifically additional mathematics and foundations of advanced mathematics (MEI). Further UCAS points can be earned upon completion of the advanced FSMQ in additional mathematics.

AQA Certificate in Mathematical Studies (Core Maths)

This new Level 3 qualification has been available from September 2015. It is designed for students who achieved a Grade 4 or above at GCSE and want to continue studying Maths. The qualification carries UCAS points equivalent to an AS level qualification.

AQA Certificate in Further Maths

This level 2 qualification has been designed to provide stretch and challenge to the most able mathematicians. This will be best suited to students who either already have, or are expected to achieve the top grades in GCSE Mathematics and are likely to progress to A level Mathematics and Further Mathematics.

Scottish qualifications

Information supplied by Scottish Qualifications Authority

In Scotland, qualifications are awarded by the Scottish Qualifications Authority (SQA), the national accreditation and awarding body. A variety of qualifications are offered, including:

- National Qualifications (National Units, National Courses and Group Awards)
- Wider Achievement Awards
- Skills for Work Courses
- Scottish Baccalaureates

Qualifications in the Scottish qualifications system sit at various levels on the Scottish Credit and Qualifications Framework (SCQF). There are 12 levels on the SCQF and each level represents the difficulty of learning involved. Qualifications in schools span SCQF levels 1 to 7.

National Qualifications (NQ)

SQA designed and developed new National Qualifications to support Curriculum for Excellence (CfE) – the new national curriculum in Scotland for young people aged 3 to 18. They are taught in schools and colleges, and by some training providers.

The National Qualifications are National 1, National 2, National 3, National 4, National 5, Higher and Advanced Higher. They range from SCQF level 1 (National 1) to SCQF level 7 (Advanced Higher).

National 1 to National 5 qualifications have been available since August 2013. The new Higher was introduced in August 2014 and the new Advanced Higher was introduced in August 2015.

National Qualifications help young people to demonstrate the skills, knowledge and understanding they have developed at school or college and enable them to prepare for further learning, training and employment.

National Units

National Units are the building blocks of National Courses and Group Awards. They are also qualifications in their own right and can be done on an individual basis, such as National 1 qualifications, which are standalone units. Units are normally designed to take 40 hours of teaching to complete and each one is assessed by completing a unit assessment. Over 3500 National Units are available, including National Literacy and Numeracy Units, which assess students' literacy and numeracy skills.

National Courses

National Courses are available at National 2, National 3, National 4, National 5, Higher and Advanced Higher levels. There are more than 60 subjects available, at various levels.

National 2, National 3 and National 4 are unit-based courses and they are assessed through internally marked unit assessments. National 4 courses also include an Added Value Unit assessment that assesses the whole course. National 2 to National 4 courses are not graded, but are assessed as pass or fail.

National 5, Higher and Advanced Higher courses are graded A to D or 'no award' and include a course assessment that takes place at the end of the course. For most subjects, the course assessment is a combination of exam(s) and coursework. SQA marks all exams and the majority of coursework.

The assessment of National 5, Higher and Advanced Higher courses has recently undergone change. Units and unit assessments are being removed from the courses, and the course assessments are being extended to assess more course content.

Skills for Work Courses

Skills for Work courses are designed to introduce school pupils to the demands and expectations of the world of work. They are available in a variety of areas such as construction, hairdressing and hospitality. They involve a strong element of learning through involvement in practical and vocational activities and develop knowledge, skills and experience that are related to employment. They are available at SCQF levels 4 to 6 and are often delivered in partnership with schools and colleges.

Group Awards

National Certificates (NCs) and National Progression Awards (NPAs) are referred to as National Qualification Group Awards. These qualifications provide students preparing for work with opportunities to develop skills that are sought after by employers. They are available at SCQF levels 2 to 6.

NCs prepare students for employment, career development or progression to more advanced study. They are available in a range of subjects, including: Sound Production, Technical Theatre, and Child, Health and Social Care.

NPAs develop specific skills and knowledge in specialist vocational areas, including Journalism, Architecture and Interior Design, and Legal Services. They are taught in partnership between schools, colleges, employers and training providers.

Awards

SQA Awards provide students with opportunities to acquire skills, recognise achievement and promote confidence through independent thinking and positive attitudes, while motivating them to be successful and participate positively in the wider community.

A variety of different awards are offered at a number of levels and cover subjects including leadership, employability and enterprise. These awards are designed to recognise the life, learning and work skills that students gain from taking part in activities such as sports, volunteering and fundraising.

Scottish Baccalaureates

Scottish Baccalaureates consist of a coherent group of Higher and Advanced Higher qualifications and, uniquely, an interdisciplinary project selected by the student in one of four broad topics – languages, science, expressive arts or social studies. The interdisciplinary project is marked at Advanced Higher level and provides students with a platform to apply their knowledge in a realistic context. Aimed at high-achieving sixth year students, the Scottish Baccalaureate encourages personalised, in-depth study and interdisciplinary learning in their final year of secondary school.

For more information on SQA and its portfolio of qualifications, visit www.sqa.org.uk or follow SQA on Twitter @sqanews.

Additional and Alternative

AQA Baccalaureate

The AQA Baccalaureate is awarded to students who achieve at least three A levels (minimum grade E or 2/3), a broader study AS level subject and the EPQ, plus they must undertake a minimum of 100 hours of 'enrichment activities'.

This is a complete curriculum programme, which adds a broader range of study, and includes the Extended Project Qualification (EPQ). This qualification is built on familiar subjects, so it can be tailored to fit in with existing curricula. It includes extracurricular activities and encourages a series of 'enrichment activities' covering personal qualities, perseverance, leadership, independence, time management, commitment and communication.

The AQA Bacc is accepted by universities; offers are based on the component parts of the baccalaureate, with students receiving their AQA Baccalaureate and enrichment certificates alongside their A level, AS level and EPQ certificates. The AQA Baccalaureate will not be available beyond 2020.

Cambridge Primary

Cambridge Primary is typically for learners aged 5-11 years. It develops learner skills and understanding through the primary years in English as a first or second language, mathematics, science, Global Perspectives™ and ICT. The flexible curriculum frameworks include optional assessment tools to help schools monitor learners' progress and give detailed feedback to parents. At the end of Cambridge Primary, schools can enter students for Cambridge Primary Checkpoint tests which are marked in Cambridge.
Website: www.cambridgeinternational.org/
programmes-and-qualifications/cambridge-primary

Cambridge ICT Starters introduces learners, typically aged 5-14 years, to the key ICT applications they need to achieve computer literacy and to understand the impact of technology on our daily lives. It can be taught and assessed in English or Spanish.

Cambridge Lower Secondary

Cambridge Lower Secondary is typically for learners aged 11-14 years. It develops learner skills and understanding in English as a first or second language, mathematics, science, Global Perspectives™ and ICT for the first three years of secondary education, and includes assessment tools. At the end of Cambridge Lower Secondary, schools can enter students for Cambridge Lower Secondary Checkpoint tests which are marked in Cambridge and provide an external international benchmark for student performance.
Website: www.cambridgeinternational.org/programmes-and-qualifications/cambridge-lower-secondary

European Baccalaureate (EB)

Not to be confused with the International Baccalaureate (IB) or the French Baccalaureate, this certificate is available in European schools and recognised in all EU countries.

To obtain the baccalaureate, a student must obtain a minimum score of 60%, which is made up from: course-work, oral participation in class and tests (40%); five written examinations (36%) – mother-tongue, first foreign language and maths are compulsory for all candidates; four oral examinations (24%) – mother tongue and first foreign language are compulsory (history or geography may also be compulsory here, dependant on whether the candidate has taken a written examination in these subjects).

Throughout the EU the syllabus and examinations necessary to achieve the EB are identical. The only exception to this rule is the syllabus for the mother tongue language. The EB has been specifically designed to meet, at the very least, the minimum qualification requirements of each member state.

Study for the EB begins at nursery stage (age four) and progresses through primary (age six) and on into secondary school (age 12).

Syllabus
Languages: Bulgarian, Czech, Danish, Dutch, English, Estonian, Finnish, Finnish as a second national language, French, German, Greek, Hungarian, Irish, Italian, Latvian, Lithuanian, Maltese, Polish, Portuguese, Romanian, Slovak, Slovenian, Spanish, Swedish, Swedish for Finnish pupils.

Literary: art education, non-confessional ethics, geography, ancient Greek, history, human sciences, Latin, music, philosophy, physical education.

Sciences: biology, chemistry, economics, ICT, integrated science, mathematics, physics.

For more information, contact:
Office of the Secretary-General of the European Schools, rue de la Science 23 – 2nd floor, B-1040 Bruxelles, Belgique
Tel: +32 (0)2 895 26 11
Website: www.eursc.eu

The International Baccalaureate (IB)

The International Baccalaureate (IB) offers four challenging and high quality educational programmes for a worldwide community of schools, aiming to develop internationally minded people who, recognizing their common humanity and shared guardianship of the planet, help to create a better, more peaceful world.

The IB works with schools around the world (both state and privately funded) that share the commitment to international education to deliver these programmes.

Schools that have achieved the high standards required for authorization to offer one or more of the IB programmes are known as IB World Schools. There are over half a million students attending almost 5000 IB World Schools in over 150 countries and this number is growing annually.

The Primary Years, Middle Years and Diploma Programmes share a common philosophy and common characteristics. They develop the whole student, helping students to grow intellectually, socially, aesthetically and culturally. They provide a broad and balanced education that includes science and the humanities, languages and mathematics, technology and the arts. The programmes teach students to think critically, and encourage them to draw connections between areas of knowledge and to use problem-solving techniques and concepts from many disciplines. They instil in students a sense of responsibility towards others and towards the environment. Lastly, and perhaps most importantly, the programmes give students an awareness and understanding of their own culture and of other cultures, values and ways of life.

A fourth programme called the IB Career-related Programme (CP) became available to IB World Schools from September 2012. All IB programmes include:
- A written curriculum or curriculum framework
- Student assessment appropriate to the age range
- Professional development and networking opportunities for teachers
- Support, authorization and programme evaluation for the school

The IB Primary Years Programme

The IB Primary Years Programme (PYP), for students aged three to 12, focuses on the development of the whole child as an inquirer, both in the classroom and in the world outside. It is a framework consisting of five essential elements (concepts, knowledge, skills, attitude, action) and guided by six trans-disciplinary themes of global significance, explored using knowledge and skills derived from six subject areas (language, social studies, mathematics, science and technology, arts, and personal, social and physical education) with a powerful emphasis on inquiry-based learning.

The most significant and distinctive feature of the PYP is the six trans-disciplinary themes. These themes are about issues that have meaning for, and are important to, all of us. The programme offers a balance between learning about or through the subject areas, and learning beyond them. The six themes of global significance create a trans-disciplinary framework that allows students to 'step up' beyond the confines of learning within subject areas:
- Who we are
- Where we are in place and time
- How we express ourselves
- How the world works
- How we organize ourselves
- Sharing the planet

The PYP exhibition is the culminating activity of the programme. It requires students to analyse and propose solutions to real-world issues, drawing on what they have learned through the programme. Evidence of student development and records of PYP exhibitions are reviewed by the IB as part of the programme evaluation process.

Assessment is an important part of each unit of inquiry as it both enhances learning and provides opportunities for students to reflect on what they know, understand and can do. The teacher's feedback to the students provides the guidance, the tools and the incentive for them to become more competent, more skilful and better at understanding how to learn.

The IB Middle Years Programme (MYP)

The Middle Years Programme (MYP), for students aged 11 to 16, comprises eight subject groups:
- Language acquisition
- Language and literature
- Individuals and societies
- Sciences
- Mathematics
- Arts
- Physical and health education
- Design

The MYP requires at least 50 hours of teaching time for each subject group in each year of the programme. In years 4 and 5, students have the option to take courses from six of the eight subject groups within certain limits, to provide greater flexibility in meeting local requirements and individual student learning needs.

Each year, students in the MYP also engage in at least one collaboratively planned interdisciplinary unit that involves at least two subject groups.

MYP students also complete a long-term project, where they decide what they want to learn about, identify what they already know, discovering what they will need to know to complete the project, and create a proposal or criteria for completing it

The MYP aims to help students develop their personal understanding, their emerging sense of self and their responsibility in their community.

The MYP allows schools to continue to meet state, provincial or national legal requirements for students with access needs. Schools must develop an inclusion/special educational needs (SEN) policy that explains assessment access arrangements, classroom accommodations and curriculum modification that meet individual student learning needs.

The IB Diploma Programme (IBDP)

The IB Diploma Programme, for students aged 16 to 19, is an academically challenging and motivating curriculum of international education that prepares students for success at university and in life beyond studies.

DP students choose at least one course from six subject groups, thus ensuring depth and breadth of knowledge and experience in languages, social studies, the experimental sciences, mathematics, and the arts. With more than 35 courses to choose from, students have the flexibility to further explore and learn subjects that meet their interest. Out of the six courses required, at least three and not more than four must be taken at higher level (240 teaching hours), the others at standard level (150 teaching hours). Students can take examinations in English, French or Spanish.

In addition, three unique components of the programme – the DP core – aim to broaden students' educational experience and challenge them to apply their knowledge and skills. The DP core – the extended essay (EE), theory of knowledge (TOK) and creativity, activity, service (CAS) – are compulsory and central to the philosophy of the programme.

The IB uses both external and internal assessment to measure student performance in the DP. Student results are determined by performance against set standards, not by each student's position in the overall rank order. DP assessment is unique in the way that it measures the extent to which students have mastered advanced academic skills not what they have memorized. DP assessment also encourages an international outlook and intercultural skills, wherever appropriate.

The IB diploma is awarded to students who gain at least 24 points out of a possible 45 points, subject to certain minimum levels of performance across the whole programme and to satisfactory participation in the creativity, activity, and service requirement.

Recognized and respected by leading universities globally, the DP encourages students to be knowledgeable, inquiring, caring and compassionate, and to develop intercultural understanding, open-mindedness and the attitudes necessary to respect and evaluate a range of viewpoints.

The IB Career Related Programme (IBCP)

The IB Career-related Programme, for students aged 16 to 19, offers an innovative educational framework that combines academic studies with career-related learning. Through the CP, students develop the competencies they need to succeed in the 21st century. More importantly, they have the opportunity to engage with a rigorous study programme that genuinely interests them while gaining transferable and lifelong skills that prepares them to pursue higher education, apprenticeships or direct employment.

CP students complete four core components – language development, personal and professional skills, service learning and a reflective project – in order to receive the International Baccalaureate Career-related Programme Certificate. Designed to enhance critical thinking and intercultural understanding, the CP core helps students develop the communication and personal skills, as well as intellectual habits required for lifelong learning.

Schools that choose to offer the CP can create their own distinctive version of the programme and select career pathways that suit their students and local community needs. The IB works with a variety of CRS providers around the world and schools seeking to develop career pathways with professional communities can benefit from our existing collaborations. All CRS providers undergo a rigorous curriculum evaluation to ensure that their courses align with the CP pedagogy and meet IB quality standards. The flexibility to meet the needs, backgrounds and contexts of learners allows CP schools to offer an education that is relevant and meaningful to their students.

Launched in 2012, there are 250 CP schools. Many schools with the IB Diploma Programme (DP) and the

Middle Years Programme (MYP) have chosen the CP as an alternative IB pathway to offer students. CP schools often report that the programme has helped them raise student aspiration, increase student engagement and retention and encouraged learners to take responsibility for their own actions, helping them foster high levels of self-esteem through meaningful achievements.

For more information on IB programmes, visit: www.ibo.org
Africa, Europe, Middle East IB Global Centre,
Churchillplein 6, The Hague, 2517JW, The Netherlands
Tel: +31 (0)70 352 6000
Email: support@ibo.org

Pearson Edexcel Mathematics Awards

Pearson's Edexcel Mathematics Awards are small, stand-alone qualifications designed to help students to develop and demonstrate proficiency in different areas of mathematics. These Awards enable students to focus on understanding key concepts and techniques, and are available across three subjects, including: Number and Measure (Levels 1 and 2), Algebra (Levels 2 and 3) and Statistical Methods (Levels 1, 2 and 3).

Designed to build students' confidence and fluency; the Awards can fit into the existing programme of delivery for mathematics in schools and colleges, prepare students for GCSE and/or GCE Mathematics, and to support further study in other subjects, training or the workplace. They offer a choice of levels to match students' abilities, with clear progression between the levels. These small, 60-70 guided learning hour qualifications are assessed through one written paper per level. Each qualification is funded and approved for pre-16 and 16-18 year old students in England and in schools and colleges in Wales.

Projects

Extended Project Qualification (EPQ)

AQA, OCR, Pearson and WJEC offer the Extended Project Qualification, which is a qualification aimed at developing a student's research and independent learning skills. The EPQ can be taken as a stand-alone qualification, and it is equivalent to half an A level in UCAS points (but only a third of performance points). It is also possible to take the EPQ as part of the AQA Baccalaureate.

Students complete a research based written report and may produce an artefact or a practical science experiment as part of their project.

Cambridge International Project Qualification (IPQ)

Cambridge International is offering a new standalone project-based qualification, which can be taken alongside Cambridge International AS & A levels. Students complete a 5000-word research project on a topic of their choice. The qualification is assessed by Cambridge International.

For more information, go to www.cambridgeinternational.org/advanced

Entry level and basic skills

Entry Level Qualifications

If you want to take GCSE or NVQ Level 1 but have not yet reached the standard required, then entry level qualifications are for you as they are designed to get you started on the qualifications ladder.

Entry level qualifications are available in a wide range of areas. You can take an entry level certificate in most subjects where a similar GCSE exists. There are also vocational entry level qualifications – some in specific areas like retail or catering and others where you can take units in different work-related subjects to get a taster of a number of career areas. Also available are entry level certificates in life skills and the basic skills of literacy and numeracy.

Anyone can take an entry level qualification – your school or college will help you decide which qualification is right for you.

Entry level qualifications are flexible programmes so the time it takes to complete will vary according to where you study and how long you need to take the qualification.

Subjects available include: Art and Design, Computer Science, English, Geography, History, Latin, Mathematics, Physical Education and Science.

Functional Skills

Functional Skills are qualifications in English and maths that equip learners with the basic practical skills required in everyday life, education and the workplace. They are available at Entry Level, Level 1 and Level 2. Functional Skills are identified as funded 'stepping stone' qualifications to English and maths GCSE for post-16 learners who haven't previously achieved a grade D in these subjects. There are part of apprenticeship completion requirements.

Vocational qualifications

Applied Generals/Level 3 Certificates

Applied General qualifications are available in Business and Science and are a practical introduction to these subjects, they are a real alternative to A level support progression to further study or employment aimed at students aged 16-18.

Developed together with teachers, schools, colleges and higher education institutions, they help learners to develop knowledge and skills.

A mixture of assessment types means learners can apply their knowledge in a practical way. An integrated approach creates a realistic and relevant qualification for learners.

AQA Technical Award

AQA's Technical Award is a practical, vocational Level 1/2 qualification for 14- to 16-year-olds to take alongside GCSEs.

The Technical Award in Performing Arts provides an introduction to life and work, equipping learners with the practical, transferable skills and core knowledge needed to progress to further general or vocational study, including Level 3 qualifications, employment or apprenticeships.

Learners are assessed on doing rather than knowing through the project-based internal assessments, where they can apply their knowledge to practical tasks. There are two internally assessed units worth 30% each, and an externally assessed exam worth 40%.

AQA Tech-levels

Level 3 technical qualifications have been designed in collaboration with employers and professional bodies. They're aimed at learners aged over 16 wanting to progress into a specific sector through apprenticeships, further study or employment. There are 16 individual qualifications within IT, Engineering, Business and Entertainment Technology. These vary in size of qualification.

Transferable skills have been contextualised explicitly within each qualification and are a mandatory part of the qualification outcome.

Learners are assessed through a combination of examinations, internally and externally assessed assignments.

BTECs

BTEC Level 2 First qualifications
ie BTEC Level 2 Diplomas, BTEC Level 2 Extended Certificates, BTEC Level 2 Certificates and BTEC Level 2 Award.

BTEC Firsts are Level 2 introductory work-related programmes covering a wide range of vocational areas including business, engineering, information technology, health and social care, media, travel and tourism, and public services.

Programmes may be taken full or part-time. They are practical programmes that provide a foundation for the knowledge and skills you will need in work. Alternatively, you can progress onto a BTEC National qualification, Applied GCE A level or equivalent.

There are no formal entry requirements and they can be studied alongside GCSEs. Subjects available include: Agriculture, Animal Care, Applied Science, Art and Design, Business, Children's Care, Learning and Development, Construction, Countryside and the Environment, Engineering, Fish Husbandry, Floristry, Health and Social care, Horse Care, Horticulture, Hospitality, IT, Land-based Technology, Business, Creative Media Production, Music, Performing Arts, Public Services, Sport, Travel and Tourism, and Vehicle Technology.

BTEC Foundation Diploma in Art and Design (QCF)
For those students preparing to go on to higher education within the field of art and design. This diploma is recognised as one of the best courses of its type in the UK, and is used in preparation for degree programmes. Units offered include researching, recording and responding in art and design, media experimentation, personal experimental studies, and a final major project.

BTEC Nationals

ie BTEC Level 3 Extended Diplomas (QCF), BTEC Level 3 Diplomas (QCF), BTEC Level 3 Subsidiary Diplomas (QCF), BTEC Level 3 Certificates (QCF)

BTEC National programmes are long-established vocational programmes. They are practical programmes that are highly valued by employers. They enable you to gain the knowledge and skills that you will need in work, or give you the choice to progress on to a BTEC Higher National, a Foundation Degree or a degree programme.

BTEC Nationals, which hold UCAS points cover a range of vocationally specialist sectors including child care, children's play, learning and development, construction, art and design, aeronautical engineering, electrical/electronic engineering, IT, business, creative and media production, performing arts, public services, sport, sport and exercise sciences and applied science. The programmes may be taken full- or part-time, and can be taken in conjunction with NVQs and/or functional skills units at an appropriate level.

There are no formal entry requirements, but if you have any of the following you are likely to be at the right level to study a BTEC national qualification.

- a BTEC Level 2 First qualification

- GCSEs – at grades A*-C in several subjects

- Relevant work experience

There are also very specialist BTEC Nationals, such as Pharmaceutical Science and Blacksmithing and Metalworking.

BTEC Higher Nationals

Known as HNDs and HNCs – ie BTEC Level 5 HND Diplomas (QCF) and BTEC Level 4 HNC Diplomas (QCF)

BTEC HNDs and HNCs are further and higher education qualifications that offer a balance of education and vocational training. They are available in over 40 work-related subjects such as Graphic Design, Business, Health and Social Care, Computing and Systems Development, Manufacturing Engineering, Hospitality Management, and Public Services.

BTEC higher national courses combine study with hands-on work experience during your course. Once completed, you can use the skills you learn to begin your career, or continue on to a related degree course.

HNDs are often taken as a full-time course over two years but can also be followed part-time in some cases.

HNCs are often for people who are working and take two years to complete on a part-time study basis by day release, evenings, or a combination of the two. Some HNC courses are done on a full-time basis.

There are no formal entry requirements, but if you have any of the following you are likely to be at the right academic level:

- at least one A level

- a BTEC Level 3 National qualification

- level 3 NVQ

BTEC specialist and professional qualifications

These qualifications are designed to prepare students for specific and specialist work activities. These are split into two distinct groups:

- Specialist qualifications (entry to Level 3)

- Professional qualifications (Levels 4-7)

Cambridge Nationals

Cambridge Nationals are vocationally-related qualifications that take an engaging, practical and inspiring approach to learning and assessment.

They are industry-relevant, geared to key sector requirements and very popular with schools and colleges because they suit such a broad range of learning styles and abilities.

Cambridge Nationals are available in: Child Development, Creative iMedia, Engineering Design, Engineering Manufacture, Enterprise and Marketing, Health and Social Care, ICT, Information Technologies, Principles in Engineering and Engineering Business, Sport Science, Sport Studies, Systems Control in Engineering. They are joint Level 1 and 2 qualifications aimed at students aged 14-16 in full-time study.

Cambridge Technicals

OCR's Cambridge Technicals are practical and flexible vocationally-related qualifications, offering students in-depth study in a wide range of subjects, including business, health and social care, IT, sport, art and design, digital media, science, performing arts and engineering.

Cambridge Technicals are aimed at young people aged 16-19 who have completed Key Stage 4 of their education and want to study in a more practical, work-related way.

Cambridge Technicals are available at Level 2 and Level 3, and carry UCAS points at Level 3.

NVQs

NVQs reward those who demonstrate skills gained at work. They relate to particular jobs and are usefully taken while you are working. Within reason, NVQs do not have to be completed in a specified amount of time. They can be taken by full-time employees or by school and college students with a work placement or part-time job that enables them to develop the appropriate skills. There are no age limits and no special entry requirements.

NVQs are organised into levels, based on the competencies required. Levels 1-3 are the levels most applicable to learners within the 14-19 phase. Achievement of Level 4 within this age group will be rare. See the OCR website for further information.

Occupational Studies (Northern Ireland)

Targeted at learners working towards and at Level 1 and 2 in Key Stage 4 within the Northern Ireland curriculum. For further information see the CCEA website.

OCR Vocational Qualifications

These are available at different levels and different sizes. Levels 1-3 are the levels most applicable to learners within the 14-19 phase. The different sizes are indicated with the use of Award, Certificate and Diploma in the qualification title and indicate the number of hours it typically takes to complete the qualification.

Vocational qualifications are assessed according to each individual specification, but may include practical assessments and/or marked assessments. They are designed to provide evidence of a student's relevant skills and knowledge in their chosen subject. These qualifications can be used for employment or as a path towards further education. See the OCR website for further details.

SVQs (Scotland)

Scottish Vocational Qualifications (SVQs) are based on national standards, which are drawn up by people from industry, commerce and education. They are studied in the workplace, in college or with training providers. Some schools offer them in partnership with colleges and employers. SVQs are available in many subject areas, from forestry to IT, management to catering, and journalism to construction.

Each unit of an SVQ defines one aspect of a job or work role and what it is to be competent in that aspect of the job.

SVQs are available at SCQF Levels 4-11 and Levels 4-7 are most applicable to learners aged 16-18.

Awarding organisations and examination dates

Awarding organisations and examination dates

In England there are four awarding organisations, each offering GCSEs, AS and A levels (Eduqas offers only reformed qualifications in England, whereas WJEC offers in England, Wales, Northern Ireland and independent regions). There are separate awarding organisations in Wales (WJEC) and Northern Ireland (CCEA). The awarding organisation in Scotland (SQA) offers equivalent qualifications.

This information was supplied by the awarding bodies and was accurate at the time of going to press. It is intended as a general guide only for candidates in the United Kingdom. Dates are subject to variation and should be confirmed with the awarding organisation concerned.

AQA

Qualifications offered:
GCSE
AS and A level
Technical Award
Foundation Certificate of Secondary Education (FCSE)
Entry Level Certificate (ELC)
Foundation and Higher Projects
Extended Project Qualification (EPQ)
AQA Baccalaureate
Applied Generals/AQA Level 3 Certificates and Extended Certificates
Functional Skills
AQA Certificate
Technical Award

Other assessment schemes:
Unit Award Scheme (UAS)

Examination dates for summer 2020: 11 May – 26 June

Contact:
Email: eos@aqa.org.uk
Website: www.aqa.org.uk
Tel: 0800 197 7162 (8am–5pm Monday to Friday)
+44 161 696 5995 (Outside the UK)

Devas Street, Manchester M15 6EX
Stag Hill House, Guildford, Surrey GU2 7XJ
Windsor House, Cornwall Road, Harrogate, HG1 2PW
2nd Floor, Lynton House, 7–12 Tavistock Square, London, WC1H 9LT

CCEA – Council for the Curriculum, Examinations and Assessment

Qualifications offered:
GCSE
GCE AS/A level
Key Skills (Levels 1-4)
Entry Level Qualifications
Occupational Studies (Levels 1 & 2)
QCF Qualifications
Applied GCSE and GCE

Contact:
Email: info@ccea.org.uk
Website: www.ccea.org.uk

29 Clarendon Road, Clarendon Dock, Belfast, BT1 3BG
Tel: (028) 9026 1200

Eduqas

Eduqas, part of WJEC, offers Ofqual reformed GCSEs, AS and A levels to secondary schools and colleges. Our qualifications are available in England, Channel Islands, Isle of Man, Northern Ireland and to the independent sector in Wales (restrictions may apply).

Qualifications offered:
GCSE (9-1)
AS
A level
Level 3

Contact:
Email: info@wjec.co.uk
Website: www.eduqas.co.uk

Eduqas (WJEC CBAC Ltd),
245 Western Avenue, Cardiff, CF5 2YX
Telephone: 029 2026 5000

IB – International Baccalaureate

Qualification offered:
IB Diploma
IB Career-related Certificate

Examination dates for summer 2020: 1 – 22 May

Contact:
Email: support@ibo.org
Website: www.ibo.org

IB Global Centre, The Hague, Churchillplein 6, 2517 JW, The Hague, The Netherlands
Tel: +31 70 352 60 00

IB Global Centre, Washington DC, 7501 Wisconsin Avenue, Suite 200 West Bethesda, Maryland 20814, USA
Tel: +1 301 202 3000

IB Global Centre, Singapore, 600 North Bridge Road, #21-01 Parkview Square, Singapore 188778
Tel: +65 6 579 5000

IB Global Centre, Cardiff, Peterson House, Malthouse Avenue, Cardiff Gate, Cardiff, Wales, CF23 8GL, UK
Email: reception@ibo.org
Tel: +44 29 2054 7777

International Baccalaureate Foundation Office, Route des Morillons 15, Grand-Saconnex, Genève, CH-1218, Switzerland
Tel: +41 22 309 2540

OCR – Oxford Cambridge and RSA Examinations – and Cambridge International

Qualifications offered by OCR or sister awarding organisation Cambridge Assessment International Education (Cambridge International) include:
GCSE
GCE AS/A level
IGCSE
International AS/A level
Extended Project
Cambridge International Project Qualification
Cambridge Pre-U
Cambridge Nationals
Cambridge Technicals
Functional Skills
FSMQ – Free Standing Maths Qualification
NVQ

Examination dates for summer 2020: 11 May to 24 June

Contact:
OCR
OCR Head Office, The Triangle Building, Shaftesbury Road, Cambridge, CB2 8EA
Website: www.ocr.org.uk
Tel: +44 1223 553998

Cambridge International
Website: www.cambridgeinternational.org
Email: info@cambridgeinternational.org
Tel: +44 1223 553554

Pearson

Qualifications offered:
Pearson's qualifications are offered in the UK but are also available through their international centres across the world. They include:
DiDA, CiDA
GCE A levels
GCSEs
Functional Skills
International GCSEs and Edexcel Certificates
ESOL (Skills for Life)
BTEC Enterprise qualifications
BTEC Entry Level, Level 1 and Level 1 Introductory
BTEC Firsts
BTEC Foundation Diploma in Art and Design
BTEC Industry Skills
BTEC International Level 3
BTEC Level 2 Technicals
BTEC Level 3 Technical Levels in Hospitality
BTEC Nationals
BTEC Specialist and Professional qualifications
BTEC Tech Awards
Higher Nationals
T Levels

Examination dates for summer 2020: 11 May – 24 June

Contact:
190 High Holborn, London WC1V 7BH

See website for specific contact details:
qualifications.pearson.com

SQA – Scottish Qualifications Authority

Qualifications offered:
National Qualifications (NQs): National 1 to National 5; Higher; Advanced Higher
Skills for Work
National Certificates (NCs)
National Progression Awards (NPAs)
Scottish Baccalaureate
Awards
Core Skills
Scottish Vocational Qualifications (SVQs)
Higher National Certificates and Higher National Diplomas (HNCs/HNDs)*

*SQA offers HNCs and HNDs to centres in Scotland. Outside of Scotland, the equivalent qualifications are the SQA Advanced Certificate and SQA Advanced Diploma.

Examination dates for summer 2020: 27 April – 4 June

Contact:
Email: customer@sqa.org.uk
Tel: 0345 279 1000
Website: www.sqa.org.uk

Glasgow – The Optima Building, 58 Robertson Street, Glasgow, G2 8DQ

Dalkeith – Lowden, 24 Wester Shawfair, Dalkeith, Midlothian, EH22 1FD

WJEC

With over 65 years' experience in delivering qualifications, WJEC is the largest provider in Wales and a leading provider in England and Northern Ireland.

Qualifications offered:
GCSE
GCE A/AS
Functional Skills
Entry Level
Welsh Baccalaureate Qualifications
Essential Skills Wales
Wider Key Skills
Project Qualifications Principal Learning
Other general qualifications such as Level 1 and Level 2 Awards and Certificates including English Language, English Literature, Latin Language, Latin Language & Roman Civilisation and Latin Literature
QCF Qualifications

Contact:
Email: info@wjec.co.uk
Website: www.wjec.co.uk

245 Western Avenue, Cardiff, CF5 2YX
Tel: 029 2026 5000

Educational organisations

Educational organisations

Artsmark

Arts Council England's Artsmark was set up in 2001, and rounds are held annually.
All schools in England can apply for an Artsmark – primary, middle, secondary, special and pupil referral units, maintained and independent – on a voluntary basis. An Artsmark award is made to schools showing commitment to the full range of arts – music, dance, drama and art and design.
Tel: 0161 934 4317
Email: artsmark@artscouncil.org.uk
Website: www.artsmark.org.uk

Association for the Education and Guardianship of International Students (AEGIS)

AEGIS brings together schools and guardianship organisations to ensure and promote the welfare of international students. AEGIS provides accreditation for all reputable guardianship organisations.
AEGIS, The Wheelhouse, Bond's Mill Estate, Bristol Road, Stonehouse, Gloucestershire GL10 3RF.
Tel: 01453 821293
Email: info@aegisuk.net
Website: www.aegisuk.net

The Association of American Study Abroad Programmes (AASAP)

Established in 1991 to represent American study abroad programmes in the UK.
Contact: Kalyn Franke, AASAP/UK,
University of Maryland in London, Connaught Hall,
36-45 Tavistock Square, London WC1H 9EX
Email: info@aasapuk.org
Website: www.aasapuk.org

The Association of British Riding Schools (ABRS)

An independent body of proprietors and principals of riding establishments, aiming to look after their interests and those of the riding public and to raise standards of management, instruction and animal welfare.
The Association of British Riding Schools, Unit 8, Bramble Hill Farm, Five Oaks Road, Slinfold, Horsham,
West Sussex RH13 0RL. Tel: 01403 790294
Email: office@abrs-info.org
Website: www.abrs-info.org

Association of Colleges (AOC)

Created in 1996 to promote the interest of further education colleges in England and Wales.
2-5 Stedham Place, London WC1A 1HU
Tel: 0207 034 9900
Email: enquiries@aoc.co.uk
Website: www.aoc.co.uk

Association of Governing Bodies of Independent Schools (AGBIS)

AGBIS supports and advises governing bodies of schools in the independent sector on all aspects of governance.
Registered charity No. 1108756
Association of Governing Bodies of Independent Schools, 3 Codicote Road, Welwyn, Hertfordshire AL6 9LY
Tel: 01438 840730
Email: office@agbis.org.uk
Website: www.agbis.org.uk

Association of Employment and Learning Providers (AELP)

AELP's purpose is to influence the education and training agenda. They are the voice of independent learning providers throughout England.
Association of Employment and Learning Providers,
2nd Floor, 9 Apex Court, Bradley Stoke, Bristol, BS32 4JT
Tel: 0117 986 5389
Email: enquiries@aelp.org.uk
Website: www.aelp.org.uk

The Association of School and College Leaders (ASCL)

Formerly the Secondary Heads Association, the ASCL is a professional association for secondary school and college leaders.
130 Regent Road, Leicester LE1 7PG
Tel: 0116 299 1122
Fax: 0116 299 1123
Email: info@ascl.org.uk
Website: www.ascl.org.uk

Boarding Schools' Association (BSA)

For information on the BSA see editorial on page 43

The British Accreditation Council (BAC)

The British Accreditation Council (BAC) has now been the principal accrediting body for the independent further and higher education and training sector for nearly 30 years. BAC-accredited institutions in the UK now number more than 300, offering everything from website design to yoga to equine dentistry, as well as more standard qualifications in subjects such as business, IT, management and law. As well as our accreditation of institutions offering traditional teaching, BAC has developed a new accreditation scheme for providers offering online, distance and blended learning. Some students may also look to study outside the UK at one of the institutions holding BAC international accreditation.
14 Devonshire Square, London, EC2M 4YT
Tel: 0300 330 1400
Email: info@the-bac.org
Website: www.the-bac.org

The British Association for Early Childhood Education (BAECE)

Promotes quality provision for all children from birth to eight in whatever setting they are placed. Publishes booklets and organises conferences for those interested in early years education and care. Registered charity Nos. 313082; SC039472
54 Clarendon Road, Watford, WD17 1DU
Tel: 01923 438 995
Email: office@early-education.org.uk
Website: www.early-education.org.uk

The Choir Schools' Association (CSA)

Represents 44 schools attached to cathedrals, churches and college chapels, which educate cathedral and collegiate choristers.
CSA Information Officer, Village Farm, The Street, Market Weston, Diss, Norfolk IP22 2NZ
Tel: 01359 221333
Email: info@choirschools.org.uk
Website: www.choirschools.org.uk

CIFE

CIFE is the professional association for independent sixth form and tutorial colleges accredited by the British Accreditation Council (BAC), the Independent Schools Council or the DfE (Ofsted). Member colleges specialise in preparing students for GCSE and A level (AS and A2) in particular and university entrance in general.
The aim of the association is to provide a forum for the exchange of information and ideas, and for the promotion of best practice, and to safeguard adherence to strict standards of professional conduct and ethical propriety. Further information can be obtained from CIFE:
Tel: 0208 767 8666
Email: enquiries@cife.org.uk
Website: www.cife.org.uk

Council of British International Schools (COBIS)

COBIS is a membership association of British schools of quality worldwide and is committed to a stringent process of quality assurance for all its member schools. COBIS is a member of the Independent Schools Council (ISC) of the United Kingdom.
COBIS, 55–56 Russell Square, Bloomsbury, London WC1B 4HP
Tel: 020 3826 7190
Email: pa@cobis.org.uk
Website: www.cobis.org.uk

Council of International Schools (CIS)

CIS is a not-for-profit organisation committed to supporting its member schools and colleges in achieving and delivering the highest standards of international education. CIS provides accreditation to schools, teacher and leader recruitment and best practice development. CIS Higher Education assists member colleges and universities in recruiting a diverse profile of qualified international students.
Schipholweg 113, 2316 XC Leiden, The Netherlands.
Tel: +31 71 524 3300
Email: info@cois.org
Website: www.cois.org

Dyslexia Action (DA)

A registered, educational charity (No. 268502), which has established teaching and assessment centres and conducts teacher-training throughout the UK. The aim of the institute is to help people with dyslexia of all ages to overcome their difficulties in learning to read, write and spell and to achieve their potential.
Dyslexia Action Training and Guild, Centurion House, London Road, Staines-upon-Thames TW18 4AX
Tel: 01784 222 304
Email: trainingcourses@dyslexiaaction.org.uk
Website: www.dyslexiaaction.org.uk

European Association for International Education (EAIE)

A not-for-profit organisation aiming for internationalisation in higher education in Europe. It has a membership of over 1800.
PO Box 11189, 1001 GD Amsterdam, The Netherlands
Tel: +31 20 344 5100
Fax: +31 20 344 5119
Email: info@eaie.org
Website: www.eaie.org

ECIS (European Collaborative for International Schools)

ECIS is a membership organisation which provides services to support professional development, good governance and leadership in international schools.
24 Greville Street,
London, EC1N 8SS
Tel: 020 7824 7040
Email: ecis@ecis.org
Website: www.ecis.org

The Girls' Day School Trust (GDST)

The Girls' Day School Trust (GDST) is one of the largest, longest-established and most successful groups of independent schools in the UK, with 4000 staff and over 20,000 students between the ages of 3 and 18. As a charity that owns and runs a family of 26 schools in England and Wales, it reinvests all its income into its schools for the benefit of the pupils. With a long history of pioneering innovation in the education of girls, the GDST now also educates boys in some of its schools, and has two coeducational sixth form colleges. Registered charity No. 306983
10 Bressenden Place, London, SW1E 5DH
Tel: 020 7393 6666
Email: info@wes.gdst.net
Website: www.gdst.net

Girls' Schools Association (GSA)

For information on the GSA see editorial on page 44

The Headmasters' and Headmistresses' Conference (HMC)

For information on the HMC see editorial on page 45

Human Scale Education (HSE)

An educational reform movement aiming for small education communities based on democracy, fairness and respect. Registered charity No. 1000400
Email: contact@hse.org.uk
Website: www.hse.org.uk

The Independent Association of Prep Schools (IAPS)

For further information about IAPS see editorial on page 46

The Independent Schools Association (ISA)

For further information about ISA see editorial on page 47

The Independent Schools' Bursars Association (ISBA)

Exists to support and advance financial and operational performance in independent schools. The ISBA is a charitable company limited by guarantee. Company No. 6410037; registered charity No. 1121757
Bluett House, Unit 11–12 Manor Farm, Cliddesden, nr Basingstoke, Hampshire RG25 2JB
Tel: 01256 330369
Email: office@theisba.org.uk
Website: www.theisba.org.uk

The Independent Schools Council (ISC)

The Independent Schools Council exists to promote choice, diversity and excellence in education; the development of talent at all levels of ability; and the widening of opportunity for children from all backgrounds to achieve their potential. Its 1280 member schools educate more than 500,000 children at all levels of ability and from all socioeconomic classes. Nearly a third of children in ISC schools receive help with fees. The Governing Council of ISC contains representatives from each of the eight ISC constituent associations listed below. See also page 42.

Members:
Association of Governing Bodies of Independent Schools (AGBIS)
Girls' Schools Association (GSA)
Headmasters' and Headmistresses' Conference (HMC)
Independent Association of Prep Schools (IAPS)
Independent Schools Association (ISA)
Independent Schools Bursars' Association (ISBA)
The Society of Heads

The council also has close relations with the BSA, COBIS, SCIS and WISC.

First Floor, 27 Queen Anne's Gate,
London, SW1H 9BU
Tel: 020 7766 7070
Fax: 020 7766 7071
Email: research@isc.co.uk
Website: www.isc.co.uk

The Independent Schools Examinations Board (ISEB)

Details of the Common Entrance examinations are obtainable from:
Independent Schools Examinations Board,
Endeavour House, Crow Arch Lane, Ringwood BH24 1HP
Tel: 01425 470555
Email: enquiries@iseb.co.uk
Website: www.iseb.co.uk
Copies of past papers can be purchased from Galore Park: www.galorepark.co.uk

The Inspiring Futures Foundation (IFF)

The IFF provides careers education and guidance to schools and students. Professional support and training is available to school staff and our Futurewise programme provides individual, web-based, support for students and their parents. Career/subject insight courses, gap-year fairs and an information service are additional elements of the service.
Tel: 01491 820381
Email: helpline@inspiringfutures.org.uk
Website: www.inspiringfutures.org.uk

International Baccalaureate (IB)

For full information about the IB see full entry on page 427.

International Schools Theatre Association (ISTA)

International body of teachers and students of theatre, run by teachers for teachers. Registered charity No. 1050103
3 Omega Offices, 14 Coinagehall St,
Helston, Cornwall TR13 8EB
Tel: 01326 560398
Email: office@ista.co.uk
Website: www.ista.co.uk

Maria Montessori Institute (MMI)

Authorised by the Association Montessori Internationale (AMI) to run their training course in the UK. Further information is available from:
26 Lyndhurst Gardens, Hampstead, London NW3 5NW
Tel: 020 7435 3646
Email: schools@mariamontessori.org
Website: www.mariamontessori.org

The National Association of Independent Schools & Non-Maintained Schools (NASS)

A membership organisation working with and for special schools in the voluntary and private sectors within the UK. Registered charity No. 1083632
PO Box 705, York YO30 6WW
Tel/Fax: 01904 624446
Email: krippon@nasschools.org.uk
Website: www.nasschools.org.uk

National Day Nurseries Association (NDNA)

A national charity that aims to promote quality in early years. Registered charity No. 1078275
NDNA, National Early Years Enterprise Centre,
Longbow Close, Huddersfield, West Yorkshire HD2 1GQ
Tel: 01484 407070
Fax: 01484 407060
Email: info@ndna.org.uk
Website: www.ndna.org.uk

NDNA Cymru, Office 3, Crown House, 11 Well Street,
Ruthin, Denbighshire LL15 1AE
Tel: 01824 707823
Email: wales@ndna.org.uk

NDNA Scotland, The Mansfield Traquair Centre,
15 Mansfield Place, Edinburgh EH3 6BB
Tel: 0131 516 6967
Email: scot@ndna.org.uk

National Foundation for Educational Research (NFER)

NFER is the UK's largest independent provider of research, assessment and information services for education, training and children's services. Its clients include UK government departments and agencies at both national and local levels. NFER is a not-for-profit organisation and a registered charity No. 313392
Head Office, The Mere, Upton Park,
Slough, Berkshire SL1 2DQ
Tel: 01753 574123
Fax: 01753 691632
Email: enquiries@nfer.ac.uk
Website: www.nfer.ac.uk

Potential Plus UK

Potential Plus UK is an independent charity that supports the social, emotional and learning needs of children with high learning potential of all ages and backgrounds. Registered charity No. 313182
Room 5 The Mansion, Sherwood Drive, Bletchley, Milton Keynes, Buckinghamshire MK3 6EB
Tel: 01908 646433
Email: amazingchildren@potentialplusuk.org
Website: www.potentialplusuk.org

Round Square

An international group of schools formed in 1967 following the principles of Dr Kurt Hahn, the founder of Salem School in Germany, and Gordonstoun in Scotland. The Round Square, named after Gordonstoun's 17th century circular building in the centre of the school, now has more than 100 member schools. Registered charity No. 327117
Round Square, First Floor, Morgan House, Madeira Walk, Windsor SL4 1EP
Tel: 01474 709843
Website: www.roundsquare.org

Royal National Children's SpringBoard Foundation

On 1 July 2017 the Royal National Children's Foundation (RNCF) merged with The SpringBoard Bursary Foundation to create the Royal National Children's SpringBoard Foundation ('Royal SpringBoard'). The newly merged charity gives life-transforming bursaries to disadvantaged and vulnerable children from across the UK.
Buckingham Suite, 7 Grosvenor Gardens,
London SW1W 0BD
Tel: 020 3405 3630
Email: admin@royalspringboard.org.uk
Website: www.royalspringboard.org.uk

School Fees Independent Advice (SFIA)

For further information about SFIA, see editorial page 40

Schools Music Association of Great Britain (SMA)

The SMA is a national 'voice' for music in education. It is now part of the Incorporated Society of Musicians
Registered charity No. 313646
Website: www.ism.org/sma

Scottish Council of Independent Schools (SCIS)

Representing more than 70 independent, fee-paying schools in Scotland, the Scottish Council of Independent Schools (SCIS) is the foremost authority on independent schools in Scotland and offers impartial information, advice and guidance to parents. Registered charity No. SC018033
61 Dublin Street, Edinburgh EH3 6NL
Tel: 0131 556 2316
Email: info@scis.org.uk
Website: www.scis.org.uk

Society of Education Consultants (SEC)

The Society is a professional membership organisation that supports management consultants who specialise in education and children's services. The society's membership includes consultants who work as individuals, in partnerships or in association with larger consultancies.
SEC, Bellamy House, 13 West Street, Cromer NR27 9HZ
Tel: 0330 323 0457
Email: administration@sec.org.uk
Website: www.sec.org.uk

The Society of Heads

For full information see editorial on page 48

State Boarding Forum (SBF)

For full information about the SBF see editorial on page 43

Steiner Waldorf Schools Fellowship (SWSF)

Representing Steiner education in the UK and Ireland, the SWSF has member schools and early years centres in addition to interest groups and other affiliated organisations. Member schools offer education for children within the normal range of ability, aged 3 to 18. Registered charity No. 295104
Steiner Waldorf Schools Fellowship® Ltd, Suite 1, 3rd Floor, Copthall House, 1 New Road, Stourbridge,
West Midlands, DY8 1PH
Tel: 01384 374116
Email: admin@steinerwaldorf.org
Website: www.steinerwaldorf.org

Support and Training in Prep Schools (SATIPS)

SATIPS aims to support teachers in the independent and maintained sectors of education. Registered charity No. 313688
West Routengill, Walden, West Burton, Leyburn,
North Yorkshire, DL8 4LF
Website: www.satips.org

The Tutors' Association

The Tutors' Association is the professional body for tutoring and wider supplementary education sector in the UK. Launched in 2013, they have over 850 members, including Individual and Corporate Members representing some 30,000 tutors throughout the UK.
Tel: 01628 306108
Email: info@thetutorsassociation.org.uk
Website: www.thetutorsassociation.org.uk

UCAS (Universities and Colleges Admissions Service)

UCAS is the organisation responsible for managing applications to higher education courses in England, Scotland, Wales and Northern Ireland. Registered charity Nos. 1024741 and SC038598
Rosehill, New Barn Lane,
Cheltenham, Gloucestershire GL52 3LZ
Tel: 0371 468 0 468
Website: www.ucas.com

UKCISA – The Council for International Student Affairs

UKCISA is the UK's national advisory body serving the interests of international students and those who work with them. Registered charity No. 1095294
Website: www.ukcisa.org.uk

United World Colleges (UWC)

UWC was founded in 1962 and their philosophy is based on the ideas of Dr Kurt Hahn (see Round Square Schools). Registered charity No. 313690.
UWC International, Third Floor, 55 New Oxford Street,
London, WC1A 1BS, UK
Tel: 020 7269 7800
Fax: 020 7405 4374
Email: info@uwcio.uwc.org
Website: www.uwc.org

World-Wide Education Service of CfBT Education Trust (WES)

A leading independent service which provides home education courses worldwide.
Waverley House, Penton,
Carlisle, Cumbria CA6 5QU
Tel: 01228 577123
Email: office@weshome.com
Website: www.weshome.com

Glossary

ACETS	Awards and Certificates in Education	AQA	Assessment and Qualification Alliance/Northern Examinations and Assessment Board	Cantab	Cambridge University
AEA	Advanced Extension Award			CATSC	Catholic Association of Teachers in Schools and Colleges
AEB	Associated Examining Board for the General Certificate of Education	BA	Bachelor of Arts		
		BAC	British Accreditation Council for Independent Further and Higher Education	CCEA	Council for the Curriculum, Examination and Assessment
AEGIS	Association for the Education and Guardianship of International Students				
		BAECE	The British Association for Early Childhood Education	CDT	Craft, Design and Technology
AGBIS	Association of Governing Bodies of Independent Schools			CE	Common Entrance Examination
		BD	Bachelor of Divinity	CEAS	Children's Education Advisory Service
AHIS	Association of Heads of Independent Schools	BEA	Boarding Educational Alliance	CertEd	Certificate of Education
AJIS	Association of Junior Independent Schools	BEd	Bachelor of Education	CIE	Cambridge International Examinations
ALP	Association of Learning Providers	BLitt	Bachelor of Letters	CIFE	Conference for Independent Education
ANTC	The Association of Nursery Training Colleges	BPrimEd	Bachelor of Primary Education	CIS	Council of International Schools
AOC	Association of Colleges	BSA	Boarding Schools' Association	CISC	Catholic Independent Schools' Conference
AP	Advanced Placement	BSc	Bachelor of Science	CLAIT	Computer Literacy and Information Technology
ASCL	Association of School & College Leaders	BTEC	Range of work-related, practical programmes leading to qualifications equivalent to GCSEs and A levels awarded by Edexcel	CNED	Centre National d'enseignement (National Centre of long distance learning)
ASL	Additional and Specialist Learning				
ATI	The Association of Tutors Incorporated			COBIS	Council of British International)

445

CSA	The Choir Schools' Association	INSET	In service training	PGCE	Post Graduate Certificate in Education
CST	The Christian Schools' Trust	ISA	Independent Schools Association	PhD	Doctor of Philosophy
DfE	Department for Education (formerly DfES and DCFS)	ISBA	Independent Schools' Bursars' Association	PL	Principal Learning
		ISCis	Independent Schools Council information service	PNEU	Parents' National Education Union
DipEd	Diploma of Education	ISC	Independent Schools Council	PYP	Primary Years Programme
DipTchng	Diploma of Teaching	ISEB	Independent Schools Examination Board	QCA	Qualifications and Curriculum Authority
EAIE	European Association for International Education	ISST	International Schools Sports Tournament	QCF	Qualifications and Credit Framework
ECIS	European Council of International Schools	ISTA	International Schools Theatre Association	RSIS	The Round Square Schools
EdD	Doctor of Education	ITEC	International Examination Council	SAT	Scholastic Aptitude Test
Edexcel	GCSE Examining group, incorporating Business and Technology Education Council (BTEC) and University of London Examinations and Assessment Council (ULEAC)	JET	Joint Educational Trust	SATIPS	Support & Training in Prep Schools/Society of Assistant Teachers in Prep Schools
		LA	Local Authority		
		LISA	London International Schools Association	SBSA	State Boarding Schools Association
		MA	Master of Arts	SCE	Service Children's Education
EFL	English as a Foreign Language	MCIL	Member of the Chartered Institute of Linguists	SCIS	Scottish Council of Independent Schools
ELAS	Educational Law Association	MEd	Master of Education	SCQF	Scottish Credit and Qualifications Framework
EPQ	Extended Project qualification	MIoD	Member of the Institute of Directors	SEC	The Society of Educational Consultants
ESL	English as a Second Language	MLitt	Master of Letters	SEN	Special Educational Needs
FCoT	Fellow of the College of Teachers (TESOL)	MSc	Master of Science	SFCF	Sixth Form Colleges' Forum
FEFC	Further Education Funding Council	MusD	Doctor of Music	SFIA	School Fees Insurance Agency Limited
FRSA	Fellow of the Royal Society of Arts	MYP	Middle Years Programme	SFIAET	SFIA Educational Trust
FSMQ	Free-Standing Mathematics Qualification	NABSS	National Association of British Schools in Spain	SMA	Schools Music Association
GCE	General Certificate of Education	NAGC	National Association for Gifted Children	SoH	The Society of Heads
GCSE	General Certificate of Secondary Education	NAHT	National Association of Head Teachers	SQA	Scottish Qualifications Authority
GDST	Girls' Day School Trust	NAIS	National Association of Independent Schools	STEP	Second Term Entrance Paper (Cambridge)
GNVQ	General National Vocational Qualifications	NASS	National Association of Independent Schools & Non-maintained Special Schools	SVQ	Scottish Vocational Qualifications
GOML	Graded Objectives in Modern Languages			SWSF	Steiner Waldorf Schools Fellowship
GSA	Girls' Schools Association	NDNA	National Day Nurseries Association	TABS	The Association of Boarding Schools
GSVQ	General Scottish Vocational Qualifications	NEASC	New England Association of Schools and Colleges	TISCA	The Independent Schools Christian Alliance
HMC	Headmasters' and Headmistresses' Conference			TOEFL	Test of English as a Foreign Language
HMCJ	Headmasters' and Headmistresses' Conference Junior Schools	NFER	National Federation of Educational Research	UCAS	Universities and Colleges Admissions Service for the UK
		NPA	National Progression Award		
HNC	Higher National Certificate	NQ	National Qualification	UCST	United Church Schools Trust
HND	Higher National Diploma	NQF	National Qualifications Framework	UKLA	UK Literacy Association
IAPS	Independent Association of Prep Schools	NQT	Newly Qualified Teacher	UKCISA	The UK Council for International Education
IB	International Baccalaureate	NVQ	National Vocational Qualifications	UWC	United World Colleges
ICT	Information and Communication Technology	OCR	Oxford, Cambridge and RSA Examinations	WISC	World International Studies Committee
IFF	Inspiring Futures Foundation (formerly ISCO)	OLA	Online Language Assessment for Modern Languages	WJEC	Welsh Joint Education Committee
IGCSE	International General Certificate of Secondary Education			WSSA	Welsh Secondary Schools Association
		Oxon	Oxford		

Index